Topics in Optimization

MATHEMATICS IN SCIENCE AND ENGINEERING

A SERIES OF MONOGRAPHS AND TEXTBOOKS

Edited by Richard Bellman

University of Southern California

1. Tracy Y. Thomas. Concepts from Tensor Analysis and Differential Geometry. Second Edition. 1965
2. Tracy Y. Thomas. Plastic Flow and Fracture in Solids. 1961
3. Rutherford Aris. The Optimal Design of Chemical Reactors: A Study in Dynamic Programming. 1961
4. Joseph LaSalle and Solomon Lefschetz. Stability by Liapunov's Direct Method with Applications. 1961
5. George Leitmann (ed.). Optimization Techniques: With Applications to Aerospace Systems. 1962
6. Richard Bellman and Kenneth L. Cooke. Differential-Difference Equations. 1963
7. Frank A. Haight. Mathematical Theories of Traffic Flow. 1963
8. F. V. Atkinson. Discrete and Continuous Boundary Problems. 1964
9. A. Jeffrey and T. Taniuti. Non-Linear Wave Propagation: With Applications to Physics and Magnetohydrodynamics. 1964
10. Julius T. Tou. Optimum Design of Digital Control Systems. 1963
11. Harley Flanders. Differential Forms: With Applications to the Physical Sciences. 1963
12. Sanford M. Roberts. Dynamic Programming in Chemical Engineering and Process Control. 1964
13. Solomon Lefschetz. Stability of Nonlinear Control Systems. 1965
14. Dimitris N. Chorafas. Systems and Simulation. 1965
15. A. A. Pervozvanskii. Random Processes in Nonlinear Control Systems. 1965
16. Marshall C. Pease, III. Methods of Matrix Algebra. 1965
17. V. E. Benes. Mathematical Theory of Connecting Networks and Telephone Traffic. 1965
18. William F. Ames. Nonlinear Partial Differential Equations in Engineering. 1965
19. J. Aczél. Lectures on Functional Equations and Their Applications. 1966
20. R. E. Murphy. Adaptive Processes in Economic Systems. 1965
21. S. E. Dreyfus. Dynamic Programming and the Calculus of Variations. 1965
22. A. A. Fel'dbaum. Optimal Control Systems. 1965

MATHEMATICS IN SCIENCE AND ENGINEERING

23. A. HALANAY. Differential Equations: Stability, Oscillations, Time Lags. 1966
24. M. NAMIK OĞUZTÖRELI. Time-Lag Control Systems. 1966
25. DAVID SWORDER. Optimal Adaptive Control Systems. 1966
26. MILTON ASH. Optimal Shutdown Control of Nuclear Reactors. 1966
27. DIMITRIS N. CHORAFAS. Control System Functions and Programming Approaches. (In Two Volumes.) 1966
28. N. P. ERUGIN. Linear Systems of Ordinary Differential Equations. 1966
29. SOLOMON MARCUS. Algebraic Linguistics; Analytical Models. 1967
30. A. M. LIAPUNOV. Stability of Motion. 1966
31. GEORGE LEITMANN (ed.). Topics in Optimization. 1967
32. MASANAO AOKI. Optimization of Stochastic Systems. 1967

In preparation

A. KAUFMANN. Graphs, Dynamic Programming, and Finite Games

MINORU URABE. Nonlinear Autonomous Oscillations

A. KAUFMANN and R. CRUON. Dynamic Programming: Sequential Scientific Management

Y. SAWARAGI, Y. SUNAHARA, and T. NAKAMIZO. Statistical Decision Theory in Adaptive Control Systems

F. CALOGERO. Variable Phase Approach to Potential Scattering

J. H. AHLBERG, E. N. NILSON, and J. L. WALSH. The Theory of Splines and Their Application

HAROLD J. KUSHNER. Stochastic Stability and Control

TOPICS IN OPTIMIZATION

EDITED BY

GEORGE LEITMANN

DEPARTMENT OF MECHANICAL ENGINEERING
UNIVERSITY OF CALIFORNIA
BERKELEY, CALIFORNIA

1967

ACADEMIC PRESS New York and London

ACADEMIC PRESS INC.
111 Fifth Avenue, New York, New York 10003

United Kingdom Edition published by
ACADEMIC PRESS INC. (LONDON) LTD.
Berkeley Square House, London W.1

LIBRARY OF CONGRESS CATALOG CARD NUMBER: 66-16442

PRINTED IN THE UNITED STATES OF AMERICA

List of Contributors

Numbers in parentheses indicate the pages on which the authors' contributions begin.

A. Blaquière (263), Faculty of Sciences, University of Paris, Paris, France.

E. K. Blum (417), Department of Mathematics, University of Southern California, Los Angeles, California.

Stephen P. Diliberto (373), Department of Mathematics, University of California, Berkeley, California.

Boris Garfinkel (3, 27), Ballistic Research Laboratories, Aberdeen Proving Ground, Maryland.[1]

Hubert Halkin (197),[2] Bell Telephone Laboratories, Whippany, New Jersey.

Henry J. Kelley (63), Analytical Mechanics Associates, Inc., Westbury, Long Island, New York.

Richard E. Kopp (63), Research Department, Grumman Aircraft Engineering Corporation, Bethpage, Long Island, New York.

G. Leitmann (263), Department of Mechanical Engineering, University of California, Berkeley, California.

A. I. Lurie (103), Leningrad Polytechnic Institute, Leningrad, USSR.

K. A. Lurie (147), Department of Mathematical Physics, A. F. Ioffe Physico-Technical Institute, Academy of Sciences of the USSR, Leningrad, USSR.

H. Gardner Moyer (63), Research Department, Grumman Aircraft Engineering Corporation, Bethpage, Long Island, New York.

Bernard Paiewonsky (391), Institute for Defense Analyses, Arlington, Virginia.

[1] Present address: Yale University Observatory, New Haven, Connecticut.
[2] Present address: Department of Mathematics, University of California, La Jolla, California.

Preface

Four years ago a multi-author volume,"Optimization Techniques with Applications to Aerospace Systems" (Academic Press, New York and London, 1962), appeared in this series. In the intervening years many facets of optimization theory and its application to problems in engineering and applied science have been explored. This book includes many results which extend or generalize the findings recorded in the earlier one.

This volume contains ten contributions to the field of optimization of dynamical systems. The reason for assembling these contributions and their publication under one cover stems from my belief that, while too long for inclusion in technical journals (some chapters are of monograph length), they deserve recording in more or less permanent format.

The book is divided into two parts of five chapters each. The investigations reported in Part 1 are based on variational techniques and constitute essentially extensions of the classical calculus of variations. Part 2 of the volume contains contributions to optimal control theory and its applications; here the arguments are primarily geometric in nature.

Some chapters deal with the solutions to particular problems while others are devoted primarily to theory. However, these latter chapters also contain problems for purposes of illustrating various aspects of the theory. Thus I hope that this volume will be of interest to both theoreticians and practitioners.

August, 1966
Berkeley, California

G. LEITMANN

Contents

Chapter 5. **The Mayer-Bolza Problem for Multiple Integrals: Some Optimum Problems for Elliptic Differential Equations Arising in Magnetohydrodynamics**

K. A. LURIE

Part 2

A Geometric Approach

Chapter 6. **Mathematical Foundations of System Optimization**

HUBERT HALKIN

Chapter 7. **On the Geometry of Optimal Processes**

A. BLAQUIÈRE AND G. LEITMANN

Chapter 10. **The Calculus of Variations, Functional Analysis, and Optimal Control Problems**

E. K. BLUM

Part 1

A Variational Approach

1

Inequalities in a Variational Problem

BORIS GARFINKEL†

BALLISTIC RESEARCH LABORATORIES,
ABERDEEN PROVING GROUND, MARYLAND

1.0 Introduction

The frequent occurrence of optimization problems with bounded *state* and *control* variables has revived the interest in the old subject of inequalities in the calculus of variations. In this chapter we are concerned with inequalities in the problem of Lagrange, illustrated by the following examples:

(a) Find the curve $y(x)$ that joins the points $(-3, -11)$ and $(2, 2)$ in the domain $y - x^3 + 3x \geq 0$, and minimizes the integral

$$\int_{-3}^{2} (1 + y'^2)^{1/2}\, dx$$

† *Present address:* Yale University Observatory, New Haven, Connecticut.

Let $Y(x)$ intersect $\phi = 0$ at $(\xi + dx, y(\xi) + dy)$. Since F may have a jump ΔF at $x = \xi$, and since $\lambda = \lambda(x)$, the *first variation* of I is given by

$$\delta I = -[\Delta F]_\xi + \int_{x_1}^{x_2} \delta F \, dx - \int_\xi^{x_2} \lambda \, \delta\phi \, dx \tag{1.10}$$

The identity

$$\delta y' = \frac{d}{dx} \delta y \tag{1.11}$$

leads to

$$\begin{aligned} \delta F &= F_y \, \delta y + F_{y'} \, \delta y' \\ &= \left(F_y - \frac{d}{dx} F_{y'}\right) \delta y + \frac{d}{dx} (F_{y'} \, \delta y) \end{aligned} \tag{1.12}$$

The integration by parts and the use of (1.7) converts (1.10) into

$$\begin{aligned} \delta I = &-[\Delta(F - y'F_{y'}) \, dx + \Delta F_{y'} \, dy]_\xi \\ &+ \int_{x_1}^{x_2} \left(F_y - \frac{d}{dx} F_{y'}\right) \delta y \, dx - \int_\xi^{x_2} \lambda \, \delta\phi \, dx \end{aligned} \tag{1.13}$$

where dx and dy inside the brackets satisfy $d\phi = 0$ at $x = \xi$. In order that I be a minimum, it is necessary that

$$\delta I \geq 0 \tag{1.14}$$

Let the arbitrary $\delta y(x)$ be successively chosen as: (1) a bilateral variation with a fixed ξ, (2) a bilateral variation with a variable ξ, and (3) a unilateral variation. Then the Dubois-Reymond lemma and (1.14) imply in succession the following three conditions: The Euler condition Ia,

$$\frac{d}{dx} F_{y'} = F_y, \qquad \lambda\phi = 0 \tag{1.15}$$

holding between corners, the Weierstrass-Erdmann *corner condition* Ib,

$$[\Delta(F - y'F_{y'}) \, dx + \Delta F_{y'} \, dy]_\xi = 0 \tag{1.16}$$

which must hold at corners for all dx and dy satisfying $d\phi = 0$, and the *convexity condition* Ic,

$$\lambda \leq 0 \tag{1.17}$$

The system of two equations (1.15) in the unknown $y(x)$ and $\lambda(x)$ defines the *extremals* of the problem. We shall use the term *extremaloid* to describe curves that satisfy condition I, which comprises Ia, Ib, and Ic. The particular extremaloid that satisfies the prescribed end-conditions will be referred to as the *test-curve*, and designated as E_{12}.

1.2 Conditions II and III

The derivation of the necessary conditions II and III does not differ essentially from that in the problem without the inequality $\phi \geq 0$. Accordingly, we merely state them here without proof.

Let the E-function be defined by

$$E \equiv F(x, y, Y') - F(x, y, y') - (Y' - y')F_{y'}(x, y, y') \tag{1.18}$$

A curve E_{12} *is said to satisfy condition* II *of Weierstrass if* $E \geq 0$ *for all* (x, y, y', λ) *of* E_{12} *and for all sets* $(x, y, Y') \neq (x, y, y')$ *that satisfy* $\phi \geq 0$. With the sign $\geq$ replaced by $>$, II becomes II′.

A curve E_{12} *is said to satisfy condition* II_N' *if there exists an N-neighborhood of* (x, y, y', λ) *on* E_{12} *with* $\lambda\phi = 0$, *in which* $E > 0$ *for all* (x, y, y', λ) *in N and for all sets* $(x, y, Y') \neq (x, y, y')$ *that satisfy* $\phi \geq 0$.

A curve E_{12} *is said to satisfy condition* III *of Legendre if* $F_{y'y'} \geq 0$ *for all* (x, y, y') *of* E_{12}. *With the sign* $\geq$ *replaced by* $>$, III *becomes* III′.

A strengthened form of III′ is III_F', which requires that $F_{y'y'} > 0$ for all (x, y) of E_{12} and for all y'. Because of the assumed continuity of f and ϕ, it is equivalent to III_F' of Bliss, which extends the condition to an F-neighborhood of (x, y). We note that III_F' implies II_N' and that the latter implies III′.

The remaining conditions IV and IV′ are discussed in Secs. 1.8 and 1.13.

PART A—CASE (a)

1.3 Preliminary Considerations

The existence and uniqueness of an extremal continuation at points that are neither corners nor junctions will be proved with the aid of the Hilbert[5] theorem. On the R- and the B-subarcs respectively, the hypothesis of the theorem is the nonvanishing of the Hilbert determinants; for $n = 1$ we write

$$\begin{aligned} H_1 &\equiv f_{y'y'} \neq 0 \qquad (R) \\ H_2 &\equiv |\phi_y|^2 \neq 0 \qquad (B) \end{aligned} \tag{1.19}$$

This condition is assured by III′ and the assumed normality $\phi_y \neq 0$ on the extremal. We note that the corresponding Euler equations (1.15) can be written

$$\begin{aligned} \frac{d}{dx} f_{y'} &= f_y, \qquad & \lambda \equiv 0 \qquad (R) \\ \frac{d}{dx} f_{y'} &= f_y + \lambda\phi_y, \qquad & \phi'' = 0 \qquad (B) \end{aligned} \tag{1.20}$$

Since y' is continuous, and since y'' and λ are generally discontinuous at junctions, it follows from the Hilbert theorem that $y''(x)$ and $\lambda(x)$ are in (C^r, D^0). That continuous transitions defined by (1.30) are not always possible will be shown in Sec. 1.4.

1.4 Singularities in Case (a)

On a composite arc, the system (1.15) is linear in the unknowns y'', λ and has the Hilbert determinant

$$H \equiv \begin{vmatrix} f_{y'y'} & -\phi_y \\ 0 & \phi \end{vmatrix} = \phi f_{y'y'} \tag{1.33}$$

A unique solution exists iff $H \neq 0$ at $x = \xi$. Accordingly, we define singular points by the condition $H = 0$, which implies $\phi = 0$ in virtue of III′. Singularities therefore occur on $\phi = 0$ in transitions classified in Table I.

TABLE I

TYPES OF TRANSITION

Type	Symbol	Name	Remarks
Region–boundary	*RB*	Entry	Nontrivial
Boundary–region	*BR*	Exit	Nontrivial
Region–region	*RR*	Nonentry	Trivial
Boundary–boundary	*BB*	Nonexit	Trivial

We have assumed that all transitions are continuous, with $\Delta y' = 0$. Accordingly, let p be defined as the least integer such that $0 \leq p \leq r$ and $y_+^{(p+2)}(\xi) \neq y_-^{(p+2)}(\xi)$ in a *nontrivial* transition.

Lemma 1a. *If* $\phi_{y'} \equiv 0$ *and if* $\phi(\xi) = 0$, *then at the point* $x = \xi$ *of a continuous nontrivial transition*

$$\Delta\phi^{(p+2)}\,\Delta\lambda^{(p)} > 0 \tag{1.34}$$

PROOF. For a nontrivial transition, an application of the jump operator Δ to the Euler equation in (1.15) yields

$$f_{y'y'}\,\Delta y''(\xi) = \phi_y\,\Delta\lambda(\xi) \tag{1.35}$$

in view of the continuity of y and y'. It follows by III′ and normality that both $\Delta y''$ and $\Delta\lambda$ vanish or do not vanish simultaneously. The definition of p and the successive differentiation of the Euler equation leads to

$$f_{y'y'}\,\Delta y^{(p+2)}(\xi) = \phi_y\,\Delta\lambda^{(p)}(\xi) \neq 0 \tag{1.36}$$

By analogous reasoning, the application of the Δ-operator to the function ϕ'' yields

$$\phi_y \, \Delta y''(\xi) = \Delta\phi''(\xi) \tag{1.37}$$

and

$$\phi_y \, \Delta y^{(p+2)}(\xi) = \Delta\phi^{(p+2)}(\xi) \tag{1.38}$$

The elimination of $\Delta y^{(p+2)}$ from Eqs. (1.38) and (1.36) now leads to

$$\Delta\phi^{(p+2)} = f_{y'y'}^{-1}(\phi_y)^2 \, \Delta\lambda^{(p)} \tag{1.39}$$

and finally, by III′ and normality, the conclusion follows.

Corollary 1a. *Under the same hypothesis*

$$\phi^{(p+2)}\lambda^{(p)} < 0 \tag{1.40}$$

where the two factors belong to the R and the B continuations respectively.

PROOF. Two cases occur, which shall be referred to as R and B.

CASE R. If ξ belongs to a R-arc, the RB and the RR transitions must be considered. For the RB transition, $\lambda(x) = 0$, $\lambda_-^{(p)}(\xi) = 0$ for $x \leq \xi$, and $\phi(x) = 0$, $\phi_+^{(p+2)}(\xi) = 0$ for $x \geq \xi$. Hence (1.34) becomes $\phi_-^{(p+2)}\lambda_+^{(p)} < 0$, where the two factors are the lowest nonvanishing derivatives at ξ. For the RR transition all the existing derivatives of $y(x)$ are continuous at ξ, so that $\phi_-^{(p+2)} = \phi_+^{(p+2)}$. Since ϕ_- refers to the same R-arc, the last two equations imply (1.40).

CASE B. If ξ belongs to a B-arc, the BR and BB transitions must be considered. Analogous reasoning shows that $\phi_+^{(p+2)}\lambda^{(p)} < 0$ and $\lambda_-^{(p)} = \lambda_+^{(p)}$, again leading to (1.40).

We shall now inquire whether the two continuations indicated in (1.40) meet both the requirements $\phi \geq 0$ and $\lambda \leq 0$. The question is settled by

Theorem 3a. *If the hypothesis of Lemma* 1a *holds, then the extremal has either two continuations or none:* (1) *for p even there exists a continuation in the region and a continuation in the boundary;* (2) *for p odd there is no continuation.*

PROOF. Case R. If ξ belongs to R-arc the dominant terms of the Taylor series expansion of $\lambda(x)$ and $\phi(x)$ about ξ in powers of $\varepsilon = |x - \xi|$ are given by

$$\begin{aligned} &\lambda(\xi + \varepsilon) = \varepsilon^p \lambda_+^{(p)}(\xi)/p! + \cdots && (RB) \\ &\phi(\xi \pm \varepsilon) = (\pm 1)^p \varepsilon^{p+2} \phi^{(p+2)}(\xi)/(p+2)! + \cdots && (RR) \end{aligned} \tag{1.41}$$

for the *RB* and the *RR* continuations respectively. Since $\phi(\xi - \varepsilon) > 0$, Eqs. (1.41) and (1.40) imply two possibilities: (1) When p is even: $\phi^{(p+2)} > 0$, $\phi(\xi + \varepsilon) > 0$, $\lambda_+^{(p)} < 0$, $\lambda(\xi + \varepsilon) < 0$. The *RB* and *RR* transitions satisfy the respective requirements $\lambda(\xi + \varepsilon) < 0$ and $\phi(\xi + \varepsilon) > 0$. Both continuations being possible, an extremaloid arc tangent to the boundary splits off a boundary subarc. (2) When p is odd: $\phi^{(p+2)} < 0$, $\phi(\xi + \varepsilon) < 0$, $\lambda_+^{(p)} > 0$, $\lambda(\xi + \varepsilon) > 0$. Both transitions violate the respective requirements, and neither continuation is possible; the extremaloid thus comes to a *dead-end*.

Case *B*. If ξ belongs to a *B*-arc, (1.41) is replaced by

$$\begin{aligned} \phi(\xi + \varepsilon) &= \varepsilon^{p+2}\phi_+^{(p+2)}(\xi)/(p+2)! + \cdots \qquad &(BR) \\ \lambda(\xi \pm \varepsilon) &= (\pm 1)^p \varepsilon^p \lambda^{(p)}(\xi)/p! + \cdots \qquad &(BB) \end{aligned} \tag{1.42}$$

Since $\lambda(\xi - \varepsilon) < 0$, (1.42) and (1.40) again imply two possibilities: (1) When p is even: $\lambda^{(p)} < 0$, $\lambda(\xi + \varepsilon) < 0$, $\phi^{(p+2)} > 0$, $\phi(\xi + \varepsilon) > 0$. Both continuations being possible at $x = \xi$, a boundary extremaloid splits off a tangent subarc. (2) When p is odd: $\lambda^{(p)} > 0$, $\lambda(\xi + \varepsilon) > 0$, $\phi^{(p+2)} < 0$, $\phi(\xi + \varepsilon) < 0$. Neither continuation being possible the extremaloid comes to a dead-end.

An illustration of the theory is furnished by the following example. Consider a boundary extremal subarc with

$$f = (1 + y'^2)^{1/2}, \qquad \phi = y - x^3$$

Then $y(x) = x^3$, $y' = 3x^2$, $y'' = 6x$, $y''' = 6$, and $\lambda(x) = 6x(1 + 9x^4)^{-3/2}$, with the aid of (1.20). At $\xi = 0$, we find $\lambda(\xi) = 0$, $\lambda'(\xi) = 6$. It follows from (1.40) that $p = 1$. Since p is odd, the diagnosis is a dead-end. A string stretched along a convex boundary $\phi = 0$ provides a physical interpretation of the fact that a geodesic $y(x)$ has no continuation beyond a point of inflection, where $y''(\xi) = 0$ and $y'''(\xi) > 0$.

More sophisticated examples can be found in problems of optimum control, such as Garfinkel.[6]

1.5 The Extremaloid Index

Since $y^{(k+2)}(x)$ at $x = \xi_-$ exists for $k = 0, 1, \ldots, r$, the successive derivatives of $\phi(x)$ and $\lambda(x)$ at $x = \xi_-$ can be determined. This can be done by the repeated differentiation of $\phi(x) = \phi(x, y(x))$ if the subarc is in R, or of the Euler equation (20.2) if the subarc is in B. Let q be the order of the lowest nonvanishing derivative of the set $(\phi^{(p+2)}, \lambda^{(p)})$ at $x = \xi_-$, and let the index $i(\xi)$ be defined as 0 if q is even, and as 1 if q is odd.

In terms of the index $i(\xi)$, the behavior of the extremaloid can be summarized by the following:

Theorem 4a. *If $\phi_{y'} \equiv 0$ and if $\phi(\xi) = 0$, then at $x = \xi$ the extremaloid either splits, undergoing both a trivial and a nontrivial transition, or it comes to a dead-end, depending on whether the index is zero or one.*

Note that the statement covers the situation $\phi' < 0$, not included in the proof based on (1.40). Here $q = i = 1$, and a dead-end occurs if a corner is excluded.

1.6 The Imbedding Construction

In order to test the sufficient conditions, the test-curve E_{12} is imbedded in families of extremals. If both end-points are in R, a typical test curve is of the structural type RBR; i.e., it contains one B-subarc. Let ξ_1 and ξ_2 refer to the points of entry and exit respectively.

In the imbedding construction, two one-parameter families $y(x, \alpha)$ and $e(x, \xi)$ will be used. The first one is the central family of R-extremals issuing from (x_1, y_1); the second is generated on the locus $\phi = 0$ by the BR transition. The existence of the latter family is assured by $\lambda < 0$ and Theorem 4a. The parameter ξ is the value of x at the point of exit. The two families are separated by their common extremal, which is the trivial continuation beyond $x = \xi_1$ of the member of $y(x, \alpha)$ that is tangent to $\phi = 0$. The union of the two families is a simply connected region.

Exclusive of the B-subarc, the test-curve E_{12} is imbedded for some $\alpha = \alpha_0$ in the central family $y(x, \alpha)$, and for $\xi = \xi_0$ in the exiting family $e(x, \xi)$, where $\xi_0 = \xi_2$. The B-subarc $\phi = 0$, being tangent to the members of the family $e(x, \xi)$, is contained in the family envelope, satisfying on $\phi = 0$ the relation

$$e_\xi(\xi, \xi) = 0 \tag{1.43}$$

From the assumed continuity of f it follows that there exists a N-neighborhood of x, y, y' on the B-subarc that is covered by the extremal family $e(x, \xi)$.

The extension of the analysis to the case of several B-subarcs presents no difficulties.

1.7 Condition IV

In view of (1.43), condition IV is stated as follows:

A curve E_{12} is said to satisfy condition IV′ if it does not contain points belonging to the envelopes, distinct from $\phi = 0$, of the families imbedding E_{12}.

The analytic statement of the condition is given by the requirement

$$\begin{aligned} y_\alpha(x, \alpha_0) &\neq 0, & x_1 < x \leq \xi_1 \\ e_\xi(x, \xi_0) &\neq 0, & \xi_0 < x \leq x_2 \end{aligned} \tag{1.44}$$

The continuity of f implies the extension of IV′ to some neighborhood N_2 of E_{12}. There the functions $\alpha(x, y)$ and $\xi(x, y)$ exist, and the *covering* of N_2 by extremals is said to be *simple*. As shown in Sec. 2.9, IV′ and $n = 1$ imply that the families $y(x, \alpha)$ and $e(x, \xi)$ are fields in N_2.

With "$\leq x_2$" in (1.44) replaced by "$< x_2$," condition IV′ becomes the necessary condition IV.

1.8 Proof of Sufficiency

Conditions I, II_N', and IV′ are sufficient for a strong relative minimum. We shall show that a test-curve E_{12} satisfying these conditions yields a lower value for the integral I than any other admissible curve joining the end-points and lying in some neighborhood M.

Let N_1 be the xy-projection of the N-neighborhood in which II_N' holds; let N_2 be the xy-neighborhood in which IV′ holds. In the light of Secs. 1.5 and 1.6, the neighborhood M defined by

$$M = N_1 \cap N_2 \tag{1.45}$$

has the following properties:

1. M is simply covered by one-parameter families $y(x, \alpha)$ and $e(x, \xi)$ of extremals.
2. Each of the two families is a field in M.
3. The boundary between the two fields is their common extremal.
4. M is the union of the two fields and is simply connected.
5. On every curve in M, the E-function, calculated with y' the slope of the field and Y' the slope of the curve, is positive for all $Y' \neq y'$. The proof of sufficiency depends on Lemmas 3 and 4 of the next chapter, and is essentially the same as the proof given there in Sec. 2.9. If the minimum is unique and if M extends over the entire region $\phi \geq 0$, then the minimum is absolute.

1.9 Numerical Example

The solution of a problem contains the following stages:

1. Construct the central family $y(x, \alpha)$ of extremals through (x_1, y_1), and a family $e(x, \xi)$ of extremals exiting from $\phi = 0$.
2. Determine the point ξ_1 of entry.
3. From the end-conditions determine the parameters α_0 and ξ_0.
4. Test the sufficient conditions.

The outline is designed for extremaloids of the type *RBR*. Degenerate cases, symbolized by *R*, *B*, *RB*, and *BR* must also be considered.

In example (a) of Sec. 1.0,

$$f = (1 + y'^2)^{1/2}, \qquad \phi = y - x^3 + 3x$$
$$x_1 = -3, \qquad y_1 = -11; \qquad x_2 = 1, \qquad y_2 = 2$$

Observe that: (1) R-extremals are straight lines, and the B-extremal is a cubic; (2) the end-points are in R, and the line joining them violates the inequality $\phi \geq 0$. We therefore seek a solution of the form RBR. The R and B types of arc are characterized in Table II, with m and b appearing as constants of integration in the solution of the Euler equations.

TABLE II

FAMILIES OF EXTREMALS

	R	B
$y(x)$	$mx + b$	$x^3 - 3x$
$\lambda(x)$	0	$6x(10 - 18x^2 + 9x^4)^{-3/2}$
$\phi(x)$	$-x^3 + (m+3)x + b$	0

The initial condition yields $b = 3m - 11$, and the central family of extremals,

$$y(x, m) = m(x + 3) - 11 \tag{1.46}$$

with the corresponding ϕ given by

$$\phi = -x^3 + (m + 3)x + 3m - 11 \tag{1.47}$$

For a continuous entry, the relations $\phi = \phi' = 0$ yield

$$m = 9, \qquad x = \xi_1 = -2 \tag{1.48}$$

which corresponds to the extremal

$$y = 9x + 16 \tag{1.49}$$

On the B-subarc,

$$y = x^3 - 3x, \qquad y' = 3x^2 - 3 \tag{1.50}$$

For a continuous exit at $x = \xi$, the relation $\Delta y' = 0$ leads to

$$y_+' = 3\xi^2 - 3 \tag{1.51}$$

The equation of the exiting family $e(x, \xi)$ can then be written as

$$\begin{aligned} y = e(x, \xi) &= 3(\xi^2 - 1)(x - \xi) + \xi^3 - 3\xi \\ &= 3(\xi^2 - 1)x - 2\xi^3 \end{aligned} \tag{1.52}$$

and

$$\lambda'\phi_{y'} + \lambda\left(\frac{d}{dx}\phi_{y'} - \phi_y\right) + \frac{d}{dx}f_{y'} - f_y = 0 \tag{1.58}$$
$$\phi' = \phi_x + \phi_y y' + \phi_{y'} y'' = 0$$

Again, the Hilbert condition is assured by III′ and the assumed normality $\phi_{y'} \neq 0$ on the extremal. It follows that y'' and λ' exist and are in C^r, and that the Euler equations have a unique solution.

Since $\phi_{y'} \neq 0$, the differentials dx and dy in (1.16) are arbitrary, and the corner condition becomes

$$\Delta(F - y'F_{y'}) = 0, \qquad \Delta F_{y'} = 0 \tag{1.59}$$

from which the two unknown y_+' and λ_+ are to be determined. Since $F = f + \lambda\phi$ and $\lambda\phi = 0$, (1.59) can be written

$$\Delta[f - y'(f_{y'} + \lambda\phi_{y'})] = 0, \qquad \Delta(f_{y'} + \lambda\phi_{y'}) = 0 \tag{1.60}$$

Theorem 1 of Sec. 1.3 remains valid; in the proof f is replaced by F, and κ is set equal to zero, again leading to

$$E(y_-', y_+') = 0 \tag{1.61}$$

at the junction. As in case (a), we limit ourselves to continuous transitions, characterized by

$$\Delta y' = 0 \tag{1.62}$$

For such transitions (1.60) implies

$$\Delta\lambda = 0 \tag{1.63}$$

so that, in contrast to case (a), the multiplier $\lambda(x)$ is continuous.

Entry is thus subject to the conditions

$$\phi = 0, \qquad \Delta y' = 0, \qquad \Delta\lambda = 0 \tag{1.64}$$

By symmetry, the conditions

$$\lambda = 0, \qquad \Delta y' = 0, \qquad \Delta\lambda = 0 \tag{1.65}$$

hold for exit. In both transitions, the unknown ξ, y_+', λ_+ are to be determined from a system of three equations. For a family $y(x, \alpha)$, the solution furnishes $\xi_1(\alpha)$ and $\xi_2(\alpha)$, which define the *entry locus* E_1 and the *exit locus* E_2 of the family. In contrast to case (a), both transitions preserve the number of degrees of freedom.

Since y' and λ are continuous, and since y'' and λ' are generally discontinuous at junctions, it follows from the Hilbert theorem that $y''(x)$ and $\lambda'(x)$ are in (C^r, D^0).

1.11 Singularities in Case (b)

For a composite arc, the system (1.15) is replaced by

$$\frac{d}{dx} F_{y'} = F_y, \qquad \frac{d}{dx}(\lambda\phi) = 0 \tag{1.66}$$

which is linear in y'', λ' and has the Hilbert determinant

$$H \equiv \begin{vmatrix} F_{y'y'} & \phi_{y'} \\ \lambda\phi_{y'} & \phi \end{vmatrix} = \phi F_{y'y'} - \lambda(\phi_{y'})^2 \tag{1.67}$$

From III′, the normality, and $\lambda\phi = 0$ it follows that $H = 0$ iff $\phi = \lambda = 0$.

Lemma 1b. *If $\phi_{y'} \neq 0$ and if $\phi(\xi) = 0$, then at the point $x = \xi$ of a continuous nontrivial transition*

$$\Delta\phi^{(p+1)}\,\Delta\lambda^{(p+1)} < 0 \tag{1.68}$$

The proof proceeds as in Lemma 1a of Sec. 1.4, with the replacement of λ, ϕ_y, ϕ'' by $-\lambda'$, $\phi_{y'}$, ϕ' respectively in (1.35–1.39).

Corollary 1b. *Under the same hypothesis,*

$$\phi_+^{(p+1)}\lambda_+^{(p+1)} > 0 \tag{1.69}$$

where the two factors belong to the R and the B continuations respectively.

The proof proceeds as in Corollary 1a of Sec. 1.4, with the replacement of $\phi^{(p+2)}$, $\lambda^{(p)}$ by $\phi^{(p+1)}$, $\lambda^{(p+1)}$ respectively.

Theorem 3b. *If the hypothesis of Lemma 1b holds, then the extremal has a unique continuation: (1) for $p + 1$ even, an R-arc continues in R, and a B-arc continues in B; (2) for $p + 1$ odd, an R-arc continues in B, and a B-arc continues in R.*

Proof. Case *R*. Equation (1.41) is replaced by

$$\begin{aligned} \lambda(\xi + \varepsilon) &= \varepsilon^{p+1}\lambda_+^{(p+1)}(\xi)/(p+1)! + \cdots && (RR) \\ \phi(\xi \pm \varepsilon) &= (\pm 1)^{p+1}\varepsilon^{p+1}\phi^{(p+1)}(\xi)/(p+1)! + \cdots && (RB) \end{aligned} \tag{1.70}$$

Then (1.70), (1.69), and $\phi(\xi - \varepsilon) > 0$ imply either (1) or (2): (1) $p + 1$ is even: the quantities $\phi^{(p+1)}$, $\phi(\xi + \varepsilon)$, $\lambda_+^{(p+1)}$, $\lambda(\xi + \varepsilon)$ are positive; no entry can occur, and the extremaloid continues in the region; (2) $p + 1$ is odd: the same quantities are negative, so that entry is the unique extremaloid continuation.

CASE B. Equation (1.42) is replaced by

$$\begin{aligned} \phi(\xi + \varepsilon) &= \varepsilon^{p+1}\phi_+^{(p+1)}(\xi)/(p+1)! + \cdots \qquad (BR) \\ \lambda(\xi \pm \varepsilon) &= (\pm 1)^{p+1}\varepsilon^{p+1}(\xi)/(p+1)! + \cdots \qquad (BB) \end{aligned} \tag{1.71}$$

Now (1.71), (1.69), and $\lambda(\xi - \varepsilon) < 0$ imply two possibilities: (1) when $p+1$ is even the quantities $\lambda^{(p+1)}$, $\lambda(\xi + \varepsilon)$, $\phi^{(p+1)}$, $\phi(\xi + \varepsilon)$ are negative; no exit can occur, and the extremaloid continues in the boundary. (2) when $p + 1$ is odd: the same quantities are positive, so that exit is the unique extremaloid continuation.

In terms of the index $i(x)$, defined in Sec. 1.5, the behavior of an extremaloid can be summarized by the following.

Theorem 4b. *If $\phi_{y'} \neq 0$ and if $\phi(\xi) = 0$, then at $x = \xi$ the extremaloid undergoes a trivial or a nontrivial transition depending on whether the index is zero or one.*

Note that the statement covers the situation $\lambda < 0$, not included in the proof based on (1.69). Here $q = i = 0$, and only the trivial transition BB occurs.

1.12 The Imbedding Construction

Since y' is not prescribed at the end-points, it is not possible to ascertain *a priori* whether the end-points of the solution curve lie in $\phi > 0$ or in $\phi = 0$. Extremals that issue from (x_1, y_1) therefore comprise a central family $y(x, \alpha)$ of R-extremals and one B-extremal, to be designated as B_1.

The entry-locus E_1 of the family $y(x, \alpha)$, and the corresponding $\xi_1(\alpha)$ are determined from the solution of (1.64). With $\xi_1(\alpha)$ known the B-subarcs are constructed as follows. Let $y = g(x, \beta)$ and $\lambda = \lambda(x, \gamma)$ be the solutions of the differential equations $\phi = 0$ and the Euler equation (1.58). Since y and λ are continuous at $x = \xi_1$, the parameters β and γ are expressed in terms of α with the aid of the equations

$$y[\xi_1(\alpha), \alpha] = g[\xi_1(\alpha), \beta], \qquad \lambda[\xi_1(\alpha), \gamma] = 0 \tag{1.72}$$

leading to $\beta = \beta(\alpha)$ and $\gamma = \gamma(\alpha)$.

With $\beta(\alpha)$ and $\gamma(\alpha)$ known, the equations of the family of B-subarcs can be written in the form $y = g(x, \alpha)$, $\lambda = \lambda(x, \alpha)$. The exit-locus E_2 of the family can then be determined from

$$\lambda(\xi_2, \alpha) = 0 \tag{1.73}$$

leading to $\xi_2 = \xi_2(\alpha)$.

The family $y(x, \alpha)$ thus generates a central family of RBR extremaloids, with $y(x, \alpha)$ assuming different functional representations on various subarcs.

In contrast to case (a), the imbedding construction extends to the entire curve E_{12}. The case of more than one B-subarc presents no difficulties.

On the B_1-extremal through (x_1, y_1), the multiplier λ is obtained from (1.58) in the form $\lambda = \lambda(x, \xi)$, where ξ is arbitrary. At every point of B_1 for which there exists a ξ such that $\lambda = 0$ and $\lambda' > 0$ an extremal exits into R. The set of such points belongs to the exit locus E_2, generating a family $e(x, \xi)$, which is enveloped by B_1. Without any loss of generality, ξ can be taken as the value of x for which $\lambda = 0$.

Condition IV′ requires that E_{12} contain no points belonging to the envelopes, distinct from B_1, of the families of extremals that imbed E_{12}. If E_{12} is imbedded for $\alpha = \alpha_0$ in the central family $y(x, \alpha)$ of extremaloids, IV′ takes the form

$$y_\alpha(x, \alpha_0) \neq 0, \qquad x_1 < x \leq x_2; \tag{1.74}$$

if E_{12} is also imbedded for $\xi = \xi_0$ in a noncentral family $e(x, \xi)$, then (1.74) is replaced by

$$\begin{matrix} y_\alpha(x, \alpha_0) \neq 0, & e_\xi(x, \xi_0) \neq 0 \\ x_1 < x \leq \xi_0, & \xi_0 < x \leq x_2 \end{matrix} \tag{1.75}$$

As in case (a), IV′ implies its extension to a neighborhood of (x, y), in which the imbedding families are fields. The proof of sufficiency is essentially the same as in case (a). A novel feature is that adjoining fields are separated by one of the loci E_1 and E_2, on which the corner condition is trivially satisfied.

1.13 Numerical Example

The solution generally involves the following stages:

(1) Construct the central family of R-extremals and the B_1-extremal through (x_1, y_1).

(2) Construct the entry and exit loci E_1 and E_2.

(3) Construct the continuations of the initial subarcs of step (1), and determine the parameters α_0 and ξ_0 from the end-conditions.

(4) Test the sufficient conditions.

In example (b) of Sec. 1.0,

$$\begin{matrix} f = y'^2, & \phi = y' - x \\ x_1 = 0, \quad y_1 = 0; & x_2 = 3, \quad y_2 = 5 \end{matrix}$$

Observe that: (1) the R-extremals are straight lines and the B-extremals are parabolas; (2) the straight line joining the end-points violates the requirement $\phi \geq 0$. Therefore we seek a solution of the structural types RBR and BR. The

R and B types of arc are characterized in Table V, with m, b, β, and γ appearing as constants of integration in the solution of Euler equations.

TABLE V

FAMILIES OF EXTREMALS

	R	B
$y(x)$	$mx + b$	$\frac{1}{2}(x^2 + \beta)$
$\lambda(x)$	0	$2(\gamma - x)$
$\phi(x)$	$m - x$	0

The initial condition yields $b = 0$ and $\beta = 0$. The central family of R-extremals can then be written as

$$y(x, m) = mx \qquad \begin{array}{ll} 0 \le x \le m & \text{if } \; m \ge 0 \\ 0 < x < \infty & \text{if } \; m < 0; \end{array} \tag{1.76}$$

the B_1-extremal is

$$y = \tfrac{1}{2}x^2, \qquad \lambda = 2(\xi - x) \qquad (0 \le x \le \xi) \tag{1.77}$$

with $\gamma = \xi$.

The entry locus E_1, obtained from (1.64), corresponds to

$$x = \xi_1 = m, \qquad y = \eta_1 = m^2 \tag{1.78}$$

The B-subarcs generated by the RB transition are determined as in (1.72), with $g = \frac{1}{2}(x^2 + \beta)$ and $\lambda = 2(\gamma - x)$, leading to

$$\beta = m^2 \qquad \gamma = m \tag{1.79}$$

and

$$y = \tfrac{1}{2}(x^2 + m^2), \qquad \lambda = 2(m - x) \tag{1.80}$$

Since $\lambda' < 0$ on the B-subarcs, including B_1, the exit locus E_2 does not exist, and we are limited to extremaloids of the type RB. The terminal condition yields $m = 1$, which corresponds to the test-curve defined by

$$\begin{array}{lll} y = x & & (0 \le x \le 1) \\ y = \tfrac{1}{2}(x^2 + 1), & \lambda = 2(1 - x) & (1 \le x \le 3) \end{array} \tag{1.81}$$

To test the sufficient conditions, we note that: (1) condition Ic is satisfied, since $\lambda \le 0$ on the B-subarc; (2) since

$$F_{y'y'} = 2 \tag{1.82}$$

condition III_F' and, *a fortiori*, II_N' are satisfied; (3) condition IV′ holds in virtue of the following relations:

$$\begin{array}{ll} y_m(x, 1) = x \neq 0, & y_m(x, 1) = 1 \neq 0 \\ 0 < x \leq 1 & 1 \leq x \leq 3 \end{array} \tag{1.83}$$

A strong relative minimum is thus assured.

The extremaloid index $i(x)$ is calculated in Table VI, which is analogous to Table III of case (a):

TABLE VI

EXTREMALOID INDEX $i(x)$

$x = m$	$\phi' = -1$	$q = 1$	$i = 1$
$x > m$	$\lambda = 2(m - x)$	$q = 0$	$i = 0$

In view of Theorem 4b, entry occurs at $x = m$, and no exit is possible for $x > m$, in agreement with previous conclusions.

If the terminal condition is replaced by $x_2 = a$, $y_2 = b$, then in various regions of the *ab*-plane the solution curve belongs to the structural types *R*, *RB*, and *B*, as indicated in Table VII.

TABLE VII

SOLUTION TYPE

Type	Location of the terminal point
R	$b \geq a^2$
RB	$\frac{1}{2}a^2 < b < a^2$
B	$b = \frac{1}{2}a^2$
No solution	$b < \frac{1}{2}a^2$

The simple covering of the region $\phi \geq 0$, $x^2 \leq 2y$ is depicted in Fig. 2. Since the minimum is unique, and since the neighborhood *M* extends over the entire region, the minimum is absolute.

1.14 Discussion of the Results

If the results of this chapter are to be extended to $n > 1$, the sufficient conditions must include the vanishing of the Hilbert integral I^* on every closed path in *M*.

2

Discontinuities in a Variational Problem

BORIS GARFINKEL†
BALLISTIC RESEARCH LABORATORIES,
ABERDEEN PROVING GROUND, MARYLAND

2.0 Introduction

The frequent occurrence of optimization problems with discontinuous control variables has focused the attention of mathematicians and engineers upon the old subject of discontinuous solutions in the calculus of variations. A solution curve is generally of class D^1, admitting discontinuities in y'.

† *Present address:* Yale University Observatory, New Haven, Connecticut.

Such discontinuities, commonly referred to as *corners*, are subject to the Weierstrass-Erdmann corner condition. Three types of corner may be distinguished: (1) *free corners*, arising from the nonconvexity of the integrand function $f(x, y, y')$ with respect to y'; (2) *reflection corners*, occurring on the boundary $\phi(x, y) = 0$ of the region $\phi \geq 0$; (3) *refraction corners*, arising from the discontinuity of f on some locus $\phi(x, y, y') = 0$.

The terms reflection and refraction have been borrowed from geometrical optics, governed by the variational Fermat principle. In this chapter we are primarily concerned with refraction in the problem of Lagrange, illustrated by the following two examples:

(a) Find the curve $y(x)$ that joins the points (0, 0) and (13, 61), and minimizes the integral

$$\int_0^{13} f\,dx$$

where $f = y'^2$ if $\phi \equiv y - \frac{1}{4}x^2 - 16 > 0$, $f = \frac{4}{3}y'^2$ if $\phi < 0$, and either value of f can be assumed if $\phi = 0$.

(b) Find the curve $y(x)$ that joins the points (0, 0) and (9, 54), and minimizes the integral

$$\int_0^{9} f\,dx$$

where $f = \frac{1}{4}y'^2 + y'$ if $\phi \equiv y' - x > 0$, $f = \frac{1}{4}y'^2 + 4$ if $\phi < 0$, and either value of f can be assumed if $\phi = 0$.

Both problems are solved in the text with the aid of the theory developed in this chapter.

The general problem can be formulated as follows. Let $\mathscr{R}$ be a set of points (x, y, w) in which the functions $f^-(x, y, w)$, $f^+(x, y, w)$, and $\phi(x, y, w)$ are defined, and have continuous derivatives up to the third order. An admissible curve $y(x)$ has its elements (x, y, y') in $\mathscr{R}$, and has a piecewise continuous first derivative y'. In the class of admissible curves, we seek a $y(x)$ that joins the fixed points (x_1, y_1) and (x_2, y_2), and minimizes the integral

$$I = \int_{x_1}^{x_2} f(x, y, y')\,dx \tag{2.1}$$

where

$$\begin{aligned} &f = f^- && \text{if} \quad \phi < 0 \\ &f = f^+ && \text{if} \quad \phi > 0 \\ &f = f^- \quad \text{or} \quad f = f^+ && \text{if} \quad \phi = 0 \end{aligned} \tag{2.2}$$

In the notation of Bolza,[1] $y(x)$ is of class (C^1, D^1), admitting a finite number of corners. Generally, y is an n-vector. In order to simplify the exposition, two assumptions will be made: (1) an admissible curve contains no more than one refraction corner; (2) $n = 1$.

A special case, solved by Bliss,[2] is characterized by the following restrictions: (1) ϕ is a function of x and y only; (2) an admissible curve contains no more than one point of $\phi = 0$. As this case does not cover situations frequently arising in optimum control,[3] there is a need for a more general solution of the refraction problem. Such a solution, removing the two restrictions imposed by Bliss, will be constructed in this chapter.

Two cases of the problem, illustrated by examples (a) and (b) above, are distinguished: (a) $\phi = \phi(x, y)$; (b) $\phi = \phi(x, y, y')$. These cases are treated in Parts A and B, respectively, following Sec. 2.1. The necessary and sufficient conditions of the calculus of variations are discussed in Secs. 2.1, 2.2, 2.7, 2.12, and 2.17–2.20; the proof of sufficiency appears in Secs. 2.9 and 2.20. In Secs. 2.3 and 2.14 the four basic types of refraction are classified, and the corner condition is used to construct a refracted continuation of an extremal. A graphical construction, based on the Zermelo diagram, is described in Secs. 2.5 and 2.14. The question of the existence and uniqueness of such continuations is investigated in Secs. 2.4 and 2.16, and the results are used in Secs. 2.6 and 2.19 to construct the fields required in sufficiency proofs. Numerical examples are worked out in Secs. 2.10 and 2.21. Finally, the results are summarized in Secs. 2.11 and 2.22.

The boundary $\phi = 0$ is the analog of the *interface* of the geometrical optics. Since two values of f are associated with a point in $\phi = 0$, we shall distinguish the two sides B^- and B^+ of the locus $\phi = 0$, with B^- corresponding to the choice $f = f^-$, and B^+ to $f = f^+$. We shall use the notation R^-, R^+ for the regions $\phi < 0$ and $\phi > 0$, denote the closures $R^- \cup B^-$ and $R^+ \cup B^+$ by $\phi \leq 0$ and $\phi \geq 0$, respectively, and follow the terminology of the last chapter in referring to arcs in R and in B as R-arcs and B-arcs, respectively.

A curve is said to be *normal* if $\phi_y \neq 0$ in case (a), and $\phi_{y'} \neq 0$ in case (b) for every (x, y, y') belonging to the curve. Normality will be assumed.

2.1 Conditions Ic and Id

Condition Ic, stated in the previous chapter as Eq. (1.84), requires the following modification:

$$\begin{aligned} \lambda \geq 0 \quad & \text{if } f = f^- \\ \lambda \leq 0 \quad & \text{if } f = f^+ \end{aligned} \tag{2.3}$$

As shown in Sec. 1.5 of Chap. 1, the condition precludes the occurrence of a *dead-end* in case (a), and assures the existence of an extremal *exiting* from the B-subarc into R. Clearly, the second part of Eq. (1.84) is satisfied if $\lambda \neq 0$.

Condition Id, which must be satisfied on $\phi \equiv 0$, is

$$f = \min(f^+, f^-) \tag{2.4}$$

In other words, on a B-subarc of a minimizing curve, f must assume the lesser of the two values f^+ and f^- for given (x, y, y'). The derivation of this condition involves the concept of a "crossover" variation, involving the exchange of the values f^+ and f^- on $\phi = 0$ without any alteration of the values x, y, y'. Such a variation is defined by

$$\begin{aligned} &\delta y(x) \equiv 0 \\ &\delta f = f^+ - f^- \quad \text{if } f = f^- \\ & = f^- - f^+ \quad \text{if } f = f^+ \end{aligned} \tag{2.5}$$

In order to derive (2.4), let the crossover variation be applied on some interval (ξ_1, ξ_2) of a B-subarc of a minimizing curve. Then the integral I of (2.1) receives an increment

$$\Delta I = \int_{\xi_1}^{\xi_2} \delta f \, dx \tag{2.6}$$

Since it is necessary that $\Delta I \geq 0$, and since (ξ_1, ξ_2) is arbitrary, it follows that $\delta f \geq 0$ for all x on the B-subarc, and (2.4) follows immediately.

Conditions Ia and Ib of the previous chapter are retained here without change; the combination Ia, b, c, d will be designated as condition I. We shall apply the term *extremaloid* to a curve that satisfies condition I, in contrast to *extremal*, which is a solution of the Euler equations. The particular extremaloid that satisfies the prescribed end-conditions will be referred to as the test-curve, and designated as E_{12}.

PART A—CASE (a)

2.2 Conditions Ia, Ib, II, and III

The necessary conditions for a strong relative minimum include I–IV; the sufficient conditions comprise I, III″, and IV′. Condition I consists of Ia, Ib, Ic, and Id, of which the last two have been discussed in Sec. 2.1.

The Euler condition Ia assumes the form

$$\begin{aligned} &\frac{d}{dx} f_{y'} = f_y \qquad \lambda \equiv 0 \qquad \text{if } \phi \neq 0 \\ &\lambda = \left(\frac{d}{dx} f_{y'} - f_y\right) / \phi_y \qquad \text{if } \phi \equiv 0 \end{aligned} \tag{2.7}$$

The corner condition Ib becomes

$$\Delta(f - y'f_{y'}) = \kappa\phi_x, \qquad \Delta f_{y'} = \kappa\phi_y \tag{2.8}$$

where Δ denotes the jump at the corner, and κ is a constant.

Condition II, stated in the previous chapter, is retained here with the E-function defined by

$$E = f(Y') - f(y') - (Y' - y')f_{y'} \tag{2.9}$$

where x, y, y' belong to the curve and $\phi(x, y) \neq 0$. The following condition II_F' will be used in the proof of sufficiency:

A curve E_{12} is said to satisfy condition II_F' if there exists an F-neighborhood of (x, y) on E_{12} such that $E > 0$ for all (x, y) in F and for all $Y' \neq y'$.

Condition III requires that $f_{y'y'} \geq 0$ for all (x, y, y') of E_{12}. Condition III″ is a strengthened form of III′ of the preceding chapter. It requires that $f_{y'y'} > 0$ for all (x, y) of E_{12} and for all y', including $y' = \pm\infty$.

We shall show that III″ implies II_F'. If $\phi(x, y) \neq 0$, define a *unilateral* F-neighborhood of (x, y) as one that contains no point of $\phi = 0$. Since f is C^3 in F, III″ implies its extension, III_F'', to F. Furthermore, the mean value theorem applied to (2.9) in F leads to

$$E = \tfrac{1}{2}(Y' - y')^2 f_{y'y'}[y' + \Theta(Y' - y')] \qquad (0 < \Theta < 1) \tag{2.10}$$

Since $f_{y'y'} > 0$ by III_F'', it follows that $E > 0$. On the other hand, if $\phi(x, y) \equiv 0$ on a subarc of E_{12}, III″ holds on both B^- and B^+. By the preceding argument, III″ can be extended to a *bilateral* F-neighborhood, again leading to $E > 0$.

The remaining conditions IV and IV′ will be discussed in Sec. 2.7.

2.3 Preliminary Considerations

Let the end-points (x_1, y_1) and (x_2, y_2) lie in $\phi < 0$ and in $\phi > 0$, respectively. The six basic transitions on $\phi = 0$, listed in Table I, include four types of refraction, as well as the *entry* and the *exit* described in the previous

TABLE I

BASIC TRANSITIONS

R^-R^+	Region → region refraction
R^-B^+	Region → boundary refraction
B^-R^+	Boundary → region refraction
B^-B^+	Boundary → boundary refraction
R^-B^-	Entry
B^+R^+	Exit

chapter. In the latter two transitions, III″ implies that the R-subarc of the minimizing curve is tangent to the locus $\phi = 0$ at the junction of the R and the B-subarcs.

From $\phi = \phi(x, y)$ we derive

$$\phi' = \phi_x + \phi_y y' \tag{2.11}$$

At a corner, the left and the right-hand values of ϕ' are

$$\phi_-' = \phi_x + \phi_y y_-', \qquad \phi_+' = \phi_x = \phi_y y_+' \tag{2.12}$$

The case of reflection, where $\phi_-'\phi_+' < 0$, has been excluded in this chapter. For refraction it is necessary that $\phi_-'\phi_+' \geq 0$, with the equality holding only where refraction is *critical*. We shall use the latter term to describe the situation where the incident or the refracted extremal lies in the locus $\phi = 0$ or is tangent to it. Refraction is thus governed by the relations

$$\Delta(f - y'f_{y'}) = \kappa\phi_x, \qquad \Delta f_{y'} = \kappa\phi_y, \qquad \phi_-'\phi_+' \geq 0 \tag{2.13}$$

of which the first two constitute the corner condition (2.8). For a given extremal $y(x)$ intersecting $\phi = 0$, the corner condition furnishes two equations from which y_+' and κ are to be determined. The nonvanishing of the Jacobian $(\phi' f_{y'y'})_+$ is sufficient for the existence of a solution. Since $f_{y'y'} > 0$ by III′, a solution exists if $\phi_+' \neq 0$. The exceptional case $\phi_+' = 0$ includes the transitions R^-B^- and R^-B^+. Then the extremal indeed has two continuations, as shown in the previous chapter, with the boundary extremal splitting off an R-extremal tangent to the boundary $\phi = 0$.

The phenomenon of *critical reflection* in geometrical optics illustrates the fact that the corner condition may give rise to an imaginary refracted continuation. The question of whether or not (2.13) has a real and unique solution will be investigated next. For this purpose we shall use the function $h(y')$ of Sec. 2.4.

2.4 The Function *h(y′)*

The slope $\tilde{y}'$ of the locus $\phi = 0$, obtained from (2.11) with $\phi' = 0$, is given by

$$\tilde{y}' = -\phi_x/\phi_y \tag{2.14}$$

Let $h(y')$ be defined on $\phi = 0$ by

$$h(y') \equiv f(y') + (\tilde{y}' - y')f_{y'} \tag{2.15}$$

We shall distinguish h^- and h^+, corresponding to $f = f^-$ and $f = f^+$, respectively. Several theorems concerning $h(y')$ will be proved.

Theorem 1. *If* (x, y, y') *belongs to an extremaloid, the function* $h(y')$ *is continuous at a corner on* $\phi = 0$.

PROOF. The left and the right-hand values of h and the jump in h are given by

$$\begin{aligned} h_- &= f^-(y_-') + (\tilde{y}' - y_-')f_{y_-'}^-, \\ h_+ &= f^+(y_+') + (\tilde{y}' - y_+')f_{y_+'}^+, \\ \Delta h &= h_+ - h_- \end{aligned} \tag{2.16}$$

in the notation of the previous chapter. Then it follows from Eqs. (2.13)–(2.15) that

$$\Delta h = \Delta(f - y'f_{y'}) + \tilde{y}'\Delta f_{y'} = 0 \tag{2.17}$$

If the transition occurs in the reverse sense; i.e., from $\phi \geq 0$ to $\phi < 0$, the superscripts + and − are to be interchanged.

Thus the corner condition can be written $\Delta h = 0$, and (2.13) becomes

$$h_+ = h_-, \qquad (y_+' - \tilde{y}')(y_-' - \tilde{y}') \geq 0 \tag{2.18}$$

from which y_+' is to be determined for given (x, y, y_-').

Lemma 1. *If* III″ *holds, then* (a) *the function* $h(y')$ *has one and only one stationary point at* $y' = \tilde{y}'$, *which is a maximum;* (b) $h(\infty) = h(-\infty) = -\infty$; (c) *if* $\max h > 0$, *then* $h(y')$ *has two distinct roots lying on the opposite sides of* $\tilde{y}'$; *if* $\max h = 0$ *there is one root* $y' = \tilde{y}'$; *if* $\max h < 0$, *there are no real roots.*

To prove (a), note that

$$h_{y'} = (\tilde{y}' - y')f_{y'y'}, \qquad h_{y'y'} = -f_{y'y'} + (\tilde{y}' - y')f_{y'y'y'} \tag{2.19}$$

Since $f_{y'y'} > 0$, it follows that $h_{y'} = 0$ implies $y' = \tilde{y}'$ and $h_{y'y'} < 0$. Thus $y' = \tilde{y}'$ yields the one and only stationary point,

$$\max_{y'} h(y') = h(\tilde{y}') = f(\tilde{y}') \tag{2.20}$$

To prove (b), we use the mean value theorem and (2.19), leading to

$$\begin{aligned} h(y') &= h(\tilde{y}') + (y' - \tilde{y}')\bar{h}_{y'} \\ &= h(\tilde{y}') - (y' - \tilde{y}')^2\bar{f}_{y'y'} \end{aligned} \tag{2.21}$$

where the bar over a letter denotes its mean value, corresponding to the argument $\tilde{y}' + \theta(y' - \tilde{y}')$ with $0 < \theta < 1$. Since $f_{y'y'} > 0$, and since $\lim f_{y'y'} \neq 0$ as $|y'| \to \infty$, the conclusion follows.

To prove (c), we use (a), (b), and the C^2 continuity of f.

The question of the existence and uniqueness of a real refracted continuation for an extremal intersecting $\phi = 0$ can now be answered.

Theorem 2. *If an extremal intersects the locus* $\phi = 0$, *and if* III″ *holds, then the corner condition* (2.18) *furnishes one real* y_+' *or none, depending on the sign of the discriminant* D *defined by*

$$D \equiv f^+(\tilde{y}') - h_- \tag{2.22}$$

Three cases arise: (a) *if* $D > 0$, *then* $y_+' \neq \tilde{y}'$; (b) *if* $D = 0$, *then* $y_+' = \tilde{y}'$; (c) *if* $D < 0$, *then* y_+' *is imaginary.*

PROOF. Consider the function

$$g(y') \equiv h^+(y') - h_- \tag{2.23}$$

Since h_- is a constant, Lemma 1 applies to $g(y')$, leading to the conclusion that $g(y')$ is maximized at $y' = \tilde{y}'$, with

$$\max g(y') = D \tag{2.24}$$

and with real roots y_1' and y_2' such that $y_1' \leq \tilde{y}' \leq y_2'$ if $D \geq 0$. Note that if the roots are distinct, only one of them satisfies the second part of Eq. (2.18), and is to be identified with y_+'.

TABLE II

THE DISCRIMINANT D

Case	Transition types	Remarks
$D > 0$	R^-R^+, B^-R^+	$y_+' \neq \tilde{y}'$
$D = 0$	R^-B^+, B^-B^+	$y_+' = \tilde{y}'$
$D < 0$	None	y_+' imaginary

The three cases of Theorem 2 are summarized in Table II for $\phi_-' > 0$. The case $D = 0$ corresponds to refraction into B. In particular, for the B^-B^+ transition, $D = 0$ implies

$$\delta \equiv f^+(\tilde{y}') - f^-(\tilde{y}') = 0 \tag{2.25}$$

in agreement with Eq. (2.4). If $\delta'(x) \neq 0$ along the extremal, then the relations

$$\delta = 0, \quad \delta' < 0; \qquad \lambda^- > 0, \quad \lambda^+ < 0 \tag{2.26}$$

comprise Ic and Id for the B^-B^+ transition. Points of $\phi = 0$ where such a transition occurs will be called *critical points*, and will be designated by x_*. Their existence is proved by the following example:

$$f^- = (3 + y'^2)^{1/2}, \qquad f^+ = \tfrac{1}{2}y'^2 + 3y - 2x^2 + 2$$
$$\phi = y - \tfrac{1}{2}x^2 = 0$$

Then Eq. (2.25) and the second part of Eq. (2.7) yield

$$\delta = 2 - (3 + x^2)^{1/2}, \qquad \lambda^- = (3 + x^2)^{-3/2}, \qquad \lambda^+ = -2$$

Clearly, $x_* = 1$ leads to $\delta = 0$, $\delta' = -\frac{1}{2}$, $\lambda^- = \frac{1}{8}$, $\lambda^+ = -2$, which satisfies (2.26).

An important consequence of Theorem 2 is the following corollary.

Corollary. *At every point of an extremaloid subarc in $\phi = 0$ there exists a refracted continuation.*

The proof depends on the observation that on a B^--arc

$$h_- = f^-(\tilde{y}'), \qquad D = f^+(\tilde{y}') - f^-(\tilde{y}') \geq 0 \tag{2.27}$$

where the latter inequality follows from Id. The same argument applies to a B^+-arc with a suitable interchange of the + and − signs.

In addition to a refracted continuation, a B-arc also has the trivial continuation and the exiting continuation, discussed in detail in the previous chapter. Altogether there are three continuations, symbolized by B^-R^+, B^-B^-, and B^-R^- respectively.

2.5 Zermelo Diagram

A useful geometrical interpretation of the corner condition and of the E-function is provided by the graph of $f = f(y')$ with (x, y) fixed.

From Eqs. (2.14), (2.15), and (2.18) it follows that: (1) the tangent to $f^-(y')$ at $y' = y_-'$, and the tangent to $f^+(y')$ at $y' = y_+'$ intersect at the point $(\tilde{y}', h_-)$; (2) y_+' and y_-' lie on the same side of $\tilde{y}'$. A geometrical construction of y_+' for given (x, y, y_-') is shown in Fig. 1.

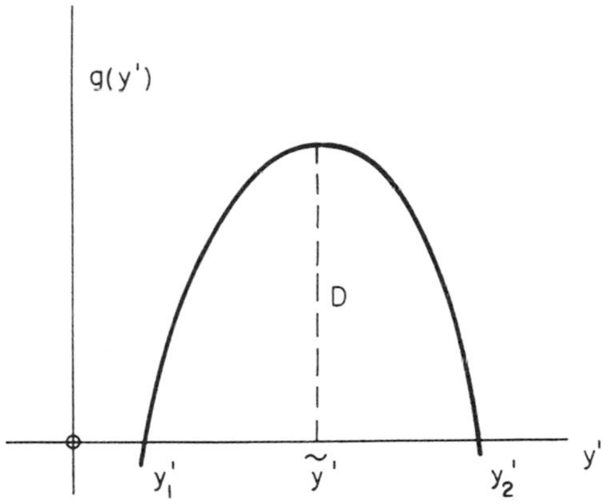

FIG. 1. Function $g(y)$.

It appears that the boundary between any two adjoining families is either their common extremal or the locus $\phi = 0$. The union of the six families is a simply-connected region.

The existence of the set S in some neighborhood of E_{12} is established in the following lemma.

Lemma 2. *There exists a neighborhood of the test-curve E_{12} that can be covered by a set of one-parameter families of extremals.*

PROOF. The interval $(\xi_1 - \varepsilon, \xi_2 + \varepsilon)$ of the locus $\phi = 0$ is decomposed into three subintervals, which will be examined in succession.

Subinterval $(\xi_1 - \varepsilon, \xi_1)$. Since an extremal through (x_1, y_1) is tangent to $\phi = 0$ at $x = \xi_1$, there exists an ε_1, such that every point in the subinterval can be reached by a member of the central family $y(x, \alpha)$. Since ξ_1 belongs to a B^--subarc of E_{12}, $D(\xi_1) > 0$ by the corollary of Sec. 2.4; furthermore, since $D(\xi)$ is continuous along $\phi = 0$, there exists an ε_2 such that $D > 0$ on the entire subinterval. Let $\varepsilon = \min(\varepsilon_1, \varepsilon_2)$. Then by Theorem 2, every member of $y(x, \alpha)$ that intersects $\phi = 0$ on $(\xi_1 - \varepsilon, \xi_1)$ has a refracted continuation in R^+.

Subinterval (ξ_1, ξ_*). By Ic and the corollary of Sec. 2.4, at every point an extremal exits from B^- into R^-, and is also critically refracted into R^+.

Subinterval $(x_*, \xi_2 + \varepsilon)$. Since $\lambda(\xi_2) < 0$ by Ic, and since $\lambda(x)$ is continuous at interior points of a B-subarc of a minimizing curve, as shown in the previous chapter, there exists an ε such that $\lambda < 0$ on the entire subinterval. By Ic and the corollary of Sec. 2.4, an extremal exits from B^+ into R^+, and is also critically refracted into R^-.

The B-subarc of E_{12}, separating adjacent families of extremals, is not a member of either. Exclusive of the B-subarc, the test-curve E_{12} is generally imbedded for some value $\alpha = \alpha_0$ in the central family $y(x, \alpha)$, and for the appropriate value $\xi = \xi_0$ in one of the families $r(x, \xi)$, $r^+(x, \xi)$, $e^+(x, \xi)$. The B-subarc of E_{12} adjoins a subset of (r, r^+, r^-, e^+, e^-), depending on the extremaloid type. A neighborhood of the subarc always includes $r(x, \xi)$, although the latter region touches $\phi = 0$ only at the point $x = \xi_1$. Parameters ξ are independent of α except in the family $r(x, \xi)$, generated by the R^-R^+ transition, where ξ is a function of α.

2.7 Condition IV′

Depending on the type of extremaloid, the neighborhood of E_{12} consists of two, four, or six families of S. We note that $\phi = 0$ is tangent to all the members of the families e^- and e^+ of exiting extremals. Consequently, the locus $\phi = 0$ is their envelope, and the relations

$$e_\xi^-(\xi, \xi) = 0, \qquad e_\xi^+(\xi, \xi) = 0 \tag{2.28}$$

are satisfied on $\phi = 0$. In view of this circumstance, condition IV′ is stated as follows.

A curve E_{12} satisfies condition IV′ if it does not contain points belonging to the envelopes, distinct from $\phi = 0$, of the families that imbed E_{12}.

The analytic formulation appears in Table IV. In the first two types.

TABLE IV

CONDITION IV′ OF JACOBI

Type	$\phi < 0$		$\phi > 0$	
R^-R^+	$y_\alpha(x, \alpha_0) \neq 0$ $x_1 \leq x \leq \xi_0$	$r_\xi(x, \xi_0) \neq 0$ $\xi_0 \leq x \leq x_2$		
$R^-B^-R^+$	$y_\alpha(x, \alpha_0) \neq 0$ $x_1 \leq x \leq \xi_1$	$r_\xi(\xi_1, \xi_1) \neq 0$ $x = \xi = \xi_1$	$r_\xi^+(\xi, \xi) \neq 0$ $\xi \leq x = \xi \leq \xi_0$	$r_\xi^+(x, \xi_0) \neq 0$ $\xi_0 \leq x \leq x_2$
$R^-B^-B^+R^+$	$y_\alpha(x, \alpha_0) \neq 0$ $x_1 \leq x \leq \xi_1$ $r_\xi^-(\xi, \xi) \neq 0$ $x_* \leq x = \xi \leq \xi_0$	$r_\xi(\xi_1, \xi_1) \neq 0$ $x = \xi = \xi_1$	$r_\xi^+(\xi, \xi) \neq 0$ $\xi_1 \leq x = \xi \leq x_*$	$e^+(x, \xi_0) \neq 0$ $\xi_0 \leq x \leq x_2$

$\xi_0 = \xi_*$; in the last one, $\xi_0 = \xi_2$. Along $\phi = 0$, no conditions have been imposed on the e-families, enveloped by $\phi = 0$; the normality $\phi_y \neq 0$ precludes the occurrence of cusps.

The continuity of f implies the extension of IV′ to a neighborhood of E_{12}. In such a neighborhood the functions $\alpha(x, y)$ and $\xi(x, y)$ exist, and the covering is said to be simple.

With "$\leq x_2$" replaced by "$< x_2$," condition IV′ becomes the necessary condition IV.

2.8 The Hilbert Integral

A field is defined as a region F of the xy-space with a slope function $p(x, y)$ having the following properties: (a) It is single-valued and is of class C^1. (b) The line integral I^* defined by

$$I^* \equiv \int h\,dx, \qquad h \equiv f(y') + (Y' - y')f_{y'}, \qquad y' = p(x, y) \tag{2.29}$$

where Y' is the slope of the path of integration, vanishes on every closed path in the region.

Since the function f must satisfy the Euler equation in order that (b) hold, it follows that the differential equation

$$y' = p(x, y) \tag{2.30}$$

is identically satisfied by a one-parameter family $y(x, \alpha)$ of extremals. By the implicit function theorem, $y = y(x, \alpha)$ can be solved for α, to yield $\alpha(x, y)$, provided $y_\alpha(x, \alpha) \neq 0$. Then in some xy-region, the function $y' = p(x, y)$, obtained by the elimination of α from $y' = y_x(x, \alpha)$, will have the property (a). Conversely, the function $p(x, y)$ so constructed has the property (b), provided $n = 1$, as has been assumed in this chapter.

Two further properties of the Hilbert integral I^* will be stated. Let I be defined by

$$I = \int f(x, y, Y')\, dx \tag{2.31}$$

and let E and C, respectively, denote an extremal of the field and any curve in the field. Then

$$I(E) = I^*(E), \qquad I(C) - I^*(C) = \int_C E\, dx \tag{2.32}$$

where the last E is the E-function with Y' the slope of C and y' the slope of the field. The result follows from the definitions (2.29) and (2.8).

In the proof of sufficiency we shall use two lemmas.

Lemma 3. *Let $\psi = 0$ be the equation of the boundary separating two adjacent fields f_1 and f_2 whose union U is a simply connected region. If the Hilbert integrand h in the direction of the locus $\psi = 0$ is continuous across $\psi = 0$, then the Hilbert integral I^* vanishes on every closed path in U.*

The proof involves the decomposition of the closed path in U into a sum of a closed path in f_1 and a closed path in f_2, with the cancellation on $\psi = 0$ of their respective contributions to I^*.

Lemma 4. *The hypothesis of Lemma* 3 *holds if the locus $\psi = 0$ is either* (1) *the common extremal of the fields f_1 and f_2 or* (2) *a locus on which the extremals of f_1 and f_2 are joined by means of the corner condition.*

PROOF. In case (1), the slope Y' of $\psi = 0$ is equal to the common value y' of the slopes of the two fields on $\psi = 0$. Hence $h^- = h^+ = f(y')$, in view of the second part of Eq. (2.29). In case (2), the equality $h^- = h^+$ is established by the argument of Theorem 1 of Sec. 2.4.

2.9 Proof of Sufficiency

Conditions I, III″, and IV′ are sufficient for strong relative minimum. We shall show that a test-curve E_{12} satisfying these conditions yields a lower value for the integral I than any other admissible curve joining the end-points and lying in some neighborhood M.

In view of the continuity of f, III″ and IV′ imply their extensions to some xy-neighborhoods, say F_1 and F_2, respectively. Let F_0 be the neighborhood of Sec. 2.6, in which the extremal families of the set S exist. In the light of Secs. 2.6 and 2.8, the neighborhood M defined by

$$M = F_0 \cap F_1 \cap F_2 \tag{2.33}$$

has the following properties:

(1) M is simply covered by one-parameter families of extremals.

(2) Each one of these families is a field in M.

(3) The boundary between any two adjoining fields is either their common extremal or the locus $\phi = 0$, on which the corner condition is satisfied by the imbedding construction.

(4) M is the union of the fields of (2), and is simply connected.

Therefore, Lemmas 3 and 4 of Sec. 2.8 apply, with the conclusion that the Hilbert integral I^* vanishes on every closed path in M.

Let E_{12} be the test-curve, and C_{12} any other curve joining the same end-points and lying in M. Since $I^*(C_{12}) = I^*(E_{12})$, we can write with the aid of (2.32)

$$I(C_{12}) - I(E_{12}) = I(C_{12}) - I^*(C_{12}) + I^*(C_{12}) - I(E_{12}) = \int_c E\,dx \tag{2.34}$$

Now III″ implies II_F', as shown in Sec. 2.2. Hence $E > 0$ on C_{12}, and

$$I(E_{12}) < I(C_{12}) \tag{2.35}$$

We have proved the following theorem.

Theorem 3. *If the locus of discontinuity of f is of the form $\phi(x, y) = 0$, and if an admissible curve satisfies* Ia, Ib, Ic, Id, III″, *and* IV′, *then it furnishes a strong relative minimum.*

If the class of admissible curves is restricted to curves containing no more than one point of $\phi = 0$, only the R^-R^+ refraction is possible. Then Id can be deleted, and the rather stringent condition III″ can be relaxed to the combination of the classical II_N' and III′. Condition IV′ is reduced to the first line of Table IV. This special case, treated by Bliss,[2] is covered by the following corollary.

Corollary. *If the class of admissible curves is restricted to curves containing no more than one point of* $\phi = 0$, *and if an admissible curve satisfies* Ia, Ib, Ic, II_N', III′, *and* IV′, *then it furnishes a strong local minimum.*

Generally, if the minimum is unique, and if M extends over the entire xy-plane, then the minimum is absolute.

2.10 Numerical Example

The solution of a problem contains the following stages:

(1) Construct the central family of extremals through (x_1, y_1).

(2) Construct the families r, r^+, e^-; determine the entry $x = \xi_1$, the critical point $x = x_*$, and the exit $x = \xi_2$.

(3) Determine the parameters α_0 and ξ_0 from the end-conditions. If there is no real solution, attack the dual problem with the end-points interchanged.

(4) Test the sufficient conditions.

In example (a) of Sec. 2.0,

$$f^- = y'^2, \qquad f^+ = \tfrac{4}{3}y'^2, \qquad \phi = y - \tfrac{1}{4}x^2 - 16$$
$$x_1 = 0, \quad y_1 = 0; \qquad x_2 = 13, \quad y_2 = 61$$

We observe that (1) extremals in R are straight lines, and the B-extremal is a parabola; (2) no tangent can be drawn to $\phi = 0$ from the initial point. Consequently, only the R^-R^+ and $R^-B^-R^+$ types of extremaloid need be considered. The R and the B types of arc are characterized in Table V with

TABLE V

FAMILIES OF EXTREMALS

	R	B
$y(x)$	$mx + b$	$\frac{1}{4}x^2 + 16$
$\lambda(x)$	0	1
$\phi(x)$	$mx + b - 16 - \frac{1}{4}x^2$	0
$\delta(x)$	—	$x/12$

m and b appearing as constants of integration in the solution of the Euler equation. The quantity $\delta(x)$ is obtained from (2.25). The initial condition furnishes $b = 0$, and the central family of extremals,

$$y(x, m) = mx \tag{2.36}$$

At a point corresponding to $x = \xi$, where the family intersects the locus $\phi = 0$, the corner condition involves the following calculations:

$$h_- = -y_-'^2 + 2\tilde{y}'y_-', \qquad h_+ = \tfrac{4}{3}(-y_+'^2 + 2\tilde{y}'y_+'), \qquad \tilde{y}' = \tfrac{1}{2}\xi \tag{2.37}$$

For the R^-R^+ transition,

$$y_-' = m = \tfrac{1}{4}\xi + 16\xi^{-1} \tag{2.38}$$

In view of the relations $h_- = h_+$ and $\phi_-' > 0$, $\phi_+' > 0$, we then obtain

$$0 < \xi \leq 8, \qquad y_+' = \tfrac{1}{2}\xi + (\tfrac{7}{64}\xi^2 - 6 + 192\xi^{-2})^{1/2} \tag{2.39}$$

The r-family of directly refracted extremals can now be written as

$$y = r(x, \xi) = [\tfrac{1}{2}\xi + (\tfrac{7}{64}\xi^2 - 6 + 192\xi^{-2})^{1/2}](x - \xi) + \tfrac{1}{4}\xi^2 + 16, \qquad 0 < \xi \leq 8 \tag{2.40}$$

The value $\xi = 8$ in (2.38) corresponds to $m = 4$ in (2.36), leading to

$$b_1: \qquad y = 4x \tag{2.41}$$

for the member of the central family tangent to $\phi = 0$. For the same value of ξ, (2.40) yields

$$b_2: \qquad y = 6x - 16 \tag{2.42}$$

for its refracted continuation. These are the boundaries b_1 and b_2, respectively, in the notation of Sec. 2.6. Since the r-family lies in the region $\phi > 0$, $y > 6x - 16$, it excludes the terminal point (13, 61). The extremaloid type R^-R^+ can therefore be dismissed.

The point of entry is given by

$$x = \xi_1 = 8, \qquad y = 32 \tag{2.43}$$

For the B^-R^+ transition, we substitute

$$y_-' = \tilde{y}' = \tfrac{1}{2}\xi \tag{2.44}$$

into (2.37), leading to

$$y_+' = \tfrac{3}{4}\xi \tag{2.45}$$

The r^+-family is then given by

$$\begin{aligned} y = r^+(x, \xi) &= \tfrac{3}{4}\xi(x - \xi) + \tfrac{1}{4}\xi^2 + 16 \\ &= \tfrac{3}{4}\xi x - \tfrac{1}{2}\xi^2 + 16, \qquad 8 \leq \xi < \infty \end{aligned} \tag{2.46}$$

The terminal condition $y(13) = 61$ yields $\xi_0 = 12$, corresponding to the extremal

$$y = 9x - 56 \tag{2.47}$$

Thus we obtain a test-curve of the type $R^-B^-R^+$, defined by

$$\begin{aligned} y &= 4x && (0 \leq x \leq 8) \\ y &= \tfrac{1}{4}x^2 + 16 && (8 \leq x \leq 12) \\ y &= 9x - 56 && (12 \leq x \leq 13) \end{aligned} \tag{2.48}$$

(see Fig. 4).

To test the sufficient conditions, we note that

(1) On the B^--subarc, $\lambda > 0$ and $\delta > 0$. Therefore Ic and Id are satisfied.

(2) III″ is satisfied, since $f^-_{y'y'} = 2$ and $f^+_{y'y'} = \frac{4}{3}$.

(3) IV′ is satisfied in virtue of the following relations:

$$\begin{array}{cc} y_m(x, 4) = x \neq 0, & r_\xi{}^+(\xi, \xi) = -\frac{1}{4}\xi \neq 0 \\ 0 < x \leq 8 & 8 \leq x = \xi \leq 12 \\ r\xi(2, 2) = -\frac{1}{2} \neq 0, & r^+(x, 12) = \frac{3}{4}x - 12 \neq 0 \\ x = \xi_1 = 2 & 12 \leq x \leq 13 \end{array} \tag{2.49}$$

A strong relative minimum is thus assured. This minimum is unique but is not absolute. For the family $r^+(x, \xi)$ in (2.46) has an envelope.

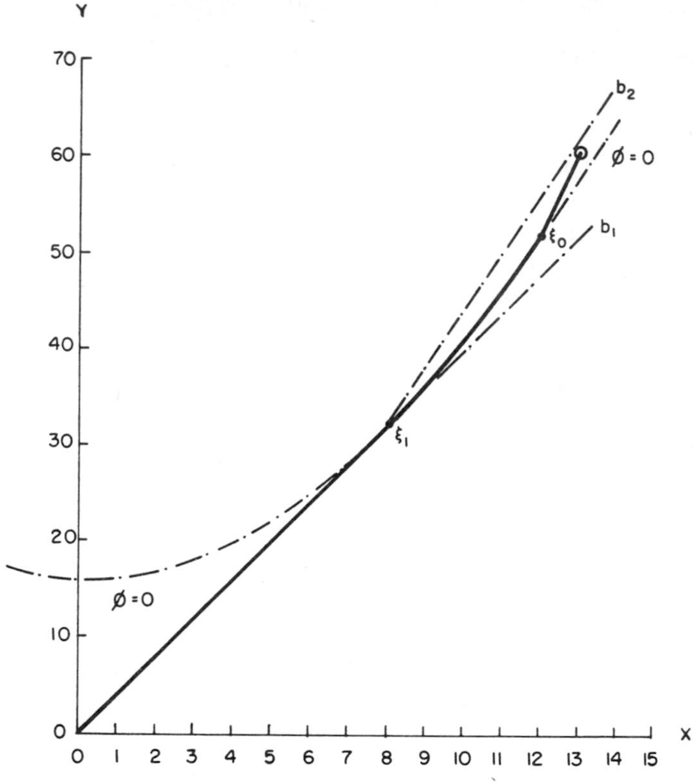

FIG. 4. The minimizing curve (solid line).

2.11 Discussion of the Results

A solution of the refraction problem in case (a) has been obtained under the following restrictions:

(1) There is only one dependent variable y.
(2) An admissible curve contains no more than one refraction corner.
(3) III″ is satisfied.

We shall discuss the possibility of the removal of these restrictions. If (1) is removed, the sufficient conditions must include the vanishing of the Hilbert integral I^* on every closed path in the M-neighborhood of E_{12}. Restriction (2) can be removed if the RB refraction does not occur on E_{12} of either the given problem or of the dual problem. Condition III″ can be regarded as a combination of III_F' with the requirement

$$\lim f_{y'y'} \neq 0 \qquad \text{as} \quad y' \to \pm\infty$$

The latter requirement can be removed if the problem can be expressed in parametric form; e.g., $f = \mu(x, y)(1 + y'^2)^{1/2}$. The entire condition III″ can be replaced by the combination of the weaker conditions III′ and II_N', if the class of admissible curves is restricted to curves containing no more than one point of $\phi = 0$.

PART B—CASE (b)

2.12 Conditions Ia, Ib, II, and III

The necessary conditions for a strong relative minimum are I, II, III, IV; the sufficient conditions comprise I, II_N', IV′. Condition I contains Ia, Ib, Ic, and Id, the last two of which were discussed in Sec. 2.1.

Conditions Ia and Ib, derived in the previous chapter for case (b), assume the forms

$$\text{Ia} \qquad \frac{d}{dx} F_{y'} = F_y \tag{2.50}$$

$$\text{Ib} \qquad \Delta(F - y'F_{y'}) = 0, \qquad \Delta F_{y'} = 0 \tag{2.51}$$

Since $F = f + \lambda\phi$ with $\lambda\phi \equiv 0$, Eqs. (2.50) and (2.51) can be written

$$\text{Ia} \qquad \frac{d}{dx} f_{y'} - f_y = 0, \qquad \lambda \equiv 0 \qquad \text{if} \quad \phi \neq 0$$

$$\lambda'\phi_{y'} + \lambda\left(\frac{d}{dx}\phi_{y'} - \phi_y\right) + \frac{d}{dx} f_{y'} - f_y = 0 \qquad \text{if} \quad \phi \equiv 0 \tag{2.52}$$

$$\text{Ib} \qquad \Delta[f - y'(f_{y'} + \lambda\phi_{y'})] = 0, \qquad \Delta(f_{y'} + \lambda\phi_{y'}) = 0 \tag{2.53}$$

It is understood that at the discontinuity, the derivatives of f with respect to its arguments are one-sided.

Condition II of the previous chapter is retained here, with the E-function defined by

$$E = F(Y') - F(y') - (Y' - y')F_{y'} \tag{2.54}$$

Condition III requires that $F_{y'y'} \geq 0$ for all (x, y, y') belonging to the curve. Conditions II_N', IV, and IV$'$ are discussed in Secs. 2.16 and 2.19.

2.13 Preliminary Considerations

At a refraction corner, with $\Delta y' \neq 0$,

$$\Delta\phi = \phi_{y'}\Delta y' \neq 0, \qquad \phi_-\phi_+ \leq 0 \tag{2.55}$$

The equality in the second part of (2.55) holds only in the case of the critical refraction. Thus, in contrast to case (a), where $\phi = 0$ and is continuous at a corner, ϕ is generally discontinuous in case (b), and need not go through value zero.

Since y' is not prescribed at x_1 and x_2, it is not possible to ascertain *a priori* whether the end-points lie in $\phi < 0$, $\phi = 0$, or $\phi > 0$. In addition to the six transitions of Sec 2.3, we must also consider the six reversed transitions R^+R^-, etc. Altogether, there are eight basic types of singly refracted extremaloids, listed in Table VI. If the structural formula is truncated from

TABLE VI

EXTREMALOID TYPES

$\Delta\phi \geq 0$	$\Delta\phi \leq 0$
$B^-R^-R^+B^+$	$B^+R^+R^-B^-$
$B^-R^-B^+R^+$	$B^+R^+B^-R^-$
$R^-B^-B^+R^+$	$R^+B^+B^-R^-$
$R^-B^-R^+B^+$	$R^+B^+R^-B^-$

either end or from both, there result 32 degenerate types, such as $R^+B^+R^-$, $R^+B^-R^+$, R^+R^-, B^+R^+, R^-, which occur in the example of Sec. 2.20.

Refraction is governed by the relations

$$\Delta(F - y'F_{y'}) = 0, \qquad \Delta F_{y'} = 0, \qquad \lambda_+\phi_+ = 0, \qquad \phi_-\phi_+ \leq 0 \tag{2.56}$$

The first two equations constitute the corner condition (2.51); the third is a consequence of the general identity $\lambda\phi \equiv 0$; the last is in (2.55). For a given extremal $y(x)$, the system (2.56) furnishes three equations, from which the three unknown $x = \xi$, y_+', λ_+ are to be determined. For refraction into the region, $\lambda_+ = 0$; for refraction into the interface, $\phi_+ = 0$ and a nonzero λ_+ is admitted.

The Jacobian determinant J of the left-hand members of the first three equations of (2.56) with respect to x, y_+', λ_+ can be expressed in the form

$$J = \Omega H_+ \tag{2.57}$$

where H is the Hilbert determinant (1.67) of the previous chapter, and the Carathéodory function Ω is defined by

$$\Omega = \Delta F_x + y_-' F_{y_+} - y_+' F_{y_-} \tag{2.58}$$

The derivation of (2.57) is based on the formulas

$$\begin{aligned} \lim_{x \to \xi + 0} \frac{d}{dx} F(x, y(x), y_+') &= (F_x)_+ + y_-' F_{y_+} \\ \frac{d}{dx}(F - y' F_{y'}) &= F_x \\ \frac{d}{dx} F_{y'} &= F_y \end{aligned} \tag{2.59}$$

holding along an extremal. Except for points of entry, where $\lambda_+ = \phi_+ = 0$, the determinant H_+ does not vanish. Thus

$$\Omega \neq 0 \tag{2.60}$$

is a sufficient condition that a solution of (2.56) exist. As in case (a), the solution may be imaginary. The question of the existence of a real refracted continuation will be investigated next.

2.14 Zermelo Diagram

To simplify the analysis, let $\phi(x, y, y')$ be written

$$\phi = y' - \tilde{y}'(x, y) \tag{2.61}$$

Then the Zermelo curve $f(y')$, with (x, y) fixed, has a left branch $f^-(y')$ and a right branch $f^+(y')$, defined on the intervals $-\infty < y' \leq \tilde{y}'$ and $\tilde{y}' \leq y' < \infty$, respectively. At $y' = \tilde{y}'$ we note the following discontinuities:

$$\Delta f = f^+(\tilde{y}') - f^-(\tilde{y}'), \qquad \Delta f_{y'} = f_{y'}^+(\tilde{y}') - f_{y'}^-(\tilde{y}') \tag{2.62}$$

Let $\mathscr{E}$ designate the special form of the E-function of (2.54) defined by

$$\begin{aligned} &\mathscr{E}(y', Y') = f(Y') - f(y') - (Y' - y') f_{y'} \\ &-\infty < y' \leq \tilde{y}' \leq Y' < \infty \qquad \text{if} \quad \Delta f \leq 0 \\ &-\infty < Y' \leq \tilde{y}' \leq y' < \infty \qquad \text{if} \quad \Delta f \geq 0 \end{aligned} \tag{2.63}$$

Clearly, $\mathscr{E}$ is the distance from the line tangent to the curve $f(y')$ at y', measured vertically to the curve at Y'.

A line is said to *support* a curve if it contains two points of the curve and does not cross it. If $f(y')$ is supported from below at points y_1' and y_2' such that

$$-\infty < y_1' \leq \tilde{y}' \leq y_2' < \infty \tag{2.64}$$

then the following relations hold:

$$\begin{gathered} \min_{Y'} \mathscr{E}(y_1', Y') = \mathscr{E}(y_1', y_2') = 0 \\ \text{if} \quad y_1' < \tilde{y}' \leq y_2' \quad \text{and} \quad \Delta f \leq 0 \end{gathered} \tag{2.65.1}$$

and

$$\begin{gathered} \min_{Y'} \mathscr{E}(y_2', Y') = \mathscr{E}(y_2', y_1') = 0 \\ \text{if} \quad y_1' = \tilde{y}' \leq y_2' \quad \text{and} \quad \Delta f \geq 0 \end{gathered} \tag{2.65.2}$$

It follows from (2.64) and (2.65) that the following relations hold at y_1' and y_2':

$$\begin{aligned} f_{y_1'} &= f_{y_2'} \qquad \text{if} \quad y_1' < \tilde{y}' < y_2' \\ f_{y_1'} &\leq f_{y_2'} \qquad \text{if} \quad (y_1' - \tilde{y}')(y_2' - \tilde{y}') = 0 \end{aligned} \tag{2.66}$$

In the first part of Eq. (2.66), the *supporting line* is a *double tangent* with y_1' and y_2' as the points of contact; in the second part of Eq. (2.66) one of the points of support is the point $\tilde{y}'$ of the discontinuity of f.

A remarkable property of the numbers y_1' and y_2' is described in the following theorem.

Theorem 4. *If the curve $f(y')$ with a jump Δf is supported from below at y_1' and y_2', then there exist numbers λ_1 and λ_2 satisfying $\lambda\phi = 0$ and the convexity condition Ic, and together with y_1' and y_2' satisfying the corner condition.*

PROOF. With (x, y) fixed, consider the system of four equations

$$\begin{gathered} f(y_1') - y_1'(f_{y_1'} + \lambda_1) = f(y_2') - y_2'(f_{y_2'} + \lambda_2) \\ f_{y_1'} + \lambda_1 = f_{y_2'} + \lambda_2 \\ \lambda_1(y_1' - \tilde{y}') = 0, \qquad \lambda_2(y_2' - \tilde{y}') = 0 \end{gathered} \tag{2.67}$$

The first two equations constitute the corner condition (2.53) with $y_-' = y_1'$, $y_+' = y_2'$, $\lambda_- = \lambda_1$, $\lambda_+ = \lambda_2$, and with $\phi_{y'} = 1$ in consequence of (2.61); the last two equations follow from the general identity $\lambda\phi = 0$. We shall show that (2.67) is satisfied by the points of support, and that λ_1 and λ_2 determined by

(2.67) satisfy Ic. Four cases are distinguished:

(1) $y_1' < \tilde{y}' < y_2'$		$\lambda_1 = \lambda_2 = 0$
(2) $y_1' < \tilde{y}' = y_2'$	$\Delta f < 0$	$\lambda_1 = 0,\ \lambda_2 < 0$
(3) $y_1' = \tilde{y}' < y_2'$	$\Delta f > 0$	$\lambda_1 > 0,\ \lambda_2 = 0$
(4) $y_1' = \tilde{y}' = y_2'$	$\Delta f = 0$	$0 < \lambda_1 < \Delta f_{y'}$
		$\lambda_2 = \lambda_1 - \Delta f_{y'} < 0$

In case (1), $f_{y_1'} = f_{y_2'}$ by the second part of Eq. (2.66), so that the supporting line becomes a double tangent. In view of (2.65), the points of contact satisfy (2.67) with $\lambda_1 = \lambda_2 = 0$. In case (2), $f_{y_1'} \leq f_{y_2'}$ by the second part of Eq. (2.66).

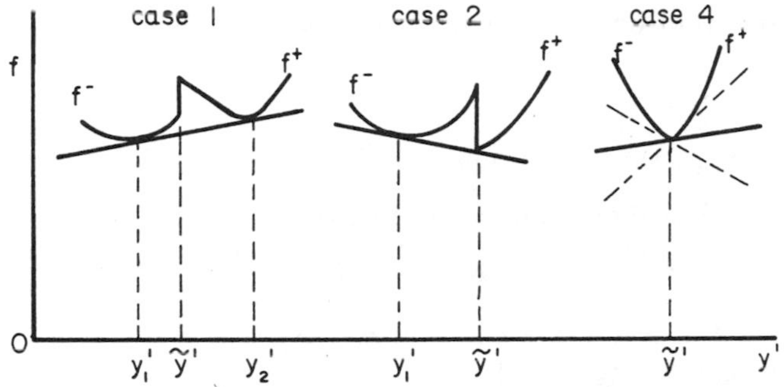

FIG. 5. The supporting line–refraction corners.

Again, the points of contact satisfy (2.67) and Ic, if we put

$$\lambda_1 = 0, \qquad \lambda_2 = f_{y_1'} - f_{y_2'} \leq 0 \tag{2.68}$$

Case (3) is treated similarly, with the choice

$$\lambda_1 = f_{y_2'} - f_{y_1'} \geq 0, \qquad \lambda_2 = 0 \tag{2.69}$$

In case (4), y_1' and y_2' are coincident, so that the supporting line is indeterminate and passes through the point $\tilde{y}'$, which is a corner and a minimum of $f(y')$. The conclusion of Theorem 4 is satisfied for any pair (λ_1, λ_2) lying in the range indicated.

The four cases of Theorem 4 can be identified with the refractions R^-R^+, R^-B^+, B^-R^+, B^-B^+, respectively, and the corresponding reverse transitions (see Fig. 5).

2.15 Corner Manifolds

If the hypothesis of Theorem 4 is satisfied, then to every (x, y) correspond real (y_1', λ_1) and (y_2', λ_2) such that $\lambda\phi = 0$. The functions $y_i'(x, y)$ and

$\lambda_i(x, y)$ for $i = 1, 2$ can be determined as the solution of (2.67). If these functions satisfy the relations

$$f_{y_1'y_1'} > 0, \qquad f_{y_2'y_2'} > 0 \tag{2.70}$$

then the two sets $M_1(x, y, y_1', \lambda_1)$ and $M_2(x, y, y_2', \lambda_2)$ are designated as *corner manifolds*. They can be used to determine the points of entry ξ_1, the points of exit ξ_2, and the points of refraction ξ_* for a family of extremals $y = y(x, \alpha)$, $\lambda = \lambda(x, \alpha)$. As shown in the previous chapter for case (b), λ vanishes at $x = \xi_1$ and $x = \xi_2$. The following cases arise:

(1) If there exists a ξ_1 such that

$$y_x(\xi_1, \alpha) = \tilde{y}'(\xi_1, y(\xi_1, \alpha)) = y_i', \qquad 0 = \lambda(\xi_1, \alpha) \neq \lambda_i \tag{2.71}$$

then the first part of Eq. (2.71) yields $\xi_1 = \xi_1(\alpha)$, which defines the *entry locus* of the family.

(2) If the relations

$$y_x(x, \alpha) = \tilde{y}'(x, y(x, \alpha)) = y_i', \qquad \lambda(x, \alpha) \neq \lambda_i \neq 0 \tag{2.72}$$

hold on some interval of x, and if there exists ξ_2 such that

$$\lambda(\xi_2, \alpha) = 0 \tag{2.73}$$

then (2.73) yields $\xi_2 = \xi_2(\alpha)$, which defines the *exit locus* of the family.

(3) If there exists a ξ_* such that

$$y_x = y_i' \neq \tilde{y}', \qquad \lambda = \lambda_i = 0 \tag{2.74}$$

or

$$y_x = y_i' = \tilde{y}', \qquad \lambda = \lambda_i \neq 0 \tag{2.75}$$

we say that the family intersects the corner manifold M_i. The intersection yields $\xi_* = \xi_*(\alpha)$, which defines the *corner locus* C of the family; its *xy*-projection can be written in the form

$$\psi(x, y) = 0 \tag{2.76}$$

Cases (2.74) and (2.75) are distinguished as refraction on R and B-subarcs, respectively.

2.16 Conditions II′ and II$_N$′

A weakened form of II′, used here, admits $E = 0$ for $Y' \neq y'$ at the corners of the curve. Indeed, with $x = \xi$, $y' = y_-'$, and $Y' = y_+'$, the E-function of (2.54) vanishes in virtue of the corner condition (2.51). Its left- and right-hand derivatives E' along an extremal assume the values $\pm\Omega$ at the corner, with Ω

defined by (2.58). The corresponding mathematical statements

$$E(y_-', y_+') = 0$$

$$E_-' = \lim_{x \to \xi - 0} \frac{d}{dx} E(y', y_+') = \Omega \qquad (2.77)$$

$$E_+' = \lim_{x \to \xi + 0} \frac{d}{dx} E(y_-', y') = -\Omega$$

are derived with the aid of (2.59). In order that II′ hold it is necessary that

$$\Omega \leq 0 \qquad (2.78)$$

Two cases arise:

(1) If $\Omega < 0$, then (2.77) implies that $E > 0$ in a neighborhood of $x = \xi$ on the refracted continuation of the extremal, and that E becomes negative for the trivial continuation $\Delta y' = 0$. More generally, let $\Omega(x)$ be defined on the extremal, with y_-' replaced by y' in (2.58), and let $\Omega^{(p)}$ be the lowest non-vanishing derivative of $\Omega(x)$ at $x = \xi$. Then the requirement

$$(-1)^p \Omega^{(p)} < 0 \qquad (2.79)$$

includes $\Omega < 0$ for the special case $p = 0$, and implies the same conclusion.

(2) If $\Omega(x) \equiv 0$ on some interval of x, then the corner condition does not yield a solution for ξ. Indeed, at every point of an extremal subarc in the corner locus $\psi' = 0$, the extremal splits into a refracted and a trivial continuation, which both satisfy $E > 0$ in the neighborhood of $x = \xi$.

The question of the existence and uniqueness of the refracted continuation can now be answered.

Theorem 5. *Let the curve $f(y')$ be supported from below by one and only one line. With the corner manifolds designated as M_1 and M_2, let an extremal intersect M_1 at $x = \xi_*$. If conditions* I *and* II′ *are satisfied for $x \leq \xi_*$, then they are also satisfied on the refracted continuation $x \geq \xi_*$, determined by the transition $M_1 \to M_2$. If $\Omega < 0$, the continuation satisfies* II *uniquely. The theorem remains valid if the subscripts* 1 *and* 2 *are interchanged.*

PROOF. The $M_1 \to M_2$ transition is characterized by

$$\begin{aligned} y_-' &= y_1', & \lambda_- &= \lambda_1 \\ y_+' &= y_2', & \lambda_+ &= \lambda_2 \end{aligned} \qquad (2.80)$$

Condition Ia is satisfied by the solution of the Euler equation with the initial conditions provided by (x, y, y_+', λ_+). The corner condition Ib, and the convexity condition Ic are satisfied by Theorem 4. Condition Id, Eq. (2.4) , holds if a corner occurs on a B-subarc, inasmuch as the curve $f(y')$ is supported from below. Observe that E_{12} satisfies II′ if and only if the tangent to the curve $f(y')$ at y' lies entirely below the curve for all (x, y, y') of E_{12}. In view of (2.70), the condition is equivalent to the requirement

$$\chi \equiv (y' - y_1')(y' - y_2') \geq 0 \tag{2.81}$$

which excludes the interval (y_1', y_2') from the domain of y'. Since χ is positive initially and vanishes at corners, $\Omega \leq 0$ implies that $\chi \geq 0$ between corners, so that II′ is satisfied.

A *unilateral* N-neighborhood of (x, y, y', λ) on E_{12} is defined as one whose xyy'-projection lies entirely in $\chi \geq 0$. Condition II_N' will be stated as follows.

A curve E_{12} is said to satisfy condition II_N' if there exists a unilateral N-neighborhood of (x, y, y', λ) on E_{12} such that $E > 0$ for all (x, y, y', λ) in N that satisfy $\lambda\phi = 0$, and for all $Y' \neq y'$.

The assumption that there be but one supporting line is removed in Sec. 2.17.

2.17 Free Corners

Generally, f is not a convex function of y'. As such, it has a supporting line for each pair of consecutive zeros of $f_{y'y'}$. Let the points of support from below be designated by y'_{1j} and y'_{2j} for $j = 1, 2, \ldots, m$. If y'_{1j} and y'_{2j} belong to the same branch of f, the corresponding corners are said to be *free*. For such corners, the results of Secs. 2.14–2.16 remain valid with the following modifications.

Theorem 4 reduces to one case, $(y_1' - \tilde{y}')(y_2' - \tilde{y}') \neq 0$, which corresponds to R^-R^- and R^+R^+ transitions. The points ξ_* of these transitions belong to some corner locus C_j and the corner manifolds M_{1j} and M_{2j}. In the proof of Theorem 5, (2.81) is replaced by

$$\begin{gathered} \chi_j = (y' - y'_{1j})(y' - y'_{2j}) \geq 0 \\ j = 1, 2, \ldots, m \\ \chi \equiv \chi_1 \cap \chi_2 \cap \cdots \chi_m \end{gathered} \tag{2.82}$$

(see Fig. 6).

The restriction (2.61) that $\phi = 0$ have only one real root can also be removed; the case of several roots $\tilde{y}_k'$ can be treated as in (2.82). The subject of free corners has been studied by Bolza,[1] Reid,[5] Graves, and others.

2.18 A Special Case

Free corners do not occur, and the testing of II_N' is considerably simplified if we impose condition III″ of Sec. 2.2. This condition implies the following consequences.

By differentiation of (2.63) we obtain

$$\mathscr{E}_{Y'} = f_{Y'} - f_{y'}, \qquad \mathscr{E}_{Y'Y'} = f_{Y'Y'}, \qquad \mathscr{E}_{y'} = -(Y' - y')f_{y'y'} \qquad (2.83)$$

and deduce the following properties of $\mathscr{E}$: (1) $\mathscr{E}$ is continuous in Y'; (2) in view of III″, the second part of Eq. (2.83) and Eq. (2.61), $\mathscr{E}_{Y'Y'} > 0$ for all Y', including $Y' = \pm\infty$. Therefore $\mathscr{E}(Y')$ has one and only one minimum m, occurring at some value $Y' = y_*'$. Accordingly, let $m(y')$ be defined by

$$m(y') = \min_{Y'} \mathscr{E}(y', Y') = \mathscr{E}(y', y_*'). \qquad (2.84)$$

The following properties of $m(y')$ are to be noted: (1) $m(y')$ is continuous;

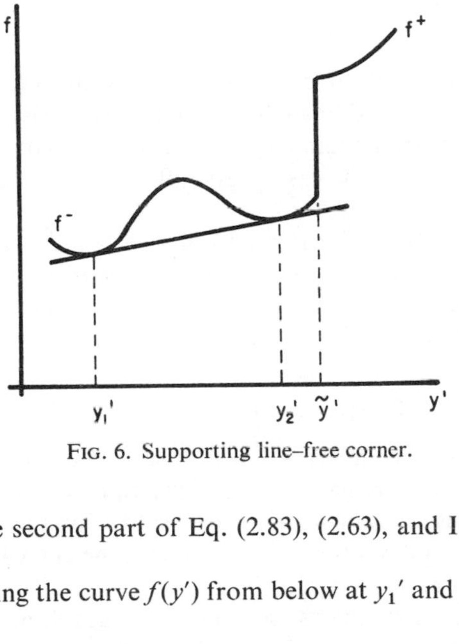

FIG. 6. Supporting line–free corner.

(2) in view of the second part of Eq. (2.83), (2.63), and III″, $m(y')$ is monotonic.

A line supporting the curve $f(y')$ from below at y_1' and y_2' is characterized by

$$\begin{aligned} m(y_1') &= 0, \quad & y_2' &= Y' = y'_* \quad & \text{if } \Delta f \leq 0 \\ m(y_2') &= 0, \quad & y_1' &= Y' = y_*' \quad & \text{if } \Delta f \geq 0 \end{aligned} \qquad (2.85)$$

The minimum m occurs either in the interior of the domain of Y' or on its boundary $Y' = \tilde{y}'$. The two cases,

$$\begin{aligned} \mathscr{E}_{Y'} = f_{y_2'} - f_{y_1'} &= 0 \quad & \text{if } & y_1' < \tilde{y}' < y_2' \\ &\geq 0 \quad & \text{if } & (y_1' - \tilde{y}')(y_2' - \tilde{y}') = 0 \end{aligned} \qquad (2.86)$$

are in accord with (2.66).

Theorem 6. *Condition* III″ *is both necessary and sufficient in order that the curve $f(y')$ with a jump discontinuity have one and only one supporting line from below, with the corresponding corner manifolds M_1 and M_2.*

PROOF. If $\Delta f \leq 0$ in (2.63), the mean value theorem leads to

$$\mathscr{E}(y', Y') = f^{+}(Y') - f^{-}(y') + \tfrac{1}{2}(Y' - y')^2 f_{y'y'}[y' + \Theta(Y' - y')], \qquad 0 < \Theta < 1 \tag{2.87}$$

Condition III′ and (2.84) respectively imply $\mathscr{E}(-\infty, Y') = \infty$ and $m(-\infty) = \infty$. Since

$$\mathscr{E}(\tilde{y}', \tilde{y}') = \Delta f \leq 0 \tag{2.88}$$

and since (2.84) implies

$$m(\tilde{y}') < \mathscr{E}(\tilde{y}', \tilde{y}') \tag{2.89}$$

we conclude that $m(\tilde{y}') < 0$. Since the continuous and monotonic function $m(y')$ changes sign in the domain $(-\infty, \tilde{y}')$, there exist a $y_1{}'$ such that $m(y_1{}') = 0$, and the corresponding $y_2{}'$ in the second part of Eq. (2.85). A similar argument applies to the case of $\Delta f \geq 0$.

Theorem 7. *If E_{12} satisfies* III″ *and $\chi(x_1) > 0$, and if it has a corner at every intersection with the corner manifolds for $\Omega < 0$, then it satisfies* II′ *and* $\text{II}_N{}'$.

The proof depends on the fact that (2.81) implies II′, and the combination of III″ and II′ implies $\text{II}_N{}'$ by the argument similar to the one in Sec. 2.2

2.19 The Imbedding Construction

Extremals that issue from (x_1, y_1) comprise a central family $y(x, \alpha)$ of R-extremals and one B-extremal, to be designated as B_1. The latter is either B^- or B^+, depending on which one satisfies Id. For these extremals, the corner manifolds M_1 and M_2 furnish the C-locus, the entry locus E_1, the exit locus E_2, and the corresponding ξ_*, ξ_1, ξ_2.

With $\xi_1(\alpha)$ known, the B-subarcs are constructed as follows. Let $y = g(x, \beta)$ and $\lambda = \lambda(x, \gamma)$ be the solutions of the differential equations $\phi = 0$ and the second part of (2.52), respectively. Since y and λ are continuous at $x = \xi_1$, the parameters β and γ are determined from the equations

$$y(\xi_1(\alpha), \alpha) = g(\xi_1(\alpha), \beta), \qquad \lambda(\xi_1(\alpha), \gamma) = 0 \tag{2.90}$$

leading to $\beta = \beta(\alpha)$ and $\gamma = \gamma(\alpha)$.

The R-extremals of the family $y(x, \alpha)$ that intersect the C-locus at $x = \xi_*(\alpha)$ generate a family of refracted extremals. The union of the two families constitutes a central family $y(x, \alpha)$ of extremaloids, with $y(x, \alpha)$ assuming different functional representations on various subarcs.

The splitting of extremals occurs in two cases described below.

(1) On the B_1-extremaloid through (x_1, y_1), the multiplier λ is obtained from the second part of (2.52) in the form $\lambda = \lambda(x, \xi)$, where ξ is arbitrary. Hence at every point of B_1 for which there exists a ξ such that $\lambda = 0$ and $\lambda' > 0$ an extremal exits into R. The set of such points belongs to the exit locus E_2, generating a family $e(x, \xi)$, which is enveloped by B_1. Without any loss of generality, ξ can be taken as the value of x at the point of exit.

(2) If an extremal subarc belongs to the C-locus, then at every point $x = \xi$ of the subarc there exists a refracted continuation, generating a family $r(x, \xi)$. Such points are characterized by $\Omega = 0$, as noted in Sec. 2.16.

Hereafter we shall assume that $\Omega \neq 0$ on E_{12}. Then E_{12} has no subarc in the C-locus $\psi \equiv 0$, and is embedded in its entirety in a family of extremaloids. It appears that the boundary between two adjacent families is one of the loci C, E_1, and E_2. It is to be noted further that the corner condition is satisfied on the C-locus, and is trivially satisfied on E_1 and E_2. The union of the families $y(x, \alpha)$, $r(x, \xi)$ is simply-connected.

Condition IV′ requires that E_{12} contain no points belonging to the envelopes, distinct from B_1, of the families of extremals that imbed E_{12}. If E_{12} is imbedded for $\alpha = \alpha_0$ in the central family $y(x; \alpha)$ of extremaloids, IV′ takes the form

$$y_\alpha(x, \alpha_0) \neq 0, \qquad x_1 < x \leq x_2; \tag{2.91}$$

if E_{12} is also imbedded for $\xi = \xi_0$ in a noncentral family, then the additional relations of the form

$$\begin{matrix} r_\xi(x, \xi_0) \neq 0, & e_\xi(x, \xi_0) \neq 0, & r_\xi(\xi, \xi) \neq 0 \\ x \geq \xi_0 & x > \xi_0 & x = \xi \end{matrix} \tag{2.92}$$

must be satisfied on the appropriate intervals of x. With " $<x_2$" in (2.91) and (2.92) replaced by " $\leq x_2$", IV′ becomes the necessary condition IV.

In view of the assumed continuity of f, IV′ implies its extension to a neighborhood of E_{12}. In such a neighborhood, the functions $\alpha(x, y)$, $\xi(x, y)$ exist, and the covering of the neighborhood by the extremals is simple.

2.20 Proof of Sufficiency

The sufficient conditions for a strong relative minimum comprise I, II_N' and IV′. We shall show that a test-curve satisfying these conditions yields a lower value for the integral I than any other admissible curve joining the end-points and lying in some neighborhood M.

Let N_1 be the xy-projection of the N-neighborhood in which II_N' holds; let N_2 be the neighborhood in which IV′ holds. Then M defined by

$$M = N_1 \cap N_2 \tag{2.93}$$

has the following properties:

(1) M is simply covered by one-parameter families of extremals.
(2) These families are fields in M.
(3) The boundary between any two adjoining fields in M is one of the loci C, E_1, E_2, on which the corner condition is satisfied by the imbedding construction.
(4) M is the union of the fields of (2) and is simply-connected.
(5) On every curve in M, the E-function, calculated with y' the slope of the field and Y' the slope of the curve, is positive for all $Y' \neq y'$.

The rest of the proof is identical with that of Sec. 2.9. We have proved the following theorem.

Theorem 8. *If the locus of the discontinuity of f is of the form $\phi(x, y, y') = 0$, and if an admissible curve satisfies the conditions* Ia, Ib, Ic, Id, II_N', *and* IV′, *then it furnishes a strong relative minimum.*

If the minimum is unique and if M extends over the entire xy-plane, then the minimum is absolute.

2.21 Numerical Example

The solution of a problem contains the following stages:

(1) Construct the central family of R-extremals and the B_1-extremal passing through (x_1, y_1).

(2) Construct the corner manifolds M_1 and M_2, and the loci C, E_1, and E_2.

(3) Construct the continuations of the initial subarcs of step (1), and determine the parameters α_0 and ξ_0 corresponding to an admissible curve.

(4) Test the sufficient conditions.

In example (b) of Sec. 2.0,

$$f^- = \tfrac{1}{4}y'^2 + y', \qquad f^+ = \tfrac{1}{4}y'^2 + 4, \qquad \phi = y' - x$$
$$x_1 = 0, \quad y_1 = 0; \qquad x_2 = 9, \quad y_2 = 54$$

Observe that extremals in R are straight lines, and extremals in B are parabolas. The R and B types of extremal are characterized in Table VII, with m, b, β, γ appearing as constants of integration in the solution of the Euler equations. The quantity $\delta(x)$ is defined in (2.25); the $\pm$ sign refers to B^+ and B^- arcs, respectively.

TABLE VII

FAMILIES OF EXTREMALS

	R	B
$y(x)$	$mx + b$	$\frac{1}{2}(x^2 + \beta)$
$\lambda(x)$	0	$\frac{1}{2}(\gamma - x)$
$\phi(x)$	$m - x$	0
$\delta(x)$	—	$\pm(x - 4)$

The initial condition yields $b = 0$, $\beta = 0$. Hence the central family of R-extremals is defined by

$$y(x, m) = mx, \qquad \lambda \equiv 0$$
$$0 \le x \le m \qquad \text{if} \quad m > 0 \qquad (R^+) \tag{2.94}$$
$$0 \le x < \infty \qquad \text{if} \quad m \le 0 \qquad (R^-);$$

the B_1^- extremal is

$$y = \tfrac{1}{2}x^2, \qquad \lambda = \tfrac{1}{2}(\xi - x), \qquad 0 \le x \le \xi \tag{2.95}$$

with $\gamma \equiv \xi$, and $\lambda(x) \ge 0$.

Since $F^-_{y'y'} = F^+_{y'y'} = 2$, condition III″ holds. By Theorem 6, there exists a unique supporting line, with corner manifolds M_1 and M_2. The latter are determined by the corner condition (2.67). With $\tilde{y}' = x$, (2.67) becomes

$$-\tfrac{1}{4}y_1'^2 - \lambda_1 y_1' = -\tfrac{1}{4}y_2'^2 + 4 - \lambda_2 y_2'$$
$$\tfrac{1}{2}y_1' + 1 + \lambda_1 = \tfrac{1}{2}y_2' + \lambda_2 \tag{2.96}$$
$$\lambda_1(y_1' - x) = 0, \qquad \lambda_2(y_2' - x) = 0$$

The solution of (2.96) appears in Table VIII and in Fig. 7.

TABLE VIII

THE CORNER MANIFOLDS

	M_1		M_2	
Domain of definition	y_1'	λ_1	y_2'	λ_2
$5 \le x < \infty$	$x - 2(x-4)^{1/2}$	0	x	$1 - (x-4)^{1/2}$
$3 \le x \le 5$	3	0	5	0
$0 \le x \le 3$	x	$(4-x)^{1/2} - 1$	$x + 2(4-x)^{1/2}$	0

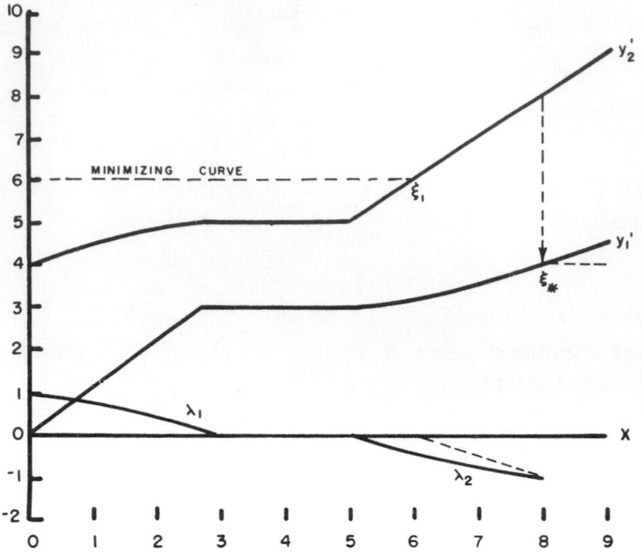

FIG. 7. The corner manifolds.

It can be shown that the initial subarcs of (2.94) and (2.95) lead to five types of extremaloid, described in Table IX. We shall confine our analysis to the case $m > 5$. It is seen from the figure that the corresponding extremaloid is $R^+B^+R^-$, and that the refraction occurs in the sense $M_2 \to M_1$. The entry locus E_1 is obtained from Eqs. (2.71) and (2.94), with $y_x = m$ and $y_2' = \tilde{y}' = x$. In parametric form, the result appears as

$$x = \xi_1 = m, \qquad y = \eta_1 = m^2 \tag{2.97}$$

As seen from Table VII, the B^+-subarc generated by the R^+B^+ transition is of the form

$$y = \tfrac{1}{2}(x^2 + \beta), \qquad \lambda = \tfrac{1}{2}(\gamma - x) \tag{2.98}$$

The parameters β and γ are determined from Eq. (2.90) with $g = \frac{1}{2}(x^2 + \beta)$, leading to

$$\beta = m^2, \qquad \gamma = m \tag{2.99}$$

Then (2.98) becomes

$$y = \tfrac{1}{2}(x^2 + m^2), \qquad \lambda = \tfrac{1}{2}(m - x) \tag{2.100}$$

The C-locus is determined from (2.75) with $i = 2$, leading to $\lambda = \lambda_2$. With the aid of Table VIII and (2.100) we obtain

$$\begin{aligned} x &= \xi_* = m + 2(m-5)^{1/2}, \\ y &= \eta_* = m^2 + 2(m-5) + 2m(m-5)^{1/2} \end{aligned} \tag{2.101}$$

The latter value of x yields

$$\lambda_- = \lambda_2 = -(m - 5)^{1/2}, \qquad y_+' = y_1' = m - 2 \tag{2.102}$$

From (2.58) we obtain

$$\Omega = -\Delta\lambda = \lambda_- - \lambda_+ \tag{2.103}$$

For the B^+R^- transition $\lambda_- \le 0$ and $\lambda_+ = 0$, so that the necessary condition $\Omega \le 0$ is satisfied. This transition generates the R^--subarc

$$y = (m - 2)x + 4m + 4(5 - m)^{1/2} - 10 \tag{2.104}$$

No further transitions being possible, the $R^+B^+R^-$ family of extremaloids is defined as in Table IX. The terminal condition $y(9) = 54$ yields $m = m_0 = 6$, corresponding to a test-curve defined by

$$\begin{aligned} &y = 6x && && (0 \le x \le 6) \\ &y = \tfrac{1}{2}x^2 + 18, && \lambda = 3 - \tfrac{1}{2}x && (6 \le x \le 8) \\ &y = 4x + 18 && && (8 \le x \le 9) \end{aligned} \tag{2.105}$$

The intersection of this solution with the corner manifolds is depicted in Fig. 7, with ξ_1 and ξ_* marked.

TABLE IX

EXTREMALOID FAMILIES

Type	Family	Range of x
$R^+B^+R^-$	$y = mx$	$(0, m)$
	$y = \frac{1}{2}(m^2 + x^2)$	$(m, m + 2(m - 5)^{1/2})$
	$\lambda = \frac{1}{2}(m - x)$	
	$y = (m - 2)x + 4m + 4(m - 5)^{1/2} - 10$	$(m + 2(m - 5)^{1/2}, \infty)$
	$5 < m < \infty$	
R^+R^-	$y = 5x$	$(0, \xi)$
	$y = 3x + 2\xi$	(ξ, ∞)
	$m = 5, \quad 3 \le \xi \le 5$	
$R^+B^-R^-$	$y = mx$	$(0, m - 2 - 2(5 - m)^{1/2})$
	$y = \frac{1}{2}(x^2 + m^2 + 4m - 8(5 - m - 24)^{1/2})$	$(m - 2 - 2(5 - m)^{1/2}, m - 2)$
	$\lambda = \frac{1}{2}(m - x) - 1$	
	$y = (m - 2)x + 4m - 4(5 - m)^{1/2} - 14$	$(m - 2, \infty)$
	$4 \le m < 5$	
B^-R^-	$y = \frac{1}{2}x^2$	$(0, \xi)$
	$\lambda = \frac{1}{2}(\xi - x)$	
	$y = \xi x - \frac{1}{2}\xi^2$	(ξ, ∞)
	$0 \le \xi \le 2$	
R^-	$y = mx$	$(0, \infty)$
	$m \le 0$	

To test the sufficient conditions, we note that

(1) On the B^+-subarc, $\lambda < 0$ and $\delta = x - 4 > 0$. Therefore Ic and Id are satisfied.

(2) III″ is satisfied, since $F^-_{y'y'} = F^+_{y'y'} = 2$.

(3) At $x = x_1 = 0$, the following values are assumed: $y' = 6$, $y_1' = 0$, $y_2' = 4$. Then (2.81) becomes

$$\chi(x_1) = 12 > 0 \tag{2.106}$$

so that II_N' holds by Theorem 7.

(4) IV′ is satisfied in virtue of the following relations:

$$\begin{aligned} y_m(x, 6) &= x && (0 < x \leq 6) \\ &= 6 && (6 \leq x \leq 8) \\ &= x + 6 && (8 \leq x \leq 9) \end{aligned} \tag{2.107}$$

We conclude that (2.105) furnishes a strong relative minimum. The other extremaloid families of Table IX do not satisfy the prescribed terminal condition for real values of the parameters. Therefore the solution (2.105) is unique.

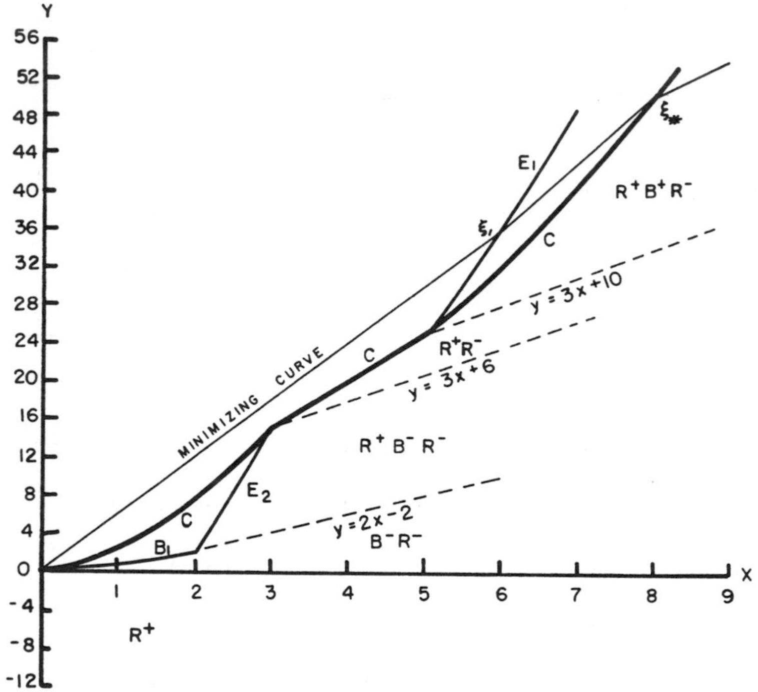

FIG. 8. The corner, the entry, and the exit loci.

The splitting of extremals occurring on the C-locus and on the B_1-subarc, as discussed in Sec. 2.19, is illustrated by the families R^+R^- and B^-R^-, respectively, with ξ replacing m as the family parameter.

To investigate the existence of the absolute minimum, we note the following:

(1) For the B^-R^- family, the range of ξ defined by $\chi \geq 0$ is $0 \leq \xi \leq 3$. For the interval $2 < \xi \leq 3$, the family overlaps with $R^+B^-R^-$ in the domain D defined by

$$\begin{aligned} &2x - 2 < y \leq \tfrac{1}{2}x^2 && (2 < x < 3) \\ &2x - 2 < y \leq 3x - \tfrac{9}{2} && (3 < x < \infty) \end{aligned} \qquad (2.108)$$

If the terminal point lies in D, there are two minima I_1 and I_2, corresponding to $R^+B^-R^-$ and B^-R^-, respectively. It can be shown that $I_1 < I_2$. Thus, if we seek the least minimum, we can eliminate the overlap by decreasing the range of ξ to $0 \leq \xi \leq 2$ as indicated in Table IX.

(2) It can be shown that the M-neighborhood of E_{12} extends over the entire half-plane $x > 0$, which is covered by the five families of Table IX without an overlap, as shown schematically in Fig. 8.

We conclude that for any choice of (x_2, y_2) there exists a unique solution, which furnishes an absolute minimum. A partial check of this statement is provided by the values $I(E_{12}) = 118\frac{2}{3}$ and $I(C_{12}) = 123$ for the curve C_{12} defined by $y = 6x$ on $0 \leq x \leq 9$.

2.22 Discussion of the Results

A solution of the refraction problem in case (b) has been obtained under the restrictions $n = 1$ and $\Omega \neq 0$. The first restriction can be removed by the requirement that I^* vanish on every closed path in M. If the second restriction is removed, subarcs in the corner locus $\psi = 0$ must be admitted. Although such subarcs cannot be imbedded in a family of extremals, the difficulty can be overcome by the replacement of II_N' by the more stringent condition III″. Indeed, the situation is quite analogous to that in case (a), with the locus $\psi = 0$ playing the role of $\phi \equiv 0$.

In conclusion we note the following application to the theory of optimum control. Let the locus of the discontinuity of f be of the form

$$\phi = \phi(x, y_i, u_j) = 0 \qquad (2.109)$$

where y_i is the set of the *state* variables, and u_j is the set of the *control* variables. Then the transformation

$$u_j = y'_{j+n} \qquad (2.110)$$

converts the problem into case (b), treated in Part B of this chapter. For a practical illustration see Garfinkel.[3]

ACKNOWLEDGMENTS

The author wishes to express his appreciation to Dr. G. T. McAllister, who contributed the construction used in Sec. 7 and has made several other useful suggestions. The author also gratefully acknowledges the aid of Mrs. Bernice Krouse, who typed the manuscript.

REFERENCES

1. O. Bolza, "Lectures on the Calculus of Variations," Chelsea, New York, 1904.
2. G. A. Bliss, A problem in the calculus of variations in which the integrand is discontinuous, *Trans. Am. Math. Soc.* **8**, 325 (1906).
3. B. Garfinkel, Minimal Problems in Airplane Performance, *Quart. Appl. Math.* **9**, 149 (1951).
4. G. A. Bliss, "Lectures on the Calculus of Variations." University of Chicago Press, Chicago, Illinois, 1946.
5. W. T. Reid, Discontinuous solutions in the non-parametric problem of Mayer, *Amer. J. Math.* **69**, 69 (1935).

3

Singular Extremals†

HENRY J. KELLEY
ANALYTICAL MECHANICS ASSOCIATES, INC.,
WESTBURY, LONG ISLAND, NEW YORK

RICHARD E. KOPP
H. GARDNER MOYER
RESEARCH DEPARTMENT, GRUMMAN AIRCRAFT ENGINEERING CORPORATION,
BETHPAGE, LONG ISLAND, NEW YORK

3.0 Introduction

Singular extremals are usually associated with variational problems which have the control variables appearing linearly in the system differential

† This work was partially supported by the U.S. Air Force Office of Scientific Research of the Office of Aerospace Research, under Contracts AF 49(638)-1207 and AF 49(638)-1512 and also by the Theoretical Division of NASA Goddard Space Flight Center under Contracts NAS 5-2535 and NAS 5-9085.

equations—singular arcs or subarcs arising when the pseudo-Hamiltonian function $\mathscr{H}$ is not explicitly a function of the control variable over a nonzero time interval. When such a situation occurs, neither the maximum principle nor the classical variational theory provide adequate tests for minimality of the arc.

The subject of singular extremals is not merely of academic interest since many problems in rocket and air vehicle flight exhibit solutions which include singular subarcs. Although the following analyses discuss explicitly only the case in which the control variable appears linearly in the system differential equations, the results are more widely applicable. Other examples which offer the possibility of singular subarcs are those problems in which the surface in "hodograph space"[1] is nonconvex. The nonconvex surfaces in these cases may be replaced by their convex hulls to obtain "relaxed" variational problems[2,3] in which appropriately chosen control variables are sectionally linear.

The possible appearance of singular subarcs in a problem is accompanied by considerable analytical difficulty. There is no general method available for determining these subarcs and the manner in which they form segments of the minimizing arc. Valuable insight into these questions is provided by the Green's theorem method of Miele.[4] This method also provides necessary and sufficient conditions for minimality, although severely restricted in its applicability in terms of number of variables present. A fairly comprehensive treatment of singular arcs in problems linear in the state has been given by LaSalle.[5] However, in such problems, singularity is equivalent to degeneracy in the sense of nonuniqueness of solution.

The present chapter will derive conditions for minimality of singular arcs over short intervals of time. The derivative material is taken mainly from four previous papers[6–9] by the authors, with extensions and considerations of the interrelationships of the two following approaches: first, a second variation test for singular subarcs employing special control variations, and second, a transformation approach to the analysis of singular subarcs. No pretense of complete treatment can be made since difficult questions on the number and sequence of singular and nonsingular subarcs remain unanswered; however, some material on junction conditions for singular arcs is included. The problem of synthesizing solutions containing singular subarcs is not considered.

3.1 Second Variation Test for Singular Extremals

3.10 Introduction

The approach presented in this section follows the work of Kopp and Moyer[6] and Kelley.[8] The positive semidefiniteness of the second variation of the payoff function is examined for a special class of explicitly defined control variations. A parameter τ of the special control variations is allowed to approach zero in the limit and the dominant term of the second variation is evaluated, providing a test for determining the minimality of the singular subarc over short lengths of arc. The special class of control variations has been constructed so that terminal conditions can be satisfied by a weak additional control variation which does not contribute to the dominant term in the second variation.

The authors are aware of some similar work concerning singular subarcs and the second variation which is being done by H. Robbins.[10] His analysis follows, somewhat, the approach used in Sec. 3.16.

3.11 Problem Formulation

In the usual format for trajectory and control problems, we are given a system of differential equations and boundary conditions

$$\begin{aligned} &\dot{x}_i = f_i(x_1, \ldots, x_n, u_1, \ldots, u_r, t), \qquad i = 1, \ldots, n \\ &x_i(t_0) = x_{i_0}, \qquad i = 1, \ldots, n \\ &x_i(t_f) = x_{i_f}, \qquad i = 1, \ldots, m, \qquad m \leq n \end{aligned} \tag{3.1†}$$

and are required to minimize a function $P(x_{m+1_f}, \ldots, x_{n_f}, t_f)$ of the open final state variables x_{i_f}. This is called the general problem of Mayer. The minimization is usually subject to explicit constraints on the control variables u_l, which require the control vector $\mathbf{u}$ to belong to a class of admissible controls U. However, such explicit constraints will present no difficulty in this analysis, since it will be assumed that the control corresponding to a singular subarc is interior to the boundary of U, as is usually the case.

Necessary conditions for P to be a minimum are that the Pontryagin pseudo-Hamiltonian function $\mathscr{H}$ be a minimum for all admissible controls:

$$\mathscr{H}(\bar{u}_1 + \Delta u_1, \ldots, \bar{u}_r + \Delta u_r) \geq \mathscr{H}(\bar{u}_1, \ldots, \bar{u}_r) \tag{3.2‡}$$

where

$$\mathscr{H} \equiv \sum_{i=1}^{n} \lambda_i f_i(x_1, \ldots, x_n, u_1, \ldots, u_r, t) \tag{3.3}$$

The λ_i variables are the usual Lagrange multipliers, and satisfy the differential equations and natural boundary conditions

$$\begin{aligned} &\dot{\lambda}_i = -\sum_{j=1}^{n} \lambda_j \frac{\partial f_j}{\partial x_i}, \qquad i = 1, \ldots, n \\ &\lambda_i(t_f) = \frac{\partial P}{\partial x_{i_f}}, \qquad i = m+1, \ldots, n \end{aligned} \tag{3.4§}$$

† Dot denotes differentiation with respect to time t.

‡ Here $\bar{u}_l$ denotes an optimal value of u_l.

§ Here it is assumed that $\lambda_0 \neq 0$. In particular, the value of λ_0 is taken to be *positive*, namely, $\lambda_0 = 1$; hence, we have a *minimum* principle.

Subarcs of the solution, along which the determinant whose elements are the second partial derivatives $\partial^2 \mathscr{H}/\partial u_k \, \partial u_s$, $k, s = 1, \ldots, r$ vanishes over a nonzero interval of time, are referred to classically as singular subarcs. In this case the maximum principle, or the Weierstrass condition (3.2), fails to determine the nature of extremal arcs over short lengths of arc. Such subarcs commonly arise in problems in which the functions f_i are linear in one or more of the control variables, the function $\mathscr{H}$ thus being correspondingly linear. Another situation which offers the possibility of singular subarcs is that in which the surface in "hodograph space" is nonconvex. This surface was defined by Contensou[1] through the equation $\dot{x}_i = f_i(x, u, t)$ with x and t fixed. In this case the surface may be replaced by its convex hull to obtain a "relaxed" variational problem[2,3] in which the functions f_i and $\mathscr{H}$ are sectionally linear in appropriately chosen control variables.

For the remainder of this analysis, we will consider the case in which a single control variable appears linearly in the system differential equations. However, this in no way limits the wider applicability of the analysis.

3.12 Second Variation

The total variation in the payoff functional P due to a variation in the control vector $\mathbf{u}$ is given[11] by

$$\begin{aligned}
\Delta P &= \sum_{i=m+1}^{n} \frac{\partial P}{\partial x_{i_f}} \Delta x_{i_f} + \frac{1}{2} \sum_{i,j=m+1}^{n} \frac{\partial^2 P(\mathbf{x}_f + \xi\, \Delta \mathbf{x}_f)}{\partial x_{i_f}\, \partial x_{j_f}} \Delta x_{i_f} \Delta x_{j_f} \\
&= \int_{t_0}^{t_f} [\mathscr{H}(\boldsymbol{\lambda}, \mathbf{x}, \mathbf{u} + \Delta \mathbf{u}, t) - \mathscr{H}(\boldsymbol{\lambda}, \mathbf{x}, \mathbf{u}, t)]\, dt \\
&\quad + \int_{t_0}^{t_f} \sum_{j=1}^{n} \frac{\partial[\mathscr{H}(\boldsymbol{\lambda}, \mathbf{x}, \mathbf{u} + \Delta \mathbf{u}, t) - \mathscr{H}(\boldsymbol{\lambda}, \mathbf{x}, \mathbf{u}, t)]}{\partial x_j} \Delta x_j \, dt \\
&\quad + \frac{1}{2} \int_{t_0}^{t_f} \sum_{s,j=1}^{n} \frac{\partial^2 \mathscr{H}(\boldsymbol{\lambda}, \mathbf{x} + \xi\, \Delta \mathbf{x}, \mathbf{u} + \Delta \mathbf{u}, t)}{\partial x_j \, \partial x_s} \Delta x_j \, \Delta x_s \, dt \\
&\quad + \frac{1}{2} \sum_{i,j=m+1}^{n} \frac{\partial^2 P(\mathbf{x}_f + \xi\, \Delta \mathbf{x}_f, t_f)}{\partial x_{i_f}\, \partial x_{j_f}} \Delta x_i(t_f)\, \Delta x_j(t_f) \qquad (0 \le \xi \le 1)
\end{aligned} \tag{3.5}$$

where

$$\begin{aligned}
\Delta \dot{x}_i &= f_i(\mathbf{x} + \Delta \mathbf{x}, \mathbf{u} + \Delta \mathbf{u}, t) - f_i(\mathbf{x}, \mathbf{u}, t), & i &= 1, \ldots, n \\
\Delta x_i(t_0) &= 0 & i &= 1, \ldots, n \\
\Delta x_i(t_f) &= 0 & i &= 1, \ldots, m
\end{aligned} \tag{3.6}$$

When one of the control variables appears linearly in $\mathscr{H}$, the first term on the right-hand side of Eq. (3.5) may be identically zero during a nonzero time interval, producing a singular subarc. In this case, the additional terms in Eq. (3.5) must be examined to determine the nature of the extremal path.

Under the assumption that the singular control is interior to its boundary, Eq. (3.5) is evaluated for variations in the singular control $\Delta u = K\,\delta u$ to second order terms in K.

$$\begin{aligned}\Delta P_2 = {} & K^2 \int_{t_0}^{t_f} \sum_{i=1}^{n} \frac{\partial^2 \mathscr{H}(\boldsymbol{\lambda}, \mathbf{x}, \mathbf{u}, t)}{\partial x_i\, \partial u}\, \delta x_i\, \delta u\, dt \\ & + \frac{K^2}{2} \int_{t_0}^{t_f} \sum_{i,j=1}^{n} \frac{\partial^2 \mathscr{H}(\boldsymbol{\lambda}, \mathbf{x}, \mathbf{u}, t)}{\partial x_i\, \partial x_j}\, \delta x_i\, \delta x_j\, dt \\ & + \frac{K^2}{2} \sum_{i,j=m+1}^{n} \frac{\partial^2 P(\mathbf{x}_f, t_f)}{\partial x_{i_f}\, \partial x_{j_f}}\, \delta x_i(t_f)\, \delta x_j(t_f) \end{aligned} \tag{3.7}$$

where

$$\begin{aligned} \delta \dot{x}_i &= \sum_{j=1}^{n} \frac{\partial f_i(\mathbf{x}, \mathbf{u}, t)}{\partial x_j}\, \delta x_j + \frac{\partial f_i(\mathbf{x}, \mathbf{u}, t)}{\partial u}\, \delta u \\ \delta x_i(t_0) &= 0, \qquad i = 1, \ldots, n \\ \delta x_i(t_f) &= 0, \qquad i = 1, \ldots, m \end{aligned} \tag{3.8}$$

The usual approach to the study of the second variation encounters difficulties as a result of the control variations appearing only linearly in Eq. (3.7). The problem of minimizing ΔP_2 subject to constraints (3.8), the classical accessory minimum problem, cannot be treated in the usual manner owing to the vanishing of $\partial^2 \mathscr{H}/\partial u^2$.

3.13 First Special Control Variation

It has long been appreciated that carefully chosen special variations are useful in deriving necessary conditions. There exists, for example, a classical derivation of the Legendre necessary condition along these lines.[12] With this in mind, we search out control variations which will satisfy boundary conditions imposed on Eq. (3.8) and which will allow the positive semidefiniteness of ΔP_2 to be tested.

The first member of a set of control variations intended to accomplish this is shown in Fig. 1 and is designated as $\varphi_0{}^1(t, \tau)$. The time $t = 0$ is designated as the center of the interval 2τ, and may occur at any interior point of the singular subarc. The parameter τ will be allowed to approach zero in the limit. Successive integrations of $\varphi_0{}^1(t, \tau)$ with respect to t are designated by $\varphi_v{}^1(t, \tau)$, that is

$$\frac{d^v \varphi_v{}^1(t, \tau)}{dt^v} = \varphi_0{}^1(t, \tau) \tag{3.9}$$

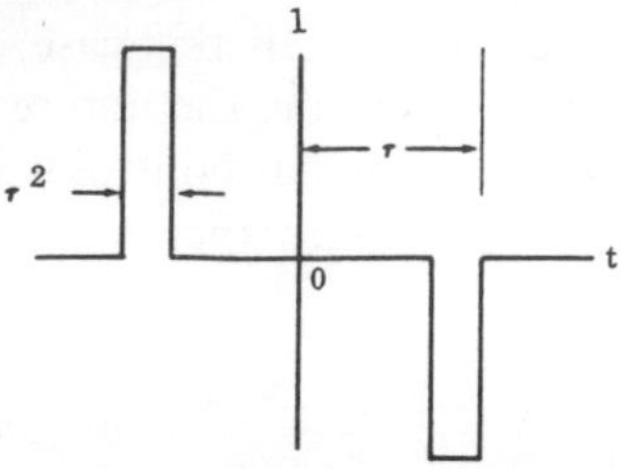

FIG. 1. $\varphi_0{}^1(t, \tau)$.

Equation (3.8) can be integrated for $\delta u = \varphi_0{}^1(t, \tau)$, subject to the initial conditions $\delta x_i(t_0) = 0$, $i = 1, \ldots, n$. For the present, the boundary conditions at t_f will be relaxed and will be satisfied later by auxiliary control variations. Let

$$\delta x_i(t) = A_{i,1}(t)\varphi_1{}^1(t, \tau) + A_{i,2}(t)\varphi_2{}^1(t, \tau) + \xi_i{}^1(t) \tag{3.10}$$

(Note that the superscripts of ξ and φ do not denote exponentiation.) Substituting Eq. (3.10) into Eq. (3.8) and equating coefficients gives

$$\begin{aligned} A_{i,1} &= \frac{\partial f_i}{\partial u} = \frac{\partial^2 \mathscr{H}}{\partial \lambda_i \, \partial u} \\ A_{i,2} &= \sum_{j=1}^{n} \frac{\partial f_i}{\partial x_j} A_{j,1} - \dot{A}_{i,1} \\ &= \sum_{j=1}^{n} \frac{\partial^2 \mathscr{H}}{\partial \lambda_i \, \partial x_j} A_{j,1} - \dot{A}_{i,1} \end{aligned} \tag{3.11}$$

and

$$\dot{\xi}_i{}^1 = \sum_{j=1}^{n} \frac{\partial f_i}{\partial x_j} \xi_j{}^1 + \left\{ \sum_{j=1}^{n} \frac{\partial f_i}{\partial x_j} A_{j,2} - \dot{A}_{i,2} \right\} \varphi_2{}^1 \tag{3.12}$$

The necessary smoothness properties of the coefficients in Eq. (3.8) required for the existence of Eqs. (3.11) and (3.12) are assumed. An evaluation of the function $\varphi_2{}^1(t, \tau)$ shows that $\xi_i{}^1(t)$ is of order τ^3; that is

$$\lim_{\tau \to 0} \frac{\xi_i{}^1(t)}{\tau^2} = 0 \tag{3.13}$$

The variation of the functional $P(\mathbf{x}, t)$ can easily be evaluated by substituting Eq. (3.10) into Eq. (3.7) and integrating by parts, retaining only the dominant terms in τ.

$$\begin{aligned} \Delta P_2 = 2\Bigg[&-\frac{1}{2}\frac{d}{dt}\left\{ \sum_{i=1}^{n} \frac{\partial^2 \mathscr{H}}{\partial u \, \partial x_i} A_{i,1} \right\} - \sum_{i=1}^{n} \frac{\partial^2 \mathscr{H}}{\partial u \, \partial x_i} A_{i,2} \\ &+ \frac{1}{2} \sum_{i,j=1}^{n} \frac{\partial^2 \mathscr{H}}{\partial x_i \, \partial x_j} A_{i,1} A_{j,1} \Bigg]_{t=0} K^2 \tau^5 + O(K^2 \tau^6) \end{aligned} \tag{3.14}$$

In this and the subsequent analysis, it is assumed that the Taylor series in τ used to evaluate ΔP_2 has a nonzero interval of convergence. A necessary condition for P to be a minimum is that $\Delta P_2 \geq 0$. Since $t = 0$ is any interior point on the singular subarc, a necessary condition for the extremal arc to be minimizing is

$$\frac{1}{2}\frac{d}{dt}\left[\sum_{i=1}^{n}\frac{\partial^2\mathscr{H}}{\partial u\,\partial x_i}A_{i,1}\right]+\sum_{i=1}^{n}\frac{\partial^2\mathscr{H}}{\partial u\,\partial x_i}A_{i,2}-\frac{1}{2}\sum_{i,j=1}^{n}\frac{\partial^2\mathscr{H}}{\partial x_i\,\partial x_j}A_{i,1}A_{j,1}\leq 0 \tag{3.15}$$

along the entire singular subarc. (The inequality is reversed for a maximum.) This can be shown to be equivalent to the condition

$$\frac{\partial}{\partial u}\left(\frac{d^2}{dt^2}\frac{\partial\mathscr{H}}{\partial u}\right)\leq 0 \tag{3.16}$$

In light of the terminal boundary conditions imposed on Eq. (3.8), one is justified in being concerned with the admissibility of such a control variation. In regard to this, the authors are prepared to give only a plausibility argument concerning the satisfaction of boundary conditions. From Eq. (3.10) it is observed that the dominant term of $\delta x_i(t_f)$ is of order τ^3 or smaller. Therefore, corrections in $\Delta x_i(t_f)$ to satisfy boundary conditions to first order in K can be made with auxiliary weak control variations Δu of order $K\tau^3$ which contribute terms of order $K^2\tau^6$ to ΔP_2. Thus, the dominant term in ΔP_2 is unchanged in Eq. (3.14). The existence of such variations is equivalent to a normality assumption. A rigorous demonstration, which would require that boundary conditions be satisfied exactly, would follow arguments similar to those used by Pontryagin and others to show that there are points that can be reached on all curves having their tangent rays interior to the cone of attainability. No attempt has been made by the authors along these lines.

3.14 Second Special Control Variation

If Eqs. (3.15) and (3.16) are met marginally (equality), the nature of the extremal subarc is still undetermined. In this case, the second member $\varphi_0{}^2(t, \tau)$ (see Fig. 2) of the class of special control variations is used and a procedure similar to that above is followed. Successive integrations of $\varphi_0{}^2(t, \tau)$ are designated by $\varphi_v{}^2(t, \tau)$, that is

$$\frac{d^v\varphi_v{}^2(t, \tau)}{dt^v} = \varphi_0{}^2(t, \tau) \tag{3.17}$$

Equation (3.8) is then solved for $\delta u = \varphi_0{}^2(t, \tau)$, subject to initial conditions $\delta x_i(t_0) = 0,\ \ i = 1, \ldots, n$ with relaxed terminal conditions as previously

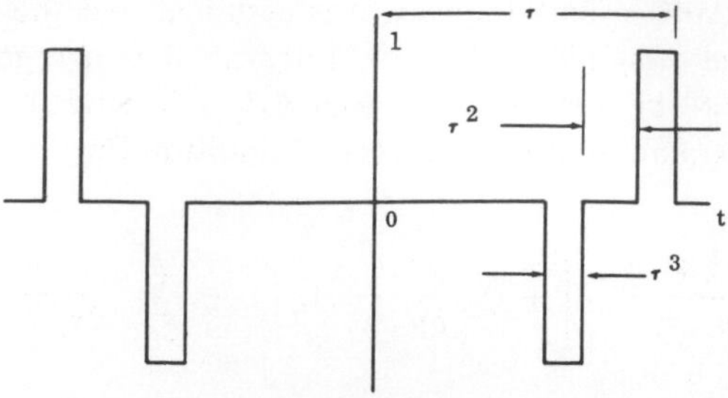

FIG. 2. $\varphi_0{}^2(t, \tau)$.

mentioned. The variations $\delta x_i(t)$ in this case are expressed by

$$\delta x_i(t) = A_{i,1}(t)\varphi_1{}^2(t, \tau) + A_{i,2}(t)\varphi_2{}^2(t, \tau) + A_{i,3}(t)\varphi_3{}^2(t, \tau) + A_{i,4}(t)\varphi_4{}^2(t, \tau) + \xi_i{}^2(t) \tag{3.18}$$

where

$$A_{i,1} = \frac{\partial f_i}{\partial u} = \frac{\partial^2 \mathscr{H}}{\partial \lambda_i\, \partial u}, \qquad A_{i,3} = \sum_{j=1}^{n} \frac{\partial^2 \mathscr{H}}{\partial \lambda_i\, \partial x_j} A_{j,2} - \dot{A}_{i,2}$$
$$A_{i,2} = \sum_{j=1}^{n} \frac{\partial^2 \mathscr{H}}{\partial \lambda_i\, \partial x_j} A_{j,1} - \dot{A}_{i,1}, \qquad A_{i,4} = \sum_{j=1}^{n} \frac{\partial^2 \mathscr{H}}{\partial \lambda_i\, \partial x_j} A_{j,3} - \dot{A}_{i,3} \tag{3.19}$$

and

$$\dot{\xi}_i{}^2 = \sum_{j=1}^{n} \frac{\partial f_i}{\partial x_j} \xi_j{}^2 + \left[\sum_{j=1}^{n} \frac{\partial f_i}{\partial x_j} A_{j,4} - \dot{A}_{i,4}\right] \varphi_4{}^2 \tag{3.20}$$

An evaluation of $\varphi_3{}^2(t, \tau)$ shows that $\xi_i{}^2(t)$ is of order τ^6.

Substituting Eq. (3.18) into Eq. (3.7) and integrating by parts gives

$$\begin{aligned}\Delta P_2 = K^2 \int_{-\tau}^{\tau} \Bigg\{ &-\frac{1}{2}\frac{d}{dt}\left[\sum_{i=1}^{n} \frac{\partial^2 \mathscr{H}}{\partial u\, \partial x_i} A_{i,1}\right] - \sum_{i=1}^{n} \frac{\partial^2 \mathscr{H}}{\partial u\, \partial x_i} A_{i,2} \\ &+ \frac{1}{2}\sum_{i,j=1}^{n} \frac{\partial^2 \mathscr{H}}{\partial x_i\, \partial x_j} A_{i,1}A_{j,1}\Bigg\}\{\varphi_1{}^2(t, \tau)\}^2\, dt \\ + K^2 \int_{-\tau}^{\tau} \Bigg\{ &\frac{1}{2}\frac{d^2}{dt^2}\left[\sum_{i=1}^{n} \frac{\partial^2 \mathscr{H}}{\partial u\, \partial x_i} A_{i,2}\right] + \frac{3}{2}\frac{d}{dt}\left[\sum_{i=1}^{n} \frac{\partial^2 \mathscr{H}}{\partial u\, \partial x_i} A_{i,3}\right] \\ &+ \sum_{i=1}^{n} \frac{\partial^2 \mathscr{H}}{\partial u\, \partial x_i} A_{i,4} - \frac{1}{2}\frac{d}{dt}\left[\sum_{i,j=1}^{n} \frac{\partial^2 \mathscr{H}}{\partial x_i\, \partial x_j} A_{i,1}A_{j,2}\right] \\ &- \sum_{i,j=1}^{n} \frac{\partial^2 \mathscr{H}}{\partial x_i\, \partial x_j} A_{i,1}A_{j,3} + \frac{1}{2}\sum_{i,j=1}^{n} \frac{\partial^2 \mathscr{H}}{\partial x_i\, \partial x_j} A_{i,2}A_{j,2}\Bigg\}\{\varphi_2{}^2(t, \tau)\}^2\, dt \\ &+ O(\tau^{12})\end{aligned} \tag{3.21}$$

The integrand of the first term on the right-hand side of Eq. (3.21) which would lead to terms of order τ^8 vanishes identically by assumption. This result is identical to the term arising out of the control variation $\varphi_0{}^1(t, \tau)$. Evaluating Eq. (3.21) and retaining only the dominant terms gives

$$\Delta P_2 = 2\left[\frac{1}{2}\frac{d^2}{dt^2}\left(\sum_{i=1}^{n}\frac{\partial^2 \mathscr{H}}{\partial u\,\partial x_i}A_{i,2}\right) + \frac{3}{2}\frac{d}{dt}\left(\sum_{i=1}^{n}\frac{\partial^2 \mathscr{H}}{\partial u\,\partial x_i}A_{i,3}\right) + \sum_{i=1}^{n}\frac{\partial^2 \mathscr{H}}{\partial u\,\partial x_i}A_{i,4}\right.$$
$$-\frac{1}{2}\frac{d}{dt}\left(\sum_{i,j=1}^{n}\frac{\partial^2 \mathscr{H}}{\partial x_i\,\partial x_j}A_{i,1}A_{j,2}\right) - \sum_{i,j=1}^{n}\frac{\partial^2 \mathscr{H}}{\partial x_i\,\partial x_j}A_{i,1}A_{j,3}$$
$$\left.+\frac{1}{2}\sum_{i,j=1}^{n}\frac{\partial^2 \mathscr{H}}{\partial x_i\,\partial x_j}A_{i,2}A_{j,2}\right]_{t=0} K^2\tau^{11} + O(\tau^{12}) \geq 0 \tag{3.22}$$

from which we obtain the second in a sequence of necessary conditions. The admissibility with regard to boundary constraints of such a control variation follows the same type of argument as before. The variation of the state variables at $t = t_f$ is of order $K\tau^6$ and, thus, terminal boundary conditions can be satisfied by auxiliary weak control variations Δu of order $K\tau^6$ which do not contribute to the dominant term in ΔP_2, as given in Eq. (3.22). The inequalities in Eq. (3.22) can be simplified to

$$\frac{\partial}{\partial u}\left(\frac{d^4}{dt^4}\frac{\partial \mathscr{H}}{\partial u}\right) \geq 0 \tag{3.23}$$

3.15 General Analysis

If the equalities are satisfied in Eqs. (3.22) and (3.23), the third control variation of the class is used and so on. The motivation for choosing such a class of control variations arises from the theory of distributions. To find $\varphi_0^{q+1}(t, \tau)$, consider the derivative of $\varphi_0{}^q(t, \tau)$ accepting the Dirac delta; approximate this distribution by a pulse of width τ^{q+2}, and scale so that the magnitude of the pulses is unity.

From the previous discussion of the control variations $\varphi_0{}^1(t, \tau)$ and $\varphi_0{}^2(t, \tau)$, it becomes evident that it is not necessary to actually construct the specific control variation, but only to be assured that such variations exist for which a constructive method has been given. With these thoughts, ΔP_2 for the qth special control variation $[\Delta u = \varphi_0{}^q(t, \tau)]$ will be evaluated.

The variation $\delta x_i(t)$ becomes

$$\delta x_i(t) = \sum_{s=1}^{2q} A_{i,s}\varphi_s{}^q(t, \tau) + \xi_i{}^q(t) \tag{3.24}$$

where $\xi_i^q(t)$ is of order $\tau^{[(q+1)(q+2)/2]}$. The coefficients $A_{i,s}$ are given by

$$A_{i,s} = \sum_{j=1}^{n} \frac{\partial^2 \mathscr{H}}{\partial \lambda_i \, \partial x_j} A_{j,s-1} - \dot{A}_{i,s-1}, \qquad s > 1 \tag{3.25}$$

where $A_{i,1} = \partial^2 \mathscr{H} / \partial \lambda_i \, \partial u$. Substituting Eq. (3.25) into Eq. (3.7) and integrating by parts gives

$$\begin{aligned}
\Delta P_2 = {} & + K^2 \int_{-\tau}^{\tau} \left\{ - \sum_{i=1}^{n} \frac{\partial^2 \mathscr{H}}{\partial u \, \partial x_i} A_{i,2} - \frac{1}{2} \frac{d}{dt} \left(\sum_{i=1}^{n} \frac{\partial^2 \mathscr{H}}{\partial u \, \partial x_i} A_{i,1} \right) \right. \\
& \left. + \frac{1}{2} \sum_{i,j=1}^{n} \frac{\partial^2 \mathscr{H}}{\partial x_i \, \partial x_j} A_{i,1} A_{j,1} \right\} \{\varphi_1^q(t, \tau)\}^2 \, dt \\
& \vdots \\
& + K^2 \int_{-\tau}^{\tau} \left\{ \sum_{s=1}^{k} \eta_{sk} + \frac{1}{2} \sum_{i,j=1}^{n} \frac{\partial^2 \mathscr{H}}{\partial x_i \, \partial x_j} A_{i,k} A_{j,k} \right\} \{\varphi_k^q(t, \tau)\}^2 \, dt \\
& \vdots \\
& + K^2 \int_{-\tau}^{\tau} \left\{ \sum_{s=1}^{q} \eta_{sq} + \frac{1}{2} \sum_{i,j=1}^{n} \frac{\partial^2 \mathscr{H}}{\partial x_i \, \partial x_j} A_{i,q} A_{j,q} \right\} \{\varphi_q^q(t, \tau)\}^2 \, dt \\
& + O(\tau^{[(q+1)(q+2)]})
\end{aligned} \tag{3.26}$$

where

$$\begin{aligned}
\eta_{1k} &= -\eta_{1,k-1}(A_{i,v+2}) - \frac{d}{dt} \{\eta_{1,k-1}(A_{i,v+1})\}, \qquad k > 1 \\
\eta_{sk} &= -\eta_{s,k-1}(A_{i,v} A_{j,w+2}) - \frac{d}{dt} \{\eta_{s,k-1}(A_{i,v} A_{j,w+1})\}, \qquad k > s > 1 \\
\eta_{11} &= -\left\{ \sum_{i=1}^{n} \left[\frac{\partial^2 \mathscr{H}}{\partial u \, \partial x_i} A_{i,2} + \frac{1}{2} \frac{d}{dt} \left(\frac{\partial^2 \mathscr{H}}{\partial u \, \partial x_i} A_{i,1} \right) \right] \right\} \\
\eta_{ss} &= -\left\{ \sum_{i,j=1}^{n} \left[\frac{\partial^2 \mathscr{H}}{\partial x_i \, \partial x_j} A_{i,s-1} A_{j,s+1} + \frac{1}{2} \frac{d}{dt} \left(\frac{\partial^2 \mathscr{H}}{\partial x_i \, \partial x_j} A_{i,s-1} A_{j,s} \right) \right] \right\}, \qquad s > 1
\end{aligned} \tag{3.27}$$

The notation $\eta_{1,k-1}(A_{i,v+2})$ designates that all terms of the form $A_{i,v}$ appearing in $\eta_{1,k-1}$ are to have their second indices increased by 2. A similar rule is used where the $A_{i,v}$ terms appear as products in the definition of $\eta_{s,k}$ in Eq. (3.27).

Let q be chosen such that the dominant term in τ for Eq. (3.26) results from the integrand which contains the term $[\varphi_q^q(t, \tau)]^2$. That is, all coefficients of $[\varphi_k^q(t, \tau)]^2$ are identically zero for $k < q$. The dominant term in Eq. (3.26) will then be of order $\tau^{[(q+1)(q+2)-1]}$. Therefore, a necessary condition for the extremal path to be minimizing is

$$\sum_{s=1}^{q} \eta_{sq} + \frac{1}{2} \sum_{i,j=1}^{n} \frac{\partial^2 \mathscr{H}}{\partial x_i \, \partial x_j} A_{i,q} A_{j,q} \geq 0 \tag{3.28}$$

To satisfy boundary conditions on $x_i(t_f)$, auxiliary control corrections are made in the remaining interval of time which will add to ΔP_2 terms which are of one degree higher in τ than those arising out of the dominant term in Eq. (3.26). Thus, they can be neglected as τ approaches zero in the limit.

Although it is not readily apparent, it will be shown in the next section that the necessary condition given by Eq. (3.28) can be expressed equivalently as

$$(-1)^k \frac{\partial}{\partial u} \left(\frac{d^{2k}}{dt^{2k}} \frac{\partial \mathscr{H}}{\partial u} \right) \geq 0 \tag{3.29}$$

We are indebted to Robbins for arriving first at this form of the test.

3.16 Alternate Development of Necessary Conditions

We consider here an alternate development of the necessary conditions expressed by Eq. (3.29). This approach proceeds similarly to a proof outlined by Robbins which was forwarded to the authors in the form of unpublished notes dated July 1964. To second-order terms in K

$$\frac{d}{dt}\left(\sum_{i=1}^{n} \delta\lambda_i \, \delta x_i \right) = - \sum_{i,j=1}^{n} \frac{\partial^2 \mathscr{H}}{\partial x_i \, \partial x_j} \delta x_i \, \delta x_j - \sum_{i=1}^{n} \frac{\partial^2 \mathscr{H}}{\partial x_i \, \partial u} \delta x_i \, \delta u + \sum_{i=1}^{n} \frac{\partial^2 \mathscr{H}}{\partial \lambda_i \, \partial u} \delta \lambda_i \, \delta u \tag{3.30}$$

where

$$\begin{aligned} \delta \dot{x}_i &= \sum_{j=1}^{n} \frac{\partial^2 \mathscr{H}}{\partial \lambda_i \, \partial x_j} \delta x_j + \frac{\partial^2 \mathscr{H}}{\partial \lambda_i \, \partial u} \delta u \\ \delta \dot{\lambda}_i &= - \sum_{j=1}^{n} \frac{\partial^2 \mathscr{H}}{\partial x_i \, \partial x_j} \delta x_j - \sum_{j=1}^{n} \frac{\partial^2 \mathscr{H}}{\partial x_i \, \partial \lambda_j} \delta \lambda_j - \frac{\partial^2 \mathscr{H}}{\partial x_i \, \partial u} \delta u \end{aligned} \tag{3.31}$$

Equation (3.30) together with Eq. (3.7) yields

$$2\Delta P_2 = \left[\int_{t_0}^{t_f} \sum_{i=1}^{n} \left(\frac{\partial^2 \mathscr{H}}{\partial x_i \, \partial u} \delta x_i + \frac{\partial^2 \mathscr{H}}{\partial \lambda_i \, \partial u} \delta \lambda_i \right) \delta u \, dt - \left[\delta x_i \, \delta \lambda_i \right]_{t_0}^{t_f} + \sum_{i,j=m+1}^{n} \frac{\partial^2 P}{\partial x_{i_f} \, \partial x_{j_f}} \delta x_{i_f} \, \delta x_{j_f} \right] K^2 \tag{3.32}$$

The boundary conditions for Eqs. (3.31) are

$$\delta x_i(t_0) = 0, \qquad i = 1, \ldots, n$$
$$\delta x_i(t_f) = 0, \qquad i = 1, \ldots, m$$

However, as before, the terminal conditions imposed on $\delta x_i(t_f)$ will be relaxed and satisfied with auxiliary control variations which will not contribute to the dominant term in ΔP_2. The special control variation $\delta u = \varphi_0{}^q(t, \tau)$ will be used, and the dominant term in τ of ΔP_2 will be evaluated.

The coefficient of δu in the integrand of Eq. (3.32) is recognized to be $\delta(\partial \mathscr{H}/\partial u)$, the first order difference between $\partial \mathscr{H}/\partial u$ with and $\partial \mathscr{H}/\partial u$ without the control variation δu along the singular subarc:

$$K\left\{\sum_{i=1}^{n} \frac{\partial^2 \mathscr{H}}{\partial u\, \partial x_i}\, \delta x_i + \frac{\partial^2 \mathscr{H}}{\partial u\, \partial \lambda_i}\, \delta \lambda_i\right\} = \delta\left(\frac{\partial \mathscr{H}}{\partial u}\right) = \frac{\partial \mathscr{H}^*}{\partial u} - \frac{\partial \mathscr{H}}{\partial u} = \frac{\partial \mathscr{H}^*}{\partial u} \tag{3.33}$$

where ( )* designates evaluation along the subarc with the control variation δu. Substituting Eq. (3.33) into Eq. (3.32) and integrating by parts q times gives

$$2\,\Delta P_2 = \left[(-1)^q \int_{t_0}^{t_f} \left\{\frac{d^q}{dt^q}\left(\frac{\partial \mathscr{H}^*}{\partial u}\right)\right\} \varphi_q{}^q(t, \tau)\, dt\right] K$$
$$+ \left[-\sum_{i=1}^{n} \delta x_i\, \delta \lambda_i\Big|_{t_f} + \sum_{i,j=m+1}^{n} \frac{\partial^2 P}{\partial x_{i_f}\, \partial x_{j_f}}\, \delta x_{i_f}\, \delta x_{j_f}\right] K^2 \tag{3.34}$$

We will now assume that the first explicit appearance of u is always in an even-order time derivative of $\partial \mathscr{H}/\partial u$. A proof of this assumption will be given subsequently. The parameter q will be chosen so that this even order is equal to $2q$. The coefficient of the $\varphi_q{}^q(t, \tau)$ term in the integrand of Eq. (3.34) can be written as

$$\frac{d^q}{dt^q}\left(\frac{\partial \mathscr{H}^*}{\partial u}\right) = \int_{-\tau}^{t} \cdots \int_{-\tau}^{\xi} \frac{d^{2q}}{dt^{2q}}\left(\frac{\partial \mathscr{H}^*}{\partial u}\right)(d\xi)^q \tag{3.35}$$

Expanding the integrand of Eq. (3.35) in a Taylor series and retaining only the dominant term in K gives

$$\frac{d^{2q}}{dt^{2q}}\left(\frac{\partial \mathscr{H}^*}{\partial u}\right) = \frac{d^{2q}}{dt^{2q}}\left(\frac{\partial \mathscr{H}}{\partial u}\right) + K \frac{\partial}{\partial u}\left[\frac{d^{2q}}{dt^{2q}}\left(\frac{\partial \mathscr{H}}{\partial u}\right)\right] \varphi_0{}^q(t, \tau)$$
$$+ K \sum_{i=1}^{n} \frac{\partial}{\partial x_i}\left[\frac{d^{2q}}{dt^{2q}}\left(\frac{\partial \mathscr{H}}{\partial u}\right)\right] \delta x_i$$
$$+ K \sum_{i=1}^{n} \frac{\partial}{\partial \lambda_i}\left[\frac{d^{2q}}{dt^{2q}}\left(\frac{\partial \mathscr{H}}{\partial u}\right)\right] \delta \lambda_i + O(K^2) \tag{3.36}$$

The first term on the right-hand side of Eq. (3.36) is identically equal to zero, along the singular subarc. It is left for the reader to verify that the dominant term in Eq. (3.34) arises from the term

$$K\frac{\partial}{\partial u}\left[\frac{d^{2q}}{dt^{2q}}\left(\frac{\partial \mathscr{H}}{\partial u}\right)\right]\varphi_0{}^q(t, \tau)$$

in Eq. (3.36) and is of order $K^2\,\tau^{[(q+1)(q+2)-1]}$. Substituting this term into Eq. (3.35) yields

$$\frac{d^q}{dt^q}\left(\frac{\partial \mathscr{H}^*}{\partial u}\right) = K\int_{-\tau}^{t}\cdots\int_{-\tau}^{\xi}\frac{\partial}{\partial u}\left[\frac{d^{2q}}{dt^{2q}}\left(\frac{\partial \mathscr{H}}{\partial u}\right)\right]\varphi_0{}^q(t, \tau)(d\xi)^q \tag{3.37}$$

The coefficient of $\varphi_0{}^q(t, \tau)$ in the integrand of Eq. (3.37) is expanded as a power series in time about $t = 0$, any interior point on the singular subarc; and the integration indicated is performed

$$\frac{d^q}{dt^q}\left(\frac{\partial \mathscr{H}^*}{\partial u}\right) = K\left\{\frac{\partial}{\partial u}\left[\frac{d^{2q}}{dt^{2q}}\left(\frac{\partial \mathscr{H}}{\partial u}\right)\right]_{t=0} + O(\tau)\right\}\varphi_q{}^q(t, \tau) \tag{3.38}$$

Equation (3.38) is now substituted into Eq. (3.34) giving

$$2\,\Delta P_2 = (-1)^q\frac{\partial}{\partial u}\left[\frac{d^{2q}}{dt^{2q}}\left(\frac{\partial \mathscr{H}}{\partial u}\right)\right]_{t=0} K^2\,\tau^{[(q+1)(q+2)-1]} + O(K^2\,\tau^{[(q+1)(q+2)]}) \tag{3.39}$$

The terms δx_i and $\delta\lambda_i$ are of order $\tau^{[(q+1)(q+2)/2]}$ and thus do not contribute to the dominant term in ΔP_2. Terminal boundary conditions on $\delta x_i(t_f)$ can be satisfied with auxiliary control variations of order $\tau^{[(q+1)(q+2)/2]}$ and also will not contribute to the dominant term in ΔP_2 as given by Eq. (3.39). Since $t = 0$ is any interior point on the singular subarc, a necessary condition for the extremal arc to be minimizing is

$$(-1)^q\frac{\partial}{\partial u}\left[\frac{d^{2q}}{dt^{2q}}\left(\frac{\partial \mathscr{H}}{\partial u}\right)\right] \geq 0 \tag{3.40}$$

along the entire singular subarc, the inequality being reversed for a maximizing extremal.

We will now proceed to prove that if $\partial\mathscr{H}/\partial u$ is successively differentiated with respect to time, then u cannot first explicitly appear in an odd order derivative. It will first be necessary to derive a few basic relationships. Given a scalar function $F(\mathbf{x}, \boldsymbol{\lambda})$, where the components of the $\mathbf{x}$ and $\boldsymbol{\lambda}$ vectors obey the differential equations $\dot{x}_i = \partial\mathscr{H}/\partial\lambda_i$ and $\dot{\lambda}_i = -\partial\mathscr{H}/\partial x_i$ $(i = 1, \ldots, n)$, then

$$\frac{d}{dt}F(\mathbf{x}, \boldsymbol{\lambda}) = \sum_{i+1}^{n}\frac{\partial F}{\partial x_i}\frac{\partial \mathscr{H}}{\partial \lambda_i} - \sum_{i=1}^{n}\frac{\partial F}{\partial \lambda_i}\frac{\partial \mathscr{H}}{\partial x_i} = -(\nabla\mathscr{H})^T S\,\nabla F \tag{3.41}$$

where

$$\nabla^T = \left[\frac{\partial}{\partial x_1}, \ldots, \frac{\partial}{\partial x_n}, \frac{\partial}{\partial \lambda_1}, \ldots, \frac{\partial}{\partial \lambda_n}\right] \tag{3.42}$$

and S is the $2n \times 2n$ matrix

$$S = \left[\begin{array}{c|c} N & I \\ \hline -I & N \end{array}\right] \tag{3.43}$$

The explicit dependence of the function F on time t is not considered; however, this assumption is not restrictive, since t can be eliminated by adjoining an additional component to the $\mathbf{x}$ vector whose derivative is equal to unity. The time derivative of the gradient of the function F is

$$\frac{d}{dt}(\nabla F) = \nabla\left(\frac{d}{dt}F\right) + [\nabla(\nabla \mathscr{H})^T]S\,\nabla F \tag{3.44}$$

The relationships $S^T = -S$ and $[\nabla(\nabla \mathscr{H})^T]^T = \nabla(\nabla \mathscr{H})^T$ are now used to obtain the remaining preliminary equations:

$$\begin{aligned}
\frac{d}{dt}[(\nabla A)^T S\,\nabla B] &= \frac{d}{dt}(\nabla A)^T S\,\nabla B + (\nabla A)^T S \frac{d}{dt}\nabla B \\
&= \left(\nabla \frac{d}{dt} A\right)^T S\,\nabla B + [\nabla(\nabla \mathscr{H})^T S\,\nabla A]^T S\,\nabla B + (\nabla A)^T S\,\nabla \frac{d}{dt} B \\
&\quad + (\nabla A)^T S\,\nabla(\nabla \mathscr{H})^T S\,\nabla B \\
&= \left(\nabla \frac{d}{dt} A\right)^T S\,\nabla B - (\nabla A)^T S\,\nabla(\nabla \mathscr{H})^T S\,\nabla B + (\nabla A)^T S\,\nabla \frac{d}{dt} B \\
&\quad + (\nabla A)^T S\,\nabla(\nabla \mathscr{H})^T S\,\nabla B \\
&= \left(\nabla \frac{d}{dt} A\right)^T S\,\nabla B + (\nabla A)^T S\,\nabla \frac{d}{dt} B
\end{aligned} \tag{3.45}$$

In the following, the term

$$\frac{\partial}{\partial u}\frac{d^k}{dt^k}\frac{\partial \mathscr{H}}{\partial u}$$

will be denoted by α_k. We will assume that the α_k $(k = 1, \ldots, p-1)$ and all their time derivatives are equal to zero. Our task is to prove that $\alpha_p = 0$ when p is odd. Using Eq. (3.41), we have

$$\alpha_p = -\left(\nabla \frac{\partial \mathscr{H}}{\partial u}\right)^T S\,\nabla \frac{d^{p-1}}{dt^{p-1}}\frac{\partial \mathscr{H}}{\partial u} + \frac{d\alpha_{p-1}}{dt} = -\left(\nabla \frac{\partial \mathscr{H}}{\partial u}\right)^T S\,\nabla \frac{d^{p-1}}{dt^{p-1}}\frac{\partial \mathscr{H}}{\partial u} \tag{3.46}$$

Similarly,

$$\alpha_{p-1} = -\left(\nabla \frac{\partial \mathscr{H}}{\partial u}\right)^T S \nabla \frac{d^{p-2}}{dt^{p-2}} \frac{\partial \mathscr{H}}{\partial u} = 0 \tag{3.47}$$

Differentiating Eq. (3.47) with respect to time and using Eq. (3.45) gives

$$\frac{d\alpha_{p-1}}{dt} = -\left(\nabla \frac{\partial \mathscr{H}}{\partial u}\right)^T S \nabla \frac{d^{p-1}}{dt^{p-1}} \frac{\partial \mathscr{H}}{\partial u} - \left(\nabla \frac{d}{dt} \frac{\partial \mathscr{H}}{\partial u}\right)^T S \nabla \frac{d^{p-2}}{dt^{p-2}} \frac{\partial \mathscr{H}}{\partial u} = 0 \tag{3.48}$$

From Eqs. (3.45) and (3.47) $d\alpha_{p-2}/dt$ is

$$\frac{d\alpha_{p-2}}{dt} = -\left(\nabla \frac{d}{dt} \frac{\partial \mathscr{H}}{\partial u}\right)^T S \nabla \frac{d^{p-3}}{dt^{p-3}} \frac{\partial \mathscr{H}}{\partial u} = 0 \tag{3.49}$$

and upon differentiating with respect to time, we have

$$\frac{d^2\alpha_{p-2}}{dt^2} = -\left(\nabla \frac{d}{dt} \frac{\partial \mathscr{H}}{\partial u}\right)^T S \nabla \frac{d^{p-2}}{dt^{p-2}} \frac{\partial \mathscr{H}}{\partial u} - \left(\nabla \frac{d^2}{dt^2} \frac{\partial \mathscr{H}}{\partial u}\right)^T S \nabla \frac{d^{p-3}}{dt^{p-3}} \frac{\partial \mathscr{H}}{\partial u} = 0 \tag{3.50}$$

Continually repeating this process yields the general equation

$$\frac{d^k\alpha_{p-k}}{dt^k} = -\left(\nabla \frac{d^{k-1}}{dt^{k-1}} \frac{\partial \mathscr{H}}{\partial u}\right)^T S \nabla \frac{d^{p-k}}{dt^{p-k}} \frac{\partial \mathscr{H}}{\partial u} - \left(\nabla \frac{d^k}{dt^k} \frac{\partial \mathscr{H}}{\partial u}\right)^T S \nabla \frac{d^{p-k-1}}{dt^{p-k-1}} \frac{\partial \mathscr{H}}{\partial u} = 0 \tag{3.51}$$

We will now assume that p is odd; that is, $p = 2v + 1$. From Eqs. (3.46), (3.48), and (3.51)

$$\alpha_p = -\left(\nabla \frac{\partial \mathscr{H}}{\partial u}\right)^T S \nabla \frac{d^{p-1}}{dt^{p-1}} \frac{\partial \mathscr{H}}{\partial u} = +\left(\nabla \frac{d}{dt} \frac{\partial \mathscr{H}}{\partial u}\right)^T S \nabla \frac{d^{p-2}}{dt^{p-2}} \frac{\partial \mathscr{H}}{\partial u}$$
$$= -\left(\nabla \frac{d^2}{dt^2} \frac{\partial \mathscr{H}}{\partial u}\right)^T S \nabla \frac{d^{p-3}}{dt^{p-3}} \frac{\partial \mathscr{H}}{\partial u} = (-1)^v \left(\nabla \frac{d^v}{dt^v} \frac{\partial \mathscr{H}}{\partial u}\right)^T S\left(\nabla \frac{d^v}{dt^v} \frac{\partial \mathscr{H}}{\partial u}\right) = 0 \tag{3.52}$$

since the quadratic form

$$Z^T S Z = 0 \tag{3.53}$$

where Z is any $2n$ vector. Therefore u cannot first appear in an odd order time derivative of $\partial \mathscr{H}/\partial u$.

3.17 Junction Conditions

Nothing has been said so far about the joining of singular subarcs with nonsingular subarcs. Although an extensive analysis on this subject is not available, it is worthwhile making some observations concerning necessary conditions at junction points.

Let us consider the possibility of joining a singular arc *a-b* to a nonsingular arc *b′-c* at time t_i with a discontinuity in the control time history, as shown in Fig. 3a. Along the singular subarc the inequality in Eq. (3.40) is satisfied, while along the nonsingular arc $(\partial \mathscr{H}/\partial u)\,\Delta u > 0$. Referring to Fig. 3a we see that Δu, which is any variation from the nonsingular subarc,

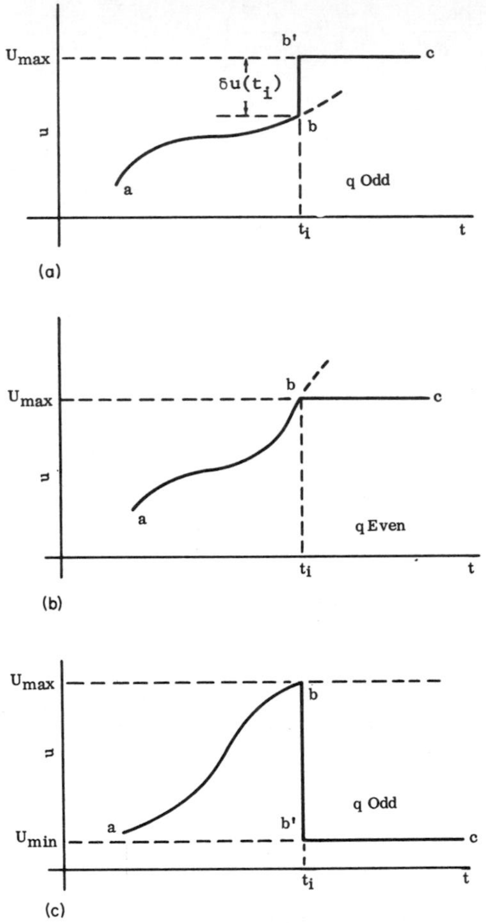

FIG. 3. Junction conditions.

must be negative—thus requiring $\partial\mathscr{H}/\partial u < 0$. However, $\partial\mathscr{H}/\partial u$ can also be evaluated in the neighborhood of the junction point on the nonsingular subarc by a Taylor series expansion, which leads to the conclusion that at the junction point

$$\frac{\partial}{\partial u}\left\{\frac{d^{2q}}{dt^{2q}}\left(\frac{\partial\mathscr{H}}{\partial u}\right)\right\} < 0 \tag{3.54}$$

In order to satisfy the inequalities in both Eqs. (3.40) and (3.54), q must be odd. A similar analysis considering a jump discontinuity in the control u to the lower boundary produces the same conclusions. Therefore, if a minimizing singular subarc is joined to a nonsingular subarc at a corner (jump discontinuity in u), q must be odd.

The situation will now be examined in which a singular subarc joins the nonsingular subarc with onset of saturation (no jump in u), as shown in Fig. 3b. In this case, an evaluation of $\partial\mathscr{H}/\partial u$ on the nonsingular subarc in the neighborhood of the junction leads to the conclusion that

$$\frac{\partial}{\partial u}\left\{\frac{d^{2q}}{dt^{2q}}\left(\frac{\partial\mathscr{H}}{\partial u}\right)\right\} > 0 \tag{3.55}$$

In this case, to satisfy the inequalities in Eqs. (3.40) and (3.55), q must be even.

We may summarize these results as follows:

(1) If q is *odd*, a jump discontinuity in control from a locally minimizing singular arc [satisfying (3.40)] to either bound will find the condition $(\partial\mathscr{H}/\partial u)$ $\Delta u \geq 0$ satisfied at slightly later t, i.e., then corner junctions are permitted. In this case, if singular control were maintained until the control saturated, the control must jump to the opposite bound, Fig. 3c.

(2) If q is *even*, jump discontinuities in control from singular arcs satisfying (3.40) in strengthened form are ruled out.

From the incompatibility of (3.40) and (3.54) in q-even problems, there is a temptation to conjecture that minimizing singular arcs of the q-even variety are isolated, except for the saturation possibility, since the most common type of junction, the corner junction, has been ruled out and, hence, that they are of only minor importance in the structure of a family of solutions. That this is not the case is illustrated by a simple example presented in Sec. 3.30 exhibiting complex junction phenomena.

3.2 A Transformation Approach to the Analysis of Singular Subarcs

3.20 Introduction

In the following section, we present an approach to the analysis of singular subarcs by means of a transformation to a new system of state variables.

such cases, we are led to an equivalent problem in a state space of smaller dimension, the z_j, $j = 1, \ldots, n-1$, becoming the state variables and $z_n = x_l$ the control variable. This change occurs through the identical vanishing of the Lagrange multiplier associated with the nth equation of state

$$\dot{z}_n = p_l + q_l u \tag{3.65}$$

In this equation, as well as in the first $n-1$ equations of state (3.59), the variables x_i are presumed eliminated in favor of the z_j by use of the inverse transformation. It should be noted that jump discontinuities in the new control variable $z_n(t) = x_l(t)$ occurring at corner points of the solution imply impulsive behavior of $u(t)$. Such behavior would be admissible in the absence of an inequality constraint on u, which we have momentarily assumed, the Weierstrass necessary condition then being directly applicable.

Unless the transformed equations are linear in the new control variable $z_n = x_l$, the Weierstrass necessary condition can be employed in conjunction with the Euler equations for the transformed problem to yield information not obtainable via the corresponding condition in the original problem. The extremals of the transformed problem are the singular extremals of the original, and those extremals satisfying the strengthened version of the Weierstrass condition are minimizing, at least over short intervals. In the special case in which the transformed equations of state (3.56) are linear in the new control variable x_l, an additional transformation to a state space of still smaller dimension is indicated.

Redirecting attention to the problem of main interest in which the inequality constraint (3.57) is operative, we perceive that the course of action just described is not open to us. We may, however, examine subarcs over which the control variable u takes on values intermediate between the specified bounds

$$u_1 < u < u_2 \tag{3.66}$$

with similar considerations in mind. If $u = \bar{u}(t)$ is the optimal control, we must, evidently, restrict attention to small variations $\delta\mu(t) = \varepsilon\eta(t)$, where $\eta(t)$ is an arbitrary, piecewise, continuous function and the magnitude of the variation ε is vanishingly small, so that $u = \bar{u} + \delta u$ satisfies (3.66). In the literature of classical variational theory, such variations are often referred to as *weak* variations and the Legendre-Clebsch condition, necessary for a *weak* relative minimum, plays a role loosely analogous to that of the Weierstrass condition whenever a restriction to vanishingly small variations is either assumed or imposed.

We rewrite Eqs. (3.59) with the notation a_j for the functions appearing on the right as

$$\dot{z}_j = a_j(x_1, \ldots, x_n, t), \qquad j = 1, \ldots, n-1 \tag{3.67}$$

and with the variables x_i eliminated in favor of z_j, as

$$\dot{z}_j = b_j(z_1, \ldots, z_n, t), \qquad j = 1, \ldots, n-1 \tag{3.68}$$

Introducing the usual Lagrange multipliers λ_j, $j = 1, \ldots, n-1$, we form the Hamiltonian

$$\mathscr{H} \equiv \sum_{j=1}^{n-1} \lambda_j b_j \tag{3.69}$$

and write the Euler-Lagrange equations corresponding to the z_j

$$\dot{\lambda}_j = -\partial \mathscr{H}/\partial z_j, \qquad j = 1, \ldots, n-1 \tag{3.70}$$

and that corresponding to z_n

$$\partial \mathscr{H}/\partial z_n = 0 \tag{3.71}$$

The Legendre-Clebsch necessary condition is

$$(\partial^2 \mathscr{H}/\partial {z_n}^2)\, \delta {z_n}^2 \geq 0 \tag{3.72}$$

for $\delta z_n \neq 0$, or

$$\partial^2 \mathscr{H}/\partial {z_n}^2 \geq 0 \tag{3.73}$$

Solutions of the system (3.68), (3.70), and (3.71) are the extremals of the transformed problem; the condition (3.73) provides an additional criterion for screening these candidates. If the left member of (3.73) is positive, the singular subarc is locally minimizing, i.e., over short time intervals; if the left member is negative, the singular subarc is locally maximizing. The vanishing of the left member of (3.73) corresponds to the special case, mentioned earlier, in which z_n enters the function $\mathscr{H}$ linearly. Thus along singular arcs of the original problem Eq. (3.73) partially fills the gap created when the Weierstrass necessary condition is being trivially satisfied.

The preceding argument lacks rigor because no account has been taken of the restriction on control variations imposed by terminal boundary conditions involving the nth state variable. It can be shown by direct calculation that the second variation test applied to a problem already transformed to canonical form produces precisely the Legendre-Clebsch criterion as given by Bliss[18] and, hence, it becomes clear that the result rests upon the same assumptions as the second variation test.

Regarding choice between the two approaches to testing singular arcs, ease of application would seem to favor the second variation test, since no laborious synthesis of a transformation is required. The transformation scheme, when it can be carried through, however, has two attributes to recommend it. One is a sufficiency statement: the strong form of (3.73) guarantees the minimizing character of the singular solution over a sufficiently short length of arc. (The strengthened Legendre-Clebsch condition insures a weak relative minimum over a sufficiently short length of arc and, since only weak variations in the new control variable z_n are admissible as a result of bounds on the control u, the restriction to a weak minimum loses significance.) The second is the convenience of the system in canonical form in analyzing the structure of the solution in terms of possible subarcs. While, in general, insufficient rules are available to permit systematic piecing together of subarc sequences into a composite solution, special cases may be more amenable to suitable specialized attacks if the canonical form is employed.

3.3 Examples

3.30 Two Elementary Examples

To illustrate the necessary condition in application of the second variation test, we will first consider two elementary examples. For the first example in our illustration, the differential equations of constraint are

$$\dot{x}_1 = u, \qquad \dot{x}_2 = x_1^2 \tag{3.74}$$

where the control u is constrained by $|u| \leq 1$. The problem is to determine $u(t)$, $t_0 \leq t \leq t_f$, so that the final value of the state variable x_2 is minimized subject to fixed values of t_0, t_f, $x_1(t_0)$, $x_2(t_0)$, and $x_1(t_f)$.

The pseudo-Hamiltonian function $\mathscr{H}$ is

$$\mathscr{H} = \lambda_1 u + \lambda_2 x_1^2 \tag{3.75}$$

where

$$\dot{\lambda}_1 = -2\lambda_2 x_1, \qquad \dot{\lambda}_2 = 0, \qquad \lambda_2(t_f) = 1$$

Along the singular subarc

$$\partial\mathscr{H}/\partial u = \lambda_1 \equiv 0 \tag{3.76}$$

thus leading to the conditions, $x_1 \equiv 0$ and $u \equiv 0$. The application of the second variation test gives

$$\frac{\partial}{\partial u}\left(\frac{d^2}{dt^2}\frac{\partial\mathscr{H}}{\partial u}\right) = -2 < 0 \tag{3.77}$$

thus satisfying the necessary condition for a minimizing extremal.

For the second example, we consider the differential equations of constraint to be

$$\dot{x}_1 = x_2, \qquad \dot{x}_2 = u, \qquad \dot{x}_3 = x_1^2 \tag{3.78}$$

where $|u| \leq 1$. The pseudo-Hamiltonian function $\mathscr{H}$ is

$$\mathscr{H} = \lambda_1 x_2 + \lambda_2 u + \lambda_3 x_1^2 \tag{3.79}$$

where

$$\dot{\lambda}_1 = -2\lambda_3 x_1, \qquad \dot{\lambda}_2 = -\lambda_1$$
$$\dot{\lambda}_3 = 0, \qquad \lambda_3(t_f) = 1$$

Along the singular subarc

$$\partial\mathscr{H}/\partial u = \lambda_2 \equiv 0 \tag{3.80}$$

thus leading to the conditions $x_1 = x_2 \equiv 0$ and $u \equiv 0$. The first application of the second variation test gives

$$\frac{\partial}{\partial u}\left(\frac{d^2}{dt^2}\frac{\partial\mathscr{H}}{\partial u}\right) = 0 \tag{3.81}$$

which is inconclusive. The next application of the second variation test gives

$$\frac{\partial}{\partial u}\left(\frac{d^4}{dt^4}\frac{\partial\mathscr{H}}{\partial u}\right) = 2\lambda_3 > 0 \tag{3.82}$$

which satisfies the necessary condition for a minimizing extremal.

Since q is even in Eq. (3.40), from the discussion of junction conditions in Sec. 3.17 one might be tempted to conjecture that such singular arcs are isolated and of only minor importance. That this is not so is illustrated by considering a problem treated recently by Johansen.[19] As part of a more complex min-max problem, Johansen treats a special case of the problem just discussed with t_0 and t_f fixed, $x_1(t_0)$ fixed, $x_2(t_0)$ unspecified, and $x_3(t_0) = 0$, with $x_1(t_f)$ and $x_2(t_f)$ unspecified. While these boundary conditions suffice to illustrate the phenomenon of interest, it will also appear for a large variety of other boundary conditions. The solution of this problem, as presented in Johansen,[19] consists of a sequence of an infinite number of switchings between $u = -1$ and $u = +1$ with the time between switchings rapidly decreasing. The limit of the sum of times between switchings is finite, with x_1 and x_2 vanishing at the limit point. Thus the joining of this arc with the singular subarc $x_1 = x_2 = 0$ is possible at the essential discontinuity of $u(t)$.

If the class of admissible functions specified in the problem statement required $u(t)$ to be piecewise continuous, one would say that no minimum exists, merely a lower bound. If $u(t)$ is required to be only measurable, however, the difficulty disappears. From an engineering viewpoint, such solutions are of interest since they can be approximated as closely as one wishes by better behaved functions. The point of the example is that singular arcs of the q-even type may play a role in solutions containing other types of arcs as subarcs.

3.31 A Servomechanism Example

In Miele[4] and Johnson and Gibson,[20] the following problem has been studied in some detail. Given the system

$$\dot{x}_1 = x_2 + y \tag{3.83}$$

$$\dot{x}_2 = -y \tag{3.84}$$

$$\dot{x}_3 = x_1{}^2/2 \tag{3.85}$$

$$|y| \leq 1 \tag{3.86}$$

the control taking the system from a specified initial state to $x_1 = x_2 = 0$ and extremizing the final value of x_3 is sought. The structure of the solution of this problem is rather complex, belying its innocuous appearance.

The Hamiltonian function is

$$\mathscr{H} = \lambda_1(x_2 + y) + \lambda_2(-y) + \lambda_3(x_1{}^2/2) \tag{3.87}$$

and the Euler-Lagrange equations are

$$\dot{\lambda}_1 = -\partial\mathscr{H}/\partial x_1 = -\lambda_3 x_1 \tag{3.88}$$

$$\dot{\lambda}_2 = -\partial\mathscr{H}/\partial x_2 = -\lambda_1 \tag{3.89}$$

$$\dot{\lambda}_3 = -\partial\mathscr{H}/\partial x_3 = 0 \tag{3.90}$$

$$\frac{\partial\mathscr{H}}{\partial y} = \lambda_1 - \lambda_2 = 0 \tag{3.91}$$

The necessary second variation condition for minimality of singular subarcs is

$$\frac{\partial}{\partial y}\left(\frac{d^2}{dt^2}\frac{\partial\mathscr{H}}{\partial y}\right) = -\lambda_3 \leq 0 \tag{3.92}$$

which indicates the possible appearance of singular subarcs in the solution of the problem of minimizing the final value of x_3 since, in this case, $\lambda_{3_f} = 1$. The test rules out the possibility of such subarcs in the problem of maximizing x_{3_f}, thus leading to the conclusion, in this case, that the optimal control is bang-bang.

The transformation scheme leads to new variables $z_1 = x_1 + x_2$, $z_2 = x_3$, $z_3 = x_2$ satisfying state equations

$$\dot{z}_1 = z_3, \qquad \dot{z}_2 = (z_1 - z_3)^2/2, \qquad \dot{z}_3 = -y \tag{3.93}$$

Identifying the Lagrange multipliers corresponding to the new variables as l_1, l_2, l_3 in order to avert possible confusion, the Hamiltonian function is

$$\mathscr{H} = l_1 z_3 + l_2[(z_1 - z_3)^2/2] + l_3(-y) \tag{3.94}$$

and the Euler-Lagrange equations are

$$\dot{l}_1 = -\partial\mathscr{H}/\partial z_1 = -l_2(z_1 - z_3) \tag{3.95}$$

$$\dot{l}_2 = -\partial\mathscr{H}/\partial z_2 = 0 \tag{3.96}$$

$$\dot{l}_3 = -\partial\mathscr{H}/\partial z_3 = -l_1 + l_2(z_1 - z_3) \tag{3.97}$$

$$\frac{\partial\mathscr{H}}{\partial y} = -l_3 = 0 \tag{3.98}$$

the latter equation being satisfied along singular subarcs. Along such subarcs the Legendre-Clebsch necessary condition

$$\partial^2\mathscr{H}/\partial {z_3}^2 = l_2 \geq 0 \tag{3.99}$$

provides the same criterion as the second variation test, namely, expressed in terms of the original multipliers corresponding to the variables x_1, x_2, x_3, the result is $\lambda_3 \geq 0$.

3.32 A Midcourse Guidance Example

As a second illustration, we examine the simplified version of the optimal midcourse guidance problem treated by Striebel and Breakwell[21] by the Green's theorem method. The equations of state are

$$\dot{x}_1 = -gx_1y + b \tag{3.100}$$

$$\dot{x}_2 = y(x_1)^{1/2} \tag{3.101}$$

The variable x_1 is the variance of an extrapolated terminal miss estimate; $b(t) \geq 0$ is an "information rate" quantity, and $g(t) > 0$, a decreasing function of t, is a measure of control effectiveness. Control linear in $x_1(t)$ has been assumed, with a "feedback gain" $y(t) \geq 0$ taking on the role of control variable in the variational problem. The terminal value of x_2, the expected propellant expenditure, is to be minimized subject to fixed initial and terminal value specifications on x_1.

Depending upon the boundary values and the given functions $g(t)$ and $b(t)$, one or more singular subarcs may appear in the solution. They are characterized by

$$x_1 = -bg/2\dot{g} \tag{3.102}$$

The necessary second variation condition takes the form

$$2\dot{g}x_1 - b\dot{g} \leq 0 \tag{3.103}$$

or

$$bg \geq 0 \tag{3.104}$$

which is satisfied, since both b and g are nonnegative from the nature of the midcourse problem.

The transformation scheme leads to new variables $z_1 = [2(x_1)^{1/2}/g] + x_2$ and $z_2 = x_1$, the latter becoming control variable along singular subarcs. Introducing multipliers l_1 and l_2 corresponding to the new variables, we have

$$\frac{\partial \mathscr{H}}{\partial z_2} = -\frac{l_1}{g}\left(\frac{b}{2} z_2^{-3/2} + \frac{\dot{g}}{g} z_2^{-1/2}\right) = 0 \tag{3.105}$$

which leads to (3.102), and

$$\frac{\partial^2 \mathscr{H}}{\partial {z_2}^2} = \frac{l_1 b}{2g} z_2^{-5/2} \geq 0 \tag{3.106}$$

Since the quantity to be minimized, in terms of the new variables, is the terminal value of $z_1 - (2/g)z_2^{1/2}$, we have $l_1 \geq 0$ and the Legendre-Clebsch condition is satisfied.

3.33 Aircraft "Energy Climb"

Equations of state corresponding to a greatly simplified model of aircraft climb performance are given by

$$\dot{h} = V \sin \gamma \tag{3.107}$$

$$\dot{V} = \frac{T - D}{m} - g \sin \gamma \tag{3.108}$$

In these equations h is altitude, V airspeed, γ the angle of the flight path to the horizontal, T engine thrust, D aerodynamic drag, m the vehicle's mass, and g the acceleration of gravity. The approximation has been made that the thrust is directed along the tangent to the flight path, and it is also usual to assume, in the course of the simplified "energy climb" analysis, that the mass m is constant, i.e., fixed at some suitable average value. A further assumption, which drastically affects the character of optimal flight path solutions, is that aerodynamic drag is a function of altitude and airspeed only $D = D(h, V)$ given by the drag for level flight. This procedure neglects induced drag changes arising from departures from level flight, possibly including substantial changes associated with maneuvering.

Under these assumptions, the flight path angle γ takes on the role of a control variable, and since only $\sin \gamma$ appears in the state equations, the substitution $u = \sin \gamma$, $-1 < u < 1$ brings the problem into the format of a single control variable appearing linearly. The version of the flight performance problem most often considered is minimum time from fixed initial h, V to fixed final h, V. It should be noted that problems whose statement includes specifications on the range variable x, having the state equation $\dot{x} = V \cos \gamma$, are not amenable to the type of analysis presently under consideration.

Analysis of the Euler-Lagrange equations for this problem leads to a singular extremal characterized by

$$V \frac{\partial}{\partial h}(T-D) - g\frac{\partial}{\partial V}(T-D) - \frac{g}{V}(T-D) = 0 \qquad (3.109)$$

which defines a curve in h, V coordinates. This model of simplified aircraft climb performance has been analyzed by numerous investigators including Kaiser,[22] Lush,[23] Rutowski,[24] and Miele,[25] the latter most comprehensively by means of his Green's theorem device. It was recognized at an early date that (3.109) corresponds to stationary points of excess power $V(T-D)$ along contours of constant energy $h + (V^2/2g)$, i.e., that the result may be stated as

$$\frac{\partial}{\partial h}[V(T-D)]\Big|_{h+(V^2/2g)=\text{const}} = 0 \qquad (3.110)$$

or as

$$\frac{\partial}{\partial V}[V(T-D)]\Big|_{h+(V^2/2g)=\text{const}} = 0 \qquad (3.111)$$

The minimum time solution will be composed, in general, of vertical climb ($\gamma = \pi/2$) subarcs, vertical dive ($\gamma = -\pi/2$) subarcs and subarcs of the singular arc.

Of main interest in connection with the subject of the present chapter is the testing of the singular extremal for minimality over short lengths of arc. The transformation scheme leads naturally to energy as a state variable $z_1 = h + (V^2/2g)$, $z_2 = h$, and the Legendre-Clebsch condition is

$$l_1 \frac{\partial^2}{\partial h^2}[V(T-D)]\Big|_{h+(V^2/2g)=\text{const}} \geq 0 \qquad (3.112)$$

Since it is clear from the interpretation of the Lagrange multiplier variables that $l_1 < 0$ for minimum time problems, the criterion follows that

$$\frac{\partial^2}{\partial h^2}[V(T-D)]\Big|_{h+(V^2/2g)=\text{const}} \leq 0 \qquad (3.113)$$

which implies that the stationary points of excess power along constant energy contours must be maxima, a result in accord with engineering intuition. The second variation test, discussed in the beginning of this chapter, leads to the identical result.

In analyses of aircraft capable of supersonic flight, the rise in drag through the region of transonic airspeeds will produce two maxima separated by a minimum in curves of excess power along contours of constant energy. Thus, a portion of the singular extremal in the vicinity of the transonic region will not furnish minimum time over short lengths of arc, and the sequence of subarcs for some specified combinations of initial and final states may be quite complex.

While analysis via the simplified model has largely been superseded in favor of more satisfactory models in applications work, it is of historical interest that some of the earliest engineering applications of variational theory encountered singular arcs; however, the accompanying mathematical difficulties were not appreciated until some time later. The relationship between optimal paths according to the simplified model and to more complex models has been investigated to a certain extent[26,27] with central portions of optimal flight paths for the complex model often resembling flight along the singular extremal of the simplified theory.

3.34 Goddard's Problem

The problem of determining the optimal thrust program for the vertical flight of a sounding rocket has been extensively studied in the astonautical literature. The state variables in this problem are altitude h, velocity v, and mass m. Using these variables, the differential constraints are

$$\dot{h} = v \tag{3.114}$$

$$\dot{v} = \frac{T - D(h, v)}{m} - g(h) \tag{3.115}$$

$$\dot{m} = -\frac{T}{c} \tag{3.116}$$

in which the rocket thrust T is bounded above and below according to

$$0 \leq T \leq \bar{T} \tag{3.117}$$

The function D is aerodynamic drag, g is the acceleration of gravity, and c is rocket exhaust velocity.

The pseudo-Hamiltonian function $\mathscr{H}$ is

$$\mathscr{H} = \lambda_1 v + \lambda_2\left[\frac{T - D(h, v)}{m} - g(h)\right] - \lambda_3 \frac{T}{c} \tag{3.118}$$

where

$$\begin{aligned} \dot{\lambda}_1 &= \lambda_2\left[\frac{1}{m}\frac{\partial D}{\partial h} + \frac{\partial g}{\partial h}\right] \\ \dot{\lambda}_2 &= -\lambda_1 + \frac{\lambda_2}{m}\frac{\partial D}{\partial v} \\ \dot{\lambda}_3 &= \frac{\lambda_2}{m^2}[T - D(h, v)] \end{aligned} \tag{3.119}$$

The singular subarc occurs when

$$\frac{\partial \mathscr{H}}{\partial T} = \frac{\lambda_2}{m} - \frac{\lambda_3}{c} \equiv 0 \tag{3.120}$$

An evaluation of the constants for the necessary second variation condition gives

$$\begin{aligned} A_{11} &= 0, & A_{12} &= \frac{1}{m} \\ A_{21} &= \frac{1}{m}, & A_{22} &= -\frac{1}{m^2}\frac{\partial D}{\partial v} - \frac{D(h, v)}{m^2 c} \\ A_{31} &= -\frac{1}{c}, & A_{32} &= 0 \end{aligned} \tag{3.121}$$

Substituting these relationships into Eq. (3.15) yields, as a necessary condition for maximum summit altitude,

$$-\frac{\lambda_1}{m^2 c} + \frac{\lambda_2}{m^3}\left[\frac{2D(h, v)}{c^2} + \frac{3}{c}\frac{\partial D}{\partial v} + \frac{\partial^2 D}{\partial v^2}\right] > 0 \tag{3.122}$$

This expression, together with the relationship

$$\frac{d}{dt}\left(\frac{\partial \mathscr{H}}{\partial T}\right) = -\frac{\lambda_1}{m} + \frac{2\lambda_2}{m^2}\frac{\partial D}{\partial v} + \frac{\lambda_2}{m^2 c} D \equiv 0 \tag{3.123}$$

satisfied along the singular subarc, gives

$$\frac{\lambda_2}{m^3}\left[\frac{D(h, v)}{c^2} + \frac{2}{c}\frac{\partial D}{\partial v} + \frac{\partial^2 D}{\partial v^2}\right] \geq 0 \tag{3.124}$$

An application of the transformation method requires the solution of the following differential equations:

$$dh/ds = q_1 = 0, \qquad dv/ds = q_2 = 1/m, \qquad dm/ds = q_3 = -1/c \tag{3.125}$$

The constants of integration are evaluated, thus leading to the transformation

$$z_1 = h, \qquad z_2 = v, \qquad z_3 = me^{v/c} \tag{3.126}$$

The differential constraints for the transformed system are

$$\begin{aligned} \dot{z}_1 &= v \\ \dot{z}_2 &= \frac{[T - D(z_1, z_2)]}{z_3}\exp(z_2/c) - g(z_1) \\ \dot{z}_3 &= -\frac{D(z_1, z_2)}{c}\exp(z_2/c) - \frac{z_3}{c}g(z_1) \end{aligned} \tag{3.127}$$

Letting z_2 take on the role of the new control variable, the new pseudo-Hamiltonian is

$$\tilde{\mathscr{H}} = l_1 z_2 - \frac{l_3}{c}\{D(z_1, z_2)\exp(z_2/c) + z_3 g(z_1)\} \tag{3.128}$$

where

$$\dot{l}_1 = \frac{l_3}{c}\left\{\exp(z_2/c)\frac{\partial D}{\partial z_1} - z_3\frac{\partial g}{\partial z_1}\right\}, \qquad \dot{l}_3 = \frac{l_3}{c}g(z_1) \tag{3.129}$$

The stationary solution of the transformed problem corresponding to the singular subarc of the original problem occurs when

$$\frac{\partial \tilde{\mathscr{H}}}{\partial z_2} = l_1 - \frac{l_3}{c}\left\{\frac{D(z_1, z_2)\exp(z_2/c)}{c} + \exp(z_2/c)\frac{\partial D}{\partial z_2}\right\} = 0 \tag{3.130}$$

The Legendre-Clebsch necessary condition requires for a maximal extremal

$$\frac{\partial^2 \tilde{\mathscr{H}}}{\partial {z_2}^2} = -\frac{l_3}{c}\exp(z_2/c)\left\{\frac{D(z_1, z_2)}{c^2} + \frac{2}{c}\frac{\partial D}{\partial z_2} + \frac{\partial^2 D}{\partial {z_2}^2}\right\} \leq 0 \tag{3.131}$$

which is identical to the expression reached by the necessary second variation condition. The advantage of employing the above variables z_1 and z_2 was first recognized by Ross,[28] who established the maximal character of the variable thrust subarc for the square-law drag case. In the case of a more general drag law, e.g., one which exhibits sharp variation in the vicinity of sonic velocity, the Legendre-Clebsch condition may rule out intermediate thrust operation over a certain velocity range. This was pointed out by Leitmann.[29]

3.35 Lawden's Spiral

Rocket flight in an inverse square law field has been studied extensively by Lawden[30,31] and others.[9] However, until recently, the nature of the singular arcs has been unresolved. A recent, rather comprehensive analysis of this problem and the singular arcs was given by Robbins.[10]

The system equations are

$$\begin{aligned} \dot{u} &= Y + (T/m)\sin\theta, & \dot{y} &= u, \\ \dot{v} &= X + (T/m)\cos\theta, & \dot{x} &= v, \\ \dot{m} &= -T/c \end{aligned} \tag{3.132}$$

where

$$Y = -\mu y/R^3, \qquad X = -\mu x/R^3, \qquad R = (x^2 + y^2)^{1/2} \tag{3.133}$$

and the problem is to choose T and θ such that $P = -m_f$ is minimized (minimum fuel) subject to the constraint $0 \leq T \leq T_{\max}$. The pseudo-Hamiltonian $\mathscr{H}$ function becomes

$$\mathscr{H} = \lambda_1\left(-\frac{\mu y}{R^3} + \frac{T}{m}\sin\theta\right) + \lambda_2\left(-\frac{\mu x}{R^3} + \frac{T}{m}\cos\theta\right) + \lambda_3 u + \lambda_4 v - \lambda_5\frac{T}{c} = 0 \tag{3.134}$$

where the λ_i are the adjoint variables and obey the differential equations

$$\dot{\lambda}_i = -\partial\mathscr{H}/\partial x_i, \qquad i = 1, \ldots, 5 \tag{3.135}$$

From the classical theory $\mathscr{H}$ is minimized with respect to T and θ giving

$$\sin\theta = -\frac{\lambda_1}{(\lambda_1{}^2 + \lambda_2{}^2)^{1/2}}, \qquad \cos\theta = -\frac{\lambda_2}{(\lambda_1{}^2 + \lambda_2{}^2)^{1/2}} \tag{3.136}$$

$$T = T_{\max} \quad \text{when} \quad \rho < 0, \qquad T = 0 \quad \text{when} \quad \rho > 0$$

where

$$\rho = \left[\frac{\lambda_1}{m}\sin\theta + \frac{\lambda_2}{m}\cos\theta - \frac{\lambda_5}{c}\right] = -\frac{(\lambda_1{}^2 + \lambda_2{}^2)^{1/2}}{m} - \frac{\lambda_5}{c} \tag{3.137}$$

The singular condition occurs when ρ identically equals zero over a nonzero interval of time. That $(\lambda_1{}^2 + \lambda_2{}^2)^{1/2}$ is then a constant derives from d/dt $(m\lambda_5) = 0$. Without loss of generality we set $(\lambda_1{}^2 + \lambda_2{}^2)^{1/2} = 1$.

Applying the first test given by Eq. (3.28) with $q = 1$, we obtain

$$\eta_{11} + \frac{1}{2}\sum_{i,j=1}^{5}\frac{\partial^2\mathscr{H}}{\partial x_i\,\partial x_j}A_{i,1}A_{j,1} \geq 0 \tag{3.138}$$

Substituting for η_{11} this expression becomes

$$-\left\{\sum_{i=1}^{5}\frac{\partial^2\mathscr{H}}{\partial T\,\partial x_i}A_{i,2} + \frac{1}{2}\frac{d}{dt}\left(\sum_{i=1}^{5}\frac{\partial^2\mathscr{H}}{\partial T\,\partial x_i}A_{i,1}\right)\right\} + \frac{1}{2}\sum_{i,j=1}^{5}\frac{\partial^2\mathscr{H}}{\partial x_i\,\partial x_j}A_{i,1}A_{j,1} \geq 0 \tag{3.139}$$

The only nonzero terms will be contributed by $(\partial^2\mathscr{H}/\partial T\,\partial x_5)A_{5,1}$ and $(\partial^2\mathscr{H}/\partial m^2)A_{5,1}^2$ where

$$\frac{\partial^2\mathscr{H}}{\partial T\,\partial x_5} = -\left\{\frac{\lambda_1}{m^2}\sin\theta + \frac{\lambda_2}{m^2}\cos\theta\right\} = \frac{1}{m^2}$$

$$\frac{\partial^2\mathscr{H}}{\partial m^2} = \frac{2}{m^3}T[\lambda_1\sin\theta + \lambda_2\cos\theta] = -\frac{2T}{m^3} \tag{3.140}$$

$$A_5 = -\frac{1}{c}$$

Evaluating Eq. (3.139) with these terms, we find that it is satisfied with the equality sign.

Applying the second test, that is Eq. (3.28) with $q = 2$, we obtain

$$\eta_{1,2} + \eta_{2,2} + \frac{1}{2} \sum_{i,j=1}^{5} \mathscr{H}_{x_i x_j} A_{i,2} A_{j,2} \geq 0 \tag{3.141}$$

where

$$\begin{aligned} \eta_{1,2} &= \sum_{i=1}^{5} \frac{\partial^2 \mathscr{H}}{\partial T\, \partial x_i} A_{i,4} + \frac{3}{2} \frac{d}{dt} \left(\sum_{i=1}^{5} \frac{\partial^2 \mathscr{H}}{\partial T\, \partial x_i} A_{i,3} \right) + \frac{1}{2} \frac{d^2}{dt^2} \left(\sum_{i=1}^{5} \frac{\partial^2 \mathscr{H}}{\partial T\, \partial x_i} A_{i,2} \right) \\ \eta_{2,2} &= - \sum_{i,j=1}^{5} \frac{\partial^2 \mathscr{H}}{\partial x_i\, \partial x_j} A_{i,1} A_{j,3} - \frac{1}{2} \frac{d}{dt} \left(\sum_{i,j=1}^{5} \frac{\partial^2 \mathscr{H}}{\partial x_i\, \partial x_j} A_{i,1} A_{j,2} \right) \end{aligned} \tag{3.142}$$

The evaluation of Eq. (3.142) shows $\eta_{1,2}$ and $\eta_{2,2}$ to be identically equal to zero. Furthermore, the only terms that contribute to the sum in Eq. (3.141) are for i and j equal to 3 and 4. Without loss of generality, we choose our coordinate system such that $x_3 = R$ and $x_4 = 0$ when the test is applied. The terms that contribute to Eq. (3.141) are:

$$\begin{gathered} \frac{\partial^2 \mathscr{H}}{\partial {x_3}^2} = -\frac{6\mu\lambda_1}{R^4}, \qquad \frac{\partial^2 \mathscr{H}}{\partial x_3\, \partial x_4} = \frac{3\mu\lambda_2}{R^4}, \qquad \frac{\partial^2 \mathscr{H}}{\partial {x_4}^2} = \frac{3\mu\lambda_1}{R^4} \\ A_{3,2} = \frac{1}{m} \sin\theta, \qquad A_{4,2} = \frac{1}{m} \cos\theta \end{gathered} \tag{3.143}$$

Substituting Eq. (3.143) into Eq. (3.141) and using Eq. (3.136), we obtain as a necessary condition

$$-\frac{3\mu \sin\theta}{m^2 R^4} \{3 - 5 \sin^2 \theta\} \geq 0 \tag{3.144}$$

From Eqs. (5.94) and (5.105) of Lawden,[31] we see that along the time-open singular arc ($\mathscr{H} = 0$) R and T/m are given by

$$R = \frac{a \sin^6 \varphi}{1 - 3 \sin^2 \varphi} \tag{3.145}$$

and

$$\frac{T}{m} = b \left(\frac{1 - 3 \sin^2 \varphi}{3 - 5 \sin^2 \varphi} \right) \left(\frac{[27 - 75 \sin^2 \varphi + 60 \sin^4 \varphi]}{\sin^{11} \varphi} \right) \tag{3.146}$$

where a and b are positive constants and φ is the angle between the thrust direction and the local horizontal. Note that φ equals θ for the position coordinates we have chosen. From Eq. (3.146) we see that $\sin\theta$ must be positive and from Eq. (3.145) that

$$0 < \sin\theta < \sqrt{\tfrac{1}{3}} \tag{3.147}$$

which violates inequality (3.144), thus showing that the singular arc is not minimizing.

Application of the transformation approach to Lawden's problem encounters two complications not met in the simpler examples treated in the preceding pages. The first complication is that two successive transformations become necessary, for reasons which will be apparent; the second complication is a proliferation of state variables, arising from the appearance of time derivatives of the second control variable θ in the transformed equations of state. The following treatment is essentially the same as the one previously given in Kelley[9] with additional material on the synthesis of transformations from Kelley.[7]

A transformation, designed to rid all save one of the state equations of the linearly appearing control variable T, is obtained by application of the method described earlier as

$$\begin{aligned} \alpha &= u\cos\theta - v\sin\theta \\ \beta &= u\sin\theta + v\cos\theta + c\log m \\ V &= -c\log m \end{aligned} \tag{3.148}$$

The inverse transformation is

$$\begin{aligned} u &= \alpha\cos\theta + \beta\sin\theta - c\log m\sin\theta \\ v &= -\alpha\sin\theta + \beta\cos\theta - c\log m\cos\theta \\ m &= e^{-V/c} \end{aligned} \tag{3.149}$$

The transformed equations of state are

$$\begin{aligned} \dot\alpha &= Y\cos\theta - X\sin\theta - (V+\beta)\omega \\ \dot\beta &= Y\sin\theta + X\cos\theta + \alpha\omega \\ \dot y &= \alpha\cos\theta + \beta\sin\theta + V\sin\theta \\ \dot x &= -\alpha\sin\theta + \beta\cos\theta + V\cos\theta \\ \dot V &= e^{V/c}T \\ \dot\theta &= \omega \end{aligned} \tag{3.150}$$

in which θ has now assumed the status of a state variable due to the appearance of its first time derivative. As previously noted, there is some freedom of choice in selection of new variables during the synthesis procedure and, in this case, the choice has been governed by simplification of subsequent manipulations. The new variable V now has acquired some of the properties of a control variable, since arbitrary weak variations in V may be approximated by suitable thrust variations satisfying the thrust inequality (3.136). However, the exceptional case has arisen in which the new variable V also appears linearly in the transformed equations of state and, as discussed earlier in this connection, a second transformation is indicated.

The result also may be obtained by the synthesis procedure as

$$\begin{aligned}\psi &= y \sin\theta + x\cos\theta + \alpha/\omega \\ \gamma &= y\cos\theta - x\sin\theta \\ \Phi &= y\sin\theta + x\cos\theta\end{aligned} \tag{3.151}$$

where the functions ψ and γ are integrals, and the function Φ is destined to assume the role of a new control variable.

The two transformations may be combined into a single transformation,[9] which may take the form

$$\begin{aligned}\psi &= y\sin\theta + x\cos\theta + (1/\omega)(u\cos\theta - v\sin\theta) \\ \beta &= c\log m + u\sin\theta + v\cos\theta \\ \gamma &= y\cos\theta - x\sin\theta \\ \Phi &= y\sin\theta + x\cos\theta \\ V &= -c\log m\end{aligned} \tag{3.152}$$

It is readily verified that this transformation is nonsingular, by noting the nonvanishing of the Jacobian determinant

$$\Delta = \frac{\partial(\psi, \beta, \gamma, \Phi, V)}{\partial(u, v, y, x, m)} = -\frac{c}{\omega m} \neq 0 \tag{3.153}$$

The equations of state in the new system of variables are obtained as

$$\dot\psi = \gamma\omega + (1/\omega)(Y\cos\theta - X\sin\theta) - (\mu/\omega)(\psi - \Phi) \tag{3.154}$$

$$\dot\beta = Y\sin\theta + X\cos\theta + \omega^2(\psi - \Phi) \tag{3.155}$$

$$\dot\gamma = \omega(\psi - 2\Phi) \tag{3.156}$$

$$\dot\Phi = \beta + \gamma\omega + V \tag{3.157}$$

$$\dot V = T/m = Te^{V/c} \tag{3.158}$$

$$\dot\theta = \omega \tag{3.159}$$

$$\dot\omega = \mu \tag{3.160}$$

It has been tacitly assumed in the course of the manipulations leading to Eqs. (3.154) through (3.160) that the steering angle θ is twice differentiable, i.e., the derivatives $\dot\theta = \omega$ and $\ddot\theta = \mu$ exist. Examination of Eqs. (3.135) and (3.136) indicates that such an assumption is justified if the gravitational force components Y and X possess first partial derivatives, except for a finite number of points along the trajectory corresponding to thrust direction reversals at which λ_1 and λ_2 vanish simultaneously. We exclude such reversal points from the segments of arc analyzed in the following.

In accordance with the objectives of the transformation, it is observed that the variables T and V appear *only* in Eqs. (3.157) and (3.158) and that, as a consequence of this, the multipliers λ_Φ and λ_V vanish along the singular subarcs. We note that the coefficients of T in Eq. (3.158) and of V in Eq. (3.157) never vanish and, accordingly, that an admissible variation in thrust δT may be found which produces an approximation as close as one wishes to an arbitrary variation $\delta\Phi(t)$, provided that the magnitude of $\delta\Phi$ is sufficiently small. With Φ in the role of control variable and small variations being assumed, the intermediate thrust arcs must satisfy the Legendre-Clebsch necessary condition for a weak relative minimum.

The Euler-Lagrange equations for the system (3.154), (3.155), (3.156), (3.159), (3.160) are

$$\dot{\lambda}_\psi = -\frac{\partial \mathscr{H}}{\partial \psi} = \lambda_\psi \frac{\mu}{\omega} - \lambda_\beta \omega^2 - \lambda_\gamma \omega \tag{3.161}$$

$$\dot{\lambda}_\beta = -\frac{\partial \mathscr{H}}{\partial \beta} = 0 \tag{3.162}$$

$$\begin{aligned} \dot{\lambda}_\gamma = -\frac{\partial \mathscr{H}}{\partial \gamma} &= -\lambda_\psi \left[\omega + \frac{1}{\omega} \frac{\partial}{\partial \gamma} (Y \cos\theta - X \sin\theta) \right] \\ &\quad - \lambda_\beta \frac{\partial}{\partial \gamma} (Y \sin\theta + X \cos\theta) \end{aligned} \tag{3.163}$$

$$\dot{\lambda}_\theta = -\frac{\partial \mathscr{H}}{\partial \theta} = -\lambda_\psi \frac{\partial}{\partial \theta} (Y \cos\theta - X \sin\theta) - \lambda_\beta \frac{\partial}{\partial \theta} (Y \sin\theta + X \cos\theta) \tag{3.164}$$

$$\begin{aligned} \dot{\lambda}_\omega = -\frac{\partial \mathscr{H}}{\partial \omega} &= -\lambda_\psi \left[\gamma - \frac{1}{\omega^2} (Y \cos\theta - X \sin\theta) + \frac{\mu}{\omega^2} (\psi - \Phi) \right] \\ &\quad - 2\lambda_\beta \omega (\psi - \Phi) - \lambda_\gamma (\psi - 2\Phi) - \lambda_\theta \end{aligned} \tag{3.165}$$

$$\begin{aligned} \frac{\partial \mathscr{H}}{\partial \Phi} &= \lambda_\psi \left[\frac{\mu}{\omega} + \frac{1}{\omega} \frac{\partial}{\partial \Phi} (Y \cos\theta - X \sin\theta) \right] \\ &\quad + \lambda_\beta \left[-\omega^2 + \frac{\partial}{\partial \Phi} (Y \sin\theta + X \cos\theta) \right] - 2\lambda_\gamma \omega = 0 \end{aligned} \tag{3.166}$$

$$\frac{\partial \mathscr{H}}{\partial \mu} = -\lambda_\psi \frac{(\psi - \Phi)}{\omega} + \lambda_\omega = 0 \tag{3.167}$$

The Legendre-Clebsch necessary condition for a weak relative minimum is

$$\frac{\partial^2 \mathscr{H}}{\partial \Phi^2}\,\delta\Phi^2 + 2\,\frac{\partial^2 \mathscr{H}}{\partial \Phi\,\partial \mu}\,\delta\Phi\,\delta\mu + \frac{\partial^2 \mathscr{H}}{\partial \mu^2}\,\delta\mu^2 \geq 0 \tag{3.168}$$

for arbitrary $\delta\Phi$, $\delta\mu$. Positive semidefiniteness of this quadratic form requires that

$$\frac{\partial^2 \mathscr{H}}{\partial \Phi^2} \geq 0 \tag{3.169}$$

$$\frac{\partial^2 \mathscr{H}}{\partial \mu^2} \geq 0 \tag{3.170}$$

$$\left(\frac{\partial^2 \mathscr{H}}{\partial \Phi^2}\right)\left(\frac{\partial^2 \mathscr{H}}{\partial \mu^2}\right) - \left(\frac{\partial^2 \mathscr{H}}{\partial \Phi\,\partial \mu}\right)^2 \geq 0 \tag{3.171}$$

We have

$$\frac{\partial^2 \mathscr{H}}{\partial \Phi^2} = \lambda_\beta \frac{\partial^2}{\partial \Phi^2}(Y \sin\theta + X\cos\theta) + \frac{\lambda_\psi}{\omega}\frac{\partial^2}{\partial \Phi^2}(Y\cos\theta - X\sin\theta) \tag{3.172}$$

$$\frac{\partial^2 \mathscr{H}}{\partial \mu^2} = 0 \tag{3.173}$$

$$\frac{\partial^2 \mathscr{H}}{\partial \Phi\,\partial \mu} = \frac{\lambda_\psi}{\omega} \tag{3.174}$$

From Eqs. (3.171), (3.173) and (3.174), it follows that $\lambda_\psi = 0$.

With this simplification and the elimination of the multiplier variables from the Euler-Lagrange equations (3.161) through (3.167), we arrive at

$$\omega^2 + \frac{\partial Z}{\partial \Phi} = 0 \tag{3.175}$$

$$-\mu + \frac{\partial Z}{\partial \gamma} = 0 \tag{3.176}$$

$$\mu\Phi + \omega^2\gamma - \left(x\frac{\partial}{\partial y} - y\frac{\partial}{\partial x}\right)Z = 0 \tag{3.177}$$

in which

$$Z \equiv Y\sin\theta + X\cos\theta \tag{3.178}$$

is the component of gravitational force along the thrust direction.

In the case of an inverse square law gravitational field

$$Y = \frac{-ky}{(x^2+y^2)^{3/2}}, \qquad X = \frac{-kx}{(x^2+y^2)^{3/2}} \tag{3.179}$$

and Eqs. (3.175), (3.176) and (3.177) become

$$\omega^2 + \frac{k(2\Phi^2 - \gamma^2)}{(\Phi^2 + \gamma^2)^{5/2}} = 0 \tag{3.180}$$

$$-\mu + \frac{3k\Phi\gamma}{(\Phi^2 + \gamma^2)^{5/2}} = 0 \tag{3.181}$$

$$\mu\Phi + \left[\omega^2 - \frac{k}{(\Phi^2 + \gamma^2)^{3/2}}\right]\gamma = 0 \tag{3.182}$$

If ω is eliminated between Eqs. (3.180) and (3.182), we obtain

$$\Phi\left[\mu - \frac{3\gamma k\Phi}{(\Phi^2 + \gamma^2)^{5/2}}\right] = 0 \tag{3.183}$$

The vanishing of the first factor $\Phi = 0$, circumferential thrust, leads to $\mu = 0$, $\omega =$ constant and

$$|\omega| = k/R^{3/2} \tag{3.184}$$

where $R = (\Phi^2 + \gamma^2)^{1/2}$ is the radius. This equation is the orbital frequency for free fall circular motion. The vanishing of the second factor indicates that Eq. (3.182) is satisfied identically along solutions of Eqs. (3.180) and (3.181), these being the equations of Lawden's[30] intermediate thrust solutions, although in rather different notation.

A further result may be obtained from analysis of the consequences of inequality (3.169), which went unnoticed in the original study.[9] Evaluation of the second partial derivative appearing in (3.169) combined with slight algebraic manipulation yields

$$\frac{\partial^2 \mathscr{H}}{\partial \Phi^2} = 3k\lambda_\beta\Phi\left[\frac{2\gamma^2}{(\Phi^2 + \gamma^2)^{7/2}} + \frac{\omega^2}{k(\Phi^2 + \gamma^2)}\right] \geq 0 \tag{3.185}$$

Since $k > 0$ and the bracketed quantity can be shown to be positive, it follows that

$$\lambda_\beta\Phi \geq 0 \tag{3.186}$$

is a necessary condition for minimality of an intermediate thrust arc. By the interpretation of Lagrange multipliers as influence functions of the functional being minimized with respect to the state variables, one can show that the multiplier λ_β will be negative for minimum fuel problems. Thus

$$\Phi = y \sin\theta + x \cos\theta \leq 0 \tag{3.187}$$

is a necessary condition requiring that the scalar product of radius vector and thrust direction be negative; i.e., the thrust must be inwardly directed if an intermediate thrust arc is minimizing. This is the same result as that obtained via the second variation test, and is the same as the result first given by Robbins.[10]

While the application of the necessary conditions rules out some members of the family of singular arcs, including Lawden's spiral arising in the time-open case, some others qualify and remain as candidates. Since this is a q-even problem ($q = 2$), corner junctions of these locally minimizing candidates with nonsingular arcs are not permissible. There remain the possibilities of control saturation junctions and "chattering" junctions, as well as the possibility that "bang-bang" thrusting arcs merely cluster around the minimizing singular arcs without ever joining with them. The structure of the family of solutions of Lawden's problem, in other words, remains largely unexplored, even after numerous efforts by qualified investigators.

References

1. P. Contensou, "Etude théorique des trajectoires optimales dans un champ de gravitation. Application au cas d'un centre d'attraction unique," *Astronaut. Acta* **8**, 134–150 (1962).
2. J. Warga, Relaxed variational problems, *J. Math. Anal. Appl.* **4**, 111–127 (1962).
3. J. Warga, Necessary conditions for minimum in relaxed variational problems, *J. Math. Anal. Appl.* **4**, 129–145 (1962).
4. A. Miele, Extremization of linear integrals by Green's theorem, *in* "Optimization Techniques" (G. Leitmann, ed.), Chapter 3, pp. 69–98. Academic Press, New York, 1962.
5. J. P. LaSalle, The time optimal control problem, *in* "Contributions to the Theory of Nonlinear Oscillations," Vol. V, pp. 1–24. Princeton Univ. Press, Princeton, New Jersey, 1960.
6. R. E. Kopp and H. G. Moyer, Necessary conditions for singular extremals, *AIAA J.* **3**, 1439–1444 (1965).
7. H. J. Kelley, A transformation approach to singular subarcs in optimal trajectory and control problems, *J. SIAM Control* **2**, 234–240 (1964).
8. H. J. Kelley, A second variation test for singular extremals, *AIAA J.* **2**, 1380–1382 (1964).
9. H. J. Kelley, Singular extremals in Lawden's problem of optimal rocket flight, *AIAA J.* **1**, 1578–1580 (1963).
10. H. M. Robbins, Optimality of intermediate-thrust arcs of rocket trajectories, *AIAA J.* **3**, 1094–1098 (1965).
11. R. E. Kopp, Pontryagin maximum principle, *in* "Optimization Techniques" (G. Leitmann, ed.), Chapter 7, pp. 255–279. Academic Press, New York, 1962.
12. R. Courant and D. Hilbert, "Methods of Mathematical Physics," Vol. 1, p. 215. Wiley (Interscience), New York, 1953.
13. F. D. Faulkner, Direct methods *in* "Optimization Techniques" (G. Leitmann, ed.), Chapter 2, pp. 33–67. Academic Press, New York, 1962.
14. F. D. Faulkner, The problem of Goddard and optimum thrust programming *in* "Advances in the Astronautical Sciences," Vol. I. Plenum Press, New York, 1957.
15. F. D. Faulkner, A degenerate problem of Bolza, *Proc. Amer. Math. Soc.* **6**, 847–854, (1955).

16. W. M. Wonham and C. D. Johnson, Optimal bang-bang control with quadratic performance index, *Proc. Fourth Joint Automatic Control Conf.*, pp. 101–112 (1963).
17. R. Courant and D. Hilbert, "Methods of Mathematical Physics," Vol. II. Wiley (Interscience), New York, 1962.
18. G. A. Bliss, "Lectures on the Calculus of Variations." Univ. of Chicago Press, Chicago, Illinois, 1946.
19. D. E. Johansen, Solution of a linear mean square estimation problem when process statistics are undefined, *Joint Automatic Control Conf. Troy, New York, June 1965.*
20. C. D. Johnson and J. E. Gibson, Singular solutions in problems of optimal control, *IEEE Trans. Automatic Control* **8**, 4–15 (1963).
21. C. T. Streibel and J. V. Breakwell, Minimum effort control in interplanetary guidance, *IAS Preprint* No. 63-80 (January, 1963).
22. F. Kaiser, Der Steigflug mit Strahlflugzeugen-Teil I, Bahngeschwindigkeit besten Steigens, *Versuchsbericht 262-02-L44*, Messerschmitt A. G., Augsburg (April, 1944). (Translated as Ministry of Supply RTP/TIB, Translation GDC/15/148 T.)
23. K. J. Lush, A review of the problem of choosing a climb technique with proposals for a new climb technique for high performance aircraft, Aeronautical Research Council Report Memo. No. 2557 (1951).
24. E. S. Rutowski, Energy approach to the general aircraft performance problem, *Aero/Space Sci. J.* **21**, 187–195 (1954).
25. A. Miele, Optimum climbing technique for a rocket-powered aircraft, *Jet Propulsion* **25**, 385–391 (1955).
26. H. J. Kelley, M. Falco and D. J. Ball, Air vehicle trajectory optimization, *SIAM Symp. Multivariable System Theory, Cambridge, Massachusetts, November 1–3, 1962.*
27. H. Heermann, The minimum time problem, *J. Astronaut. Sci.* **2**, 93–107 (1964).
28. S. Ross, Minimality for problems in vertical and horizontal rocket flight, *Jet Propulsion* **28**, 55–56 (1958).
29. G. Leitmann, An elementary derivation of the optimal control conditions, *in Proc. 12th Intern. Astronaut. Congr., 1961* (R. M. L. Baker and M. W. Makemson, eds.), pp. 275–298. Academic Press, New York, 1963.
30. D. F. Lawden, Optimal intermediate-thrust arcs in a gravitational field, *Astronaut. Acta* **8**, 106–123 (1962).
31. D. F. Lawden, "Optimal Trajectories for Space Navigation," Butterworth, Washington, D.C., 1963.

4

Thrust Programming in a Central Gravitational Field

A. I. LURIE

LENINGRAD POLYTECHNIC INSTITUTE, LENINGRAD, USSR

4.1 General Equations Governing the Motion of a Boosting Vehicle in a Central Gravitational Field

4.11 The Equations of Motion: Vector Form

Let **r** denote the position vector of the center of mass of a vehicle, this vector originating at the attractive center. Furthermore, let **v** denote the velocity vector. These vectors together determine the instantaneous position of the orbital plane Π. The angular momentum vector of a unit mass

$$\mathbf{k} = \mathbf{r} \times \mathbf{v} = k\mathbf{n} \tag{4.1}$$

is directed along the normal (its unit vector being **n**) to the orbital plane.

The differential equations governing the motion of the center of mass can be written down in the following form:†

$$\dot{\mathbf{r}} = \mathbf{v}, \qquad \dot{\mathbf{v}} = -(\mu/r^3)\mathbf{r} + \mathbf{w} \tag{4.2}$$

Here μ denotes a constant equal to the product of the attractive mass and the gravitational constant; **w** denotes thrust acceleration,

$$\mathbf{w} = (cq/m)\mathbf{e} = w\mathbf{e} \tag{4.3}$$

c denotes the exhaust speed, and q the mass flow rate; the latter satisfies the equation of the flow rate

$$\dot{m} = -q \tag{4.4}$$

Last, we shall denote by **e** the unit vector in the direction of the thrust; thus,

$$1 - \mathbf{e} \cdot \mathbf{e} = 0 \tag{4.5}$$

We observe, in conclusion, that according to the angular momentum theorem,

$$\dot{\mathbf{k}} = \mathbf{r} \times \mathbf{w} \tag{4.6}$$

4.12 Statement of the Problem

The vectors **r** and **v** and the mass m will further be defined as the "coordinates"‡ of the system whereas the quantities **e**, c, and q will serve as "controls." The latter will be subjected to some additional constraints depending on the type of the boosting device considered (see Sec. 4.13).

† The dot denotes differentiation with respect to time t; in the case of vectors, such differentiation is relative to an "inertial" frame.

‡ The components of **r** and **v** together with m are the "state variables" of the system.

The coordinates belong to the class of continuous functions of time on the interval $[0, t_1]$. In what follows their initial values will always be assumed prescribed:

$$t = 0; \qquad \mathbf{r} = \mathbf{r}^0, \quad \mathbf{v} = \mathbf{v}^0, \quad m = m^0 \tag{4.7}$$

Their values $\mathbf{r}^1$, $\mathbf{v}^1$, m^1 at the right side of the interval are subjected to the following system of conditions:

(1) the vectors $\mathbf{r}^1$, $\mathbf{v}^1$ are connected by the relations

$$t = t_1; \qquad \varphi_l(\mathbf{r}^1, \mathbf{v}^1) = 0, \qquad l = 1, 2, \dots, r \leq 6 \tag{4.8}$$

where the quantity t_1 is either prescribed *a priori* ($t_1 = t_1{}^*$) or unknown;

(2) either the final mass is assumed known, i.e.,

$$t = t_1; \qquad m = m^1 = m_*{}^1 \tag{4.9}$$

or else minimum fuel consumption is required, i.e.,

$$J = m^0 - m^1 = \min \tag{4.10}$$

(3) the requirement (4.10) is replaced by the minimum time condition (the quick-operation problem), i.e.,

$$J = t_1 = \min \tag{4.11}$$

where now m^1 is either prescribed or unknown.

The basic problem is to prescribe the thrust operation, that is, to determine the time dependence of the control functions $\mathbf{e}$, c, and q in the class of piece-wise-continuous functions, in such a way as to satisfy the conditions formulated above.

4.13 The Boosting Devices

In what follows, we shall consider three types of boosting devices:

(1) Devices which guarantee the constant magnitude of the thrust-acceleration vector ($w = \text{const}$) while the exhaust speed c is either constant or is given as a function of time.

The flow rate equation can now be integrated to give

$$m = m^0 \exp\left(-w \int_0^t \frac{dt}{c}\right)$$

and the mass is then excluded from future consideration. The quick-operation requirement now guarantees the minimum of fuel consumption. The vector $\mathbf{e}$ serves as the control function.

(2) Propulsive power limited boosters (plasma or ionic). Now the quantities c and q are also treated as controls, and are connected by the relation

$$\mathcal{N}(t) = \tfrac{1}{2}c^2 q = \tfrac{1}{2}(m^2 w^2/q), \qquad \mathcal{N}_{\min} \leq \mathcal{N}(t) \leq \mathcal{N}_{\max} \tag{4.12}$$

where $\mathcal{N}(t)$ is the propulsive power.

Following the technique suggested in Leitmann[1] and in Miele[2] we can write these inequalities in the form of equalities

$$[\mathcal{N}_{\max} - \mathcal{N}(t)][\mathcal{N}(t) - \mathcal{N}_{\min}] - \nu_2{}^2 = 0 \tag{4.13}$$

where the quantity ν_2 is treated as an artificial (or auxiliary) "control."

(3) Mass flow rate limited booster (chemical rockets). Here the exhaust speed is assumed constant and the flow rate bounded, i.e.,

$$c = \text{const}, \qquad 0 \leq q(t) \leq q_{\max} \tag{4.14}$$

Now q and ν_3 serve as the control functions, so that

$$q(t)[q_{\max} - q(t)] - \nu_3{}^2 = 0 \tag{4.15}$$

4.14 The Mayer-Bolza Problem

In the fundamental papers[1-5] the formulated problem is treated from the point of view of the Mayer-Bolza problem which is well known in the calculus of variations. A detailed account of the latter problem was given by Bliss;[6] various recent publications can also be noted.[7,8] Different topics on the optimal control of rocket flight are analyzed in Tarasov.[9]

We introduce three types of the Lagrange multipliers.

(1) The vectors $\boldsymbol{\lambda}_r$, $\boldsymbol{\lambda}_v$, and also the scalar λ_m for boosting devices of the second and third types. With the aid of these multipliers, we construct the "Hamiltonian" corresponding to the right-hand sides of the equations of motion and flow rate:

$$H_\lambda = \boldsymbol{\lambda}_r \cdot \mathbf{v} - \boldsymbol{\lambda}_v \cdot \mathbf{r}(\mu/r^3) + \boldsymbol{\lambda}_v \cdot \mathbf{e}w \tag{4.16$_1$†}$$

$$H_\lambda = \boldsymbol{\lambda}_r \cdot \mathbf{v} - \boldsymbol{\lambda}_v \cdot \mathbf{r}(\mu/r^3) + \boldsymbol{\lambda}_v \cdot \mathbf{e}(cq/m) - \lambda_m q \tag{4.16$_{2,3}$}$$

(2) Scalar multipliers μ_e, μ_κ, corresponding to the finite constraints imposed on the "control functions." These multipliers appear in the second term of the Hamiltonian

$$H_\mu = \mu_e(1 - \mathbf{e} \cdot \mathbf{e}) = 0 \tag{4.17$_1$}$$

$$H_\mu = \mu_e(1 - \mathbf{e} \cdot \mathbf{e}) + \mu_1(c^2 q - 2\mathcal{N}) + \mu_2[(\mathcal{N}_{\max} - \mathcal{N})(\mathcal{N} - \mathcal{N}_{\min}) - \nu_2{}^2] = 0 \tag{4.17$_2$}$$

$$H_\mu = \mu_e(1 - \mathbf{e} \cdot \mathbf{e}) + \mu_3[q(q_{\max} - q) - \nu_3{}^2] = 0 \tag{4.17$_3$}$$

† A subscript to an equation number refers to the corresponding type of boosting device.

(3) Constant scalar multipliers ρ_l, introduced for the derivation of the boundary conditions. These multipliers serve for the formulation of the "indicating function"

$$\theta = J + \theta_1, \quad \theta_1 = \sum_{l=1}^{r} \rho_l \varphi_l(\mathbf{r}^1, \mathbf{v}^1) + \rho_t(t_1 - t_1{}^*) + \rho_m(m^1 - m_*{}^1) = 0 \quad (4.18)$$

Here we have denoted by J the functional (4.10) or (4.11) to be minimized. If the quantities t_1 and (or) m^1 are not known *a priori*, then ρ_t and (or) ρ_m are assumed to be zero.

Having set the variation of the functional

$$I = \theta + \int_0^{t_1} (\boldsymbol{\lambda}_r \cdot \dot{\mathbf{r}} + \boldsymbol{\lambda}_v \cdot \dot{\mathbf{v}} - H_\lambda - H_\mu + \lambda_m \dot{m})\, dt \quad (4.19)$$

equal to zero, we arrive at three groups of equations; namely, equations of stationarity, the Erdmann-Weierstrass conditions at the points t_* of possible lack of continuity of the "controls," and boundary conditions for the Lagrange multipliers $\boldsymbol{\lambda}_r$, $\boldsymbol{\lambda}_v$, λ_m and for the Hamiltonian H_λ. These requirements are complemented by the fundamental Weierstrass necessary criterion for a minimum. We construct the function E, having for the above-described types of boosting devices the following form:

$$E = \boldsymbol{\lambda}_v \cdot (\mathbf{e} - \mathbf{e}^*) \quad (4.20)_1$$

$$E = (1/m)\boldsymbol{\lambda}_v \cdot (cq\mathbf{e} - c^*q^*\mathbf{e}^*) - \lambda_m(q - q^*) \quad (4.20)_2$$

$$E = (c/m)\boldsymbol{\lambda}_v \cdot (q\mathbf{e} - q^*\mathbf{e}^*) - \lambda_m(q - q^*) \quad (4.20)_3$$

Here the asterisk denotes an admissible control which satisfies the constraints imposed on the control functions. The Weierstrass criterion requires that

$$E \geq 0 \quad (4.21)$$

4.15 Conditions of Stationarity

These conditions constitute the system of differential equations and finite relations for the Lagrange multipliers of the first and the second types; namely,

$$\dot{\boldsymbol{\lambda}}_v = -\text{grad}_v\, H_\lambda = -\boldsymbol{\lambda}_r \quad (4.22)$$

$$\dot{\boldsymbol{\lambda}}_r = -\text{grad}_r\, H_\lambda = \frac{\mu}{r^3}\left(\boldsymbol{\lambda}_v - 3\frac{\boldsymbol{\lambda}_v \cdot \mathbf{r}}{r^2}\mathbf{r}\right) \quad (4.23)$$

$$\dot{\lambda}_m = -\partial H_\lambda/\partial m = \boldsymbol{\lambda}_v \cdot \mathbf{e}(cq/m^2) \quad (4.24)_{2,3}$$

$$\text{grad}_{\mathbf{e}}(H_\lambda + H_\mu) = w\boldsymbol{\lambda}_v - 2\mu_e\mathbf{e} = 0 \tag{4.25$_1$}$$

$$\text{grad}_{\mathbf{e}}(H_\lambda + H_\mu) = (cq/m)\boldsymbol{\lambda}_v - 2\mu_e\mathbf{e} = 0 \tag{4.25$_{2,3}$}$$

$$\left.\begin{aligned} \frac{\partial(H_\lambda + H_\mu)}{\partial q} &= \boldsymbol{\lambda}_v \cdot \mathbf{e}\frac{c}{m} - \lambda_m + c^2\mu_1 = 0, \\ \frac{\partial(H_\lambda + H_\mu)}{\partial c} &= \frac{1}{q}\left(\frac{1}{m}\boldsymbol{\lambda}_v \cdot \mathbf{e} + 2\mu_1 c\right) = 0 \\ \frac{\partial H_\mu}{\partial \mathcal{N}} &= -2\mu_1 + \mu_2(\mathcal{N}_{\max} + \mathcal{N}_{\min} - 2\mathcal{N}) = 0, \end{aligned}\right\} \tag{4.26$_2$}$$

$$\left.\begin{aligned} \frac{\partial H_\mu}{\partial \nu_2} &= -\mu_2\nu_2 = 0 \\ \frac{\partial(H_\lambda + H_\mu)}{\partial q} &= \boldsymbol{\lambda}_v \cdot \mathbf{e}\frac{c}{m} - \lambda_m + \mu_3(q_{\max} - q) = 0, \\ \frac{\partial H_\mu}{\partial \nu_3} &= -\mu_3\nu_3 = 0 \end{aligned}\right\} \tag{4.26$_3$}$$

4.16 Equations Valid for all Types of Boosting Devices

Such equations are the stationarity conditions (4.22), (4.23), and (4.25). From Eq. (4.25) it follows that the vectors $\boldsymbol{\lambda}_v$ and $\mathbf{e}$ are parallel to each other; the Weierstrass condition now shows that they are equally directed. In fact, the unknown control function should be chosen among the admissible ones and, therefore, it becomes clear that the Weierstrass criterion must be valid for $c = c^*$, $q = q^*$. Now we see that inequality $(4.20)_1$ is true for all types of devices considered. Having now set $\boldsymbol{\lambda}_v = \tilde{\lambda}_v\mathbf{e}$, where $\tilde{\lambda}_v = \pm\lambda_v = \pm|\boldsymbol{\lambda}_v|$, we get

$$E = (cq/m)\boldsymbol{\lambda}_v \cdot (\mathbf{e} - \mathbf{e}^*) = (cq/m)\tilde{\lambda}_v(1 - \mathbf{e} \cdot \mathbf{e}^*) \geq 0, \qquad \tilde{\lambda}_v = \lambda_v$$

this being the required relation. Thus, we have

$$\boldsymbol{\lambda}_v = \lambda_v\mathbf{e} \tag{4.27}$$

On eliminating the quantity $\boldsymbol{\lambda}_r$ from Eq. (4.23) by use of (4.22), and choosing the notation $\boldsymbol{\lambda}$ for $\boldsymbol{\lambda}_v$, we arrive at the second-order differential equation for the vector $\boldsymbol{\lambda}$

$$\ddot{\boldsymbol{\lambda}} = (\mu/r^3)[3(\boldsymbol{\lambda} \cdot \mathbf{r}/r^2)\mathbf{r} - \boldsymbol{\lambda}] \tag{4.28}$$

This completes the system of stationary conditions for the first type of boosting devices.

4.17 Additional Conditions of Stationarity: Boosting Devices of the Second Type

Now it will be supposed that the exhaust speed is finite. From this assumption it follows due to Eq. (4.12) that the mass flow rate $q \neq 0$; having eliminated μ_1 from Eq. $(4.26)_2$, we assert with the help of Eqs. (4.27) and $(4.24)_2$ that

$$\lambda_m = \frac{c\lambda}{2m}, \qquad \frac{\dot{\lambda}_m}{\lambda_m} = \frac{2\lambda}{m}, \qquad \lambda_m = \frac{A}{m^2}, \qquad \lambda = \frac{2A}{mc} \tag{4.29}$$

A being an integration constant. Now we have

$$c = \frac{2A}{\lambda m}, \qquad \mathcal{N} = \tfrac{1}{2}c^2 q = \frac{2A^2}{\lambda^2 m^2}\, q, \qquad w = \frac{cq}{m} = \frac{2A}{\lambda m^2}\, q$$

and, by virtue of the flow rate equation (4.4),

$$\lambda = A\,\frac{w}{\mathcal{N}}, \qquad \frac{q}{m^2} = \left(\frac{1}{m}\right)^{\bullet} = \frac{w^2}{2\mathcal{N}}, \qquad \frac{1}{m} - \frac{1}{m^0} = \frac{1}{2}\int_0^t \frac{w^2}{\mathcal{N}}\, dt$$

On eliminating the quantity μ_1, the third equation $(4.26)_2$ can be presented in the following form: $\lambda/mc + \mu_2(\mathcal{N}_{\max} + \mathcal{N}_{\min} - 2\mathcal{N}) = 0$ and so the assumption $\mu_2 = 0$† leads to $\lambda = 0$, $\boldsymbol{\lambda} = 0$, $\dot{\boldsymbol{\lambda}} = 0$, $\lambda_m = 0$. It will become clear from material following that this leads to a contradiction with the boundary conditions of the problem of fuel consumption minimization as well as with those of the problem of minimizing t_1. Thus the assumption $\mu_2 = 0$ should be withdrawn, and there remain the possibilities $v_2 = 0$ and $\mathcal{N} = \mathcal{N}_{\max}$ or $\mathcal{N} = \mathcal{N}_{\min}$. But from the Weierstrass condition it now becomes clear that we must retain only the first possibility. Indeed, turning to Eq. $(4.20)_2$ and taking Eqs. (4.27) and (4.29) into consideration, we arrive at the inequalities:

$$\tfrac{1}{2}c(q + q^*) - c^*q^* \geq 0, \qquad \frac{\mathcal{N}}{c}\left(1 + \frac{\mathcal{N}^*}{\mathcal{N}}\right) - \frac{2\mathcal{N}^*}{c^*} > 0$$

Of the three admissible control functions, c^*, q^*, and $\mathcal{N}^*$ only two are independent, and the third may be chosen arbitrarily; setting $c = c^*$, we see from the second inequality that $\mathcal{N} - \mathcal{N}^* \geq 0$, and setting $q = q^*$, we infer from the first inequality that $c \geq c^*$, or equivalently, $\mathcal{N} \geq \mathcal{N}^*$. But the quantity $\mathcal{N}^*$ may be chosen arbitrarily near to $\mathcal{N}_{\max}$ without violation of inequalities (4.12), and from here it follows that these inequalities require that $\mathcal{N} = \mathcal{N}_{\max}$.

† On a nonzero interval.

We have now deduced that for the type of boosting devices considered, the vector $\boldsymbol{\lambda}$ given by

$$\boldsymbol{\lambda} = \frac{A}{\mathcal{N}_{\max}} \mathbf{w} = \frac{A}{\mathcal{N}_{\max}} \left(\dot{\mathbf{v}} + \frac{\mu}{\tau^3} \mathbf{r} \right) \tag{4.30}$$

differs from $\mathbf{w}$ only by a constant multiplier, and the mass is determined from the equation

$$\frac{1}{m} - \frac{1}{m^0} = \frac{1}{2\mathcal{N}_{\max}} \int_0^t \left| \dot{\mathbf{v}} + \frac{\mu}{r^3} \mathbf{r} \right|^2 dt \tag{4.31}$$

4.18 Additional Conditions of Stationarity: Boosting Devices of the Third Type

Instead of λ_m, it seems now convenient to introduce the quantity η called the switching function:

$$\eta = (c/m)\lambda - \lambda_m \tag{4.32}$$

From Eq. $(4.24)_3$ it follows that the switching function satisfies the differential equation

$$\dot{\eta} = (c/m)\dot{\lambda} \tag{4.33}$$

Equations $(4.26)_3$ can now be presented as follows:

$$\eta + \mu_3(q_{\max} - 2q) = 0 \qquad \mu_3 \nu_3 = 0$$

From the assumption $\nu_3 = 0$ and Eq. (4.15) we deduce that the mass flow rate must assume only one of its limiting values $q = 0$ or $q = q_{\max}$. The Weierstrass criterion Eq. $(4.20)_3$ is now written in the form $\eta(q - q^*) \geq 0$ and there appears the possibility of two regimes, the regime of maximum thrust

$$q = q_{\max} \qquad \text{when} \quad \eta > 0 \tag{4.34$_*$}$$

and that of moving along a Keplerian arc

$$q = 0 \qquad \text{when} \quad \eta < 0 \tag{4.34$_{**}$}$$

At the instant of switching, the Lagrange multipliers and, consequently, η and $\dot{\eta}$, suffer no discontinuity. Thus, we have

$$\eta(t_*) = 0 \tag{4.35}$$

and $\dot{\eta}(t_* - 0) > 0$ when the vehicle proceeds from a Keplerian arc to the maximum thrust regime, and $\eta(t_* - 0) < 0$ during the inverse maneuver. The case $\dot{\eta}(t_*) = 0$ is doubtful since the sign of the second derivative $\ddot{\eta}(t_* \pm 0)$ (which is discontinuous) provides no information about the subsequent regime. None of the three possibilities can as yet be withdrawn. These are (1) conservation of the preceding regime if the sign of $\eta(t)$ is conserved;

(2) transition from the maximum thrust regime to moving along a Keplerian arc when $\eta(t)$ goes over from negative values to positive ones, and (3) the inverse transition when previously negative values of $\eta(t)$ become positive.

In what was stated above, it had been supposed that $v_3 = 0$; one cannot, however, withdraw the possibility that $v_3 \neq 0$ on some time-interval (t_*, t_{**}). In this case

$$0 \leq q(t) \leq q_{\max}, \qquad \eta \equiv 0 \tag{4.36}$$

Here we have the regime of "singular control"† with variable thrust; now the mass flow rate is some unknown function of time determined from the second Eq. (4.36) and from the equation of motion:

$$q = \frac{m}{c}\left(\dot{\mathbf{v}} \cdot \mathbf{e} + \frac{\mu}{r^3}\mathbf{r} \cdot \mathbf{e}\right) \tag{4.37}$$

where, however, no further integration is as yet required.

We see now that with the condition $\dot{\eta}(t_*) = 0$ we cannot exclude the possibility that an arc of "singular control" is included in the solution, if we can simultaneously retain the continuity of $\mathbf{r}$ and $\mathbf{v}$. In the "singular control" regime, $\dot{\lambda} = 0$ and $\lambda = m\lambda_m/c$ is a constant different from zero, since the assumption $\lambda \equiv 0$ would be equivalent to the vanishing of all Lagrange multipliers $(\boldsymbol{\lambda}, \dot{\boldsymbol{\lambda}}, \lambda_m)$; such vanishing is presumed impossible in the Mayer-Bolza problem. The constant λ is now determined from the requirement of continuity at the moment t_*, and it remains to verify that the vectors $\boldsymbol{\lambda}$, $\dot{\boldsymbol{\lambda}}$ and the Hamiltonian H_λ are continuous (of course, $|\dot{\boldsymbol{\lambda}}| \neq \dot{\lambda} = 0$). So long as $\lambda \neq 0$, the verification reduces to checking the continuity of the vectors $\mathbf{e}$ and $\dot{\mathbf{e}}$.

The moment $t_{**} - 0$ of termination of the "singular control" is as yet unknown; this moment is probably not that when $q(t)$ reaches either $q = 0$ or $q = q_{\max}$, because the quantity q can be discontinuous. It seems useful to retain t_{**} as the unknown quantity determined by boundary conditions (see also Sec. 4.62*a*).

4.2 Integrals of the Basic System of Equations

4.21 Scalar Integral

The equations of motion and the mass flow rate equation together with the stationarity conditions allow the first integral,

$$H_\lambda = h \tag{4.38}$$

expressing the constancy of the Hamiltonian.

† See Chapter 3.

For boosting devices of the first type, by virtue of Eqs. (4.16), (4.22), and (4.27), this integral can be presented in the form

$$-\dot{\boldsymbol{\lambda}} \cdot \mathbf{v} - \boldsymbol{\lambda} \cdot \mathbf{r}(\mu/r^3) + w\lambda = h \tag{4.39$_1$}$$

For boosting devices of the second type, we infer from Eqs. $(4.16)_2$ and (4.29) that

$$-\dot{\boldsymbol{\lambda}} \cdot \mathbf{v} - \boldsymbol{\lambda} \cdot \mathbf{r}(\mu/r^3) + \tfrac{1}{2}\lambda w = h \tag{4.39$_2$}$$

In this equation, we may replace the vector $\boldsymbol{\lambda}$ by the proportional vector $\mathbf{w}$, so that

$$-\dot{\mathbf{w}} \cdot \mathbf{v} - \mathbf{w} \cdot \mathbf{r}(\mu/r^3) + \tfrac{1}{2}w^2 = h_1, \qquad h_1 = (\mathcal{N}_{\max}/A)h$$

Last, taking account of Eq. (4.32) for the switching function, we see that for the third type of booster

$$-\dot{\boldsymbol{\lambda}} \cdot \mathbf{v} - \boldsymbol{\lambda} \cdot \mathbf{r}(\mu/r^3) + \eta q = h \tag{4.39$_3$}$$

Here q is constant ($q_{\max}$ or zero) if $\eta \neq 0$, and $q = q(t)$ if $\eta = 0$.

It can be immediately verified by differentiation that (4.38) in fact is an integral of the equations noted above.

The calculation proceeds identically for all cases concerned, and therefore we shall only analyze the first one. In view of the relations

$$\dot{\boldsymbol{\lambda}} = \dot{\lambda}\mathbf{e} + \lambda\dot{\mathbf{e}}, \qquad \mathbf{e} \cdot \dot{\mathbf{e}} = 0, \qquad \dot{\boldsymbol{\lambda}} \cdot \mathbf{w} = \dot{\lambda}w$$

we present the result of differentiation of Eq. $(4.39)_1$ in the following way

$$\left(\ddot{\boldsymbol{\lambda}} + \frac{\mu}{r^3}\boldsymbol{\lambda} - \frac{3\mu}{r^5}\boldsymbol{\lambda} \cdot \mathbf{r}\,\mathbf{r}\right) \cdot \mathbf{v} + \dot{\boldsymbol{\lambda}} \cdot \left(\dot{\mathbf{v}} + \frac{\mu}{r^3}\mathbf{r} - \mathbf{w}\right) = 0 \tag{4.40}$$

It is observed that the vectors in brackets vanish due to the equations of motion together with those of stationarity, Eq. (4.28). We shall make use of Eq. (4.40) in Sec. 4.23.

4.22 Vector Integral

The system of Eqs. (4.2) and (4.28) complemented with condition (4.27) also allows a vector integral. Consider the vector product of both sides of Eq. (4.28) with the vector $\mathbf{r}$; in view of Eqs. (4.2) and (4.27), we get

$$\ddot{\boldsymbol{\lambda}} \times \mathbf{r} + \boldsymbol{\lambda} \times \frac{\mu}{r^3}\mathbf{r} = \ddot{\boldsymbol{\lambda}} \times \mathbf{r} - \boldsymbol{\lambda} \times \dot{\mathbf{v}} = \frac{d}{dt}(\dot{\boldsymbol{\lambda}} \times \mathbf{r} - \boldsymbol{\lambda} \times \mathbf{v}) = 0$$

so that

$$\dot{\boldsymbol{\lambda}} \times \mathbf{r} - \boldsymbol{\lambda} \times \mathbf{v} = \mathbf{a} = a\boldsymbol{\sigma} \tag{4.41}$$

Here $\mathbf{a}$ denotes a constant vector, $a = |\mathbf{a}|$; $\boldsymbol{\sigma}$ is a constant unit vector.

The subsequent results of this paper are based to a considerable extent upon the use of both scalar and vector integrals. The existence of the first one is very well known while the second has been mentioned neither in the fundamental papers,[1-5] nor in a more recent publication[10]; in Isayev and Sonin[11] it was observed that the vector integral exists in a special case of plane motion, but no use was made of this fact.†

4.23 The Equivalence among Different Systems of Equations

Differentiating Eq. (4.41) and making use of the equations of motion Eqs. (4.2), we arrive at the relation

$$\left(\ddot{\boldsymbol{\lambda}} + \frac{\mu}{r^3}\boldsymbol{\lambda}\right) \times \mathbf{r} = 0 \tag{4.42}$$

From this we deduce that the vector in brackets is collinear with $\mathbf{r}$ and therefore may be presented as $b\mathbf{r}$, b being a scalar multiplier. Substitution in Eq (4.40) now shows that

$$\left(b - \frac{3\mu}{r^5}\boldsymbol{\lambda}\cdot\mathbf{r}\right)\mathbf{r}\cdot\mathbf{v} = 0$$

where we have eliminated the second term in view of Eq. (4.2). Thus, we have

$$b = \frac{3\mu}{r^5}\boldsymbol{\lambda}\cdot\mathbf{r}, \qquad \ddot{\boldsymbol{\lambda}} + \frac{\mu}{r^3}\boldsymbol{\lambda} = \frac{3\mu}{r^5}\boldsymbol{\lambda}\cdot\mathbf{r}\,\mathbf{r} \quad \text{when} \quad \mathbf{r}\cdot\mathbf{v} \neq 0$$

It is now clear that in view of the equations of motion (4.2), the second-order equation (4.28) is equivalent to the pair of first-order equations (4.39) and (4.41); these involve four scalar constants: h and the vector $\mathbf{a}$. The case $\mathbf{r}\cdot\mathbf{v} = 0$, corresponding to spherical orbits, requires separate consideration.

4.24 The First-Order Differential Equation for the Vector $\boldsymbol{\lambda}$

Having constructed the scalar product of Eq. (4.41) by $\mathbf{r}$, $\mathbf{v}$, and $\mathbf{k}$, respectively, and accounting for Eqs. (4.1), we obtain

$$\boldsymbol{\lambda}\cdot\mathbf{k} = a\boldsymbol{\sigma}\cdot\mathbf{r} \tag{4.43}$$

$$\dot{\boldsymbol{\lambda}}\cdot\mathbf{k} = a\boldsymbol{\sigma}\cdot\mathbf{v} \tag{4.44}$$

$$(\dot{\boldsymbol{\lambda}}\cdot\mathbf{r} + \boldsymbol{\lambda}\cdot\mathbf{v})\mathbf{r}\cdot\mathbf{v} - (\dot{\boldsymbol{\lambda}}\cdot\mathbf{v}r^2 + \boldsymbol{\lambda}\cdot\mathbf{r}v^2) = a\boldsymbol{\sigma}\cdot\mathbf{k} \tag{4.45}$$

It should be noted that expression (4.43) represents an integral of Eq. (4.44) [see Eqs. (4.3), (4.6), and (4.27)].

† See also Melbourne and Sauer[20].

If $\mathbf{r}\cdot\mathbf{v}\neq 0$, we can determine from Eqs. (4.44), (4.45), and (4.39) the covariant components $\dot{\boldsymbol{\lambda}}\cdot\mathbf{r}$, $\dot{\boldsymbol{\lambda}}\cdot\mathbf{v}$, and $\dot{\boldsymbol{\lambda}}\cdot\mathbf{k}$ of the vector $\dot{\boldsymbol{\lambda}}$ in the vector basis $\mathbf{r}$, $\mathbf{v}$, $\mathbf{k}$. With these components we may form the following expression for this vector:

$$\dot{\boldsymbol{\lambda}} = 1/k^2(\dot{\boldsymbol{\lambda}}\cdot\mathbf{r}\ \mathbf{v}\times\mathbf{k} + \dot{\boldsymbol{\lambda}}\cdot\mathbf{v}\,\mathbf{k}\times\mathbf{r} + \dot{\boldsymbol{\lambda}}\cdot\mathbf{k}\,\mathbf{k})$$

This is just the differential equation required; on substitution for $\dot{\boldsymbol{\lambda}}\cdot\mathbf{r}$, $\dot{\boldsymbol{\lambda}}\cdot\mathbf{v}$, and $\dot{\boldsymbol{\lambda}}\cdot\mathbf{k}$, this equation can be presented as

$$\dot{\boldsymbol{\lambda}} = \frac{1}{\mathbf{r}\cdot\mathbf{v}}\left[\boldsymbol{\lambda}\cdot(\mathbf{v}\times\mathbf{n})\mathbf{v}\times\mathbf{n} - \frac{\mu}{r^3}\boldsymbol{\lambda}\cdot\mathbf{r}\,\mathbf{r} + a\left(\boldsymbol{\sigma}\cdot\mathbf{n}\,\mathbf{v}\times\mathbf{n} + \frac{1}{k}\mathbf{r}\cdot\mathbf{v}\,\boldsymbol{\sigma}\cdot\mathbf{v}\,\mathbf{n}\right) + \mathbf{r}\vartheta\right] \tag{4.46}$$

where

$$\vartheta = w\lambda - h, \qquad \vartheta = \tfrac{1}{2}w\lambda - h, \qquad \vartheta = \eta q - h \qquad (4.47)_{1,2,3}$$

for boosters of the first, second, and third types, respectively.

4.25 Orbital Axes

Determine an orthogonal orbital triad by a triplet of unit vectors: $\mathbf{e}_r$ and $\mathbf{e}_\varphi$, lying in the instantaneous orbital plane Π, and the vector $\mathbf{n}$ perpendicular to this plane, where

$$\mathbf{e}_r = \frac{\mathbf{r}}{r}, \qquad \mathbf{e}_\varphi = \mathbf{n}\times\mathbf{e}_r, \qquad \mathbf{n} = \frac{1}{k}\mathbf{r}\times\mathbf{v} \tag{4.48}$$

Let $\boldsymbol{\omega}$ stand for the angular velocity vector of this triad $\boldsymbol{\omega} = \omega_r\mathbf{e}_r + \omega_\varphi\mathbf{e}_\varphi + \omega_n\mathbf{n}$ and let us determine its components along the orbital axes. Taking account of kinematic relations

$$\begin{aligned}
\dot{\mathbf{e}}_r &= \boldsymbol{\omega}\times\mathbf{e}_r = -\mathbf{n}\omega_\varphi + \mathbf{e}_\varphi\omega_n\\
\dot{\mathbf{e}}_\varphi &= \boldsymbol{\omega}\times\mathbf{e}_\varphi = -\mathbf{e}_r\omega_n + \mathbf{n}\omega_r\\
\dot{\mathbf{n}} &= \boldsymbol{\omega}\times\mathbf{n} = -\mathbf{e}_\varphi\omega_r + \mathbf{e}_r\omega_\varphi
\end{aligned}$$

we construct the following expressions for the vectors $\mathbf{v}$ and $\mathbf{k}$:

$$\begin{aligned}
\mathbf{v} &= (r\mathbf{e}_r)^{\cdot} = \dot{r}\mathbf{e}_r + r(-\mathbf{n}\omega_\varphi + \mathbf{e}_\varphi\omega_n)\\
\mathbf{k} &= \mathbf{r}\times\mathbf{v} = r^2(\omega_\varphi\mathbf{e}_\varphi + \omega_n\mathbf{n})
\end{aligned}$$

Observe now that the vector $\mathbf{v}$ lies in the Π plane and the vector $\mathbf{k}$ is directed perpendicularly to it; from here we deduce that

$$\omega_\varphi = 0, \qquad \omega_n = \frac{k}{r^2}, \qquad \mathbf{v} = v_r\mathbf{e}_r + \frac{k}{r}\mathbf{e}_\varphi, \qquad v_r = \dot{r} \tag{4.49}$$

It remains now to determine ω_r; to do this substitute the expression for $\mathbf{v}$ above into the equation of motion (4.2) so that

$$\dot{\mathbf{v}} = \ddot{r}\mathbf{e}_r + \dot{r}\frac{k}{r^2}\mathbf{e}_\varphi + \left(\frac{\dot{k}}{r} - \dot{r}\frac{k}{r^2}\right)\mathbf{e}_\varphi + \frac{k}{r}\left(-\mathbf{e}_r\frac{k}{r^2} + \mathbf{n}\omega_r\right) = -\frac{\mu}{r^2}\mathbf{e}_r + w\mathbf{e} \tag{4.50}$$

Let α_1, α_2, and α_3 denote the direction cosines of the thrust vector relative to the orbital axes; namely,

$$\mathbf{e} = \alpha_1\mathbf{e}_r + \alpha_2\mathbf{e}_\varphi + \alpha_3\mathbf{n} \tag{4.51}$$

where it is of course understood that

$$\alpha_1^2 + \alpha_2^2 + \alpha_3^2 = 1 \tag{4.52}$$

Turning back now to Eq. (4.50), we obtain first, the equations of motion in the instantaneous orbital plane

$$\dot{r} = v_r, \qquad \dot{v}_r = \frac{k^2}{r^3} - \frac{\mu}{r^2} + w\alpha_1, \qquad \dot{k} = rw\alpha_2, \qquad \left(w = \frac{cq}{m}\right) \tag{4.53}$$

and, second, the expression for the vector

$$\boldsymbol{\omega} = \frac{k}{r^2}\mathbf{n} + w\frac{r}{k}\alpha_3\mathbf{e}_r \tag{4.54}$$

The differential equations of the orbital triad's rotation can now be presented in the form

$$\dot{\mathbf{e}}_r = \frac{k}{r^2}\mathbf{e}_\varphi, \qquad \dot{\mathbf{e}}_\varphi = -\frac{k}{r^2}\mathbf{e}_r + \frac{wr}{k}\alpha_3\mathbf{n}, \qquad \dot{\mathbf{n}} = -\frac{wr}{k}\alpha_3\mathbf{e}_\varphi \tag{4.55}$$

Let $\mathbf{e}^*$ denote the vector whose components along orbital axes are equal to $\dot{\alpha}_1$, $\dot{\alpha}_2$, $\dot{\alpha}_3$. We may write

$$\dot{\mathbf{e}} = \mathbf{e}^* + \boldsymbol{\omega}\times\mathbf{e} = \left(\dot{\alpha}_1 - \frac{k}{r^2}\alpha_2\right)\mathbf{e}_r + \left(\dot{\alpha}_2 + \frac{k}{r^2}\alpha_1 - \frac{rw}{k}\alpha_3^2\right)\mathbf{e}_\varphi + \left(\dot{\alpha}_3 + \frac{wr}{k}\alpha_2\alpha_3\right)\mathbf{n} \tag{4.56}$$

Consider now the angular velocity vector $\mathbf{v}$ of the vector $\mathbf{e}$; one may of course set $\mathbf{v}\cdot\mathbf{e} = 0$. The relation between vectors $\boldsymbol{\omega}$ and $\mathbf{v}$ is given by

$$\dot{\mathbf{e}} = \mathbf{v}\times\mathbf{e} = \mathbf{e}^* + \boldsymbol{\omega}\times\mathbf{e}, \qquad \mathbf{v} = \mathbf{e}\times(\mathbf{v}\times\mathbf{e}) = \boldsymbol{\omega} + \mathbf{e}\times\mathbf{e}^* - \boldsymbol{\omega}\cdot\mathbf{e}\mathbf{e} \tag{4.57}$$

The vector $\boldsymbol{\sigma}$ which enters into the expression for the vector integral, is of constant direction; from this we infer that

$$\dot{\boldsymbol{\sigma}} = \boldsymbol{\sigma}^* + \boldsymbol{\omega} \times \boldsymbol{\sigma} = 0$$

and having denoted by σ_s its components along the orbital axes, we arrive at the following equations:

$$\dot{\sigma}_1 = \frac{k}{r^2}\sigma_2, \qquad \dot{\sigma}_2 = -\frac{k}{r^2}\sigma_1 + \frac{r}{k}w\alpha_3\sigma_3, \qquad \dot{\sigma}_3 = -\frac{r}{k}w\alpha_3\sigma_2 \tag{4.58}$$

Equations (4.58) obviously allow the integral

$$\sigma_1{}^2 + \sigma_2{}^2 + \sigma_3{}^2 = 1 \tag{4.59}$$

this relation connects the initial values as well, namely,

$$(\sigma_1{}^0)^2 + (\sigma_2{}^0)^2 + (\sigma_3{}^0)^2 = 1 \tag{4.60}$$

For reference axes we choose the orbital axes $\mathbf{e}_r{}^0$, $\mathbf{e}_\varphi{}^0$, and $\mathbf{n}^0$ at the initial instant. On these axes, the orbital triad can be oriented by means of three Euler angles Ω, i, and u; these are, respectively, the longitude of an ascending node, the instantaneous inclination of orbital plane Π to the plane Π^0 (of the vectors $\mathbf{e}_r{}^0$, $\mathbf{e}_\varphi{}^0$), and the angle in the Π plane between the direction $\mathbf{m}$ of the ascending node and that of the position vector $\mathbf{r}$. The angular velocity vector can be presented in terms of the derivatives of the Euler angles, that is,

$$\boldsymbol{\omega} = \dot{\Omega}\mathbf{n}^0 + \frac{di}{dt}\mathbf{m} + \dot{u}\mathbf{n} \tag{4.61}$$

Comparison with Eq. (4.54) leads to the system of differential equations

$$\frac{di}{dt} = \frac{r}{k}w\alpha_3 \cos u, \qquad \dot{\Omega} = \frac{r}{k}w\alpha_3(\sin u/\sin i), \qquad \dot{u} = \frac{k}{r^2} - \frac{r}{k}w\alpha_3 \sin u \cot i \tag{4.62}$$

Integration of this system provides no new constants because we have already assumed the initial values of the Euler angles to be zero.

We may obtain a more symmetrical form of these equations if we introduce the complex Cayley-Klein parameters α and β, satisfying

$$\dot{\alpha} = \frac{i}{2}\left(\frac{k}{r^2}\alpha + w\frac{r}{k}\alpha_3\beta\right), \qquad \dot{\beta} = \frac{i}{2}\left(-\frac{k}{r^2}\beta + \frac{wr}{k}\alpha_3\alpha\right) \tag{4.63}$$

where†

$$\alpha = \cos(i/2)\exp[(i/2)(\Omega + u)], \qquad \beta = i \sin(i/2)\exp[(i/2)(\Omega - u)] \tag{4.64}$$

† There should be no confusion between $i = (-1)^{1/2}$ and the angle i, since this angle appears only as the argument of trigonometric functions.

Equations (4.63) are integrated with the initial conditions $\alpha = 1$, $\beta = 0$. Note that the components σ_s of the vector $\boldsymbol{\sigma}$ are expressed through their initial values and the Cayley-Klein parameters in the following way:

$$\begin{aligned} \sigma_1 + i\sigma_2 &= (\sigma_1{}^0 + i\sigma_2{}^0)\bar{\alpha}^2 - (\sigma_1{}^0 - i\sigma_2{}^0)\beta^2 + 2\sigma_3{}^0\bar{\alpha}\beta \\ \sigma_1 - i\sigma_2 &= -(\sigma_1{}^0 + i\sigma_2{}^0)\bar{\beta}^2 + (\sigma_1{}^0 - i\sigma_2{}^0)\alpha^2 + 2\sigma_3{}^0\alpha\bar{\beta} \\ \sigma_3 &= -(\sigma_1{}^0 + i\sigma_2{}^0)\bar{\alpha}\bar{\beta} - (\sigma_1{}^0 - i\sigma_2{}^0)\alpha\beta + \sigma_3{}^0(\alpha\bar{\alpha} - \beta\bar{\beta}) \end{aligned} \tag{4.65}$$

the overbar denoting the complex-conjugate quantities.

4.26 The Differential Equations Written Relative to the Orbital Axes

With the aid of Eqs. (4.27) and (4.56) we may replace the differential equation (4.56) by the following system:

$$\begin{aligned} \frac{\dot{\lambda}}{\lambda} = \frac{1}{\lambda}\dot{\boldsymbol{\lambda}} \cdot \mathbf{e} = \frac{1}{\mathbf{r} \cdot \mathbf{v}} \Bigg\{ &|\mathbf{e} \cdot (\mathbf{v} \times \mathbf{n})|^2 - \frac{\mu}{r^2}\alpha_1{}^2 \\ &+ \frac{a}{\lambda}\left[\sigma_3\, \mathbf{e} \cdot (\mathbf{v} \times \mathbf{n}) + \frac{\mathbf{r} \cdot \mathbf{v}}{k} \boldsymbol{\sigma} \cdot \mathbf{v}\, \alpha_3\right] + r\alpha_1 \frac{\vartheta}{\lambda} \Bigg\} \end{aligned} \tag{4.66}$$

$$\begin{aligned} \mathbf{e}^* + \boldsymbol{\omega} \times \mathbf{e} = \frac{1}{\mathbf{r} \cdot \mathbf{v}} \Bigg\{ &\mathbf{e} \cdot (\mathbf{v} \times \mathbf{n})\mathbf{e} \times [(\mathbf{v} \times \mathbf{n}) \times \mathbf{e}] - \frac{\mu}{r^2}\alpha_1 \mathbf{e} \times (\mathbf{r} \times \mathbf{e}) \\ &+ \frac{a}{\lambda}\left[\sigma_3 \mathbf{e} \times \{(\mathbf{v} \times \mathbf{n}) \times \mathbf{e}\} + \frac{\mathbf{r} \cdot \mathbf{v}}{k} \boldsymbol{\sigma} \cdot \mathbf{v}\, \mathbf{e} \times (\mathbf{n} \times \mathbf{e})\right] + \mathbf{e} \times (\mathbf{r} \times \mathbf{e})\frac{\vartheta}{\lambda} \Bigg\} \end{aligned} \tag{4.67}$$

where, if $\alpha_3 \neq 0$, we have according to Eq. (4.43)

$$\lambda = ar\sigma_1/k\alpha_3 \tag{4.68}$$

If $\alpha_3 = 0$ (it will be seen later that this equation holds in a special case of plane motion), then the last relation is dropped (at the same time we shall observe that $\sigma_1 = 0$, $\sigma_2 = 0$).

4.3 Boundary Conditions: Various Types of Motion

4.31 General Boundary Problem

At the instant t_1 the position and velocity of the vehicle will be assumed prescribed: $\mathbf{r}^1 = \mathbf{r}_*{}^1$, $\mathbf{v}^1 = \mathbf{v}_*{}^1$. By a traditional technique we can now determine the values of $\mathbf{r}^1$, $\mathbf{v}^1$, k^1 and the position of the orbital triad—the vectors $\mathbf{e}_r{}^1$, $\mathbf{e}_\varphi{}^1$, $\mathbf{n}^1$ (either the Euler angles, the Cayley-Klein or Hamilton-Rodriques parameters, etc.). The term θ_1 in Eq. (4.18) for the indicating function can now be presented as

$$\theta_1 = \boldsymbol{\rho}_1 \cdot (\mathbf{r}^1 - \mathbf{r}_*{}^1) + \boldsymbol{\rho}_2 \cdot (\mathbf{v}^1 - \mathbf{v}_*{}^1) + \rho_t(t_1 - t_1{}^*) + \rho_m(m^1 - m_*{}^1) = 0 \tag{4.69}$$

where $\boldsymbol{\rho}_1$, $\boldsymbol{\rho}_2$ denote the Lagrange multipliers. Since multipliers $\boldsymbol{\lambda}^1$, $\dot{\boldsymbol{\lambda}}^1$ and the boundary value of the Hamiltonian $H_\lambda{}^1$ are determined from the relations

$$\boldsymbol{\lambda}^1 = -\operatorname{grad}_{\mathbf{v}^1} \theta_1, \qquad \dot{\boldsymbol{\lambda}}^1 = \operatorname{grad}_{\mathbf{r}^1} \theta_1, \qquad \lambda_m{}^1 = -\frac{\partial \theta}{\partial m_1}, \qquad H_\lambda{}^1 = \frac{\partial \theta}{\partial t_1} = h \tag{4.70}$$

we have $\boldsymbol{\lambda}^1 = -\boldsymbol{\rho}_2, \dot{\boldsymbol{\lambda}}^1 = \boldsymbol{\rho}_1$, and no information about boundary values of $\boldsymbol{\lambda}$ and $\dot{\boldsymbol{\lambda}}$ can now be supplied. If the minimized functional is given by Eq. (4.10), then $\rho_m = 0$ and

$$\lambda_m{}^1 = 1, \qquad h = \rho_t \tag{4.71}$$

that is, h stays unknown if t_1 is presumed fixed, and vanishes when t_1 is not prescribed.

If, however, time is minimized [the functional is given by Eq. (4.11)], then $\rho_t = 0$ and $h = 1$, $\lambda_m{}^1 = \rho_m$, that is, $\lambda_m{}^1$ remains undetermined when m^1 is prescribed and vanishes otherwise.

4.32 Turning of the Orbital Plane

The unit normal $\mathbf{n}^1 = \mathbf{n}_*{}^1$ to the instantaneous orbital plane Π^1 is assumed given at the instant t_1 so that

$$\theta_1 = \boldsymbol{\rho} \cdot (\mathbf{n}^1 - \mathbf{n}_*{}^1) = \boldsymbol{\rho} \cdot \left(\frac{\mathbf{r}^1 \times \mathbf{v}^1}{|\mathbf{r}^1 \times \mathbf{v}^1|} - \mathbf{n}_*{}^1 \right)$$

With the aid of Eq. (4.70) we get

$$\dot{\boldsymbol{\lambda}}^1 = \frac{1}{|\mathbf{r}^1 \times \mathbf{v}^1|} \operatorname{grad}_{\mathbf{r}_1} \mathbf{r}^1 \cdot (\mathbf{v}^1 \times \boldsymbol{\rho}) - \frac{\boldsymbol{\rho} \cdot (\mathbf{r}^1 \times \mathbf{v}^1)}{|\mathbf{r}^1 \times \mathbf{v}^1|^2} \operatorname{grad} |\mathbf{r}^1 \times \mathbf{v}^1|$$

$$= \frac{1}{|\mathbf{r}^1 \times \mathbf{v}^1|^3} [\mathbf{v}^1 \times \boldsymbol{\rho} \, |\mathbf{r}^1 \times \mathbf{v}^1|^2 - \boldsymbol{\rho} \cdot (\mathbf{r}^1 \times \mathbf{v}^1) \mathbf{v}^1 \times (\mathbf{r}^1 \times \mathbf{v}^1)]$$

and setting $\boldsymbol{\rho}^* = (1/k^1)\boldsymbol{\rho}$, this becomes

$$\dot{\boldsymbol{\lambda}}^1 = \mathbf{v}^1 \times \boldsymbol{\rho}^* - \boldsymbol{\rho}^* \cdot \mathbf{n}^1 \, \mathbf{v}^1 \times \mathbf{n}^1 = \mathbf{v}^1 \times [\mathbf{n}^1 \times (\boldsymbol{\rho}^* \times \mathbf{n}^1)]$$

The vector $\boldsymbol{\lambda}^1$ can be calculated in the same way. We write

$$\dot{\boldsymbol{\lambda}}^1 = \mathbf{v}^1 \times \mathbf{b}, \qquad \boldsymbol{\lambda}^1 = \mathbf{r}^1 \times \mathbf{b}, \qquad \mathbf{b} = \mathbf{n}^1 \times (\boldsymbol{\rho}^* \times \mathbf{n}^1) \tag{4.72}$$

where **b** denotes a vector lying in the Π^1 plane since $\mathbf{b}\ \mathbf{n}^1 = 0$. The pair of vectors $\dot{\boldsymbol{\lambda}}^1$ and $\boldsymbol{\lambda}$ is perpendicular to the pairs of vectors ($\mathbf{v}^1$ and $\mathbf{b}$, $\mathbf{r}^1$ and $\mathbf{b}$) disposed in the Π^1 plane; from here it follows that $\boldsymbol{\lambda}^1$ and $\dot{\boldsymbol{\lambda}}^1$ and, consequently, $\mathbf{e}^1$ and $\dot{\mathbf{e}}^1$ are collinear with **n**, so that

$$\alpha_1{}^1 = 0, \qquad \alpha_2{}^1 = 0, \qquad \alpha_3{}^1 = \varepsilon = \pm 1 \tag{4.73}$$

and Eqs. (4.56) and (4.52) show that

$$\dot{\alpha}_1{}^1 = 0, \qquad \dot{\alpha}_2{}^1 = (r^1/k^1)w^1, \qquad \dot{\alpha}_3{}^1 = 0$$

Turning now to vector integral (4.41), we see that

$$a\boldsymbol{\sigma} = (\mathbf{v}^1 \times \mathbf{b}) \times \mathbf{r}^1 - (\mathbf{r}^1 \times \mathbf{b}) \times \mathbf{v}^1 = \mathbf{b} \times (\mathbf{r}^1 \times \mathbf{v}^1) = k\mathbf{b} \times \mathbf{n} \tag{4.74}$$

and this means (since for nonplane motion we have $a \neq 0$ as will be shown below) that the vector $\boldsymbol{\sigma}$ is disposed in the Π^1 plane and is perpendicular to **b**. We now have

$$\boldsymbol{\sigma} \cdot \mathbf{n}^1 = 0, \qquad \sigma_3{}^1 = 0, \qquad \sigma_1{}^1 = \sin\mu, \qquad \sigma_2{}^1 = \cos\mu \tag{4.75}$$

where the angle μ is introduced by the relation $\mathbf{b} = b(\mathbf{e}_r{}^1 \cos\mu + \mathbf{e}_\varphi{}^1 \sin\mu)$.

Projecting now the vector $\boldsymbol{\sigma}$ onto the initial system of axes, we arrive at relations

$$\begin{aligned} \sigma_1{}^0 &= \cos\Omega^1 \sin(\mu + u^1) + \cos i^1 \sin\Omega \cos(\mu + u^1) \\ \sigma_2{}^0 &= \sin\Omega^1 \sin(\mu + u^1) - \cos i^1 \cos\Omega \cos(\mu + u^1) \\ \sigma_3{}^0 &= -\sin i^1 \cos(\mu + u^1) \end{aligned} \tag{4.76}$$

where Ω^1 and i^1 are prescribed angles which determine $\mathbf{n}^1$ in the initial system of orbital axes.

From Eqs. (4.46) and (4.68) we deduce [having also taken Eq. (4.72) into account]

$$\lambda^1/a = \varepsilon(r^1/k^1)\sin\mu, \qquad \vartheta^1 = 0 \tag{4.77}$$

This relation shows, in particular, that ε and $\sin\mu$ have the same sign.

4.33 Three-Dimensional Motions

Equations (4.66) and (4.67) may [in view of Eq. (4.68)] be presented in the following form:

$$\begin{aligned} \frac{\dot{\lambda}}{\lambda} = \frac{1}{v_r}\left(\frac{k^2}{r^3} - \frac{\mu}{r^2}\right)\alpha_1{}^2 - 2\frac{k}{r^2}\alpha_1\alpha_2 + \frac{v_r}{r}(1 - \alpha_1{}^2) \\ + \frac{k\alpha_3}{r^2\sigma_1}\left[\sigma_2\alpha_3 + \sigma_3\left(-\alpha_2 + \frac{k}{rv_r}\alpha_1\right)\right] + \frac{\alpha_1}{v_r}\vartheta\frac{k\alpha_3}{ar\sigma_1} \end{aligned} \tag{4.78}$$

$$\dot{\alpha}_1 = \frac{1}{v_r}\left(\frac{k^2}{r^3} - \frac{\mu}{r^2}\right)\alpha_1(1-\alpha_1{}^2) + 2\frac{k}{r^2}\alpha_1{}^2\alpha_2 - \frac{v_r}{r}(1-\alpha_1{}^2)\alpha$$
$$+ \frac{k\alpha_3}{r^2\sigma_1}\left[\alpha_1(\alpha_2\sigma_3 - \alpha_3\sigma_2) + \sigma_3\frac{k}{rv_r}(1-\alpha_1{}^2)\right] + \frac{1-\alpha_1{}^2}{v_r}\vartheta\frac{k\alpha_3}{ar\sigma_1} \quad (4.79)$$

$$\dot{\alpha}_2 = -\frac{1}{v_r}\left(\frac{k^2}{r^3} - \frac{\mu}{r^2}\right)\alpha_1{}^2\alpha_2 - 2\frac{k}{r^2}\alpha_1{}^2\alpha_2 + \frac{v_r}{r}\alpha_1{}^2\alpha_2$$
$$- \frac{k\alpha_3}{r^2\sigma_1}\left[\alpha_2\alpha_3\sigma_2 + \sigma_3(1-\alpha_2{}^2) - \sigma_3\frac{k}{rv_r}\alpha_1\alpha_2\right] - \frac{\alpha_1\alpha_2}{v_r}\vartheta\frac{k\alpha_3}{ar\sigma_1} + \frac{r}{k}w\alpha_3{}^2 \quad (4.80)$$

$$\dot{\alpha}_3 = -\frac{1}{v_r}\left(\frac{k^2}{r^3} - \frac{\mu}{r^2}\right)\alpha_1{}^2\alpha_3 + 2\frac{k}{r^2}\alpha_1\alpha_2\alpha_3 + \frac{v_r}{r}\alpha_1{}^2\alpha_3$$
$$+ \frac{k\alpha_3}{r^2\sigma_1}\left[\alpha_2\alpha_3\sigma_3 + \sigma_2(1-\alpha_3{}^2) - \sigma_3\frac{k}{rv_r}\alpha_1\alpha_3\right] - \frac{\alpha_1\alpha_3}{v_r}\vartheta\frac{k\alpha_3}{ar\sigma_1} - \frac{r}{k}w\alpha_2\alpha_3 \quad (4.81)$$

Equation (4.78) follows immediately from Eqs. (4.68) and (4.79)–(4.81) together with (4.58); this equation is used to formulate expression (4.33) for the switching function.

In the most difficult case of boosters of the third type, we have 11 unknown quantities, namely

$$r, v, k, m, \alpha_1, \alpha_2, \alpha_3, \sigma_1, \sigma_2, \sigma_3, \eta \quad (4.82)$$

To determine all these, we have the three differential equations of motion Eqs. (4.53), the flow rate equation (4.4), Eqs. (4.79), (4.63), or (4.62) for determination of the Cayley-Klein parameters (or Euler angles) to express the values of σ_s [by virtue of Eqs. (4.65)], and equation (4.33) for the switching function. For fixed values of r^0, $v_r{}^0$, k^0 and m^0, the expression for the Cauchy integral will include nine constants $\alpha_s{}^0$, $\sigma_s{}^0$, η^0, h, and a; of these only seven may be treated as independent since $\alpha_s{}^0$ and $\sigma_s{}^0$ must satisfy relations (4.52) and (4.59).

In the general boundary problem, when, for instance, t_1 is minimized and terminal mass is prescribed, the constant h equals unity, but t_1 enters into the set of constants; we have then to determine seven quantities out of just the same number of conditions which express that r^1, v^1, k^1, and m^1 together with Euler angles Ω^1, i^1, and u^1 are given. If, however, the mass is not prescribed, then $\lambda_m{}^1$ is equal to zero and the seventh condition is given by $\eta^1 = (c/m^1)\, ar^1\sigma^1/k^1\alpha_3{}^1$. This relation follows immediately from Eqs. (4.32) and (4.68).

Some items concerning the problem of integration of the basic equations when moving along Keplerian arcs as well as those about matching of various solutions at points of switching will be developed below in Sec. 4.36.

In problems formulated for boosting devices of the first type ($w = \text{const.}$), the flow rate equation and that for the switching function are deleted, and the time t_1 is minimized. We must then find six independent constants ($\alpha_s{}^0$, $\sigma_s{}^0$, a, t_1). This number is reduced to five in the problem of turning the orbital plane, since by virtue of Eq. (4.76) we may express $\sigma_s{}^0$ through one constant μ. The five equations for these constants are given by two of the trio of Eqs. (4.73), two equations prescribing the fixed values for Ω^1 and i^1, and, last, the relation $wa \sin \mu = \varepsilon(k^1/r^1)$ which follows from Eqs. (4.77) and $(4.47)_1$.

4.34 Plane Motions

For motions along plane orbits, the vector $\mathbf{n}$ remains constant, $\dot{\mathbf{n}} = 0$; also [by Eq. (4.55)] $\alpha_3 = 0$, which means that thrust acts in the orbital plane. The vector $\boldsymbol{\lambda}$ is disposed in the same plane, and Eqs. (4.43) and (4.58) now show that $\boldsymbol{\sigma}$ is collinear with $\mathbf{n}$: $\sigma_1 = 0, \sigma_2 = 0, \sigma_3 = \pm 1$, and $\mathbf{a} = \tilde{a}\mathbf{n}$ where $\tilde{a} = \pm a$. Setting now $\alpha_1 = \cos \psi$, $\alpha_2 = \sin \psi$ where ψ is the angle between $\mathbf{e}$ and the radius vector, we arrive at a pair of differential equations equivalent to Eqs. (4.78)–(4.81); it should be mentioned that Eq. (4.68) has now been deleted, and we must again introduce λ into Eqs. (4.78)–(4.81).

We get

$$\frac{\dot{\lambda}}{\lambda} = -\frac{1}{v_r}\left(\frac{v_r{}^2}{r} + \frac{\mu}{r^2} - \frac{k^2}{r^3}\right)\cos^2\psi + \frac{v_r}{r} - 2\frac{k}{r^2}\sin\psi\cos\psi$$

$$+ \frac{a}{\lambda r}\left(-\sin\psi + \frac{k}{rv_r}\cos\psi\right) + \frac{\cos\psi}{v_r}\frac{\vartheta}{\lambda} \tag{4.83}$$

$$\dot{\psi} = \frac{1}{v_r}\left(\frac{v_r{}^2}{r} + \frac{\mu}{r^2} - \frac{k^2}{r^3}\right)\cos\psi\sin\psi - 2\frac{k}{r^2}\cos^2\psi$$

$$-\frac{\tilde{a}}{\lambda r}\left(\cos\psi + \frac{k}{rv_r}\sin\psi\right) - \frac{\sin\psi}{v_r}\frac{\vartheta}{\lambda} \tag{4.84}$$

These equations must be used together with Eqs. (4.53), (4.4), and (4.33). They combine into a system of the seventh order, and nine constants enter into the general solution. The order can be reduced to the sixth in the case of boosters of the first type. Considerable simplification may then be achieved, since there is no necessity to observe the sign of the switching function, and transitions from one regime to another are absent in this case.

The solution to the (plane) general boundary problem for boosters of the third type reduces to the determination of five constants (for fixed values of r^0, v^0, k^0, and m^0). Four equations arise from the prescription of the values for r^1, v^1, k^1, and the angle

$$\varphi^1 - \varphi^0 = \int_0^{t_1} \frac{k}{r^2}\, dt \tag{4.85}$$

This angle gives the change in true anomalies. Let, for instance, m^1 be minimized and t_1 given; the fifth equation will then be written as $\eta^1 = (c/m)\lambda^1 - 1$.

4.35 Special Case of Plane Motion

This case holds whenever $\sigma_3 = 0$. Under this condition, it follows from Eq. (4.58) that either $\alpha_3 = 0$ or $\sigma_2 = 0$. In the first case we have, according to Sec. 4.34, $\sigma_1 = 0$, $\sigma_2 = 0$, and $\mathbf{a} = 0$; and in the second case Eq. (4.58) shows that $\sigma_1 = 0$.

In both cases, $\mathbf{a} = 0$, the constant $\tilde{a}$ drops out of Eqs. (4.83)–(4.84) and the solution to the general boundary problem is no longer possible. The problem is soluble if we prescribe, at the right end, not the vectors $\mathbf{r}^1$, $\mathbf{v}^1$ themselves but their scalar invariants r^1, v^1, $\mathbf{r}^1 \cdot \mathbf{v}^1$. Indeed, if the indicating function is presented by the relation

$$\theta_1 = \theta_1(r^1, v^1, \mathbf{r}^1 \cdot \mathbf{v}^1)$$

we have [see Eq. (4.70)]

$$\dot{\boldsymbol{\lambda}}^1 = \frac{\partial \theta_1}{\partial r^1}\frac{\mathbf{r}^1}{r^1} + \frac{\partial \theta_1}{\partial \mathbf{r}^1 \cdot \mathbf{v}^1}\mathbf{v}^1, \qquad \boldsymbol{\lambda}^1 = -\frac{\partial \theta_1}{\partial v^1}\frac{\mathbf{v}^1}{v^1} - \frac{\partial \theta_1}{\partial \mathbf{r}^1 \cdot \mathbf{v}^1}\mathbf{r}^1$$

and substitution into the vector integral Eq. (4.41) shows that $\mathbf{a} = 0$.

The differential equation (4.83) is now written as follows:

$$\frac{\dot{\lambda}}{\lambda} = \frac{v_r}{r} - \left(\dot{\psi} + \frac{2k}{r^2}\right)\cot\psi$$

$$\frac{\vartheta}{\lambda} = \left(\frac{v_r^{\,2}}{r} + \frac{\mu}{r^2} - \frac{k^2}{r^3}\right)\cos\psi - \frac{v_r}{\sin\psi}\dot{\psi} + \frac{2k}{r^2}\cos^2\psi \tag{4.86}$$

The elimination of λ from these equations is uniquely performed for any prescribed ϑ. We have

$$\left(\frac{\vartheta}{\lambda}\right)^{\boldsymbol{\cdot}} = \frac{\dot{\vartheta}}{\lambda} - \frac{\vartheta}{\lambda}\frac{\dot{\lambda}}{\lambda} = \frac{\dot{\eta} q}{\lambda} - \frac{\vartheta}{\lambda}\frac{\dot{\lambda}}{\lambda} = \left(\frac{cq}{m} - \frac{\vartheta}{\lambda}\right)\frac{\dot{\lambda}}{\lambda} = \left(w - \frac{\vartheta}{\lambda}\right)\frac{\dot{\lambda}}{\lambda}$$

Here ϑ is taken in the form of Eq. $(4.47)_3$. By an analogous argument, Eqs. $(4.47)_1$ and $(4.47)_2$ become, respectively,

$$\left(\frac{\vartheta}{\lambda}\right)^{\cdot} = \frac{h}{\lambda}\frac{\dot{\lambda}}{\lambda} = \left(w - \frac{\vartheta}{\lambda}\right)\frac{\dot{\lambda}}{\lambda}$$

$$\left(\frac{\vartheta}{\lambda}\right)^{\cdot} = \left(\frac{1}{2}\frac{A}{\mathcal{N}_{\max}}\lambda - \frac{h}{\lambda}\right)^{\cdot} = \left(\frac{1}{2}\frac{A}{\mathcal{N}_{\max}}\lambda + \frac{h}{\lambda}\right)\frac{\dot{\lambda}}{\lambda} = \left(w - \frac{\vartheta}{\lambda}\right)\frac{\dot{\lambda}}{\lambda}$$

On substitution for $\dot{\lambda}/\lambda$ and ϑ/λ in these expressions we arrive (in view of the equations of motion) at the second-order equation

$$\ddot{\psi} + \left(\dot{\psi} + \frac{k}{r^2}\right)\left(\dot{\psi} + \frac{2k}{r^2}\right)\cot\psi + 3\frac{\mu}{r^3}\cos\psi\sin\psi$$
$$+ 2\frac{v_r}{r}\dot{\psi} + \frac{w}{r}\sin\psi = 0 \tag{4.87}$$

Sometimes it may be preferable to introduce the criterion

$$\zeta = \frac{\eta}{\lambda} \tag{4.88}$$

instead of η. Eq. (4.33) is then replaced by

$$\dot{\zeta} = \left(\frac{c}{m} - \zeta\right)\frac{\dot{\lambda}}{\lambda} = \left(\frac{c}{m} - \zeta\right)\left[\frac{v_r}{r} - \left(\dot{\psi} + \frac{2k}{r^2}\right)\cot\psi\right] \tag{4.89}$$

Equation (4.87) should be referred to when the initial value of the radial velocity component v_r is equal to zero (thrust imposed either at the perigee or at the apogee of an orbit).

Consider, for example, the problem of minimization of time, and let the functional relation $\varphi(r^1, v^1) = 0$ be prescribed at the right end of the time interval. Then $\theta = t_1 + \rho\varphi(r^1, v^1)$ and by virtue of Eqs. (4.70), (4.27), and (4.57) we have

$$\boldsymbol{\lambda}^1 = \lambda^1(\mathbf{e}_r{}^1\cos\psi^1 + \mathbf{e}_\varphi{}^1\sin\psi^1) = -\rho\frac{\partial\varphi}{\partial v^1}\frac{\mathbf{v}^1}{v^1} = -\frac{\rho}{v^1}\frac{\partial\varphi}{\partial v^1}\left(v_r{}^1\mathbf{e}_r{}^1 + \frac{k^1}{r^1}\mathbf{e}_\varphi{}^1\right)$$

$$\dot{\boldsymbol{\lambda}}^1 = (\dot{\lambda}^1\cos\psi^1 - \lambda^1 v_3{}^1\sin\psi^1)\mathbf{e}_r{}^1 + (\dot{\lambda}^1\sin\psi^1 + \lambda^1 v_3{}^1\cos\psi^1)\mathbf{e}_\varphi{}^1$$
$$= \rho\frac{\partial\varphi}{\partial r^1}\mathbf{e}_r{}^1$$

where $h = 1$, $v_3{}^1 = \dot{\psi}^1 + k^1/(r^1)^2$. Having eliminated $\dot{\lambda}^1/\lambda^1$ and ρ/λ^1 from the four resulting equations, we arrive at the three boundary conditions required:

$$\cot\psi^1 = \frac{v_r{}^1 r^1}{k^1}, \qquad \dot{\psi}^1 = -\frac{k^1}{(r^1)^2}\left(1 + \frac{d\ln v^1}{d\ln r^1}\right), \qquad \varphi(r^1, v^1) = 0$$

For example, if $\varphi = (v^1)^2 - \alpha(\mu/r^1) = 0$, then

$$\frac{d \ln v^1}{d \ln r^1} = -\frac{1}{2}, \qquad \dot{\psi}^1 = -\frac{1}{2}\frac{k^1}{(r^1)^2}$$

Here $\alpha = 1$ for the problem of acceleration to orbital velocity, and $\alpha = 2$ for escape velocity.

In the problem of transfer to a circular orbit

$$\theta = \rho_1\left[(v^1)^2 - \frac{\mu}{r^1}\right] + \rho_2 \mathbf{r}^1 \cdot \mathbf{v}^1$$

and having eliminated ρ_1/λ, ρ_2/λ, and $\dot{\lambda}/\lambda$ from the four resulting equations, we arrive at the relations

$$\dot{\psi}^1 = -\frac{v^1}{2r^1}(1 + 3\cos\psi^1), \qquad (v^1)^2 = \frac{\mu}{r^1}, \qquad v_r{}^1 = 0$$

4.36 Moving along a Keplerian Arc

The differential equation (4.28) for the vector $\boldsymbol{\lambda}$ gives only an equation of variations for the system of the equations of motion. In fact, we have

$$\delta\dot{\mathbf{r}} = \delta\mathbf{v}, \qquad \delta\dot{\mathbf{v}} = -\delta\frac{\mu}{r^3}\mathbf{r} = \frac{\mu}{r^3}\left(3\frac{\mathbf{r}\cdot\delta\mathbf{r}}{r^2}\mathbf{r} - \delta\mathbf{r}\right)$$

and it suffices to put $\delta\mathbf{r} = \boldsymbol{\lambda}$, $\delta\mathbf{v} = \dot{\boldsymbol{\lambda}}$. But the solution of the equations of motion is well known, and the derivatives of the position vector $\mathbf{r}$ with respect to six constants of the motion lead to a system of linearly independent solutions to the equations of the variations. Having combined some linear forms of these derivatives, we obtain the system of vectors[12]

$$\mathbf{q}_1 = \left[\frac{r}{p}(1 - \varepsilon^2) - \frac{3n(t - t_0)}{2(1 - \varepsilon^2)^{1/2}}\varepsilon\sin\varphi\right]\mathbf{e}_r - \frac{3n(t - t_0)}{2(1 - \varepsilon^2)^{1/2}}(1 + \varepsilon\cos\varphi)\mathbf{e}_\varphi$$

$$\mathbf{q}_2 = -\cos\varphi\,\mathbf{e}_r + \frac{2 + \varepsilon\cos\varphi}{1 + \varepsilon\cos\varphi}\sin\varphi\,\mathbf{e}_\varphi$$

$$\mathbf{q}_3 = \sin\varphi\,\mathbf{e}_r + \frac{2 + \varepsilon\cos\varphi}{1 + \varepsilon\cos\varphi}\cos\varphi\,\mathbf{e}_\varphi, \qquad \mathbf{q}_4 = \frac{r(1 - \varepsilon^2)}{p}\mathbf{e}_\varphi$$

$$\mathbf{q}_5 = \frac{r(1 - \varepsilon^2)}{p}\cos\varphi\,\mathbf{n}, \qquad \mathbf{q}_6 = [r(1 - \varepsilon^2)/p]\sin\varphi\,\mathbf{n}$$

together with their derivatives

$$\frac{1}{n}\dot{\mathbf{q}}_1 = -\left[\frac{\varepsilon \sin\varphi}{2(1-\varepsilon^2)^{1/2}} - \frac{3}{2}n(t-t_0)\frac{p^2}{(1-\varepsilon^2)^2 r^2}\right]\mathbf{e}_r - \frac{1+\varepsilon\cos\varphi}{2(1-\varepsilon^2)^{1/2}}\mathbf{e}_\varphi$$

$$\frac{1}{n}\dot{\mathbf{q}}_2 = -\frac{p}{r(1-\varepsilon^2)^{3/2}}\left(-\sin\varphi\,\mathbf{e}_r + \frac{\varepsilon+\cos\varphi}{1+\varepsilon\cos\varphi}\mathbf{e}_\varphi\right)$$

$$\frac{1}{n}\dot{\mathbf{q}}_3 = -\frac{p}{r(1-\varepsilon^2)^{3/2}}\left(\cos\varphi\,\mathbf{e}_r + \frac{\sin\varphi}{1+\varepsilon\cos\varphi}\mathbf{e}_\varphi\right)$$

$$\frac{1}{n}\dot{\mathbf{q}}_4 = \frac{1}{(1-\varepsilon^2)^{1/2}}[-(1+\varepsilon\cos\varphi)\mathbf{e}_r + \varepsilon\sin\varphi\,\mathbf{e}_\varphi]$$

$$\frac{1}{n}\dot{\mathbf{q}}_5 = -\frac{\sin\varphi}{(1-\varepsilon^2)^{1/2}}\mathbf{n}, \qquad \frac{1}{n}\dot{\mathbf{q}}_6 = \frac{\cos\varphi+\varepsilon}{(1-\varepsilon^2)^{1/2}}\mathbf{n}$$

By φ we have denoted the true anomaly (measured from the ellipse's perigee). The expressions for r, v_r, and $k = r^2\dot{\varphi}$ are well known:

$$r = \frac{p}{1+\varepsilon\cos\varphi}, \qquad v_r = \frac{np\varepsilon}{(1-\varepsilon^2)^{3/2}}\sin\varphi, \qquad k = \frac{np^2}{(1-\varepsilon^2)^{3/2}}$$

$$[n = (\mu/p^3)^{1/2}(1-\varepsilon^2)^{3/2}]$$

The constants of a Keplerian orbit and the true anomaly at the moment of transfer are expressed through r_*, v_{r_*}, and k_* according to the relations

$$p = \frac{k_*^2}{\mu}, \qquad 1 - \frac{k_*^2}{r_*\mu} = \varepsilon\cos\varphi_*, \qquad \frac{v_{r_*}k_*}{\mu} = \varepsilon\sin\varphi_*$$

so that

$$\varepsilon = \left[1 - 2\frac{k_*^2}{\mu^2}\left(\frac{\mu}{r*} - \frac{v_*^2}{2}\right)\right]^{1/2} = \left(1 + 2h_1\frac{k_*^2}{\mu^2}\right)^{1/2}$$

where h_1 denotes a constant (energy) of the Keplerian orbit; the moment of passing through perigee, t_0, is determined either by well known formulas or from the tables of solutions of the Keplerian equation.

We can now present the solution of Eq. (4.28) in the following form:

$$\boldsymbol{\lambda} = \sum_{\kappa=1}^{6} C_\kappa \mathbf{q}_\kappa, \qquad \dot{\boldsymbol{\lambda}} = \sum_{\kappa=1}^{6} C_\kappa \dot{\mathbf{q}}_\kappa \tag{4.90}$$

In accordance with the Erdmann-Weierstrass condition, we must choose the constants C_κ in such a way that the vectors $\boldsymbol{\lambda}$ and $\dot{\boldsymbol{\lambda}}$ and the Hamiltonian H_λ are continuous at the point of discontinuity of the control function (at this point $\eta = 0$).

From Eq. (4.39)$_1$ taken along the Keplerian arc ($w = 0$) we get

$$\sum_{\kappa=1}^{6} C_\kappa \left[\dot{\mathbf{q}}_\kappa \cdot \left(\mathbf{e}_r v_r + \mathbf{e}_\varphi \frac{k}{r} \right) + \frac{n^2 p^3}{(1-\varepsilon^2)^3 r^2} \mathbf{q}_\kappa \cdot \mathbf{e}_r \right] = -h$$

Only the first term on the left-hand side of this equation differs from zero; we find

$$C_1 = -2h[(1-\varepsilon^2)/n^2 p] = -(h/h_1)[p/(1-\varepsilon^2)] \tag{4.91}$$

An analogous calculation with the vector integral Eq. (4.41) shows that

$$\tfrac{1}{2}(-3C_1 + \varepsilon C_2)[np/(1-\varepsilon^2)^{1/2}]\mathbf{n} + [np/(1-\varepsilon^2)^{1/2}](C_5 \mathbf{i}_1 + C_6 \mathbf{i}_2) = a\boldsymbol{\sigma}$$

where $\mathbf{i}_1$ is a unit vector directed to the perigee of the orbit, and $\mathbf{i}_2 = \mathbf{n} \times \mathbf{i}_1$. Thus, we have

$$a\sigma_3 = \tfrac{1}{2}(-3C_1 + \varepsilon C_2) \tag{4.92}$$

$$\begin{aligned} a\sigma_1 &= (C_5 \cos\varphi + C_6 \sin\varphi)[np/(1-\varepsilon^2)^{1/2}] \\ a\sigma_2 &= (-C_5 \sin\varphi + C_6 \cos\varphi)[np/(1-\varepsilon^2)^{1/2}] \end{aligned} \tag{4.93}$$

The values of σ_3 and of the components of $\boldsymbol{\sigma}$ along fixed directions $\mathbf{i}_1$ and $\mathbf{i}_2$ have naturally become constant; one could have foreseen the values of σ_1 and σ_2 in view of Eq. (4.68), using an independent variable φ ($d\varphi = k/r^2\, dt$).

The coefficients C_3 and C_4 have dropped from the scalar and vector integrals. To determine these, we must use the first of Eqs. (4.90); this equation shows that

$$\sum_{\kappa=1}^{4} C_\kappa \mathbf{q}_\kappa \cdot \mathbf{e}_r = \lambda\alpha_1, \qquad \sum_{\kappa=1}^{4} C_\kappa \mathbf{q}_\kappa \cdot \mathbf{e}_\varphi = \lambda\alpha_2, \qquad (C_5 \mathbf{q}_5 + C_6 \mathbf{q}_6) \cdot \mathbf{n} = \lambda\alpha_3 \tag{4.94}$$

The last relation can be rewritten as

$$\lambda\alpha_3 = \frac{r}{p}(1-\varepsilon^2)(C_5 \cos\varphi + C_6 \sin\varphi) = \frac{r}{k} a\sigma_1$$

and from here we arrive at Eq. (4.68).

The thrust direction program is now determined by the following formulas:

$$\alpha_1 \sum_{\kappa=1}^{4} C_\kappa \mathbf{q}_\kappa^* \cdot \mathbf{e}_r^* = \alpha_1^* \sum_{k=1}^{4} C_\kappa \mathbf{q}_\kappa \cdot \mathbf{e}_r, \text{ etc.}$$

The relations determining the coefficients C_κ through the values of $a\sigma_\kappa$, α_κ, r, k, and v_r at the moment t_* are rather involved, in general, and there is no need to write them down here; these relations can immediately be derived with the aid of the equations cited above. Remarkable simplification ($C_1 = 0$) is obtained if $h = 0$: such is the situation in the problem of minimization of fuel consumption where t_1 is not fixed.

From Eq. (4.33) and in view of the constancy of mass m along the Keplerian arc we find

$$\eta = \frac{c}{m_*}(\lambda - \lambda_*) \tag{4.95}$$

Determination of the vector $\boldsymbol{\lambda}$ (in the plane motion problem) has been discussed.[3] It is obvious from what has been said above that this determination requires no further integrations.

4.36a The $\boldsymbol{\lambda}$ vector in the special case of a plane motion problem and when $h=0$. So long as $\tilde{a} = 0$, it follows immediately from Eqs. (4.92) and (4.93) that $C_1 = C_2 = C_5 = C_6 = 0$; the constant parameters C_3 and C_4 are determined from Eqs. (4.94). These equations are now written in the form

$$C_3 \sin\varphi = \lambda\cos\psi, \qquad C_3 \frac{2+\varepsilon\cos\varphi}{1+\varepsilon\cos\varphi}\cos\varphi + C_4\frac{1-\varepsilon^2}{1+\varepsilon\cos\varphi} = \lambda\sin\psi$$

Having replaced in these relations $\cos\varphi$ and $\sin\varphi$ by r and v_r, respectively, we arrive at the formula

$$\tan\psi = \frac{r}{v_r}\left(\frac{k_*}{r^2} + \mathfrak{D}\right), \qquad \mathfrak{D} = (\mu/p^3)^{1/2}[-1 + \varepsilon(1-\varepsilon^2)^{1/2}(C_4/C_3)]$$

This relation can also be obtained after integration of Eq. (4.84) under the assumptions $\tilde{a} = 0$, $\vartheta = \eta q = 0$. There is no trouble in combining the expressions for λ and the η criterion. Consideration of the ζ criterion leads to a more compact expression. We write the differential equation (4.89) in the form

$$-\left[\ln\left(\frac{c}{m_*} - \zeta\right)\right]^{\cdot} = \left[\ln\frac{r}{\sin\psi}\right]^{\cdot} - 2\frac{k}{r^2}\cot\psi = \left[\ln\frac{r}{\sin\psi}\right]^{\cdot} - \left[\ln\frac{r^2}{k/\mathfrak{D} + r^2}\right]^{\cdot}$$

and having determined the integration constant and taken care of the expression for $\tan\psi$, we arrive at the relation

$$\zeta = \frac{c}{m_*}\left(1 - \frac{v_r}{v_{r*}}\frac{\cos\psi_*}{\cos\psi}\right)$$

4.4 Orbits on a Spherical Surface

4.41 The Statement of the Problem of Spherical Motions

For motion on a spherical surface, the $\mathbf{r}$-coordinate is subjected to the condition

$$\mathbf{r}\cdot\mathbf{r} = r^2 = \text{const} \tag{4.96}$$

We must now introduce an additional term into the functional (4.19), this term being

$$\frac{1}{2}\int_0^{t_1} \nu(\mathbf{r}\cdot\mathbf{r} - r^2)\, dt$$

where ν denotes a Lagrange multiplier. This will add the term $\nu\mathbf{r}$ to the stationarity condition Eq. (4.23), and Eq. (4.28) will then be rewritten in the form

$$\ddot{\boldsymbol{\lambda}} = \frac{\mu}{r^3}\left(3\,\frac{\boldsymbol{\lambda}\cdot\mathbf{r}}{r^2}\,\mathbf{r} - \boldsymbol{\lambda}\right) - \nu\mathbf{r} \tag{4.97}$$

All the other equations remain unchanged. It is readily observed that the term $\nu\mathbf{r}$ in Eq. (4.97) is collinear with $\mathbf{r}$ and has no influence on the derivation of the vector integral (see Sec. 4.22) or on the construction of the scalar integral (since the value of H_λ stays the same). But in the preceding Section (Sec. 4.23), the collinearity of the vectors $\ddot{\boldsymbol{\lambda}} + (\mu/r^3)\boldsymbol{\lambda}$ and $\mathbf{r}$ followed immediately from the vector integral and the equations of motion. Thus, when using the integrals (4.39) and (4.41) (together with the equations of motion, flow rate, and switching function), one need not worry about the validity of Eq. (4.97): this one may be satisfied by suitable choice of ν. It would be a mistake to consider spherical motions on the basis of the differential equation (4.28).

4.42 The Differential Equations of Spherical Motions

For spherical motions,

$$\mathbf{r}\cdot\mathbf{r} = r^2 = \text{const}, \qquad \mathbf{r}\cdot\mathbf{v} = 0, \qquad v_r = 0 \tag{4.98}$$

The equations of motion are written in the form

$$w\alpha_1 = \frac{\mu}{r^2} - \frac{k^2}{r^3}, \qquad \dot{k} = rw\alpha_2, \qquad \left(w = \frac{cq}{m}\right) \tag{4.99}$$

Consider now Eqs. (4.78)–(4.81). Having retained in these equations only the terms containing v_r in the denominator, we arrive at the single relation (resulting from all equations considered)

$$\left(\frac{k^2}{r^3} - \frac{\mu}{r^2}\right)\alpha_1 + \frac{k^2}{r^3}\frac{\sigma_3}{\sigma_1}\alpha_3 + \vartheta\,\frac{k\alpha_3}{ar\sigma_1} = 0 \tag{4.100}$$

From Eqs. (4.80) and (4.81) we deduce the relation which does not include v_r, namely,

$$\dot{\alpha}_2 - \frac{\dot{\alpha}_3}{\alpha_3}\alpha_2 = -2\frac{k}{r^2}\alpha_1 - \frac{k}{r^2\sigma_1}(\sigma_2\alpha_2 + \sigma_3\alpha_3) + w\frac{r}{k}(1 - {\alpha_1}^2) \tag{4.101}$$

As was demonstrated in Sec. 4.35, the function ϑ satisfies the differential equation

$$\left(\frac{\vartheta}{\lambda}\right)^{\bullet} = \left(w - \frac{\vartheta}{\lambda}\right)\frac{\dot{\lambda}}{\lambda} = \left(w - \frac{\vartheta}{\lambda}\right)\left(\frac{k}{r^2}\frac{\sigma_2}{\sigma_1} - \frac{r}{k} w\alpha_2 - \frac{\dot{\alpha}_3}{\alpha_3}\right) \tag{4.102}$$

Note that, for boosters of the third type, this equation presents a modification of the differential equation for the switching function η; the latter can be expressed through ϑ [see Eq. $(4.47)_3$].

Nine quantities k, m, α_s, σ_s, and ϑ are thus connected by ten equations, these equations being: Eq. (4.99) of motion; Eq. (4.4) of mass flow rate; four equations (4.100)–(4.102) and (4.52); and, last, the three equations of (4.58). But we observe that Eq. (4.102) may be rewritten with the aid of Eqs. (4.100) and (4.99) in the form

$$\left(w{\alpha_1}^2 - \frac{k^2}{r^3}\frac{\sigma_3}{\sigma_1}\alpha_3\right)^{\bullet} = \left[w(1 - {\alpha_1}^2) + \frac{k^2}{r^3}\frac{\sigma_3}{\sigma_1}\alpha_3\right]\left(\frac{k}{r^2}\frac{\sigma_2}{\sigma_1} - \frac{r}{k} w\alpha_2 - \frac{\dot{\alpha}_3}{\alpha_3}\right) \tag{4.103}$$

and this one is obviously satisfied in view of the remaining equations (this point may readily be verified by differentiation). The value of $\dot{\alpha}_1$ is then determined by differentiation from the equations of motion (4.99), namely,

$$\dot{\alpha}_1 = -\frac{q}{m}\alpha_1 - \frac{2k}{r^2}\alpha_2 \tag{4.104}$$

The values of $\dot{\alpha}_2$ and $\dot{\alpha}_3$ follow from Eq. (4.101) together with the relation $\alpha_1\dot{\alpha}_1 + \alpha_2\dot{\alpha}_2 + \alpha_3\dot{\alpha}_3 = 0$.

Thus, Eq. (4.102) is withdrawn from further use, and Eq. (4.101) serves only for calculation of the switching function in view of Eq. $(4.47)_3$.

We arrive at eight equations for just the same number of unknowns k, m, α_s, and σ_s.

4.43 Spherical Motions when $w = \text{const}$ (Devices of the First Type)

For simplicity, we introduce nondimensional variables

$$\nu = \frac{k}{r}\left(\frac{r}{\mu}\right)^{1/2}, \qquad \left(\frac{\mu}{r^3}\right)^{1/2} t = nt = \tau, \qquad w\frac{r^2}{\mu} = \zeta \tag{4.105}$$

Here ν denotes the ratio of speed $v = k/r$ to that along a Keplerian orbit of the same radius, n represents angular speed in the same orbit, and ζ the ratio of thrust to gravitational force† also in the same orbit. With minimization

† There should be no danger of confusing this notation with that for the switching function, because the latter does not appear in this section.

of time t_1 in mind, we write, in view of Eq. $(4.47)_1$ that $\vartheta/\lambda = w - h/\lambda = w - 1/\lambda = w - v\alpha_3/a\sigma_1$ and Eqs. (4.99)–(4.102) will now be rewritten (a prime denoting differentiation with respect to τ) as

$$\alpha_1 = \frac{1 - v^2}{\zeta}, \quad v' = \zeta\alpha_2 \tag{4.99$_1$}$$

$$\alpha_3 = \frac{\sigma_1}{v\zeta} \frac{\zeta^2 - (1 - v^2)^2}{\delta - v\sigma_3} \qquad \left(\delta = \frac{1}{an}\right) \tag{4.100$_1$}$$

$$\alpha_2' - \frac{\alpha_3'}{\alpha_3}\alpha_2 = -2v\alpha_1 - \frac{v}{\sigma_1}(\sigma_2\alpha_2 + \sigma_3\alpha_3) + \frac{\zeta}{v}(1 - \alpha_1^2) \tag{4.101$_1$}$$

One of the two latter equations follows from the others. It seems natural to retain the finite relation Eq. $(4.100)_1$. The equations already written must, of course, be complemented by Eqs. (4.58) and (4.52). The latter equation, together with Eqs. $(4.99)_1$ and $(4.100)_1$, leads to the relation

$$(v')^2 + (1 - v^2)^2 + \frac{\sigma_1^2}{v^2} \frac{[\zeta^2 - (1 - v^2)^2]^2}{(\delta - v\sigma_3)^2} = \zeta^2 \tag{4.106}$$

In this equation, the values of σ_3 and σ_1 are expressed by Eqs. (4.65) through the Cayley-Klein parameters, these being determined from the system of Eqs. (4.59). This system may now be presented as

$$\alpha' = \frac{i}{2}\left[v\alpha + \frac{\sigma_1}{v^2}\frac{\zeta^2 - (1 - v^2)^2}{\delta - v\sigma_3}\beta\right], \qquad \beta' = \frac{i}{2}\left[-v\beta + \frac{\sigma_1}{v^2}\frac{\zeta^2 - (1 - v^2)^2}{\delta - v\sigma_3}\alpha\right] \tag{4.107}$$

and a pair of equations for the complex conjugate values $\bar{\alpha}$ and $\bar{\beta}$. The equations are integrated with initial conditions $\alpha^0 = 1$, $\bar{\alpha}^0 = 1$, $\beta^0 = 0$, $\bar{\beta}^0 = 0$. Note that the following integral is valid:

$$\alpha\bar{\alpha} + \beta\bar{\beta} = 1 \tag{4.108}$$

The constants v^0, $\sigma_s^{\,0}$, and δ will enter into the general solution. For the general boundary problem there are prescribed the values of v^0 and v^1 together with the vectors $\mathbf{e}_r^{\,1}$ and $\mathbf{e}_\varphi^{\,1}$ giving the position of the mass center and its velocity direction at the instant t_1. For a fixed value of v^0, at the right end the following conditions should be satisfied:

$$v^1 = v(\sigma_s^{\,0}, \delta, t_1)$$

$$\alpha_1 = \alpha(\sigma_s^{\,0}, \delta, t_1), \qquad \bar{\alpha}^1 = \bar{\alpha}(\sigma_s^{\,0}, \delta, t_1)$$

$$\beta^1 = \beta(\sigma_s^{\,0}, \delta, t_1), \qquad \bar{\beta}^1 = \bar{\beta}(\sigma_s^{\,0}, \delta, t_1)$$

Of these relations only four may be treated as independent because the Cayley-Klein parameters are connected by Eq. (4.108). On the other hand, we have also four independent constants among $\sigma_s{}^0$, δ, and t_1 at our disposal. It is stressed that the values of $\alpha^1, \bar{\alpha}^1, \beta^1, \bar{\beta}^1$ are determined by those prescribed for

$$\mathbf{e}_r{}^1, \mathbf{e}_\varphi{}^1, \mathbf{n}^1 = \mathbf{e}_r{}^1 \times \mathbf{e}_\varphi{}^1$$

4.43a Turning of a circular orbit. Consider the partial solution to the problem of the preceding section constructed under the condition that thrust be collinear with the normal $\mathbf{n}$ to the instantaneous orbital plane:

$$\alpha_1 = 0, \qquad \alpha_2 = 0, \qquad \alpha_3 = \pm 1 = \varepsilon \tag{4.109}$$

From $(4.99)_1$ it follows that for motion of this kind $\nu = 1$, which means that the speed is held constant and equal to that on a circular orbit of radius r. In view of Eq. $(4.100)_1$ [or Eq. (4.106)] we obtain the equation

$$\varepsilon\zeta\sigma_1 + \sigma_3 = \delta \tag{4.110}$$

equivalent to the stationarity condition for the simplest case considered. The differential equations (4.58) can now be written in the form

$$\sigma_1{}' = \sigma_2, \qquad \sigma_2{}' = -\sigma_1 + \varepsilon\zeta\sigma_3, \qquad \sigma_3{}' = -\varepsilon\zeta\sigma_2 \tag{4.111}$$

According to these equations, the τ-derivative of the left-hand side of Eq. (4.110) vanishes, and from this we deduce that the corresponding situation is realizable.

Equations (4.107) now present a differential system with constant coefficients, namely,

$$\alpha' = \frac{i}{2}(\alpha + \varepsilon\zeta\beta) \qquad \beta' = \frac{i}{2}(-\beta + \varepsilon\zeta\alpha) \tag{4.112}$$

whose general solution is

$$\alpha = \alpha^0\kappa_1 + \beta^0\kappa_2, \qquad \beta = \alpha_0\rho_1 + \beta_0\rho_2 \tag{4.113}$$

Here we have introduced a system of solutions with the unit matrix of initial conditions:

$$\begin{aligned} \kappa_1(\tau) &= \cos^2(\chi/2)\, e^{i\omega} + \sin^2(\chi/2)\, e^{-i\omega}, & \rho_1(\tau) &= \tfrac{1}{2}\varepsilon \sin\chi\,(e^{i\omega} - e^{-i\omega}) \\ \kappa_2(\tau) &= \tfrac{1}{2}\varepsilon \sin\chi\,(e^{i\omega} - e^{-i\omega}), & \rho_2(\tau) &= \sin^2(\chi/2)\, e^{i\omega} + \cos^2(\chi/2)\, e^{-i\omega} \end{aligned} \tag{4.114}$$

where

$$\tan\chi = \zeta, \qquad \omega = \tau/(2\cos\chi) \tag{4.115}$$

The table of cosines (Table I) corresponds to the values of $\alpha = 1$, $\beta = 0$, that is, to the transfer from the initial position of an orbital triad. The equation of motion of the center of mass is now formulated with the aid of the first line of this table:

$$\mathbf{r} = r\mathbf{e}_r = r[\mathbf{e}_r^{\,0}(\sin^2\chi + \cos^2\chi\cos 2\omega) + \mathbf{e}_\varphi^{\,0}\cos\chi\sin 2\omega + \mathbf{n}^0\varepsilon\sin\chi\cos\chi(1-\cos 2\omega)] \tag{4.116}$$

From this equation it is easy to deduce that the following relations are valid:

$$\mathbf{r}\cdot\mathcal{N} = r\sin\chi, \qquad \mathcal{N} = \mathbf{e}_r^{\,0}\sin\chi + \varepsilon\mathbf{n}^0\cos\chi \tag{4.117}$$

These relations show that an orbit is a minor circle of a sphere resulting from its intersection with the plane perpendicular to the vector $\mathcal{N}$ and moved the distance $r \sin \chi$ from the attractive center.

TABLE I

COSINES

	$\mathbf{e}_r^{\,0}$	$\mathbf{e}_\varphi^{\,0}$	$\mathbf{n}^0$
$\mathbf{e}_r$	$\sin^2\chi + \cos^2\chi\cos 2\omega$	$\cos\chi\sin 2\omega$	$\varepsilon\cos\chi\sin\chi\,(1-\cos 2\omega)$
$\mathbf{e}_\varphi$	$-\cos\chi\sin 2\omega$	$\cos 2\omega$	$\varepsilon\sin\chi\sin 2\omega$
$\mathbf{n}$	$\varepsilon\cos\chi\sin\chi\,(1-\cos 2\omega)$	$-\varepsilon\sin\chi\sin 2\omega$	$\cos^2\chi + \sin^2\chi\cos 2\omega$

The formulated solution does not allow one to prescribe an *a priori* direction of the vector $\mathbf{n}^1$ normal to the instantaneous Π^1 plane. Indeed, this direction is fixed by two angles Ω^1 and i^1, while we have only one quantity $2\omega_1 = \tau_1/\cos\chi$ at our disposal. This is the reason why it would seem reasonable to obtain a solution by changing at some suitable instant the thrust direction by 180° (going from $\alpha_3 = \varepsilon$ to $\alpha_3 = -\varepsilon$). Under this assumption, we have [see Eq. (4.113)]

$$0 \le \tau \le \tau_* - 0 \qquad \alpha_3 = \varepsilon \qquad \alpha = \kappa_1^{\,+}(\tau), \qquad \beta = \rho_1^{\,+}(\tau)$$

$$\tau_* + 0 \le \tau \le \tau_1 \qquad \alpha_3 = -\varepsilon \qquad \alpha = \alpha_*\kappa_1^{\,-}(\tau-\tau_*) + \beta_*\kappa_2^{\,-}(\tau-\tau_*)$$

$$\beta = \alpha_*\rho_1^{\,-}(\tau-\tau_*) + \beta_*\rho_2^{\,-}(\tau-\tau_*)$$

where $\kappa_i^{\,+}$, $\rho_i^{\,+}$ are determined by Eqs. (4.114), and $\kappa_i^{\,-}$, $\rho_i^{\,-}$ by the same equations with ε replaced by $-\varepsilon$. We get

$$\alpha^1 = \alpha(\tau_1) = \kappa_1^{\,+}(\tau_*)\kappa_1^{\,-}(\tau_1-\tau_*) + \rho_1^{\,+}(\tau_*)\kappa_2^{\,-}(\tau_1-\tau_*)$$

and

$$\beta^1 = \beta(\tau_1) = \kappa_1^{\,+}(\tau_*)\rho_1^{\,-}(\tau_1-\tau_*) + \rho_1^{\,+}(\tau_*)\rho_2^{\,-}(\tau_1-\tau_*)$$

and after the calculation, in view of Eqs. (4.114), we obtain

$$\alpha^1 = i \cos \chi \sin \omega_1 + \cos \omega_1 + \sin^2 \chi [\cos (\omega_1 - 2\omega_*) - \cos \omega_1] \qquad (4.118)$$
$$\beta^1 = \varepsilon \sin \chi\{\cos \chi [\cos(\omega_1 - 2\omega_*) - \cos \omega_1] - i \sin \chi \sin(\omega_1 - 2\omega_*)\}$$
$$(\omega_1 = \tau_1/2 \cos \chi, \qquad \omega_* = \tau_*/2 \cos \chi)$$

The unknown parameters τ_* and τ_1 are the least positive roots of the system of equations

$$\alpha^1\bar{\alpha}^1 - \beta^1\bar{\beta}^1 = \cos i^1, \qquad 2\alpha^1\beta^1 = i \sin i^1 \exp(i\Omega^1) \qquad (4.119)$$

For $0 \leq \tau \leq \tau_1 - 0$, an orbit is combined of two parts of minor circles equally removed from the attractive center; their common tangent at the point $r\mathbf{e}_r(\tau_*)$ is directed along the vector $\mathbf{e}_\varphi(\tau_*)$, and the vectors $\mathcal{N}_1$ and $\mathcal{N}_2$ serve as normals to the circles' planes. Since thrust ceases its action at the instant $\tau_1 + 0$, the Keplerian orbit becomes a major circle whose plane is suitably oriented in space (its normal given by $\mathbf{n}^1$).

In the problem considered above, the stationarity conditions and the Weierstrass criterion have resulted in the single requirement equation (4.110). This condition is valid for either of the transfers $\mathbf{e}_r^0 \to \mathbf{e}_r^*$ and $\mathbf{e}_r^* \to \mathbf{e}_r^1$ taken separately; but for the equivalent transfer $\mathbf{e}_r^0 \to \mathbf{e}_r^1$ it may be satisfied only under the additional requirement $\sigma_1(\tau_*) = 0$, since $\boldsymbol{\sigma}$ is a constant vector and its components σ_s along the orbital axes must be continuous functions of τ. But as long as $\alpha_1 = 0$, $\alpha_2 = 0$, $\alpha_3 = \varepsilon$, we may write

$$\boldsymbol{\lambda} = \lambda \mathbf{n}\varepsilon = \frac{ar}{k}\sigma_1\mathbf{n} = \frac{r^2}{\delta\mu}\sigma_1\mathbf{n}, \qquad \boldsymbol{\lambda}' = \frac{r^2}{\delta\mu}(\sigma_2\mathbf{n} - \varepsilon\zeta\sigma_1\mathbf{e}_\varphi)$$

and

$$\boldsymbol{\lambda}(\tau_*) = 0, \qquad \boldsymbol{\lambda}'(\tau_*) = \frac{r^2}{\delta\mu}\sigma_2(\tau_*)\mathbf{n}^*, \qquad (H_\lambda)_{\tau=\tau_*} = 0$$

We have arrived at a contradiction with the equality $h = 1$ so that one of the Erdmann-Weierstrass conditions is violated, and the transfer $\mathbf{e}_r^0 \to \mathbf{e}_r^1$ is not an optimal one.

It was postulated at the very outset that the thrust vector may be arbitrarily oriented relative to the orbital axes; it seems probable that under this assumption the minimum time requirement can be realized only when there is a component of thrust in the instantaneous orbital plane. The above partial solution does not meet this condition.

4.43b Optimal turning of the plane of a circular orbit. We now alter the statement of the problem: it will be assumed in what follows that the orbit is a spherical curve and the thrust acceleration (of bounded magnitude) is collinear with the normal to the instantaneous orbital plane. Under these conditions, the velocity will stay constant in magnitude and collinear with $\mathbf{e}_\varphi$ (this statement comes from the equation of motion $(4.99)_1$). The other equations of motion reduce to Eqs. (4.55). In view of the nondimensional notation introduced above, we may present Eqs. (4.55) in the form

$$\mathbf{e}_r' = \mathbf{e}_\varphi, \qquad \mathbf{e}_\varphi' = -\mathbf{e}_r + \varepsilon\zeta\mathbf{n}, \qquad \mathbf{n}' = -\varepsilon\zeta\mathbf{e}_\varphi \tag{4.120}$$

where $|\varepsilon(\tau)| \leq 1$. The choice of the "control" $\varepsilon(t)$ must be such as to minimize the transition time from the initial position of the orbital plane to the terminal one described by the normal vector $\mathbf{n}^1 = \tilde{\mathbf{n}}^1$. In this connection, we give the indicating function in the form $\theta = \tau_1 + \boldsymbol{\rho}\cdot(\mathbf{n}^1 - \tilde{\mathbf{n}}^1)$.

We introduce three Lagrange vectors $\boldsymbol{\lambda}_1$, $\boldsymbol{\lambda}_2$, and $\boldsymbol{\lambda}_3$, and write the Hamiltonian $H_\lambda = \boldsymbol{\lambda}_1\cdot\mathbf{e}_\varphi - \boldsymbol{\lambda}_2\cdot\mathbf{e}_r + \varepsilon\zeta(\boldsymbol{\lambda}_2\cdot\mathbf{n} - \boldsymbol{\lambda}_3\cdot\mathbf{e}_\varphi)$.

From Pontryagin's maximum principle it follows that $\varepsilon(\tau)$ may take either of its limiting values

$$\varepsilon = +1 \quad \text{if} \quad \boldsymbol{\lambda}_2\cdot\mathbf{n} - \boldsymbol{\lambda}_3\cdot\mathbf{e}_\varphi > 0$$
$$\varepsilon = -1 \quad \text{if} \quad \boldsymbol{\lambda}_2\cdot\mathbf{n} - \boldsymbol{\lambda}_3\cdot\mathbf{e}_\varphi < 0.$$

The moment of switching τ_* is found from the equation

$$\boldsymbol{\lambda}_2{}^*\cdot\mathbf{n}^* - \boldsymbol{\lambda}_3{}^*\cdot\mathbf{e}_\varphi{}^* = 0 \tag{4.121}$$

The stationarity conditions lead to the linear system

$$\boldsymbol{\lambda}_1' = \boldsymbol{\lambda}_2, \qquad \boldsymbol{\lambda}_2' = -\boldsymbol{\lambda}_1 + \varepsilon\zeta\boldsymbol{\lambda}_3, \qquad \boldsymbol{\lambda}_3' = -\varepsilon\zeta\boldsymbol{\lambda}_2 \tag{4.122}$$

whose partial solution is $\boldsymbol{\lambda}_1 = \mathbf{e}_r$, $\boldsymbol{\lambda}_2 = \mathbf{e}_\varphi$, $\boldsymbol{\lambda}_3 = \mathbf{n}$; the general solution, including nine arbitrary constants, may be presented in the form

$$\boldsymbol{\lambda}_1 = \mathsf{A}\cdot\mathbf{e}_r, \qquad \boldsymbol{\lambda}_2 = \mathsf{A}\cdot\mathbf{e}_\varphi, \qquad \boldsymbol{\lambda}_3 = \mathsf{A}\cdot\mathbf{n}$$

where through A we have denoted a constant tensor of the second rank. The boundary conditions may be formulated in terms of the indicating function introduced above; these conditions are

$$\boldsymbol{\lambda}_1{}^1 = 0, \qquad \boldsymbol{\lambda}_2{}^1 = 0, \qquad H_\lambda{}^1 = 1 \tag{4.123}$$

Having presented A as a sum of three dyadics

$$\mathsf{A} = \mathbf{a}_1\mathbf{e}_r{}^1 + \mathbf{a}_2\mathbf{e}_\varphi{}^1 + \mathbf{a}\mathbf{n}^1$$

we find that $\mathbf{a}_1 = 0$ and $\mathbf{a}_2 = 0$. The solution of Eqs. (4.122) with the boundary conditions of Eq. (4.123) is now given by

$$\boldsymbol{\lambda}_1 = \mathbf{a}\mathbf{e}_r\cdot\mathbf{n}^1, \qquad \boldsymbol{\lambda}_2 = \mathbf{a}\mathbf{e}_\varphi\cdot\mathbf{n}^1, \qquad \boldsymbol{\lambda}_3 = \mathbf{a}\mathbf{n}\cdot\mathbf{n}^1$$

where $\mathbf{a}$ is a constant vector collinear with the Lagrange multipliers $\boldsymbol{\lambda}_s$.

The scalar integral which expresses the constancy of the Hamiltonian is now transformed into

$$(\mathbf{n}^1 \times \mathbf{a}) \cdot (\mathbf{n} + \varepsilon\zeta \mathbf{e}_r) = 1 \tag{4.124}$$

and the notation $\mathbf{n}^1 \times \mathbf{a} = (1/\delta)\boldsymbol{\sigma}$ allows us to present it in the form of Eq. (4.110). The vector $\boldsymbol{\sigma}$ now turns out to be disposed in the Π^1 plane in accordance with boundary condition, Eq. (4.75), previously found in the general problem of turning the orbital plane.

An instant τ_* may be determined from Eq. (4.121) transformed into

$$\mathbf{a} \cdot (\mathbf{n}^* \mathbf{e}_\varphi{}^* \cdot \mathbf{n}^1 - \mathbf{e}_\varphi{}^* \mathbf{n}^* \cdot \mathbf{n}^1) = \mathbf{a} \cdot [\mathbf{n}^1 \times (\mathbf{n}^* \times \mathbf{e}_\varphi{}^*)]$$
$$= (\mathbf{a} \times \mathbf{n}^1) \cdot (\mathbf{n}^* \times \mathbf{e}_\varphi{}^*) = 0$$

or, equivalently,

$$(1/\delta)\boldsymbol{\sigma} \cdot \mathbf{e}_r{}^* = 0, \qquad \sigma_1(\tau_*) = 0.$$

Nothing prevents us from assuming that the latter condition is satisfied. From Eq. (4.124) we also infer that $\varepsilon(\tau_1)\zeta\sigma(\tau_1) = \delta$, and $\varepsilon(\tau_1) = \operatorname{sgn} \sigma_1(\tau_1)$. This relation serves for the choice of the sign of $\varepsilon(\tau_1)$. This conclusion is also confirmed by Eq. (4.77).

The stationarity conditions and the Weierstrass criterion (maximum principle) are satisfied in the statement of the problem above, while the expressions for the $\boldsymbol{\lambda}$-vectors and the Hamiltonian [see Eqs. (4.121)] leave no doubt that the Erdmann-Weierstrass conditions are also fulfilled. The differential equations of motion [Eqs. (4.120)] were analyzed above in the equivalent form, Eq. (4.112). The orbit so found consists of two parts of minor circles and is optimal for the statement of the problem formulated in this Section; the minimum time and the switching instant may be calculated from Eqs. (4.119). This minimum is of course larger than that obtained for a more general problem when we allow the components of thrust to be disposed in the instantaneous orbital plane.

The problem of turning the plane of a circular orbit has been analyzed by others.[13,14,15]

4.5 Boosting Devices of Limited Propulsive Power

4.51 The Differential Equations of Motion

In Sec. 4.17 it was shown that for this type of booster the vector $\boldsymbol{\lambda}$ differs from the thrust acceleration vector only by the constant multiplier $A/\mathcal{N}_{\max}$. With this in mind, we place the expression (4.30) for the vector $\boldsymbol{\lambda}$ in the differential equation (4.28) and arrive at the fourth-order differential equation for the vector **r**, namely,

$$\mathbf{L}(\mathbf{r}) = \left(\ddot{\mathbf{r}} + \frac{\mu}{r^3}\mathbf{r}\right)^{\cdot\cdot} - \frac{\mu}{r^3}\left(3\,\frac{\ddot{\mathbf{r}}\cdot\mathbf{r}}{r^2}\,\mathbf{r} + 2\,\frac{\mu}{r^3}\,\mathbf{r} - \ddot{\mathbf{r}}\right) = 0 \qquad (4.125)$$

The total fuel consumption will be presumed to be minimized; in this case

$$\theta = -m^1 + \theta_1(\mathbf{r}^1, \dot{\mathbf{r}}^1) + \rho_t(t_1 - t_1{}^*) \qquad (4.126)$$

where $\rho_t = h$; and if t_1 is not prescribed, then $h = 0$. The boundary conditions at the right end are formulated through the vector **r**; in view of Eqs. (4.30) and (4.70), these conditions are written as

$$t = t_1, \qquad \left(\ddot{\mathbf{r}} + \frac{\mu}{r^3}\mathbf{r}\right)^{\cdot}_{t_1} = \operatorname{grad}_{\mathbf{r}^1}\theta_1,$$
$$\left(\ddot{\mathbf{r}} + \frac{\mu}{r^3}\mathbf{r}\right)_{t_1} = -\operatorname{grad}_{\dot{\mathbf{r}}^1}\theta_1, \qquad H_\lambda\big|_{t_1} = h \qquad (4.127)$$

At the left end the vectors $\mathbf{r}^0$, $\dot{\mathbf{r}}^0$ are presumed to be fixed. The expression for H_λ will be written below.

4.51a. Scalar and vector integrals. Substitution of Eq. (4.30) into Eqs. $(4.39)_2$ and (4.41) transforms these integrals into

$$H_\lambda = -(\ddot{\mathbf{r}}\cdot\dot{\mathbf{r}})^{\cdot} + \frac{3}{2}\,\ddot{\mathbf{r}}\cdot\ddot{\mathbf{r}} - \frac{\mu}{r^3}\left[\frac{\mu}{2r} + \dot{\mathbf{r}}\cdot\dot{\mathbf{r}} - \frac{3}{r^2}\,(\mathbf{r}\cdot\dot{\mathbf{r}})^2\right] = h \qquad (4.128)$$

$$(\ddot{\mathbf{r}}\times\mathbf{r})^{\cdot} - 2\left(\ddot{\mathbf{r}} + \frac{\mu}{r^3}\mathbf{r}\right)\times\dot{\mathbf{r}} = \mathbf{b} = b\boldsymbol{\sigma} \qquad (4.129)$$

where **b** and h denote constants. By the same argument as in Sec. 4.23, it can be shown that the system of Eqs. (4.128) and (4.129), now containing four constants, is equivalent to the initial equation (4.125) under the additional requirement $\mathbf{r}\cdot\dot{\mathbf{r}} \neq 0$. Equation (4.68) which may also be presented in the form

$$w\alpha_3 k = \left|\ddot{\mathbf{r}} + \frac{\mu}{r^3}\mathbf{r}\right| |\mathbf{r}\times\dot{\mathbf{r}}|\,\alpha_3 = \left(\ddot{\mathbf{r}} + \frac{\mu}{r^3}\mathbf{r}\right)\cdot\mathbf{n}\,|\mathbf{r}\times\dot{\mathbf{r}}| = \left(\ddot{\mathbf{r}} + \frac{\mu\mathbf{r}}{r^3}\right)\cdot(\mathbf{r}\times\dot{\mathbf{r}}) = br\sigma_1$$

provides the first integral of Eq. (4.129). This relation may also be written in the easily verified form

$$\mathbf{r}\cdot(\dot{\mathbf{r}}\times\ddot{\mathbf{r}}) = b\boldsymbol{\sigma}\cdot\mathbf{r} \qquad (4.130)$$

Having constructed the cross-product of Eq. (4.129) with $\dot{\mathbf{r}}$ and $\ddot{\mathbf{r}}$, we obtain

$$\mathbf{r}\cdot(\dot{\mathbf{r}}\times\dddot{\mathbf{r}}) = b\boldsymbol{\sigma}\cdot\dot{\mathbf{r}} \qquad (4.131)$$

and

$$\mathbf{r}\cdot(\ddot{\mathbf{r}}\times\dddot{\mathbf{r}}) = b\boldsymbol{\sigma}\cdot(\ddot{\mathbf{r}} + (\mu/r^3)\mathbf{r}] \qquad (4.132)$$

the latter by use of Eq. (4.130). We may disregard Eq. (4.131) because it is an immediate consequence of Eq. (4.130). The problem has now been reduced to the system of three scalar equations (4.128), (4.130) and (4.132). These equations determine covariant components of the vector $\dddot{\mathbf{r}}$ in the vector basis $\mathbf{r} \times \dot{\mathbf{r}}$, $\mathbf{r} \times \ddot{\mathbf{r}}$, $\dot{\mathbf{r}}$, and with their aid this vector is expanded along the axes of the conjugate basis

$$(1/b\Delta)(\mathbf{r} \times \ddot{\mathbf{r}}) \times \dot{\mathbf{r}},\ (1/b\Delta)\dot{\mathbf{r}} \times (\mathbf{r} \times \dot{\mathbf{r}}),\ (1/b\Delta)(\mathbf{r} \times \dot{\mathbf{r}}) \times (\mathbf{r} \times \ddot{\mathbf{r}})$$

where [see Eq. (4.130)]

$$b\Delta = \mathbf{r} \cdot \dot{\mathbf{r}}(\mathbf{r} \times \dot{\mathbf{r}}) \cdot \ddot{\mathbf{r}} = \mathbf{r} \cdot \dot{\mathbf{r}}\, b\, \boldsymbol{\sigma} \cdot \mathbf{r} \tag{4.133}$$

We arrive at the following result:

$$\dddot{\mathbf{r}}\Delta = \boldsymbol{\sigma} \cdot \mathbf{r}\left\{\mathbf{r}\left[\dot{\mathbf{r}} \cdot \dot{\mathbf{r}}\frac{\mu}{r^3} + \frac{1}{2}\left(\ddot{\mathbf{r}} \cdot \ddot{\mathbf{r}} - \frac{\mu^2}{r^4}\right) - h + \frac{3\mu}{r^5}(\mathbf{r} \cdot \dot{\mathbf{r}})^2\right] - \dot{\mathbf{r}}\,\mathbf{r} \cdot \dot{\mathbf{r}}\frac{2\mu}{r^3}\right\}$$
$$+ \boldsymbol{\sigma} \cdot \dot{\mathbf{r}}\,\dot{\mathbf{r}} \times (\ddot{\mathbf{r}} \times \mathbf{r}) + \boldsymbol{\sigma} \cdot \ddot{\mathbf{r}}\,\dot{\mathbf{r}} \times (\mathbf{r} \times \dot{\mathbf{r}}) \tag{4.134}$$

This result is valid when $\mathbf{r} \cdot \dot{\mathbf{r}} \neq 0$ and $b \neq 0$ (except for spherical and plane motions). The three differential equations (4.134) of the third order allow an integral (4.130). The system depends on three independent constants; namely, the constant unit vector $\boldsymbol{\sigma}$ and h and one other constant, b, which enters into the first integral. The control program for the thrust acceleration is determined from the relation

$$\mathbf{w} = \ddot{\mathbf{r}} + (\mu/\tau^3)\mathbf{r} \tag{4.135}$$

4.52 Plane Motions

For the motion along plane orbits, the vectors $\mathbf{r}$, $\dot{\mathbf{r}}$, $\ddot{\mathbf{r}}$, $\dddot{\mathbf{r}}$ are coplanar, and from Eqs. (4.130)–(4.132) it is readily seen that $\mathbf{b} = \tilde{b}\mathbf{n}$, $\tilde{b} = \pm b$. Equation (4.129) can now be presented in the form $\ddot{\mathbf{r}} \times \mathbf{r} = [\ddot{\mathbf{r}} + 2(\mu/r^3)\mathbf{r}] \times \dot{\mathbf{r}} + \tilde{b}\mathbf{n}$.

Consider now the vector product of this equation with $\dot{\mathbf{r}}$; having replaced $\dddot{\mathbf{r}} \cdot \dot{\mathbf{r}}$ in the resulting expression with the aid of Eq. (4.128), we arrive at the following presentation of the vector $\dddot{\mathbf{r}}$:

$$\dddot{\mathbf{r}}\,\mathbf{r} \cdot \dot{\mathbf{r}} = \mathbf{r}\left[\frac{1}{2}\left(\ddot{\mathbf{r}} \cdot \ddot{\mathbf{r}} - \frac{\mu^2}{r^4}\right) + \frac{\mu}{r^3}\dot{\mathbf{r}} \cdot \dot{\mathbf{r}} + \frac{3\mu}{r^5}(\mathbf{r} \cdot \dot{\mathbf{r}})^2 - h\right]$$
$$- \dot{\mathbf{r}}\frac{2\mu}{r^3}\mathbf{r} \cdot \dot{\mathbf{r}} - \dot{\mathbf{r}} \times (\dot{\mathbf{r}} \times \ddot{\mathbf{r}}) + \tilde{b}\,\dot{\mathbf{r}} \times \mathbf{n} \tag{4.136}$$

We now have a system of two third-order differential equations containing two constants $\tilde{b}$, h. For the special case of plane motion, $\tilde{b} = 0$.

4.53 Spherical Motions

In accordance with what has been stated in Sec. 4.4, the differential equation of motion Eq. (4.125) should be complemented by the term $\nu\mathbf{r}$ collinear with $\mathbf{r}$. But this term obviously does not change the form of the integrals (4.128), (4.129). Combined, they present the differential equations of the problem.

In terms of the nondimensional variables of (4.105), these equations are written as follows:

$$\begin{aligned} -(\mathbf{e}_r'' \cdot \mathbf{e}_r')' + \tfrac{3}{2}\mathbf{e}_r'' \cdot \mathbf{e}_r'' + \mathbf{e}_r'' \cdot \mathbf{e}_r &= \tfrac{1}{2} \\ (\mathbf{e}_r'' \times \mathbf{e}_r)' - 2(\mathbf{e}_r'' + \mathbf{e}_r) \times \mathbf{e}_r' &= \boldsymbol{\sigma}\delta \end{aligned} \tag{4.137}$$

where we have accounted for $\mathbf{e}_r \cdot \mathbf{e}_r' = 0$ and $\mathbf{e}_r' \cdot \mathbf{e}_r' = -\mathbf{e}_r \cdot \mathbf{e}_r''$, and τ_1 had been presumed *a priori* unknown ($h = 0$).

We must adjoin to these equations the following kinematic relations

$$\mathbf{e}_r' = v\mathbf{e}_\varphi, \qquad \mathbf{e}_\varphi' = -v\mathbf{e}_r + \frac{\rho}{v}\mathbf{n}, \qquad \mathbf{n}' = -\frac{\rho}{v}\mathbf{e}_\varphi \tag{4.138}$$

where v denotes the speed and ρ the component of the thrust acceleration along the normal to the instantaneous orbital plane, both parameters presented in nondimensional form. These quantities will from now on be treated as new dependent variables.

We write

$$\mathbf{e}_r'' = v'\mathbf{e}_\varphi - v^2\mathbf{e}_r + \rho\mathbf{n} \tag{4.139}$$

Substitution into Eqs. (4.137) leads to the four relations

$$\rho v = \sigma_1\delta \tag{4.140}$$

$$(v'/v)\rho + \rho' = \sigma_2\delta \tag{4.141}$$

$$\frac{1}{2v}[(1 - v^2)^2 - z'^2 - \rho^2] = \sigma_3\delta \tag{4.142}$$

$$\rho^2 = \tfrac{1}{3} + \tfrac{2}{3}v^2 + \tfrac{2}{3}vv'' - \tfrac{1}{3}v'^2 - v^4 \tag{4.143}$$

where we have already used Eq. (4.143) for presentation of Eq. (4.142). Only two of these four relations may be treated as independent. Indeed, since $\boldsymbol{\sigma}$ is a constant unit vector, we have

$$\sigma_1' = v\sigma_2, \qquad \sigma_2' = -v\sigma_1 + \frac{\rho}{v}\sigma_3, \qquad \sigma_3' = -\frac{\rho}{v}\sigma_2, \qquad \sigma_1^2 + \sigma_2^2 + \sigma_3^2 = 1 \tag{4.144}$$

It is obvious that Eq. (4.141) is a consequence of Eq. (4.140). Furthermore, we arrive at Eq. (4.141) by differentiation of Eq. (4.142) and use of Eq. (4.143). It remains only to require that the right-hand sides of Eqs. (4.140)–(4.142) be connected by the second equation of Eqs. (4.144). This condition is equivalent to the differential relation

$$\rho'' + \frac{v'}{v}\rho' = \frac{\rho}{v^2}(1 - 2\rho^2 - 2v^4) \tag{4.145}$$

which must be treated together with Eq. (4.143). The first integral of the system of Eqs. (4.143) and (4.145) is already known: we mean the last of Eqs. (4.144) expressed in terms of the left-hand sides of Eqs. (4.140)–(4.142). We have five free parameters—four constants of integration and τ_1—at our disposal, and it is necessary to choose them in such a way as to satisfy prescribed values of v^0, v^1, and Euler angles Ω^1, i^1, u^1. In this way we infer that the general boundary problem for spherical motion is well formulated. The program of thrust operation is determined from Eqs. (4.135) and (4.139):

$$\mathbf{w} = (\mu/r^2)(\mathbf{e}_r'' + \mathbf{e}_r) = (\mu/r^2)[(1 - v^2)\mathbf{e}_r + v'\mathbf{e}_\varphi + \rho\mathbf{n}] \tag{4.146}$$

The control program when the thrust vector is directed along the normal to the instantaneous orbital plane is by no means optimal because the values $v = 1$ and $\rho = \pm 1$ do not present a partial solution to the system of equations (4.143) and (4.145). These equations could have been satisfied by setting the values of v^2 and ρ^2 equal to 1/4 and 7/16, respectively, but for the regime of constant speed ($v = 1/2$) one can choose τ_1 so as to prescribe only one of the three Euler angles Ω^1, i^1, u^1.

4.54 An Application of the Ritz Method

One could have derived the solution of the thrust–acceleration control problem under limited propulsive power without reducing it to the Mayer-Bolza problem as it was done above. In fact, turning back to the basic equations (4.2), (4.3), (4.4), and (4.12), we can write

$$w^2 = \left|\ddot{\mathbf{r}} + \frac{\mu}{r^3}\mathbf{r}\right|^2 = \frac{c^2}{m^2}q^2 = 2\mathcal{N}\frac{q}{m^2} = 2\mathcal{N}\left(\frac{1}{m}\right)^{\cdot} \tag{4.147}$$

and, consequently,

$$\tilde{I} = \frac{1}{\tilde{m}^1} - \frac{1}{m^0} = \frac{1}{2}\int_0^{t_1}\frac{1}{\mathcal{N}}\left|\ddot{\mathbf{r}} + \frac{\mu}{r^3}\mathbf{r}\right|^2 dt \tag{4.148}$$

Note that the magnitude of the acceleration w depends on two independent functions of time: $\mathcal{N}(t)$ and $q(t)$. We might, indeed, choose some program for

$\mathcal{N}(t)$ and by suitable alteration of the flow rate law $q(t)$ obtain any functional dependence of $w(t)$ prescribed from the outset. Thus, it becomes obvious that we have independent quantities under the sign of the integral in Eq. (4.128). From this point and taking Eq. (4.12) into account, we deduce the following inequality:

$$\tilde{I} \geq I = \frac{1}{2\mathcal{N}_{\max}} \int_0^{t_1} \left| \ddot{\mathbf{r}} + \frac{\mu}{r^3}\mathbf{r} \right|^2 dt = \frac{1}{m^1} - \frac{1}{m^0} \tag{4.149}$$

The problem of minimum fuel consumption (maximum final mass m^1) is reduced to the determination of the law $\mathbf{r}(t)$ of motion, this law leading to the minimum value of integral (4.149). When t_1 is fixed equal to $t_1{}^*$, this provides the "simplest problem" of the calculus of variations, and if t_1 is not prescribed we arrive at the problem with free boundary.

If boundary values of $\mathbf{r}^1$, $\mathbf{v}^1$, t_1 are connected by the relation

$$\theta = \theta_1(\mathbf{r}^1, \dot{\mathbf{r}}^1) + h(t_1 - t_1{}^*) = 0 \tag{4.150}$$

one must set the first variation of

$$\Omega_2 = \theta_1(\mathbf{r}^1, \dot{\mathbf{r}}^1) + h(t_1 - t_1{}^*) + \frac{1}{2}\int_0^{t_1} \left(\ddot{\mathbf{r}} \cdot \ddot{\mathbf{r}} + 2\frac{\mu}{r^3}\mathbf{r} \cdot \ddot{\mathbf{r}} + \frac{\mu^2}{r^4} \right) dt \tag{4.151}$$

equal to zero.

Note that the upper limit of the integral must also be varied; we get

$$\delta\Omega_2 = \int_0^{t_1} \mathbf{L}(\mathbf{r}) \cdot \delta\mathbf{r}\, dt + \left\{ \left(\ddot{\mathbf{r}} + \frac{\mu}{r^3}\mathbf{r} + \operatorname{grad}_{\dot{\mathbf{r}}^1} \theta_1 \right) \cdot \Delta\dot{\mathbf{r}} \right.$$
$$\left. - \left[\left(\ddot{\mathbf{r}} + \frac{\mu}{r^3}\mathbf{r} \right)^{\cdot} - \operatorname{grad}_{\mathbf{r}^1} \theta_1 \right] \cdot \Delta\mathbf{r} \right\}_{t=t_1} - [(H)_{t_1} - h]\,\delta t_1 = 0 \tag{4.152}$$

where Δ denotes the total variations at the right end:

$$\Delta\mathbf{r}^1 = \delta\mathbf{r}^1 + \dot{\mathbf{r}}^1\,\delta t_1, \qquad \Delta\dot{\mathbf{r}}^1 = \delta\dot{\mathbf{r}}^1 + \ddot{\mathbf{r}}^1\,\delta t_1 \tag{4.153}$$

The left end is assumed fixed ($\delta\mathbf{r}^0 = 0$, $\delta\dot{\mathbf{r}}^0 = 0$); in Eq. (4.152) H means the left-hand side of Eq. (4.128), $\mathbf{L}(\mathbf{r})$ denotes the differential operator (4.125).

The requirement that the first variation must vanish leads, of course, to differential equation (4.125) with boundary conditions equation (4.70).

We may now use the Ritz method to minimize integral I in Eq. (4.149), and so determine the vector $\mathbf{r}(t)$. The latter is to be found in the class of functions continuous with their derivatives up to third order, and satisfying the complemented boundary conditions. Having chosen functions of this class containing some unknown constants $C_1, \ldots, C_s$, we obtain the minimum problem for the function $I(C_1, \ldots, C_s)$ of these constants. This problem is obviously reduced to a system of s finite equations for the same number of constants C_s. If "geometrical" boundary conditions are prescribed (the vectors $\mathbf{r}^1$ and $\dot{\mathbf{r}}^1$) and t_1 is fixed, then the choice of a suitable expression for $\mathbf{r}(t)$ is fairly easy; this case is quite difficult to solve in the equivalent Mayer-Bolza problem since the values of $\boldsymbol{\lambda}^1$ and $\dot{\boldsymbol{\lambda}}^1$ are all unknown. Inversely, the case of $\boldsymbol{\lambda}^1 = 0$, $\dot{\boldsymbol{\lambda}}^1 = 0$ treated as the simplest one in the Mayer-Bolza problem, corresponds to "statical" boundary conditions (in terms used in the problem of bending of plates), and under these conditions there arise difficulties in the construction of a suitable expression for $\mathbf{r}(t)$. From Eq. (4.152) it follows, however, that one need not trouble much about "statical" conditions since they are met automatically when $\delta\mathbf{r}^1 = 0$, $\delta\dot{\mathbf{r}}^1 = 0$ (and $\delta t_1 = 0$) and I attains its minimum value. It is, of course, obvious that one can hardly rely upon such a solution in practice.

The reader may find a very detailed account of optimal problems for boosters of limited propulsive power in Grodzovskii *et al.*[16] who also presented an extensive bibliography.

4.6 Singular Control Regimes†

4.61 Statement of the Variational Problem

It was noted in Sec. 4.8 that for boosting devices of limited flow rate the possibility of "singular control" regimes cannot be excluded. In such regimes, the mass flow rate is determined by Eq. (4.37) under additional constraints expressed by inequalities (4.14).

For a "singular control" program, Eq. (4.36) is satisfied; from this it follows that the derivative $\dot{\eta}$ of the switching function is also equal to zero, and from Eq. (4.33) we infer that $\dot{\lambda} = 0$, $\lambda = \text{const}$. The differential equation (4.28) becomes, in view of Eq. (4.27), the equation for unit vector $\mathbf{e}$ of the thrust direction:

$$\mathbf{L}(\mathbf{e}, \mathbf{r}) = \ddot{\mathbf{e}} + \frac{\mu}{r^3}\left(\mathbf{e} - \frac{3}{r^2}\,\mathbf{r}\cdot\mathbf{e}\,\mathbf{r}\right) = 0 \tag{4.154}$$

We might derive this result immediately from the variational problem for minimum fuel consumption. From Eq. (4.4) we find

$$\frac{cq}{m} = -c\frac{\dot{m}}{m} = \left|\ddot{\mathbf{r}} + \frac{\mu}{r^3}\mathbf{r}\right|, \qquad \ln\frac{m^0}{m^1} = I = \frac{1}{c}\int_0^{t_1}\left|\ddot{\mathbf{r}} + \frac{\mu}{r^3}\mathbf{r}\right| dt \tag{4.155}$$

where

$$\left|\ddot{\mathbf{r}} + \frac{\mu}{r^3}\mathbf{r}\right| = \left(\ddot{\mathbf{r}} + \frac{\mu}{r^3}\mathbf{r}\right)\cdot\mathbf{e} \tag{4.156}$$

† For a general discussion of singular control, see Chapter 3.

The problem is reduced (like that considered in Sec. 4.54) to the calculation of the first variation of the functional

$$\Omega_3 = \theta_1(\mathbf{r}^1, \dot{\mathbf{r}}^1) + h(t_1 - t_1{}^*) + \int_0^{t_1} \left| \ddot{\mathbf{r}} + \frac{\mu}{r^3}\mathbf{r} \right| dt \tag{4.157}$$

Note that the upper limit must also be free; we have

$$\delta\Omega_3 = \operatorname{grad}_{\mathbf{r}^1} \theta_1 \cdot \Delta\mathbf{r}^1 + \operatorname{grad}_{\dot{\mathbf{r}}^1} \theta_1 \cdot \Delta\dot{\mathbf{r}}^1 + h\,\delta t_1 + \left(\ddot{\mathbf{r}} + \frac{\mu}{r^3}\mathbf{r}\right) \cdot \mathbf{e}|_{t_1}\delta t_1$$
$$+ \frac{1}{2}\int_0^{t_1} \frac{1}{|\ddot{\mathbf{r}} + (\mu/r^3)\mathbf{r}|}\,\delta\left[\left(\ddot{\mathbf{r}} + \frac{\mu}{r^3}\mathbf{r}\right) \cdot \left(\ddot{\mathbf{r}} + \frac{\mu}{r^3}\mathbf{r}\right)\right] dt \tag{4.158}$$

where Δ denotes the total variation.

The variation of the expression in square brackets is now transformed into

$$\frac{1}{2}\delta\left[\left(\ddot{\mathbf{r}} + \frac{\mu}{r^3}\mathbf{r}\right) \cdot \left(\ddot{\mathbf{r}} + \frac{\mu}{r^3}\mathbf{r}\right)\right] = \left(\ddot{\mathbf{r}} + \frac{\mu}{r^3}\mathbf{r}\right) \cdot \delta\ddot{\mathbf{r}} + \frac{\mu}{r^3}\left[\left(\ddot{\mathbf{r}} + \frac{\mu}{r^3}\mathbf{r}\right) \cdot \delta\mathbf{r}\right.$$
$$\left. - \frac{3}{r^2}\left(\ddot{\mathbf{r}} + \frac{\mu}{r^3}\mathbf{r}\right) \cdot \mathbf{r}\,\mathbf{r} \cdot \delta\mathbf{r}\right]$$

Now, taking Eq. (4.156) into account, we may present the integrand in the following form:

$$\mathbf{e} \cdot \delta\ddot{\mathbf{r}} + \frac{\mu}{r^3}\left[\mathbf{e} \cdot \delta\mathbf{r} - \frac{3}{r^2}\mathbf{e} \cdot \mathbf{r}\,\mathbf{r} \cdot \delta\mathbf{r}\right] = (\mathbf{e} \cdot \delta\dot{\mathbf{r}})^{\cdot} - (\dot{\mathbf{e}} \cdot \delta\mathbf{r})^{\cdot} + \mathbf{L}(\mathbf{e}, \mathbf{r}) \cdot \delta\mathbf{r}$$

In view of Eq. (4.156), after integration we obtain the following expression for the first variation:

$$\delta\Omega_3 = \int_0^{t_1} \mathbf{L}(\mathbf{e}, \mathbf{r}) \cdot \delta\mathbf{r}\, dt + (\operatorname{grad}_{\mathbf{r}^1} \theta_1 - \dot{\mathbf{e}}^1) \cdot \Delta\mathbf{r}^1$$
$$+ (\operatorname{grad}_{\dot{\mathbf{r}}^1} \theta_1 + \mathbf{e}^1) \cdot \Delta\dot{\mathbf{r}}^1 + (h - H)_{t_1}\,\delta t_1 \tag{4.159}$$

where

$$H = -\left(\dot{\mathbf{e}} \cdot \dot{\mathbf{r}} + \frac{\mu}{r^3}\mathbf{r} \cdot \mathbf{e}\right) \tag{4.160}$$

This expression coincides with that for the previously introduced quantity H_λ (see Eqs. (4.39)) for $\lambda = \text{const}$ and $\eta = 0$. Setting the first variation equal to zero, we arrive at the differential equation (4.154) and boundary conditions Eq. (4.70), where now we must set $\lambda = \text{const}$.

4.62 The Differential Equations

The unknown function—the mass flow rate $q(t)$—is excluded from the problem formulation: this function is determined from Eq. (4.37) after the whole solution is found. It is required to determine the vector $\mathbf{r}$ and the unit vector $\mathbf{e}$ from Eq. (4.154) and the equation

$$\left(\ddot{\mathbf{r}} + \frac{\mu}{r^3}\mathbf{r}\right) \times \mathbf{e} = 0 \tag{4.161}$$

resulting from the equation of motion after elimination of $q(t)$. This system allows both vector and scalar integrals

$$\dot{\mathbf{e}} \times \mathbf{r} - \mathbf{e} \times \dot{\mathbf{r}} = \mathbf{a} = u\boldsymbol{\sigma} \tag{4.162}$$

$$H = -\left(\dot{\mathbf{e}} \cdot \dot{\mathbf{r}} + \frac{\mu}{r^3}\mathbf{r} \cdot \mathbf{e}\right) = h \tag{4.163}$$

From Eq. (4.57) we get

$$\dot{\mathbf{e}} = \mathbf{v} \times \mathbf{e}, \qquad \ddot{\mathbf{e}} = \dot{\mathbf{v}} \times \mathbf{e} - v^2\mathbf{e} \tag{4.164}$$

and substitution into Eq. (4.154) gives

$$\dot{\mathbf{v}} \times \mathbf{e} - v^2\mathbf{e} = \frac{\mu}{r^3}(3\mathbf{e}_r\alpha_1 - \mathbf{e}) \qquad (\alpha_1 = \mathbf{e}_r \cdot \mathbf{e})$$

This relation shows that

$$v^2 = \frac{\mu}{r^3}(1 - 3\alpha_1{}^2), \qquad \dot{\mathbf{v}} = \frac{3\mu}{r^3}\alpha_1\, \mathbf{e} \times \mathbf{e}_r \tag{4.165}$$

From the first of these relations we deduce the inequality $\alpha_1 \le 1/\sqrt{3}$ noted in the literature.[17]

4.62a Plane motion.[18,19] In Eqs. (4.83) and (4.84) we set $\dot{\lambda}/\lambda = 0$ and $\vartheta/\lambda = 0$, and arrive at a pair of equations which may be transformed into

$$-\frac{h}{r} = \frac{\mu}{r^3}\cos\psi + \tilde{v}^2\cos\psi - \tilde{v}\left(\frac{\dot{r}}{r}\sin\psi + \dot{\psi}\cos\psi\right) \tag{4.166}$$

$$-\frac{\tilde{a}}{r} = 2\tilde{v}\cos\psi - \left(\frac{\dot{r}}{r}\sin\psi + \dot{\psi}\cos\psi\right) \tag{4.167}$$

We have denoted by $\tilde{v}$ the component of the vector $\mathbf{v}$ along the normal $\mathbf{n}$ to the orbital plane, so that

$$\mathbf{v} = \tilde{v}\mathbf{n}, \qquad \tilde{v} = \dot{\psi} + k/r^2 = \dot{\psi} + \dot{\varphi} \tag{4.168}$$

From Eq. (4.165) it follows that

$$\tilde{v}^2 = \frac{\mu}{r^3}(1 - 3\cos^2\psi), \qquad \dot{\tilde{v}} = -\frac{3\mu}{r^3}\sin\psi\cos\psi \tag{4.169}$$

Equations (4.166) and (4.167) together with the first Eq. (4.169) show that

$$\tilde{a}\tilde{v} = h + \frac{3\mu}{r^2}\cos^3\psi \tag{4.170}$$

$$\left(h + \frac{3\mu}{r^2}\cos^3\psi\right)^2 = \mu\frac{\tilde{a}^2}{r^3}(1 - 3\cos^2\psi) \tag{4.171}$$

and differentiation of Eq. (4.170) yields, in view of the second Eq. (4.169), that

$$2\frac{\dot{r}}{r}\cos^2\psi + 3\dot{\psi}\sin\psi\cos\psi = \frac{\tilde{a}}{r}\sin\psi \tag{4.172}$$

This equation must be solved together with Eq. (4.167). We have

$$\frac{\dot{r}}{r} = \frac{2\sin\psi}{3 - 5\cos^2\psi}\left(\frac{\tilde{a}}{r} + 3v\cos\psi\right) \tag{4.173}$$

$$\dot{\psi} = \frac{1}{\cos\psi\,(3 - 5\cos^2\psi)}\left[\frac{\tilde{a}}{r}(1 - 3\cos^2\psi) - 4v\cos^3\psi\right] \tag{4.174}$$

Equation (4.171) determines r in terms of ψ and of constants $\tilde{a}$, h. The other unknowns v, $\dot{r}$ and $\dot{\psi}$ are also expressed through the same quantities [see Eqs. (4.170), (4.173), and (4.174)]; after determining the values of v and $\dot{\psi}$, we also find $\dot{\varphi}$. It is easily seen that substitution of these values of $\dot{r}$ and $\dot{\psi}$ into the equation resulting from Eq. (4.170) after differentiation leads to an identity. In this calculation, we made use of Eq. (4.169) for $\dot{\tilde{v}}$; this could have been avoided since the initial system of Eqs. (4.166) and (4.167), together with the first of Eqs. (4.169), suffice for the determination of the three unknowns r, ψ and k.

The result may be presented explicitly[18] if t_1 is not fixed so that $h = 0$. Then, in view of (4.169), we get

$$\frac{\mu}{r} = \frac{\tilde{a}^2}{9}\frac{1 - 3\cos^2\psi}{\cos^6\psi} \tag{4.175}$$

and

$$r\tilde{v} = \frac{a}{3}\frac{1 - 3\cos^2\psi}{\cos^3\psi}, \qquad \dot{r} = 2\tilde{a}\frac{1 - 2\cos^2\psi}{3 - 5\cos^2\psi}\frac{\sin\psi}{\cos^2\psi} \tag{4.176}$$

$$r\dot{\psi} = -\frac{\tilde{a}}{3\cos\psi}\frac{1 - 3\cos^2\psi}{3 - 5\cos^2\psi}, \qquad r\dot{\varphi} = \frac{\tilde{a}}{3\cos^3\psi}\frac{1 - 3\cos^2\psi}{3 - 5\cos^2\psi}(3 - 4\cos^2\psi) \tag{4.177}$$

From Eq. (4.176) we get

$$\frac{d\varphi}{d\psi} = 4 - \frac{3}{\cos^2 \psi}, \qquad \varphi = 4\psi - 3 \tan \psi + C_1 \tag{4.178}$$

All unknown quantities are expressed parametrically through the angle ψ between the thrust vector and the position vector. With the aid of Eqs. (4.175) and (4.177) we may also present time in terms of the same parameter:

$$\frac{\tilde{a}^3}{27\mu} dt = -\frac{3 - 5 \cos^2 \psi}{(1 - 3 \cos^2 \psi)^2} \cos^7 \psi \, d\psi \tag{4.179}$$

Integration introduces one more constant, C_2. Turning now to Eq. (4.37), we infer [see also Eq. (4.163)] that

$$\frac{q}{m} = \frac{1}{c}\left[(\mathbf{v} \cdot \mathbf{e})^{\cdot} + \frac{2\mu}{r^2} \cos \psi\right], \qquad \ln \frac{m_0}{m} = \frac{1}{c} \mathbf{v} \cdot \mathbf{e} + 2\mu \int_0^t \frac{\cos \psi}{r^2} dt \tag{4.180}$$

This relation also determines the mass together with the flow rate q; one must also check the fulfillment of inequalities (4.14).

The general solution depends on four constants $\tilde{a}$, C_1, C_2, and m_0. It is obvious from its structure that we may choose these constants so as to assign prescribed initial values to the mass, true anomaly φ^0, and only two of the three quantities r^0, $r^0\dot{\varphi}^0$, and $\dot{r}^0$; at the right side there remains the possibility of only one quantity to be prescribed, this prescription being achieved by suitable choice of t_1. If it is required to include an arc of singular control in the program, then at the switching point not only "coordinates" r, φ, $\dot{r}$, and $r\dot{\varphi}$ but also "controls" ψ and $\dot{\psi}$ must be continuous as required by the Erdmann-Weierstrass conditions. Such continuous transition is possible only under fairly specialized boundary conditions.

References

1. G. Leitmann, On a class of variational problems in rocket flight, *J. Aerospace Sci.* **26**, 586–591 (1959).
2. A. Miele, General variational theory of flight paths of rocket-powered aircraft, missiles and satellite carriers, *Astronaut. Acta* **4**, 264–288 (1958).
3. D. F. Lawden, Interplanetary rocket trajectories, *Advan. Space Sci. Techn.* **1**, 1–53 (1959).
4. D. F. Lawden, Optimal programming of rocket thrust direction, *Astronaut. Acta* **1**, 41–56 (1955).
5. G. Leitmann, Minimum transfer time for a power-limited rocket, *J. Appl. Mech.* **28**, 1–8 (1961).
6. G. A. Bliss, "Lectures on the Calculus of Variations." Univ. of Chicago Press, Chicago, Illinois, 1946.

7. V. A. Troitskii, O variatsionnysh zadachakh optimizatsii processov upravlenua (On variational problems of control processes), *Prikl. Mat. Mekh.* **26**, 29–38 (1962).
8. L. D. Berkovitz, Variational methods in problems of control and programming, *J. Math. Anal. Appl.* **3**, 145–187 (1961).
9. E. V. Tarasov, "Optimal'nie rezhimi poliota letatel'nykh apparatov" ("Optimal Regimes of Flight"). Oborongiz, Moscow, 1963.
10. L. Dahlard, Application of Pontryagin's maximum principle in determining the control of a variable mass-vehicle, *Progr. Astron. Rocketry* **8**, 21–29 (1962).
11. V. K. Isayev and V. V. Sonin, Ob odnoi nelineinoi zadache optimal'nogo upravleniia (On certain non-linear problems of optimal control), *Avtomat. Telemekh.* (*Automat. Remote Control*) **23**, 1117–1129 (1962).
12. A. I. Lurie, Svobodnoe padenie material'noi tochki v Kabine sputnika (Free fall of a material point inside of a satellite's cabin), *Prikl. Mat. Mekh.* **27**, 3–9 (1963).
13. V. F. Illarionov and L. M. Shkadov, Povorot ploskosti krugovoi orbiti sputnika [Turning of the satellite's orbital plane (circular orbit)], *Prikl. Mat. Mekh.* **26**, 15–21 (1962).
14. H. Lass and C. Solloway, Motion of a satellite under the influence of a constant normal thrust, *ARS J.* **32**, 97–100 (1962).
15. Yu. P. Gus'kov, Metod upravleniia povorotom ploskosti krugovoi orbiti sputnika (Method of control over the satellite's orbital plane turning), *Prikl. Mat. Mekh.* **27**, 578–582 (1963).
16. G. L. Grodzovskii, Yu. P. Ivanov, and V. V. Tokarev, Mekhanika kosmicheskogo poliota s maloi tiagoi (Mechanics of the low-thrust space flight), I; *Inzh. Zh.* **3**, 590–616 (1963); II: *ibid.* **3**, 748–768 (1963); III; *ibid.* **4**, 168–195 (1964).
17. B. D. Fried, Trajectory optimization for powered flight in two or three dimensions, *in* "Space Technology." Chap. IV. Wiley, New York, 1959.
18. D. F. Lawden, Optimal powered arcs in an inverse square law field, *ARS J.* **31**, 566–568 (1961).
19. D. F. Lawden, Optimal intermediate-thrust arcs in a gravitational field, *Astronaut. Acta* **8**, 106–123 (1962).
20. W. G. Melbourne and C. G. Sauer, Jr., Optimum interplanetary rendezvous with power-limited vehicles, *AIAA J.* **1**, 54–60 (1963).

5

The Mayer-Bolza Problem for Multiple Integrals: Some Optimum Problems for Elliptic Differential Equations Arising in Magnetohydrodynamics

K. A. LURIE

DEPARTMENT OF MATHEMATICAL PHYSICS,
A. F. IOFFE PHYSICO-TECHNICAL INSTITUTE, ACADEMY OF SCIENCES OF THE USSR,
LENINGRAD, USSR

5.0 Introduction

In recent years, considerable interest has arisen in optimum problems for objects whose characteristics are continuously distributed in space and time. Problems of that kind appear in various branches of mathematical physics, especially in continuum mechanics and electromagnetic theory; e.g., different problems of continuous heating in metallurgy, of drying processes,[1,2] some problems in the theory of growth of crystals,[3] in the theory of flight,[4] and so on. In short, optimum problems naturally arise for any continuous system controlled from outside. The control itself may be either concentrated or distributed in space; the latter case seems to be most difficult in practice, but simultaneously most promising from the point of view of optimization. In what follows, there will be presented an example of distributed control over the conductivity of the working fluid in magnetohydrodynamical channel flow, and we shall be able to estimate the advantages in power generation gained from it. Control over the conductivity of gas flow seems to be quite possible even now; it is very likely that analogous controls would become possible in such "classical" fields as mechanics of structures; if so, we should be led to optimum problems in the mathematical theory of elasticity.

It seems worthwhile to add that not any admissible but only optimal control need be realizable in practice. Moreover, in certain cases we may considerably simplify theoretical considerations by extending the class of admissible controls so that some physically unrealizable controls will be included as mathematically admissible. In a variety of practically important cases, the resulting optimal control will be realizable; if not, we may inquire into the possibilities of its approximate realization, and so on. These considerations will be illustrated in Sec. 5.3.

Mathematically, the optimum problems in question may be described as variational problems of the Mayer-Bolza type with partial differential equations as side conditions. There may be distinguished a class of optimum problems with integral equations as side conditions. Methods of solution for such problems began to be investigated only very recently. Bellman and Osborn[5] applied dynamic programming to the derivation of the well-known Hadamard formula for the variation of Green's function of the Laplace operator. Butkovsky and Lerner[6] formulated a very general optimum problem for systems with distributed parameters. Their work was followed by a series of publications by Butkovsky[7,8] in which there was demonstrated an analog of Pontryagin's maximum principle for optimum problems with distributed parameters and with integral equations as side conditions.

The case of constraints formulated by partial differential equations has also been examined by different writers. A. I. Egorov[2] has given the optimality conditions for processes described by quasilinear hyperbolic equations. Yu. V. Egorov[9] has outlined analogous conditions for a class of equations in Banach space, this class including hyperbolic and parabolic equations.

There is a vast class of optimum problems for hyperbolic equations which has been studied for a long time by different authors: namely, the determination of optimum forms of nozzles and bodies of revolution in hypersonic gas flow. In this field, there can be mentioned well-known papers by Guderley and Hantsch,[10] Rao,[11] and Shmiglevsky.[12,13] In these investigations, however, it has been possible (due to the special form of isoperimetric conditions:

given total length of a body or a nozzle) to reduce an optimum problem with two independent variables to a one-dimensional optimum problem.

The general case was only recently considered by Guderley and Armitage.[14] In their paper, the reduction to a one-dimensional problem is no longer possible because of a more general type of isoperimetric condition (area of the nozzle's surface given). Guderley and Armitage formulated only Euler equations and natural boundary conditions; the Weierstrass condition remained beyond the scope of their work. These ideas were quite recently exploited by Kraiko.[15]

The present author has considered a general problem of optimization with partial differential equations of any type given as side conditions.[16] The investigation was carried out according to traditional methods of the calculus of variations, the necessary condition of Weierstrass having been considered equivalent to an analog of Pontryagin's maximum principle. In the following sections, a detailed outline of these considerations will be given, together with an illustration of general principles by means of an example from magnetohydrodynamics.

5.1 Optimum Problems for Partial Differential Equations: Necessary Conditions for Optimality

5.11 Formulation of the Problem

Let S denote a closed domain in the xy plane with piecewise continuous boundaries Σ_1, Σ_2 (Fig. 1). In this domain, let us consider a system of partial differential equations

$$\Xi_i \equiv \frac{\partial z^i}{\partial x} - X_i(z, \zeta, u; x, y) = 0$$

$$\mathrm{H}_i \equiv \frac{\partial z^i}{\partial y} - Y_i(z, \zeta, u; x, y) = 0 \tag{5.1}$$

$$\frac{\partial Xi}{\partial y} - \frac{\partial Yi}{\partial x} = 0, \qquad i = 1, \dots, n$$

The latter equations contain total derivatives with respect to all the arguments included.

Vector functions $z = (z^1, \dots, z^n)$, $\zeta = (\zeta^1, \dots, \zeta^\nu)$ of the arguments x, y describe the mechanical system itself, while the functions $u = (u^1, \dots, u^p)$ of the same arguments present the "distributed controls." The couple of vector functions z, ζ will be called the state of a system.

Equations (5.1) present a standard form of any system of partial differential equations (so-called special case of the Pfaffian system).[17] In other words, any such system may be written in the form (5.1) (with the number of dependent variables increased if necessary). It should be mentioned that the presence of ζ variables is typical for the majority of applications. For example, the Helmholtz equation $z^1_{xx} + z^1_{yy} + uz^1 = 0$ is equivalent to the system

$$z_x^{\ 1} = z^2, \quad z_y^{\ 1} = z^3; \qquad z_x^{\ 2} = -\zeta^2 - uz^1, \quad z_y^{\ 2} = \zeta^1; \qquad z_x^{\ 3} = \zeta^1, \quad z_y^{\ 3} = \zeta^2$$

The wave equation $z^1_{yy} - (kz_x^{\ 1})_x = 0$ is evidently identical to the system

$$z_x^{\ 1} = -\zeta^1/k, \quad z_y^{\ 1} = \zeta^2; \qquad z_x^{\ 2} = \zeta^2, \quad z_y^{\ 2} = -\zeta^1$$

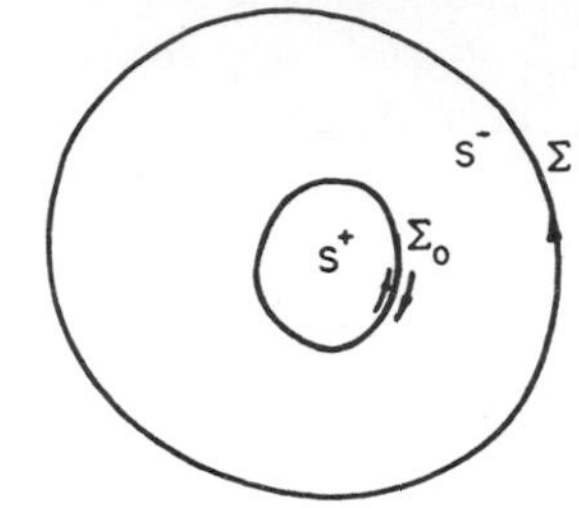

FIG. 1. Closed domain in xy plane.

The form (5.1) corresponds to the problems in a sense more general than those given by differential equations of higher order. For example, the system

$$z_x^{\ 1} = \zeta^1, \quad z_y^{\ 1} = -\zeta^2 + u; \qquad z_x^{\ 2} = \zeta^2, \quad z_y^{\ 2} = \zeta^1$$

is equivalent to equations

$$\Delta z^1 = \partial u/\partial y, \qquad \Delta z^2 = -\partial u/\partial x$$

only if u is differentiable. Note that the latter pair of equations contains derivatives of the control and not the control itself. The class of optimum problems for higher-order equations depending on controls (and not on their derivatives) was examined by A. I. Egorov.[2]

Returning to (5.1), let us formulate the restrictions imposed on the control functions. The first r_1 of these restrictions will be expressed by finite equalities

$$G_k(u; x, y) = 0, \qquad k = 1, \ldots, r_1 \tag{5.2}$$

the remaining $r - r_1$ having the form of finite inequalities

$$G_k(u; x, y) \geq 0, \qquad k = r_1 + 1, \ldots, r \leq p \tag{5.3}$$

Suppose that the first $n_1 \leq n$ functions z^i are prescribed at Σ_1, this boundary assumed known.

So far we have

$$z^i|_{\Sigma_1} = z_1{}^i(t), \qquad i = 1, \dots, n_1 \tag{5.4}$$

The number n_1 is determined by the conditions of any given problem.

The outer curve Σ_2 is not assumed known *a priori*; it is only supposed that along it there are prescribed $n_2 \leq n$ ordinary differential equations of the form

$$\Theta_{i_k} = \frac{dz^{i_k}}{dt} - T_{i_k}(z, v; t) = 0 \qquad i_k = i_1, \dots, i_{n_2} \tag{5.5}$$

These equations involve a set of functions

$$v^\kappa = v^\kappa(t) \qquad \kappa = 1, \dots, \pi$$

of the parameter t, which will be called boundary controls. The values of z^{i_k} $(t = 0)$ are assumed known. The boundary controls are also connected by constraints expressed by equalities

$$g_k(v; t) = 0 \qquad k = 1, \dots, \rho_1 \tag{5.6}$$

and inequalities

$$g_k(v; t) \geq 0 \qquad k = \rho_1 + 1, \dots, \rho \leq \pi \tag{5.7}$$

The total number of these constraints is equal to $\rho \leq \pi$.

It is essential that there will be supposed to exist a solution of Eqs. (5.1), (5.4), (5.5) under the restrictions (5.2), (5.3), (5.6), (5.7) imposed on the control functions. This requirement is satisfied for any properly formulated physical problem, and we may say that it produces a recipe for distinguishing between ζ and u variables in basic equations (5.1). In fact, the u variables are distinguished because they serve as immediate control variables. On the other hand, the ζ variables cannot be altered directly from outside, and generally there is no proper solution to Eqs. (5.1), (5.4), (5.5) when ζ variables are prescribed more or less arbitrarily on S. The existence of such solutions for some u would be equivalent to the nonuniqueness of the solution z, ζ for the u in question. In what follows, we shall not consider such cases.

The Mayer-Bolza problem is now formulated as follows. In a suitable class of functions, determine the state variables z^i, ζ^j and controls u^k, v^κ so as to minimize the functional

$$J = \iint_S F(z, \zeta, u; x, y)\, dx\, dy + \oint_{\Sigma_1} f_1(z, t)\, dt + \oint_{\Sigma_2} f_2(z, v; t)\, dt \tag{5.8}$$

subject to side conditions (5.1)–(5.7). The functions X_i, Y_i, F, f_1, f_2 are assumed differentiable with respect to all their arguments.

In the following section we shall explain the notion of "suitable class" of functions because this point is essential to the very existence of the solution to the optimal problem.

5.12 Admissible Controls and Possible Behavior of State Variables

For further consideration, it is necessary to specify the class of admissible controls and possible behavior of state variables. The "distributed controls" will be assumed to belong to a class of functions no less wide than the class of piecewise continuous functions of two independent variables. Possible discontinuities of distributed controls may occur along smooth, closed, isolated curves Σ_0. In what follows, we shall suppose for the sake of simplicity that there is one such discontinuity along a curve Σ_0 lying entirely inside S, and that this curve may be continuously deformed to any of the boundary curves Σ_1 or Σ_2.

The state variables z^i are assumed continuous across the curve Σ_0; the variables ζ^j are in general discontinuous but their values on both sides of Σ_0 are connected by the requirement that the tangential derivatives $\partial z^i/\partial t$ along Σ_0 be continuous, i.e.,

$$[X_i x_t + Y_i y_t]_-^+ = 0, \qquad i = 1, \ldots, n \tag{5.9}$$

Boundary controls v also will be assumed to belong to a class of functions no less wide than that of the piecewise continuous functions of t. For simplicity, there will be hypothesized only one point t_* of such discontinuity, this point being a point of continuity for $z^i(t)$ and a corner point of the curve Σ_2. The latter assumption is necessary for discontinuity of dz^{i_k}/dt across t_*, because otherwise we should have permitted some line of discontinuity of $\partial z^{i_k}/\partial x$, $\partial z^{i_k}/\partial y$ starting from t_* on the boundary Σ_2 and going inside S. Such a line of discontinuity can only be connected with a jump of the distributed control u across it, but we have already assumed above that there is no such line intersecting the boundaries Σ_1 or Σ_2.†

5.13 Euler Equations and Natural Boundary Conditions

First we shall try to transform the restrictions (5.3) and (5.7) expressed by inequalities to others expressed by equalities. In a traditional way,[18] we introduce (real) artificial controls $u_* = (u_*^{r_1+1}, \ldots, u_*^{r})$, $v_* = (v_*^{\rho_1+1}, \ldots, v_*^{\rho})$ by virtue of the following equations:

$$G_k^* \equiv G_k(u; x, y) - (u_*^k)^2 = 0, \qquad k = r_1 + 1, \ldots, r \tag{5.10}$$

$$g_k^* \equiv g_k(u; x, y) - (v_*^k)^2 = 0, \qquad k = \rho_1 + 1, \ldots, \rho \tag{5.11}$$

†*Note added in proof:* In hyperbolic problems, a corner point of the boundary may initiate some line of discontinuity of the first derivatives going inside S without any jump of the distributed control across it (see Kraiko[15]).

these equations now taking the place of (5.3) and (5.7). So far we have passed from a closed region of control variation to an open region, but for an increased number of control functions.

To proceed, let us now introduce the Lagrange multipliers

$$\xi_i^{\pm}(x, y), \quad \eta_i^{\pm}(x, y), \qquad i = 1, \dots, n$$
$$\Gamma_k^{\pm}(x, y), \quad k = 1, \dots, r_1; \qquad \Gamma_k^{*\pm}(x, y), \quad k = r_1 + 1, \dots, r$$
$$\theta_{i_k}(t), \quad i_k = i_1, \dots, i_{n_2}$$
$$\gamma_k(t), \quad k = 1, \dots, \rho_1; \qquad \gamma_k{}^*(t), \quad k = \rho_1 + 1, \dots, \rho$$

With the aid of these multipliers, we construct a functional

$$\Pi = J + \iint_{S^+} (\xi^+\Xi^+ + \eta^+\mathrm{H}^+ + \Gamma^+G^+ + \Gamma^{*+}G^{*+})\, dx\, dy$$
$$+ \iint_{S^-} (\xi^-\Xi^- + \eta^-\mathrm{H}^- + \Gamma^-G^- + \Gamma^{*-}G^{*-})\, dx\, dy$$
$$+ \oint_{\Sigma_2} (\theta\Theta + \gamma g + \gamma^* g^*)\, dt \tag{5.12}$$

Here S^+ denotes a region bounded by the curves Σ_1 and Σ_0, S^-, a region bounded by Σ_0 and Σ_2 (Fig. 1); the products of vector functions are interpreted as scalar products.

The functional Π is always equal to J, these two being simultaneously stationary.

Let L, l_1, l_2 denote the Lagrangians

$$\begin{aligned} L &= F + \xi\Xi + \eta\mathrm{H} + \Gamma G + \Gamma^* G^* \\ l_1 &= f_1, \qquad l_2 = f_2 + \theta\Theta + \gamma g + \gamma^* g^* \end{aligned} \tag{5.13}$$

The first variation of Π is composed of double integrals, line integrals along Σ_1, Σ_0, Σ_2, and nonintegral terms.

The double-integral part of the first variation is equal to

$$\iint_{S^+} \left(\frac{\partial L^+}{\partial z^{i+}} - \frac{\partial \xi_i{}^+}{\partial x} - \frac{\partial \eta_i{}^+}{\partial y}\right) \delta z^{i+}\, dx\, dy + \iint_{S^-} \left(\frac{\partial L^-}{\partial z^{i-}} - \frac{\partial \xi_i{}^-}{\partial x} - \frac{\partial \eta_i{}^-}{\partial y}\right) \delta z^{i-}\, dx\, dy$$
$$+ \iint_{S^+} \frac{\partial L^+}{\partial \zeta^{j+}} \delta\zeta^{j+}\, dx\, dy + \iint_{S^-} \frac{\partial L^-}{\partial \zeta^{j-}} \delta\zeta^{j-}\, dx\, dy + \iint_{S^+} \frac{\partial L^+}{\partial u^{k+}} \delta u^{k+}\, dx\, dy$$
$$+ \iint_{S^-} \frac{\partial L^-}{\partial u^{k-}} \delta u^{k-}\, dx\, dy + \iint_{S^+} \frac{\partial L^+}{\partial u_*^{k+}} \delta u_*^{k+}\, dx\, dy + \iint_{S^-} \frac{\partial L^-}{\partial u_*^{k-}} \delta u_*^{k-}\, dx\, dy \tag{5.14}$$

Consider the line integral $\oint_\Sigma f\,dt$ where f denotes the limiting value on the curve Σ of the function determined in the domain bounded by Σ and continuously differentiable there up to the curve Σ. To take the variation of this integral, one should follow the rule

$$\delta \oint_\Sigma f\,dt = \oint_\Sigma \delta f\,dt + \oint_\Sigma \left(\frac{f}{\rho} + \frac{\partial f}{\partial n}\right) \delta n\,dt \tag{5.15}$$

Here ρ denotes the radius of curvature of Σ, and δn the variation of the outer normal to this curve.

In the expression for the first variation there appears an integral along Σ_1, namely,

$$\oint_{\Sigma_1} \left(\frac{\partial l_1}{\partial z^{i+}} + \xi_i^+ \frac{dy}{dt} - \eta_i^+ \frac{dx}{dt}\right) \delta z^{i+}\,dt \tag{5.16}$$

The analogous integral taken along Σ_0 is

$$\oint_{\Sigma_0} \left\{\left[\left(\xi_i \frac{dy}{dt} - \eta_i \frac{dx}{dt}\right) \delta z^i\right]_-^+ + (L)_-^+ \delta n\right\} dt \tag{5.17}$$

To construct an integral along Σ_2, it is necessary to take into account the discontinuity of boundary controls. This may be actually done at a corner point t_* on the curve Σ_2. We have ($\delta_\alpha{}^\beta$ denotes Kronecker symbol)

$$\oint_{\Sigma_2} \left[\left(\xi_i^- \frac{dy}{dt} - \eta_i^- \frac{dx}{dt} + \frac{\partial l_2}{\partial z^{i-}} - \frac{d\theta_{i_k}}{dt} \delta_i^{i_k}\right) \delta z^{i-} \right.$$
$$\left. + \frac{\partial l_2}{\partial v^\kappa} \delta v^\kappa + \frac{\partial l_2}{\partial v_*{}^\kappa} \delta v_*{}^\kappa + \left(L^- + \frac{l_2}{\rho_2} + \frac{\partial l_2}{\partial n}\right) \delta n \right] dt + (\theta_{i_k}\, \delta z^{i_k})_+^- \tag{5.18}$$

The last term in this formula denotes a contribution to the first variation from the corner point t_*, and is equal to the difference between the expressions in brackets taken just before and after t_* (the words "before" and "after" correspond to the positive direction determined on Σ_2).

Along the line Σ_0 we have

$$\delta f = \Delta f - \frac{\partial f}{\partial n} \delta n \tag{5.19}$$

Here Δf denotes total variation of f.

The functions z^i are supposed continuous across Σ_0, this being also true for their total variations. The functions ζ^j and u^k are discontinuous across Σ_0. So far we can write (5.17) in the following way:

$$\oint_{\Sigma_0} \left\{\left(\xi_i \frac{dy}{dt} - \eta_i \frac{dx}{dt}\right)_-^+ \Delta z^i + \left[L - \left(\xi_i \frac{dy}{dt} - \eta_i \frac{dx}{dt}\right) \frac{\partial z^i}{\partial n}\right]_-^+ \delta n\right\} dt \tag{5.20}$$

At the point t_* of discontinuity of the boundary controls on Σ_2 there applies the relation $\delta z^i = \Delta z^i - (\text{grad } z^i \cdot \delta \mathbf{r})$. Here $\delta \mathbf{r}$ denotes a variation of the position vector of the corner point.

Taking into account the continuity of the total variations of z^i at the corner point, we may present the last term in (5.18) in the following form:

$$[\theta_{i_k}(t_*)]_+^- \Delta z^{i_k}(t_*) - [\theta_{i_k}(t_*) \text{ grad } z^{i_k}]_+^- \cdot \delta \mathbf{r} \tag{5.21}$$

The first variation of Π is composed by summing up expressions (5.14), (5.16), (5.18) and (5.20).

Now we can follow the usual argument of the calculus of variations to derive necessary conditions of stationarity.

We have:

In the regions $S^\pm$,

$$\frac{\partial \xi_i^\pm}{\partial x} + \frac{\partial \eta_i^\pm}{\partial y} - \frac{\partial L^\pm}{\partial z^{i\pm}} = 0, \quad i = 1, \ldots, n; \qquad \frac{\partial L^\pm}{\partial \zeta^{j\pm}} = 0, \quad j = 1, \ldots, v$$

$$\frac{\partial L^\pm}{\partial u^{k\pm}} = 0, \quad k = 1, \ldots, p; \qquad \frac{\partial L^\pm}{\partial u_*^{k\pm}} \equiv -2\Gamma_k^{*\pm} u_*^{k\pm} = 0, \quad k = r_1 + 1, \ldots, r \tag{5.22}$$

Along the line Σ_1,

$$\frac{\partial l_1}{\partial z^{i+}} + \xi_i^+ \frac{dy}{dt} - \eta_i^+ \frac{dx}{dt} = 0, \qquad i = n_1 + 1, \ldots, n \tag{5.23}$$

Along the line Σ_2,

$$\delta_i^{i_k} \frac{d\theta_i}{dt} - \frac{\partial l_2}{\partial z^{i-}} - \xi_i^- \frac{dy}{dt} + \eta_i^- \frac{dx}{dt} = 0, \quad i = 1, \ldots, n \tag{5.24}$$

$$\frac{\partial l_2}{\partial v^\kappa} = 0, \quad \kappa = 1, \ldots, \pi, \qquad \frac{\partial l_2}{\partial v_*{}^\kappa} = 2\gamma_\kappa{}^* v_*{}^\kappa - 0, \quad \kappa = \rho_1 + 1, \ldots, \rho$$

$$L^- + \frac{l_2}{\rho_2} + \frac{\partial l_2}{\partial n} = 0$$

At the point t_* of discontinuity of boundary controls,

$$\theta_{i_k}^-(t_*) = \theta_{i_k}^+(t_*), \qquad i_k = i_1, \ldots, i_{n_2}$$
$$\theta_{i_k}^-(t_*) \text{ grad } z^{i_k -}(t_*) = \theta_{i_k}^+(t_*) \text{ grad } z^{i_k +}(t_*) \tag{5.25}$$

Along the line Σ_0 of discontinuity of distributed controls,

$$\left(\xi_i \frac{dy}{dt} - \eta_i \frac{dx}{dt}\right)_-^+ = 0, \qquad i = 1, \ldots, n$$

$$\left[L - \left(\xi_i \frac{dy}{dt} - \eta_i \frac{dx}{dt}\right) \frac{\partial z^i}{\partial n}\right]_-^+ = 0 \tag{5.26}$$

The last equation can be transformed by the aid of the Hadamard-Hugoniot theorem and the first of Eqs. (5.26); we may write

$$(L)_-^+ - \xi_i^+(z_x{}^i)_-^+ - \eta_i(z_y{}^i)_-^+ = 0 \tag{5.27}$$

The stationarity conditions (5.22)–(5.26) may be rewritten in a Hamiltonian form. To do this, we first introduce "impulses" $\partial L/\partial z_x{}^i$, $\partial L/\partial z_y{}^i$, and make certain that these are just the same as Lagrange multipliers ξ_i, η_i.

Let H denote the "Hamiltonian"

$$\mathsf{H} = [z_x{}^i L_{z_x{}^i} + z_y{}^i L_{z_y{}^i} - L]_{z_x{}^i = X_i, z_y{}^i = Y_i} = \xi X + \eta Y - F - \Gamma G - \Gamma^* G^* \tag{5.28}$$

The following relations are evident:

$$\begin{aligned} &\mathsf{H}_x = -L_x, \quad \mathsf{H}_y = -L_y, \quad \mathsf{H}_{z^i} = -L_{z^i}, \quad \mathsf{H}_{\zeta^j} = -L_{\zeta^j} \\ &\mathsf{H}_{u^k} = -L_{u^k}, \quad \mathsf{H}_{u_*{}^k} = -L_{u_*{}^k}, \quad \mathsf{H}_{\xi_i} = X_i, \quad \mathsf{H}_{\eta_i} = Y_i \end{aligned} \tag{5.29}$$

Making use of these formulas, let us replace the first pair of Eqs. (5.1) and the first of Eqs. (5.22) with the following relations:

$$z_x{}^i = \frac{\partial \mathsf{H}}{\partial \xi_i}, \qquad z_y{}^i = \frac{\partial \mathsf{H}}{\partial \eta_i}, \qquad \frac{\partial \xi_i}{\partial x} + \frac{\partial \eta_i}{\partial y} = -\frac{\partial \mathsf{H}}{\partial z^i} \tag{5.30}$$

These equations have just the same form as the canonical equations of Volterra.[19] The coincidence is as yet, however, merely formal because the H function is by no means Hamiltonian until we eliminate the variables ζ^j and controls u by the aid of the rest of Eqs. (5.22). This is the argument for the quotation marks in the definition of H above [Eq. (5.28)].

The other equations may also be rewritten in a similar way. We have

$$\begin{aligned} &\frac{\partial \mathsf{H}}{\partial \zeta^j} = 0, \quad j = 1, \ldots, v; \qquad \frac{\partial \mathsf{H}}{\partial u^k} = 0, \quad k = 1, \ldots, p \\ &\frac{\partial \mathsf{H}}{\partial u_*{}^k} \equiv 2\Gamma_k{}^* u_*{}^k = 0, \quad k = r_1 + 1, \ldots, r \end{aligned} \tag{5.31}$$

Equation (5.27) can be represented in the following form:

$$(\mathsf{H})_-^+ = z_x^{i-}(\xi_i)_-^+ + z_y^{i-}(\eta_i)_-^+ \tag{5.32}$$

By the same argument we can see that the "impulses" $\partial l_2/\partial z_t^{i_k}$ calculated from the Lagrangian l_2 [Eq. (5.13)] coincide with the Lagrange multipliers θ_{i_k}. We introduce the "Hamiltonian"

$$\mathsf{h} = [z_t{}^i l_{2 z_t{}^i} - l_2]_{z_t{}^{i_k} = T_{i_k}} = \theta_{i_k} T_{i_k} - f_2 - \gamma g - \gamma^* g^* \tag{5.33}$$

and write down the "canonical equations"

$$\frac{dz^{i_k}}{dt} = \frac{\partial \mathsf{h}}{\partial \theta_{i_k}}, \qquad \frac{d\theta_{i_k}}{dt} = -\frac{\partial \mathsf{h}}{\partial z^{i_k}} + \xi_{i_k}^- \frac{dy}{dt} - \eta_{i_k}^- \frac{dx}{dt} \tag{5.34}$$

The control variables v^κ, $v_*{}^\kappa$ are to be eliminated from h with the aid of relations

$$\frac{\partial \mathsf{h}}{\partial v^\kappa} = 0, \quad \kappa = 1, \dots, \pi; \qquad \frac{\partial \mathsf{h}}{\partial v_*{}^\kappa} \equiv 2\gamma^* v_*{}^\kappa = 0, \quad \kappa = \rho_1 + 1, \dots, \rho \tag{5.35}$$

5.14 The Weierstrass Condition

In this section, we present a detailed derivation of the necessary condition for a minimum. Its analog for an ordinary Mayer-Bolza problem is well known as the Weierstrass condition. First of all, we shall formulate the basic theorem.

Let us denote by $E^{(1)}$ and $E^{(2)}$ the Weierstrass functions

$$\begin{aligned} E^{(1)} = {} & L(z, Z_x, Z_y, \mathrm{Z}, U, U_* ; \xi, \eta, \Gamma, \Gamma^*, x, y) \\ & - L(z, z_x, z_y, \zeta, u, u_* ; \xi, \eta, \Gamma, \Gamma^*, x, y) \\ & - (Z_x{}^i - z_x{}^i) \frac{\partial L}{\partial z_x{}^i} - (Z_y{}^i - z_y{}^i) \frac{\partial L}{\partial z_y{}^i} \end{aligned} \tag{5.36}$$

$$\begin{aligned} E^{(2)} = {} & l_2(z, Z_t, V, V_* ; \theta, \gamma, \gamma^*, t) \\ & - l_2(z, z_t, v, v_* ; \theta, \gamma, \gamma^*, t) - (Z_t^{i_\kappa} - z_t^{i_\kappa}) \frac{\partial l_2}{\partial z_t^{i_\kappa}} \end{aligned} \tag{5.37}$$

In these formulas z, ζ, u and v correspond to the optimum values of state variables and controls, and Z, Z, U, V denote any set of admissible functions which satisfy the conditions formulated in Sec. 5.12.

The Weierstrass conditions necessary for a strong relative minimum reduce to the following inequalities

$$E^{(1)} \geq 0, \qquad E^{(2)} \geq 0 \tag{5.38}$$

The demonstration will be based on the assumption that the extremal surface S bounded by closed curves Σ_1 and Σ_2 may be imbedded in a family of integral surfaces $S(b)$ bounded by the curves Σ_1 and $\Sigma_2(b)$, depending on $n_1 + n_2$ parameters b_i $(i = 1, \dots, n_1 + n_2)$.

In this family we define the functions

$$\begin{gathered} z^i(b; x, y), \quad i = 1, \dots, n; \qquad \zeta^j(b; x, y), \quad j = 1, \dots, \nu \\ u^k(b; x, y), \quad k = 1, \dots, p \end{gathered} \tag{5.39}$$

and along the boundary curves Σ_1 and $\Sigma_2(b)$ the functions

$$\begin{gathered} z_2{}^i(b; t), \quad \zeta_2{}^j(b; t), \quad u_2{}^k(b; t), \quad v^\kappa(b, t) \\ x(b; t), \quad y(b; t) \quad \text{along } \Sigma_2(b) \end{gathered} \tag{5.40}$$

Both sets of functions are determined in such a way that they satisfy Eqs. (5.1)–(5.7) and convert into the functions corresponding to the extremal surface $S(\Sigma_1, \Sigma_2)$ under vanishing of the parameters b_i.

In what follows, it will be supposed that all restrictions imposed on the control variables are already expressed by finite equalities (cf. Sec. 5.13).

Let Σ' denote a smooth closed curve bounding the region S' and lying entirely inside S^+ or S^- so that the curves Σ' and Σ_0 have no common points. Let us also choose some (noncorner) point t' on the curve $\Sigma_2(t' \neq t_*)$.† Consider now a closed curve Σ_e' drawn outside Σ' parallel to it at the distance $e > 0$ and let $S_e' - S'$ denote a ring-shaped region bounded by both curves.

The equations of Σ' and Σ_e' are as follows

$$\begin{array}{lll} (\Sigma') & x = x'(t), & y = y'(t) \\ (\Sigma_e') & x = x'(t) + e\cos nx, & y = y'(t) + e \cos ny \end{array} \tag{5.41}$$

Here $\cos nx$, $\cos ny$ denote direction cosines of the outer normal to Σ'. When $e = 0$, the curves Σ' and Σ_e' coincide and the region $S_e' - S'$ vanishes. The part of $S(b)$ lying outside Σ_e' will be denoted by $S_b - S_e'$.

Consider the following sets of functions:

$$\begin{array}{llll} z_1{}^i(b, e; x, y), & \zeta_1{}^j(b, e; x, y), & u^k(b; x, y), & (x, y) \in S' \\ Z^i(b, e; x, y), & \mathrm{Z}^j(b, e;, x, y), & U^k(x, y), & (x, y) \in S_e' - S' \\ z_3{}^j(b, e; x, y), & \zeta_3{}^j(b, e; x, y), & u^k(b; x, y), & (x, y) \in S_b - S_e' \end{array} \tag{5.42}$$

The first and the third of these families satisfy Eqs. (5.1) and (5.2), together with the boundary conditions (5.4); the second satisfies the same equations with z^i replaced by Z^i, and so on.

In the same way, we consider a segment $(t', t' + \varepsilon)$ on the curve $\Sigma_2(b)$ $(0 \leq t \leq t_2)$ and introduce two families of functions

$$\begin{array}{c} Z_2{}^i(b, e; t), \quad \mathrm{Z}_2{}^j(b; e; t), \quad u_2{}^k(b; t), \quad V^\kappa(t), \qquad t' \leq t \leq t' + \varepsilon \\ z_2{}^i(b, e, \varepsilon; t), \quad \zeta_2{}^j(b, e, \varepsilon; t), \quad u_2{}^k(b; t), \quad v^\kappa(b; t) \\ 0 < t < t', \qquad t' + \varepsilon < t < t_2 \end{array} \tag{5.43}$$

These functions satisfy Eqs. (5.5), (5.6), and corresponding initial conditions (see Sec. 5.11).

For the sake of brevity, we introduce the notation

$$\begin{array}{llll} \delta_b z_\alpha{}^i = \dfrac{\partial z^i}{\partial b_\alpha}, & \delta_b \zeta_\alpha{}^j = \dfrac{\partial \zeta^j}{\partial b_\alpha}, & \delta_b u_\alpha{}^k = \dfrac{\partial u^k}{\partial b_\alpha}, & \delta_b v_\alpha{}^\kappa = \dfrac{\partial v^\kappa}{\partial b_\alpha} \\ \delta_e z^i = \dfrac{\partial z^i}{\partial e}, & \delta_e \zeta^j = \dfrac{\partial \zeta^j}{\partial e}, & \delta_\varepsilon z^i = \dfrac{\partial z^i}{\partial \varepsilon}, & \delta_\varepsilon \zeta^j = \dfrac{\partial \zeta^j}{\partial \varepsilon} \end{array} \tag{5.44}$$

† Here and henceforth we do not differentiate the notation used for surfaces and curves and their projections onto the xy plane.

The sets of functions constructed above are subjected to the following conditions:

The sets (5.42) to

$$\begin{aligned} Z^i(b, e; x, y)\,\big|_{\Sigma'} &= z_1{}^i(b, e; x, y)\,\big|_{\Sigma'} \\ Z^i(b, e; x, y)\,\big|_{\Sigma_e'} &= z_3{}^i(b, e; x, y)\,\big|_{\Sigma_e'} \\ \operatorname{grad}(Z^i - z^i)\,\big|_{\Sigma'} &= \mathbf{n}[\delta_e z_3{}^i - \delta_e z_1{}^i]\big|_{\Sigma'} = \mathbf{n}[(\delta_e z^i)_1^3]_{\Sigma'} \end{aligned} \tag{5.45}$$

the last equation being valid in the limit $e = 0$.

The sets (5.43) to

$$\begin{aligned} Z_2{}^i(b, e; t) &= z_2{}^i(b, e, \varepsilon; t') \\ Z_2{}^i(b, e; t' + \varepsilon) &= z_2{}^i(b, e, \varepsilon; t' + \varepsilon) \\ Z_{2t}^i(t') &= z_{2t}^i(t') + \delta_\varepsilon z_2{}^i(t') \end{aligned} \tag{5.46}$$

Now we consider the functional

$$\begin{aligned} \Pi(b, e, \varepsilon) = \iint_{S'} L[z_1(b, e; x, y), z_{1x}(b, e; x, y), z_{1y}(b, e; x, y), \\ \zeta_1(b, e; x, y), u(b; x, y)]\, dx\, dy \\ + \iint_{S_e' - S'} L[Z(b, e; x, y), Z_x(b, e; x, y), Z_y(b, e; x, y), \\ \mathbf{Z}(b, e; x, y), U(x, y)]\, dx\, dy \\ + \iint_{S_b - S_e'} L[z_3(b, e; x, y), z_{3x}(b, e; x, y), z_{3y}(b, e; x, y), \\ \zeta_3(b, e; x, y), u(b; x, y)]\, dx\, dy + \oint_{\Sigma_1} l_1[z(b, e; t)]\, dt \\ + \left[\int_0^{t'} + \int_{t'+\varepsilon}^{t_2}\right] l[z_2(b, e, \varepsilon; t), z_{2t}(b, e, \varepsilon; t), v(b; t)]\, dt \\ + \int_{t'}^{t'+\varepsilon} l[Z_2(b, e; t), Z_{2t}(b, e; t), V(t)]\, dt \end{aligned} \tag{5.47}$$

Making use of the stationarity conditions (5.22)–(5.26), we may write

$$\left.\frac{\partial \Pi}{\partial b_\alpha}\right|_{e=\varepsilon=0} = 0 \tag{5.48}$$

and

$$\begin{aligned} \left.\frac{\partial \Pi}{\partial e}\right|_{e=\varepsilon=0} = \oint_{\Sigma'} \Big[L(z, Z_x, Z_y, \mathbf{Z}, U) - L(z, z_x, z_y, \zeta, u) \\ - \left(\frac{\partial L}{\partial z_x{}^i} (\delta_e z^i)_1^3 \cos(nx) + \frac{\partial L}{\partial z_y{}^i} (\delta_e z^i)_1^3 \cos(ny)\right)\Big]\, dt \end{aligned} \tag{5.49}$$

$$\left.\frac{\partial \Pi}{\partial \varepsilon}\right|_{e=\varepsilon=0} = l_2(z_2, Z_{2t}, V; t') - l_2(z_2, z_{2t}, v; t') - \left.\frac{\partial l_2}{\partial z_{2t}^i}\right|_{t'} \delta_\varepsilon z_2{}^i(t') \tag{5.50}$$

Let us now take advantage of boundary conditions (5.4) and those prescribed for the z^{i_k} functions at the point $t = 0$ on Σ_2. These conditions provide n_1 finite relations among the parameters b_i, and n_2 relations among b_i, e and ε. Suppose now that it is possible to determine from these equations all the b_i as functions of e and ε, these functions vanishing when $e = \varepsilon = 0$.

That total differential of $\Pi(b, e, \varepsilon)$ evaluated for $e = \varepsilon = 0$ on the extremal is now equal to

$$d\Pi = \left[\frac{\partial \Pi}{\partial e} + \frac{\partial \Pi}{\partial b}\frac{\partial b}{\partial e}\right]_{e=\varepsilon=0} de + \left[\frac{\partial \Pi}{\partial \varepsilon} + \frac{\partial \Pi}{\partial b}\frac{\partial b}{\partial \varepsilon}\right]_{e=\varepsilon=0} d\varepsilon$$

This expression can be modified by virtue of (5.45), (5.46) and (5.48)–(5.50) to the form

$$d\Pi = \left[\oint_{\Sigma'} E^{(1)}\,dt\right] de + E^{(2)}(t')\,d\varepsilon \tag{5.51}$$

To make Π (and J) minimum, it is necessary that $d\Pi \geq 0$.

Note that only positive values of e, ε (or de and $d\varepsilon$) correspond to admissible surfaces (boundary curves). This is equivalent to the requirement that

$$\oint_{\Sigma'} E^{(1)}\,dt \geq 0, \qquad E^{(2)}(t') \geq 0$$

The arbitrariness of the curve Σ' on the extremal surface and of the point t' on its boundary lead us now to the Weierstrass conditions (5.38). These conditions can be rewritten in terms of the "Hamiltonians" H and h [see Eqs. (5.28) and (5.30)], the modified form being

$$\begin{gathered}\mathsf{H}(z, \mathbf{Z}, U, U_* ; \xi, \eta, \Gamma, \Gamma^*) \leq \mathsf{H}(z, \zeta, u, u_* ; \xi, \eta, \Gamma, \Gamma^*)\\ \mathsf{h}(z, V, V_* ; \theta, \gamma, \gamma^*) \leq \mathsf{h}(z, v, v_* ; \theta, \gamma, \gamma^*)\end{gathered} \tag{5.52}$$

We stress that the "admissible" variables $\mathbf{Z}$, U included here are to be so chosen as to satisfy Eq. (5.9) which expresses the continuity of z^i across any admissible line; in particular, for elliptic problems this means that the values x_t, y_t are arbitrary except for the restriction $x_t^2 + y_t^2 = 1$.

This formulation of the Weierstrass conditions provides an analog to the well-known maximum principle derived by Pontryagin for ordinary minimum problems.[20] We may add that the "artificial controls" u_* and v_* do not actually enter into the expressions for H and h [Eqs. (5.28), (5.30)]. Lastly, inequalities (5.52) are also valid for corner lines (and points) due to considerations of continuity.

5.2 Optimum Problems in the Theory of Magnetohydrodynamical Channel Flow

The motion of a conducting fluid through magnetic fields is characterized by some peculiar effects studied by means of magnetohydrodynamics (mhd).

The most interesting and important applications of mhd are connected with the problem of power generation. In this problem, there is a variety of difficulties caused by technical restrictions currently in effect.

It is necessary, for example, to maintain highly intensive magnetic fields in large volumes to keep the conductivity of the working gas sufficiently high, to reduce the flow of heat to the walls of a channel, and so on.

The variety of different demands (which are sometimes conflicting) attaches considerable importance to considerations of optimality of power generation design, and the problems concerned are of great significance for applications of mhd.

Theoretical aspects of the power generation problem are based upon the investigations of the mhd channel flow. Corresponding calculations are often carried out according to the so-called one-dimensional approximation when only the dependence upon the longitudinal coordinate is considered. This approximation provides considerable information about certain obstacles to the intensification of the power conversion process, but of course it does not take into account two- and three-dimensional phenomena connected with the bending of the current lines inside the channel. This bending reduces the total current emitted from the electrodes and consequently presents an additional source of loss in the device. The reader is referred to a detailed survey[21] of the most important losses in the channel of a mhd generator.

Methods of optimization of mhd conversion regimes are largely determined by the nature of the losses to be decreased. There may be outlined a group of factors which can be considered as controls within the one-dimensional approximation, and suitable choice of these factors may well reduce the corresponding losses. The factors in question are the distribution of the external magnetic field along the channel, the choice of the channel's length and its transverse dimensions, and the selection of the initial data. One can indicate various criteria of optimization. Either the total current I flowing from the electrodes to the outer load R or the value of Joule heating Q are often chosen for such criteria. We can also introduce the effectivity μ defined as the ratio $IR/(IR + Q)$. Optimum regimes are characterized either by the maximum value of I (or of μ) or by the minimum value of Q.

Some one-dimensional optimum problems in magnetohydrodynamics have already been examined in the literature.[22,23] It should be noted that there is no principal difference between these problems and those arising in the theory of rocket flight. In both cases, optimum problems for ordinary differential equations are encountered.

The theory of mhd power conversion presents, however, more complicated two-dimensional optimum problems connected with so-called end effects in a mhd channel. In such a channel, there is observed a sort of current loss caused by inversely directed currents induced at the ends of a zone occupied by the external magnetic field. In other words, some part of the total current is branched out into the current loops inside those regions of the channel that are free of electromotive forces, instead of being turned into the external network. It is important to minimize losses of that kind, and such minimization can be effected in different ways. We may, for example, arrange either the optimum distribution of the conductivity of the working gas or the optimum distribution of the external magnetic field. Both factors are to be so chosen as to decrease end losses to the greatest possible extent.

The same argument may be followed to formulate several more complicated problems. Of these, we shall outline the optimum problems with the Hall effect taken into account.

Two-dimensional effects inside of an mhd channel have already been considered in the literature. For a bibliography, the reader is referred to the references at the end of this chapter, but we shall outline the main points in what follows.

In magnetohydrodynamics, the current density $\mathbf{j}$ depends on the electric field $\mathbf{E}$, magnetic field $\mathbf{H}$, and velocity $\mathbf{v}$ of the conducting fluid according to Ohm's law. For many interesting applications, this law can be written in the following form:

$$\mathbf{j} = \sigma \left(\mathbf{E} + \frac{1}{c} \mathbf{v} \times \mathbf{H} \right) \tag{5.53}$$

Here σ denotes the conductivity of the fluid and c the speed of light.

By virtue of the Maxwell equation

$$\text{curl } \mathbf{E} = -\frac{1}{c} \frac{\partial \mathbf{H}}{\partial t} \tag{5.54}$$

we may eliminate the electric field $\mathbf{E}$ from Eq. (5.53), the resulting equation taking the form

$$\frac{\partial \mathbf{H}}{\partial t} = \text{curl } (\mathbf{v} \times \mathbf{H}) - \text{curl } \nu_m \text{ curl } \mathbf{H} \tag{5.55}$$

It can be readily verified that the second term in the right-hand side of this equation prevails over the first term if

$$\text{Re}_m = \frac{VL}{\nu_m} \ll 1 \tag{5.56}$$

Here L and V denote typical linear dimension and speed of the fluid, respectively; $\nu_m = c^2/4\pi\sigma$ represents the so-called magnetic viscosity. The parameter Re_m is called the magnetic Reynolds number. It is clear from Eq. (5.55) that for small values of Re_m we can to a first approximation neglect the dependence of **H** on the velocity **v** of the conducting fluid. In this approximation, only the external magnetic field should be taken into account. This situation is typical for power conversion conditions where we have, for example:

$$L = 10^2 \text{ cm}, \qquad V = 10^5 \text{ cm/sec}, \qquad \nu_m = 10^9 \text{ cm}^2/\text{sec}, \qquad \text{Re}_m = 10^{-2}$$

Some additional remarks concerning the velocity of the working fluid are to be made. In general, the velocity distribution is governed by the totality of the basic equations of mhd.[24] In certain circumstances, however, it is possible to separate the equations for the velocity from those for the magnetic field and electric currents. A detailed account of such possibilities can be found elsewhere.[25] For our present aim, it suffices to restrict the analysis to those cases when the density of the Lorentz force is small compared with that of the inertial force. The ratio of the two is characterized by the so-called mhd parameter of interaction

$$N = \frac{\sigma {B_0}^2 h}{\rho_0 V}$$

Here B_0 and ρ_0 denote typical values of the magnetic field and gas density, respectively; h represents a typical transverse dimension.

We shall suppose that $N \ll 1$, this assumption corresponding to the weak interaction between the flow and the outer load. In fact, from this it follows that the influence of the outer load on the velocity distribution is negligible, and that one can treat this distribution as given from the outside.

This is equivalent to the assumption that the supply of kinetic energy of the working gas dominates that part of it which is converted into electricity.

So far, the inequalities $\text{Re}_m \ll 1$, $N \ll 1$ allow us to treat the distributions of magnetic induction, $\mathbf{B} = \mathbf{H}$ and the velocity **v** of the working gas as given functions of the coordinates. The outcome is not only a considerable simplification of the fundamental equations, but also permits us to treat the functions **B** and **v** as control functions. Under the formulated assumptions, the mhd equations reduce to Eqs. (5.53) and (5.54) combined with the equation of continuity

$$\operatorname{div} \mathbf{j} = 0 \tag{5.57}$$

for the electric current density **j**. Let us now suppose that there is only one component of the velocity **v**, namely, $\mathbf{v} = V(y)\mathbf{i}_1$ and a single component of magnetic induction, $\mathbf{B} = -B(x)\mathbf{i}_3$. Having denoted by $\rho(x, y)$ the specific resistance of the working fluid at the point (x, y), we may write the fundamental equations in the following form ($\partial/\partial t = 0$):

$$\operatorname{div} \mathbf{j} = 0, \qquad \mathbf{j} = \rho^{-1}\left(-\operatorname{grad} z^1 + \frac{1}{c}\mathbf{v} \times \mathbf{B}\right) \tag{5.58}$$

Here we have introduced the following notation: $\mathbf{E} = -\operatorname{grad} z^1$ and $\mathbf{j} = -\operatorname{curl} \mathbf{i}_3 z^2$, z^1 and z^2 being the electric potential and current function, respectively.

The system (5.58) was examined by various authors for a variety of boundary conditions and under different assumptions about the functions $\rho = \rho(x)$, $V(y)$, $B(x)$, these functions in all cases being given.

For optimum problems corresponding to Eqs. (5.58) it is typical that the functions ρ, V, and B are treated as control functions. There is a variety of ways to obtain distributed control of this kind. We can alter the magnetic field distribution by a suitable choice of currents in the exciting magnet networks. To obtain control over the conductivity distribution, we may use numerous methods of ionization, especially those connected with seeding the vapors of certain alkali metals such as cesium or potassium into the working gas.[18] On the other hand, we may considerably reduce the conductivity of the hot gas by seeding some quantities of electronegative gases into it (for instance, sulfur hexafluoride or water vapor).[26]

It is of great importance that there always exist some well-determined intervals for possible values of the control functions. The lower and upper limits of such intervals are determined by the technology now available, and may be either constant or varying with the coordinates. The closed character of an admissible region for the values of control functions appears to be of special importance for those optimum problems which depend linearly on the control functions. An absence of boundaries for the values of the control functions is equivalent in such cases to an absence of optimum control itself.

One may observe from Eqs. (5.58) that there is a considerable mathematical difference between two possible cases of optimization. On the one hand, we may treat $\rho(x, y)$ as fixed, and $V(y)$ and $B(x)$ as variable controls to be determined. Inversely, we may fix the functions $V(y)$ and $B(x)$, and try to prescribe an optimum control $\rho(x, y)$. In problems of the first type, the controls enter into the free term of the basic equations (5.58). This is why such problems can, in principle, be reduced to the simplest variational problems, this reduction being always possible if Green's function is assumed known. Only if it is difficult to construct Green's function may it be practically impossible to realize such a reduction.

On the contrary, problems of the second type cannot be reduced to the simplest problems, for we cannot construct Green's function so long as optimal control $\rho(x, y)$ is unknown. In what follows, we shall examine problems of the second type: the functions $V(y)$ and $B(x)$ will be assumed fixed, while $\rho(x, y)$ will represent an unknown optimum control to be determined together with the state variables.

5.3 Application to the Theory of MHD Power Generation: Minimization of End Effects in an MHD Channel[27]

5.31 Basic Equations and Statement of the Problem

Consider the rectilinear motion $\{\mathbf{v} = [V(y), 0, 0]\}$ of a conducting fluid along a plane channel of width 2δ. Let the specific resistance $\rho(x, y)$ of the fluid be restricted by (constant) limits $\rho_{\min}$ and $\rho_{\max}$. The walls of the channel will be assumed insulating everywhere except for two sections of equal length 2λ occupied by ideally conducting electrodes located opposite each other on different walls (Fig. 2). Electrodes are connected through the outer load R.

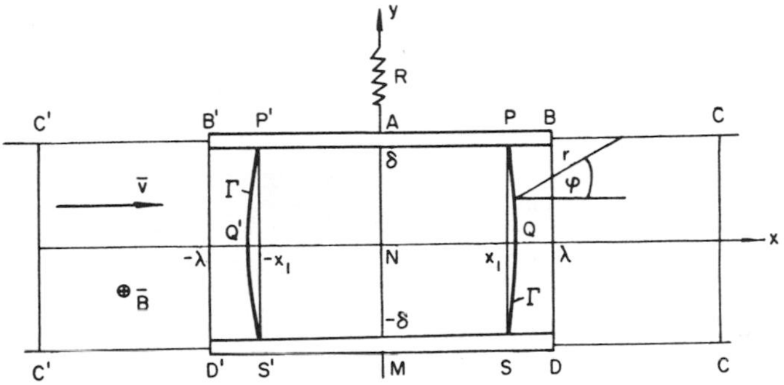

FIG. 2. Scheme of mhd-conversion device.

As soon as the transverse magnetic field $\mathbf{B} = -\mathbf{i}_3 B(x)$ is imposed on the moving fluid, an electric current of density $\mathbf{j}(\zeta^1, \zeta^2)$ is induced inside the channel, and through the outer load there flows total current equal to

$$I = \int_{-\lambda}^{\lambda} \zeta^2(x, \pm\delta)\, dx \tag{5.59}$$

Provided the magnetic Reynolds number Re_m is small compared with unity, we may neglect the induced magnetic field as compared with the external field; if, moreover, the mhd parameter of interaction N is also small, it is possible to neglect the Lorentz force in the dynamic equation so that the velocity distribution will be considered as prescribed by the purely hydrodynamical problem of rectilinear motion in a channel. These two assumptions simplify the basic mhd equations[24] to the form (5.58). Having introduced the notation (see Sec. 5.3)

$$\mathbf{j} = -\operatorname{curl} \mathbf{i}_3 z^2, \qquad j_x = \zeta^1, \qquad j_y = \zeta^2 \tag{5.60}$$

we may present the system (5.58) and Eq. (5.59) in the following standard form:

$$\frac{\partial z^1}{\partial x} = -\rho\zeta^1, \qquad \frac{\partial z^1}{\partial y} = -\rho\zeta^2 + \frac{VB}{c}, \qquad \frac{\partial}{\partial x}\left(\frac{VB}{c} - \rho\zeta^2\right) + \frac{\partial}{\partial y}\rho\zeta^1 = 0$$

$$\frac{\partial z^2}{\partial x} = \zeta^2, \qquad \frac{\partial z^2}{\partial y} = -\zeta^1, \qquad \frac{\partial \zeta^1}{\partial x} + \frac{\partial \zeta^2}{\partial y} = 0 \tag{5.61}$$

$$I = z^2(\lambda, \pm\delta) - z^2(-\lambda, \pm\delta)$$

According to the preceding discussion, we subject the function $\rho(x, y)$ to inequalities

$$\rho_{\min} \leq \rho(x, y) \leq \rho_{\max} \tag{5.62}$$

the limits $\rho_{\min}$ and $\rho_{\max}$ being known and constant. The upper limit corresponds to the resistance of the fluid when all external ionization factors are withdrawn, the lower limit characterizes the maximum number of ionization possibilities.

It seems relevant to write down the second-order equations for z^1, z^2 following from (5.61) on elimination of the ζ variables. These equations are

$$\frac{\partial}{\partial x}\frac{1}{\rho}\frac{\partial z^1}{\partial x} + \frac{\partial}{\partial y}\frac{1}{\rho}\frac{\partial z^1}{\partial y} = \frac{1}{c}\frac{\partial}{\partial y}\frac{VB}{\rho}$$

$$\frac{\partial}{\partial x}\rho\frac{\partial z^2}{\partial x} + \frac{\partial}{\partial y}\rho\frac{\partial z^2}{\partial y} = \frac{1}{c}\frac{\partial}{\partial x}VB \tag{5.63}$$

As to the complementary boundary conditions, we shall examine the situation when the walls of a channel are as described above. The boundary conditions will be discussed in Secs. 5.34 and 5.35.

At infinity, the components ζ^1, ζ^2 of the current density will be assumed to vanish.

The basic problem is to choose the optimum control function $\rho(x, y)$ in a class of functions of two independent variables including all piecewise continuous functions satisfying inequalities (5.62) in such a way as to furnish the maximum value of the functional I [Eq. (5.59)].

5.32 Euler Equations and Boundary Conditions

Following the technique outlined in Sec. 5.13, we construct the H function corresponding to the basic system (5.61):

$$\mathsf{H} = -\xi_1\rho\zeta^1 + \xi_2\zeta^2 + \eta_1\left(\frac{VB}{c} - \rho\zeta^2\right) - \eta_2\zeta^1$$
$$-\Gamma^*[(\rho_{\max} - \rho)(\rho - \rho_{\min}) - {\rho_*}^2] \tag{5.64}$$

Here ρ_* denotes an artificial control variable defined by the equation

$$(\rho_{\max} - \rho)(\rho - \rho_{\min}) - \rho_*{}^2 = 0 \tag{5.65}$$

and ξ_i, η_i $(i = 1, 2)$ represent the Lagrange multipliers. These multipliers satisfy the Euler equations [cf. Eq. (5.22)]

$$\begin{gathered}
\frac{\partial \xi_1}{\partial x} + \frac{\partial \eta_1}{\partial y} = 0, \qquad \frac{\partial \xi_2}{\partial x} + \frac{\partial \eta_2}{\partial y} = 0 \\
\rho \xi_1 + \eta_2 = 0, \qquad \rho \eta_1 - \xi_2 = 0 \\
\zeta^1 \xi_1 + \zeta^2 \eta_1 - \Gamma^*(2\rho - \rho_{\max} - \rho_{\min}) = 0, \qquad \Gamma^* \rho_* = 0
\end{gathered} \tag{5.66}$$

The first two pairs of these equations can be modified to an equivalent form with the aid of the "flow functions" $\omega_1(x, y)$, $\omega_2(x, y)$ defined as follows:

$$\begin{aligned}
\xi_1 &= -\partial\omega_1/\partial y \qquad \eta_1 = \partial\omega_1/\partial x \\
\xi_2 &= -\partial\omega_2/\partial y \qquad \eta_2 = \partial\omega_2/\partial x
\end{aligned} \tag{5.67}$$

We observe that the first pair of Eqs. (5.66) is identically satisfied, the second pair now being rewritten in the following way:

$$\rho\, \partial\omega_1/\partial y = \partial\omega_2/\partial x, \qquad \rho\, \partial\omega_1/\partial x = -\partial\omega_2/\partial y \tag{5.68}$$

On rearranging these equations, we get

$$\begin{aligned}
\frac{\partial}{\partial x}\rho\frac{\partial\omega_1}{\partial x} + \frac{\partial}{\partial y}\rho\frac{\partial\omega_1}{\partial y} &= 0 \\
\frac{\partial}{\partial x}\frac{1}{\rho}\frac{\partial\omega_2}{\partial x} + \frac{\partial}{\partial y}\frac{1}{\rho}\frac{\partial\omega_2}{\partial y} &= 0
\end{aligned} \tag{5.69}$$

Boundary conditions for the Lagrange multipliers ξ_i, η_i (or, equivalently, for ω_1, ω_2) are defined by initial boundary conditions for the variables z^1, z^2 together with the functional I to be maximized. We put off the formulation of these conditions to Secs. 5.34 and 5.35.

The last pair of Eqs. (5.66) show that two types of solutions are possible: the solutions characterized by the relations $\rho_* = 0$, $\Gamma^* \neq 0$, and those described by $\rho_* \neq 0$, $\Gamma^* = 0$.

For the first type of these solutions, it is seen from Eq. (5.65) that the control function $\rho(x, y)$ can take on only the limiting values $\rho_{\min}$ or $\rho_{\max}$, these values being optimum controls. But the Euler equations themselves provide no information about conditions necessary for realization of any regime of control $\rho(x, y)$ (sign of Γ^*).

For solutions of the second type, the control $\rho(x, y)$ does not generally take on limiting values. Moreover, restriction (5.62) on the control function is not

under additional conditions $\psi = \chi + \varphi$, $\chi = \text{const}$, and to require that the corresponding value of A be nonnegative. The function $f(\varphi, \chi + \varphi)$ of the φ variable is readily seen to be maximum when $\varphi = -(\chi/2)$, that is, for the direction bisecting the acute angle χ. For this direction

$$f_{\max} = f(-\chi/2, \chi/2) = S_{\max}\, j|\text{grad}\ \omega_2|\cos^2(\chi/2)$$

The corresponding value of A is equal to

$$A_{\max} = j|\text{grad}\ \omega_2|[S_{\max}\cos^2(\chi/2) - \cos\chi]$$

According to the preceding discussion, we must have

$$S_{\max}\cos^2(\chi/2) - \cos\chi \leq 0$$

or

$$\chi \leq \arccos p \tag{5.75}$$

where the parameter p is determined by the relation

$$p = \frac{\rho_{\max} - \rho_{\min}}{\rho_{\max} + \rho_{\min}} \tag{5.76}$$

Now let us take into account that $\mathbf{j} \cdot \text{grad}\ \omega_2 > 0$, whence it follows that $|\chi| \leq \pi/2$. We observe that inequality (5.75) presents an upper limit for the value of acute angle χ between the vectors $\mathbf{j}$ and grad ω_2. The value of the limit depends on the parameter p; this limit being equal to $\pi/2$ when $p = 0$, and to zero when $p = 1$.

By analogous argument, we observe that in the second case outlined above the inequalities

$$\mathbf{j} \cdot \text{grad}\ \omega_2 < 0, \qquad \chi \geq \pi - \arccos p \tag{5.77}$$

are necessary for optimality. The second inequality of (5.77) presents a lower limit for obtuse angle χ between the vectors $\mathbf{j}$ and grad ω_2. This limit depends on the value of p and is equal to $\pi/2$ when $p = 0$, and to π when $p = 1$.

It must be added that the condition $A = 0$ can be satisfied only along some separate curves, not inside any two-dimensional regions, the latter case being impossible since A contains the noninvariant term $Sj_n\, \partial\omega_2/\partial n$. This remark shows that there can be no regime of "singular controls" in the two-dimensional problem considered.[28]

We summarize the results of this section in the following form:

Theorem. *The functional* [*Eq.* (5.59)] *can achieve its maximum value under restrictions* (5.61) *and* (5.62) *only for the following values of the control function* $\rho(x, y)$:

$$\begin{aligned} &(1) \qquad \rho = \rho_{\max}, \qquad \mathbf{j} \cdot \text{grad}\ \omega_2 > 0, \qquad \chi \leq \arccos p \\ &(2) \qquad \rho = \rho_{\min}, \qquad \mathbf{j} \cdot \text{grad}\ \omega_2 < 0, \qquad \chi \geq \pi - \arccos p \end{aligned} \tag{5.78}$$

where the parameter p is defined by Eq. (5.76).

It is worthwhile to make some additional observations regarding this theorem. In our preceding considerations concerning the Weierstrass condition, we have never utilized the functional I itself. The statement of the theorem is therefore true for any functional depending only on the boundary values of the state variables. The case of the functional $(-I)$ to be minimized allows, however, an immediate interpretation of the Weierstrass condition. This interpretation proceeds from certain intuitive considerations, not rigorous but quite instructive in themselves. More precisely, we may in a sense approximate the continuous medium—the conducting fluid flowing through the external magnetic field—by an arbitrarily complicated linear network containing concentrated resistances and perhaps electromotive forces, the latter corresponding to a zone occupied by the magnetic field. We may distinguish some (arbitrary) resistance as the outer load R, and try to calculate the total current I through this resistance. It is readily observed from Kirchhoff's laws that the current I flowing through any resistance R depends on any other resistance ρ of the network according to the relation

$$I = \frac{a\rho + b}{c\rho + d} \tag{5.79}$$

where the coefficients a, b, c, and d depend linearly on R and all other resistances of the network, and a, b also contain linearly the included electromotive forces. If we now admit the resistance ρ to vary within the limits $(\rho_{\min}, \rho_{\max})$, then we can readily observe from Eq. (5.79) that only limiting values of ρ can be optimum, for the right-hand side of Eq. (5.79) is monotonic everywhere.

We have now arrived at the statement of the theorem, but of course without any criteria for distinction between the two regimes.

It can be added that by quite the same argument we can get analogous results for the electromotive forces (that is, for the VB/c term in the basic system (5.61), considered as the control term) but this investigation lies beyond our present discussion.

5.34 The Case of a Homogeneous Magnetic Field[27]

For the case of constant conductivity of the working fluid throughout the channel, the current distribution was examined by Vatazhin.[29]

In what follows, we shall outline the solution of the optimum problem to illustrate our general considerations.

Boundary conditions indicating the constancy of the potential along the electrodes and the vanishing of the normal component of the current density along the insulators, as well as the conditions at infinity and Ohm's law for the outer load, may be expressed as follows:

$$
\begin{aligned}
&z^1(x, \pm\delta) = z_{\pm}{}^1 = \text{const}, \qquad |x| < \lambda \\
&z^2(x, \pm\delta)|_{x>\lambda} = z_+{}^2 = \text{const}, \qquad z^2(x, \pm\delta)|_{x<-\lambda} = z_-{}^2 = \text{const} \\
&z^1(\infty, \delta) - z^1(\infty, -\delta) = z^1(-\infty, \delta) - z^1(-\infty, -\delta) \\
&\qquad = \frac{1}{c} B \int_{-\delta}^{\delta} V\, dy = \varepsilon \\
&z^2(\infty, \pm\delta) - z^2(-\infty, \pm\delta) = R^{-1}(z_+{}^1 - z_-{}^1)
\end{aligned}
\tag{5.80}
$$

For the Lagrange multipliers, the boundary conditions must be constructed in view of relations (5.80) among the boundary values of the state variables z^1 and z^2 or, equivalently, among their variations.

In view of the last Eq. (5.61) (the functional $-I$ to be minimized) together with Eqs. (5.66), we write the first variation of the functional $-I$ [cf. Eq. (5.12)] as follows (Fig. 2):

$$
\begin{aligned}
&\left(\int_C^B + \int_{C'}^{B'}\right) [\eta_1 \delta z^1 + \eta_2 \delta z^2]\, dt \\
&\qquad - \left(\int_{C'}^{D'} + \int_D^C\right) [\eta_1 \delta z^1 + \eta_2 \delta z^2]\, dt \\
&\qquad + \int_B^{B'} [\eta_1 \delta z^1 + \eta_2 \delta z^2]\, dt - \int_{D'}^{D} [\eta_1 \delta z^1 + \eta_2 \delta z^2]\, dt \\
&\qquad - \int_{C'(\delta)}^{C'(-\delta)} [\xi_1 \delta z^1 + \xi_2 \delta z^2]\, dt + \int_{C(-\delta)}^{C(\delta)} [\xi_1 \delta z^1 + \xi_2 \delta z^2]\, dt \\
&\qquad - \delta z_+{}^2 + \delta z_-{}^2
\end{aligned}
\tag{5.81}
$$

The variations entering into these relations are not independent but are subjected to constraints arising from Eqs. (5.80) after taking variations. Conditions at infinity immediately follow from those on the vertical paths $\overline{C'(-\delta)C'(\delta)}$ and $\overline{C(-\delta)C(\delta)}$ after moving both to infinity. We get (Fig. 2):

On electrodes $B'B$ and $D'D$, $\eta_2 = 0$.

On insulators $C'B'$, BC, $C'D'$ and DC, $\eta_1 = 0$.

At infinity,

$$
\int_{C'(\delta)}^{C'(-\delta)} \xi_1\, dt = \int_{C(-\delta)}^{C(\delta)} \xi_1\, dt = 0
$$

$$
\int_{C'(\delta)}^{C'(-\delta)} \xi_2\, dt = \int_{C(-\delta)}^{C(\delta)} \xi_2\, dt = 0
$$

The other terms remaining in Eq. (5.81) combine into the relation

$$\left[\int_C^B \eta_2\,dt - \int_D^C \eta_2\,dt - 1\right]\delta z_+{}^2 + \left[\int_{B'}^{C'} \eta_2\,dt - \int_{C'}^{D'} \eta_2\,dt + 1\right]\delta z_-{}^2$$
$$+ \int_B^{B'} \eta_1\,dt \cdot \delta z_+{}^1 - \int_{D'}^{D} \eta_1\,dt \cdot \delta z_-{}^1 = 0 \tag{5.82}$$

The variations in the left-hand side are connected by the relation [cf. Eq. (5.80)]

$$\delta z_+{}^1 - \delta z_-{}^1 = R(\delta z_+{}^2 - \delta z_-{}^2)$$

This relation permits us to eliminate $\delta z_+{}^1$ from Eq. (5.82), the resulting equation having all the variations independent and the corresponding coefficients equal to zero.

We may write

$$\int_B^{B'} \eta_1\,dt = \int_{D'}^{D} \eta_1\,dt$$

$$\int_C^B \eta_2\,dt - \int_D^C \eta_2\,dt - 1 = -R\int_B^{B'} \eta_1\,dt$$

$$\int_{B'}^{C'} \eta_2\,dt - \int_{C'}^{D'} \eta_2\,dt + 1 = R\int_{D'}^{D} \eta_1\,dt$$

The boundary conditions just obtained may be rewritten with the aid of the "flow-functions" ω_1 and ω_2. We get:

On the electrodes,

$$\omega_2(x, \pm\delta) = \omega_{2\pm} = \text{const}, \qquad \partial\omega_1/\partial y = 0 \tag{5.83}$$

On the insulators,

$$\omega_1(x, \pm\delta)|_{x>\lambda} = \omega_{1+} = \text{const}, \qquad \omega_1(x, \pm\delta)|_{x<-\lambda} = \omega_{1-} = \text{const}$$
$$\partial\omega_2/\partial y = 0 \tag{5.84}$$

At infinity,

$$\omega_1(\infty, \delta) = \omega_1(\infty, -\delta), \qquad \omega_1(-\infty, \delta) = \omega_1(-\infty, -\delta)$$
$$\omega_2(\infty, \delta) = \omega_2(\infty, -\delta), \qquad \omega_2(-\infty, \delta) = \omega_2(-\infty, -\delta) \tag{5.85}$$

In addition to these conditions, we have

$$\omega_{2+} - \omega_{2-} + 1 = R[\omega_{1+} - \omega_{1-}] \tag{5.86}$$

If now we introduce the function u by virtue of the relation

$$u = z^1 - \frac{B}{c}\int_0^y V\,dy \tag{5.87}$$

then we may write Eqs. (5.58) in the following form:

$$\frac{\partial z^2}{\partial y} = \frac{1}{\rho}\frac{\partial u}{\partial x}, \qquad \frac{\partial z^2}{\partial x} = -\frac{1}{\rho}\frac{\partial u}{\partial y} \tag{5.88}$$

the vector **j** being equal to

$$\mathbf{j} = -\frac{1}{\rho}\,\text{grad}\, u \tag{5.89}$$

We observe that Eqs. (5.88) coincide with those of (5.68), if we substitute in the latter the function u for ω_2, and z^2 for ω_1.

Having compared the boundary conditions (5.80) and (5.83)–(5.86), we see that, for any $\rho(x, y)$, we may write

$$z^2 = \varepsilon\omega_1, \qquad u = \varepsilon\omega_2 \tag{5.90}$$

These relations show that the vectors **j** and grad ω_2 are antiparallel everywhere in the channel ($\chi = \pi$); the Weierstrass condition (5.78) now shows that in the optimum regime we must have $\rho = \rho_{\min}$ throughout the channel. This result seems to be in complete accord with physical considerations.

We would certainly have arrived at this statement on investigating Vatazhin's solution,[29] but then we could have verified the optimality of $\rho = \rho_{\min}$ only relative to the class of functions which are constant everywhere. Utilizing the general method[16,27] (cf. Sec. 5.2), we have stated this optimality relative to a wider class of functions of two independent variables. There is, in general, no possibility of obtaining any analytical solution for arbitrary functions of that class.

Figure 4 shows the ratio $I_{\infty c}/I_{\infty\lambda}$ of the total current gained under optimum

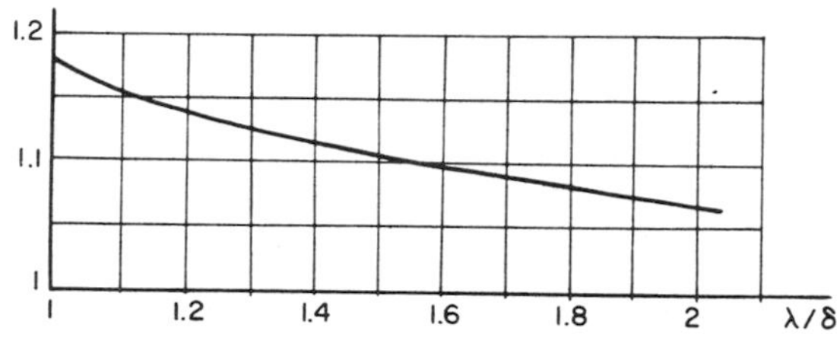

FIG. 4. Dependence of the ratio $I_{\infty c}/I_{\infty\lambda}$ on λ/δ.

conditions $(I_{\infty c})$[29] to that obtained when the conductivity ρ^{-1} vanishes outside the electrode zone. The parameter α is equal to the ratio $K(k')/K(k)$, $k = \exp(-\pi\lambda/\delta)$, $k^2 + k'^2 = 1$; $K(k)$ being the complete elliptic integral of the first kind. The ratio $R/\rho_{\min}$ is taken as equal to unity. We see that the difference between $I_{\infty\lambda}$ and $I_{\infty c}$ vanishes when the parameter λ/δ goes to infinity.

5.35 The Case of the Magnetic Field Varying along the Channel[30]

For a homogeneous magnetic field, we have just seen that for optimum conditions, the conductivity is uniform and constant throughout the channel. This result changes qualitatively when the magnetic field is assumed to vary along the channel. In the latter case, we obtain discontinuities in the optimum distribution of conductivity.

Consider, for instance, the case when the magnetic field is presented by an even function of x vanishing outside the electrode zone. The velocity of the fluid will be assumed constant. We are going to prove that the distribution $\rho = \text{const}$ throughout the channel is not optimal under these conditions.

For the case of $\rho = \text{const}$, the current distribution was investigated by Vatazhin.[29] The vector $\mathbf{j}$ may be generally given as the sum of two parts: the vector $\mathbf{j}^{(1)}$ generated by the motion of the working fluid in a homogeneous magnetic field of intensity

$$\mathbf{B} = -B_0\mathbf{i}_3, \qquad B_0 = -\frac{R}{2\rho\delta}\int_{-\lambda}^{\lambda} B(x)\,dx \tag{5.91}$$

and the vector $\mathbf{j}^{(2)}$ with components $[0, (1/\rho c)VB(x)]$. The vector lines $\mathbf{j}^{(1)}$ and $\mathbf{j}$ are presented by Figs. 5a, and 5b, respectively.[29]

It follows from Eqs. (5.89) and (5.90) (where we must now put $\varepsilon < 0$) that the vector lines grad ω_2 are parallel to those of $\mathbf{j}^{(1)}$.

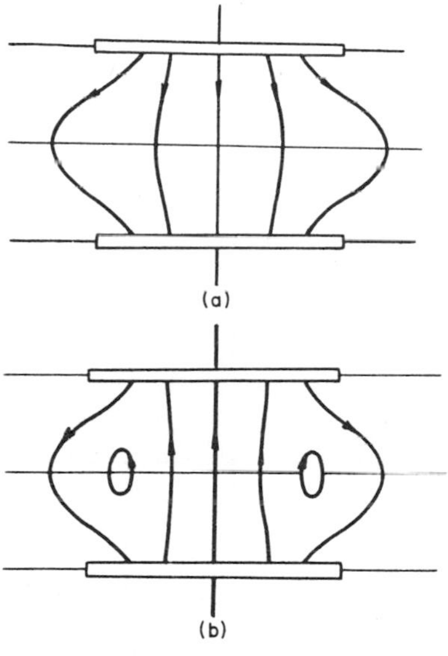

FIG. 5. Vector lines of $\mathbf{j}^{(1)}$ and $\mathbf{j}$ (Sec. 5.35).

Comparison of Figs. 5a and 5b shows that the Weierstrass condition (see theorem) is not satisfied because the vector lines **j** and grad ω_2 intersect each other in acute as well as in obtuse angles, this being in contradiction with the presupposed constancy of the conductivity.

It can be shown by more detailed consideration that the mutual orientation of the vector lines corresponds to the regime $\rho = \rho_{\min}$ roughly speaking in the electrode zone, and to the regime $\rho = \rho_{\max}$ in the outer region. Physically, this means that for optimization of the current distribution, it is necessary to intensify the current density inside of the electrode zone and to reduce that in the outer part of the channel to the greatest possible extent.

Analogously, it can be shown that the regime of constant conductivity is by no means optimal when the magnetic field zone passes the limits prescribed by the electrode zone.

So far there arises the problem of determination of the lines of discontinuity dividing the regions of different regimes of conductivity. In what follows, we shall present a formulation of this problem where it will be supposed that, in general, the magnetic field zone spreads out of the electrode zone.

Along the unknown lines Σ_0 of discontinuity there applies the condition that the tangential component of the electric field intensity is continuous, the same being also true for the normal component of the current density. These conditions can be expressed as follows:†

$$[z^i]_2^1 = 0, \qquad i = 1, 2 \tag{5.92}$$

Now we must formulate the Erdmann-Weierstrass conditions along the line Σ_0 [cf. Eqs. (5.26)]. We get

$$[\omega_i]_2^1 = 0, \quad i = 1, 2 \tag{5.93}$$

$$\frac{\partial \omega_1}{\partial t}\left[\frac{\partial z^1}{\partial n}\right]_2^1 + \frac{\partial \omega_2}{\partial t}\left[\frac{\partial z^2}{\partial n}\right]_2^1 = 0 \tag{5.94}$$

Here we have denoted by $\mathbf{t}(x_t, y_t)$, $\mathbf{n}(y_t, -x_t)$ the tangential and normal directions, respectively, to the line Σ_0.

We may represent Eqs. (5.92)–(5.94) in an equivalent form. To do this, let us expand the functions z^i into the sums

$$z^i = \mathrm{P}^i + F^i, \qquad \mathrm{P}^i = \int_{\Sigma_0} \mu^i \ln \frac{1}{r}\, dt \tag{5.95}$$

Here F^i denotes a suitably chosen solution to the corresponding Eq. (5.63), continuous together with its first derivatives everywhere inside the channel.

† We attach the index "1" to quantities defined inside the region where $\rho = \rho_{\max}$ (regime 1), and the index "2" to those for the region where $\rho = \rho_{\min}$ (regime 2).

The first term in the right-hand side of Eq. (5.95) is responsible for discontinuity of the normal derivatives of z^i across the line Σ_0, these variables themselves being continuous across it [cf. Eq. (5.92)]. We observe, for example, that representation (5.95) of the function z^1 satisfies the corresponding relation (5.92) identically. The other relation (5.92), written in terms of z^1, leads immediately to the integral equation for the density μ^1.

To derive this equation, let us consider the well-known relations for the limiting values of normal derivatives of the potential of a surface distribution[31]:

$$\begin{aligned}\left(\frac{\partial \mathrm{P}^i}{\partial n_0}\right)_{\text{in}} &= \pi\mu^i + \int_{\Sigma_0} \mu^i \frac{\cos\psi_0}{r_0}\, dt \\ \left(\frac{\partial \mathrm{P}^i}{\partial n_0}\right)_{\text{out}} &= -\pi\mu^i + \int_{\Sigma_0} \mu^i \frac{\cos\psi_0}{r_0}\, dt\end{aligned} \tag{5.96}$$

Here ψ_0 denotes an angle between the normal $\mathbf{n}_0$ to the curve Σ_0 and the radius vector $\mathbf{r}_0$ of the running point relative to the pole at the point of observation.

The relation $[z^2]_2^1 = 0$ is equivalent to

$$\frac{1}{\rho_{\max}}\left(\frac{\partial z^1}{\partial n}\right)_1 + \frac{VB}{c\rho_{\max}} x_t = \frac{1}{\rho_{\min}}\left(\frac{\partial z^1}{\partial n}\right)_2 + \frac{VB}{c\rho_{\min}} x_t$$

Having now substituted the corresponding expressions in the latter equation by virtue of Eqs. (5.95) and (5.96), we get

$$\mu^1 - \frac{p}{\pi}\int_{\Sigma_0} \mu^1 \frac{\cos\psi_0}{r_0}\, dt = \frac{p}{\pi}\frac{\partial F^1}{\partial n_0} + \frac{p}{\pi}\frac{VB}{c} x_t \tag{5.97}$$

The parameter p is defined by Eq. (5.76); $\mathbf{n}_0$ denotes the normal to Σ_0 external to region 1 where $\rho = \rho_{\max}$.

By the same argument, we proceed to the formulation of the related equations for the density μ^2, as well as for the densities ν_1, ν_2 corresponding to the "flow-functions" ω_1, ω_2 [cf. Eqs. (5.69)].

The last Erdmann-Weierstrass condition (5.94) may now be rewritten as follows:

$$\left(\int_{\Sigma_0} \mu^2 \frac{\sin\psi_0}{r_0}\, dt + \frac{\partial F^2}{\partial t}\right)\nu_2 + \left(\int_{\Sigma_0} \nu_2 \frac{\sin\psi_0}{r_0}\, dt + \frac{\partial G_2}{\partial t}\right)\mu^2 = 0 \tag{5.98†}$$

It remains now to develop a recipe for the determination of the function F^1 in the right-hand side of Eq. (5.97). The determination of this function reduces to the boundary problem generated by the initial problem formulated for the state variable z^1. More precisely, we assume for simplicity that the magnetic field vanishes outside the electrode zone, and that the velocity of the

† Function G_2 corresponds to F^2 for ω_2.

working fluid is constant. Under these assumptions, we suppose that the following distribution of conductivity is optimum: in the middle region $PP'Q'S'SQP$ (cf. Fig. 2) all disposed within the limits of the electrode zone, there is the regime $\rho = \rho_{\min}$; in the symmetrically disposed outer regions (including infinity), there is the regime $\rho = \rho_{\max}$. Needless to say, the (symmetrical) lines $S'Q'P'$ and PQS of discontinuity of the control function $\rho(x, y)$ are to be determined together with the solution to the optimum problem. We shall only suppose in what follows that these lines have their ends on the electrodes (cf. Fig. 6).

Under the assumptions formulated, we observe that the boundary problem for the determination of F^1 may be stated in the following way [see Eqs. (5.63) and (5.80)].† It is required to determine a harmonic function F^1 in the half-strip $x \geq 0$, $|y| < \delta$ by the following conditions along the boundaries:

$$
\begin{aligned}
F^1(x, \pm\delta) &= z_+{}^1 - \int_{\Sigma_0} \mu^1 \ln\frac{1}{r}\, dt\Big|_{y=\pm\delta}, \qquad x < \lambda \\
\frac{\partial F^1}{\partial x} &= -\frac{\partial}{\partial x}\int_{\Sigma_0} \mu^1 \ln\frac{1}{r}\, dt, \quad x = 0, \quad |y| < \delta \\
\frac{\partial F^1}{\partial y} &= -\frac{\partial}{\partial y}\int_{\Sigma_0} \mu^1 \ln\frac{1}{r}\, dt, \quad \lambda < x < \infty, \quad y = \pm\delta
\end{aligned}
\tag{5.99}
$$

At infinity, the derivatives $\partial F^1/\partial x$, $\partial F^1/\partial y$ are equal to zero.

The constant difference $z_+{}^1 - z_-{}^1$ is calculated by virtue of Ohm's law for the outer load, namely,

$$
2R\int_0^\lambda \frac{1}{\rho}\left(\frac{VB}{c} - \frac{\partial z^1}{\partial y}\right)\Big|_{y=\pm\delta} dx = z_+{}^1 - z_-{}^1
$$

An analogous problem had been examined by Vatazhin;[32] following his paper we introduce the analytic function

$$
\Phi^1 = \frac{\partial F^1}{\partial x} - i\frac{\partial F^1}{\partial y} = u + iv; \qquad u = \frac{\partial F^1}{\partial x}; \qquad v = -\frac{\partial F^1}{\partial y} \tag{5.100}
$$

satisfying the boundary conditions (for notation see Fig. 6)

$$
u = \int_{\Sigma_0} \mu^1 \frac{\cos\varphi}{r}\, dt \equiv C(x, y) \qquad \text{along BA, AM, MD}
$$

$$
v = -\int_{\Sigma_0} \mu^1 \frac{\sin\varphi}{r}\, dt \equiv -S(x, y) \qquad \text{along CB, DC}
$$

† The postultimate Eq. (5.80) must now be replaced by $z^1(\pm\infty, y) = 0$.

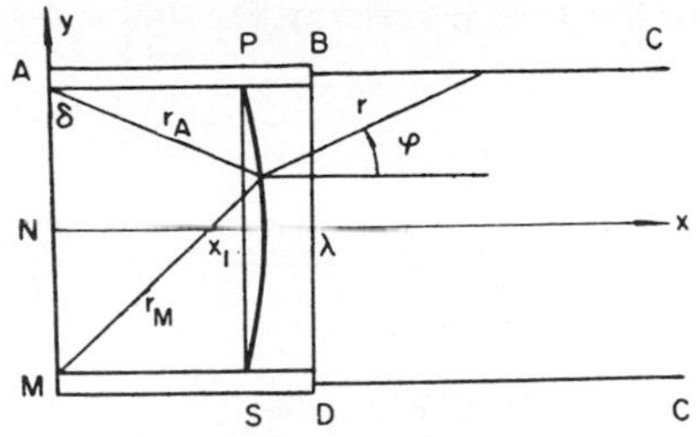

FIG. 6. Notations for calculations of Sec. 5.35.

$$\Phi^1(\infty) = 0$$

$$- \int_0^{\delta} v(0, y)\, dy + \frac{1}{2}\left[\int_{\Sigma_0} \mu^1 \ln \frac{1}{r_A}\, dt - \int_{\Sigma_0} \mu^1 \ln \frac{1}{r_A}\, dt\right]$$

$$= \frac{R}{\rho_{\min}} \int_0^{x_1} v(x, \delta)\, dx + \frac{R}{\rho_{\max}} \int_{x_1}^{\lambda} v(x, \delta)\, dx$$

$$+ \frac{R}{\rho_{\min}} \int_0^{x_1} dx \left(\int_{\Sigma_0} \mu^1 \frac{\sin \varphi}{r}\, dt\right)_{y=\delta} + \frac{R}{\rho_{\max}} \int_{x_1}^{\lambda} dx \left(\int_{\Sigma_0} \mu^1 \frac{\sin \varphi}{r}\, dt\right)_{y=\delta}$$

$$+ \frac{R}{\rho_{\min}} \frac{V}{c} \int_0^{x_1} B(x)\, dx + \frac{R}{\rho_{\max}} \frac{V}{c} \int_{x_1}^{\lambda} B(x)\, dx \tag{5.101}$$

The analytic function

$$w = \tau + i\omega = \frac{\sin(\pi i z/2\delta)}{\cosh(\pi\lambda/2\delta)}, \qquad z = x + iy \tag{5.102}$$

realizes the conformal mapping of the half-strip $x \geq 0$, $|y| \leq \delta$ into the upper half-plane. Corresponding points are denoted on Fig. 7.

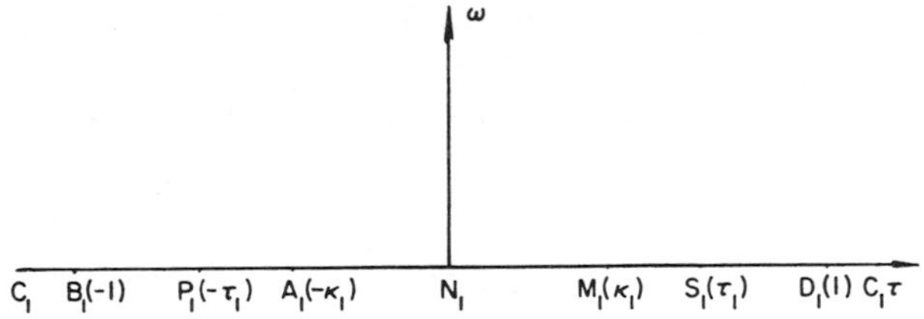

FIG. 7. Points corresponding to one another under conformal mapping.

On the boundary of the mapped region, the following relations are satisfied:

$$\tau = -\frac{\cosh(\pi x/2\delta)}{\cosh(\pi\lambda/2\delta)}, \qquad x \geq 0, \quad y = \delta$$

$$\tau = -\frac{\sin(\pi y/2\delta)}{\cosh(\pi\lambda/2\delta)}, \qquad x = 0, \quad |y| \leq \delta \tag{5.103}$$

$$\tau = \frac{\cosh(\pi x/2\delta)}{\cosh(\pi\lambda/2\delta)}, \qquad x \geq 0, \quad y = -\delta$$

We must now construct the function $\Phi^1[z(w)] = \Phi_1{}^1(w) = u_1 + iv_1$ which is analytic in the upper half-plane, vanishes at infinity, and satisfies mixed boundary conditions along the real axis

$$u_1 = C_1(\tau) \quad \text{if} \quad -1 < \tau < 1, \quad \omega = 0$$

$$v_1 = -S_1(\tau) \quad \text{if} \quad 1 < |\tau| < \infty, \quad \omega = 0$$

$$-\frac{2\delta}{\pi}\int_0^{k_1} \frac{v_1(\tau, 0)}{(k_1{}^2 - \tau^2)^{1/2}}\,d\tau = R\frac{2\delta}{\pi}\left[\frac{1}{\rho_{\min}}\int_{k_1}^{\tau_1} \frac{v_1(\tau, 0)}{(\tau^2 - k_1{}^2)^{1/2}}\,d\tau \right.$$
$$\left. + \frac{1}{\rho_{\max}}\int_{\tau_1}^{1} \frac{v_1(\tau, 0)}{(\tau^2 - k_1{}^2)^{1/2}}\,d\tau\right] + R\left[\frac{N_1}{\rho_{\min}} + \frac{N_2}{\rho_{\max}}\right]$$
$$- \tfrac{1}{2}[\mathrm{P}^1(0, \delta) - \mathrm{P}^1(0, -\delta)] \tag{5.104}$$

Here we have introduced the following notation:

$$C_1(w) = -\left.\frac{\partial \mathrm{P}^1}{\partial x}\right|_{z=z(w)} = \left(\int_{\Sigma_0} \mu^1 \frac{\cos\varphi}{r}\,dt\right)_{z=z(w)}$$

$$S_1(w) = -\left.\frac{\partial \mathrm{P}^1}{\partial y}\right|_{z=z(w)} = \left(\int_{\Sigma_0} \mu^1 \frac{\sin\varphi}{r}\,dt\right)_{z=z(w)}$$

$$N_1 = \int_0^{x_1} S(x, \delta)\,dx + \frac{V}{c}\int_0^{x_1} B(x)\,dx$$

$$N_2 = \int_{x_1}^{\lambda} S(x, \delta)\,dx + \frac{V}{c}\int_{x_1}^{\lambda} B(x)\,dx$$

$$k_1 = \frac{1}{\cosh(\pi\lambda/2\delta)}, \qquad \tau_1 = \frac{\cosh(\pi x_1/2\delta)}{\cosh(\pi\lambda/2\delta)} \tag{5.105}$$

This problem can be immediately solved by virtue of the Keldish-Sedov formula.[33] We get

$$\Phi_1{}^1(w) = \frac{1}{\pi i g(w)}\left\{-i\int_{-\infty}^{1} \frac{1}{\theta - w}\left(\frac{|\theta| + 1}{|\theta| - 1}\right)^{1/2} S_1(\theta)\, d\theta\right.$$

$$\left. - i\int_{-1}^{1} \frac{1}{\theta - w}\left(\frac{1 - \theta}{1 + \theta}\right)^{1/2} C_1(\theta)\, d\theta - i\int_{1}^{\infty} \frac{1}{\theta - w}\left(\frac{\theta - 1}{\theta + 1}\right)^{1/2} S_1(\theta)\, d\theta\right\}$$

$$+ \frac{\gamma}{[(w-1)(w+1)]^{1/2}}, \qquad g(w) = \left(\frac{w - 1}{w + 1}\right)^{1/2} \tag{5.106}$$

In this formula we have taken the branch of the square root which is positive along that part of the real axis where $\tau > 1$. The constant parameter γ can be determined from the last of Eqs. (5.104). Having set $w = \tau$, $|\tau| < 1$ in Eq. (5.106), we get

$$v_1(\tau, 0) = v_1{}^*(\tau, 0) - \frac{\gamma}{(1 - \tau^2)^{1/2}} - \Lambda(\tau)$$

$$v_1{}^*(\tau, 0) = \frac{1}{\pi}\left(\frac{1 + \tau}{1 - \tau}\right)^{1/2}\left\{\int_{-\infty}^{-1} \frac{1}{\theta - \tau}\left(\frac{|\theta| + 1}{|\theta| - 1}\right)^{1/2} S_1(\theta)\, d\theta\right.$$

$$\left. + \int_{1}^{\infty} \frac{1}{\theta - \tau}\left(\frac{\theta - 1}{\theta + 1}\right)^{1/2} S_1(\theta)\, d\theta\right\}$$

$$\Lambda(\tau) = \frac{1}{\pi}\left[\int_{1}^{1} \frac{C_1(\theta)\left(\dfrac{\theta - 1}{\theta + 1}\cdot\dfrac{\tau + 1}{\tau - 1}\right)^{1/2} - C_1(\tau)}{\theta - \tau}\, d\theta + C_1(\tau)\ln\frac{1 - \tau}{1 + \tau}\right] \tag{5.107}$$

Having substituted this expression for $v_1(\tau, 0)$ into Eq. (5.104), we calculate the constant parameter γ. After simple but rather extensive calculations (see Appendix) we arrive at the following result:

$$\gamma = \pi\left\{2\delta K(k_1)\left[1 + \frac{R}{\rho_{\min}}\alpha^* - R\left(\frac{1}{\rho_{\min}} - \frac{1}{\rho_{\max}}\right)\alpha^{**}\right]\right\}^{-1}$$

$$\times\left(R\left[\frac{N_1{}^*}{\rho_{\min}} + \frac{N_2{}^*}{\rho_{\max}}\right] - \frac{1}{2}[\mathrm{P}^1(0, \delta) - \mathrm{P}^1(0, -\delta)] - \frac{2\delta}{\pi}\lambda_0^{k_1}\right.$$

$$+ \frac{4\delta}{\pi^2}\int_1^{\infty} \frac{\theta}{(\theta^2 - 1)^{1/2}} S_1(\theta)\, d\theta\left\{\frac{\theta^2 - 1}{\theta^2}\Pi\left(\frac{\pi}{2}, -\frac{k_1{}^2}{\theta^2}, k_1\right)\right.$$

$$+ \frac{R}{\rho_{\min}}\Pi\left(\frac{\pi}{2}, \frac{k_1'^2}{\theta^2 - 1}, k_1'\right) - R\left(\frac{1}{\rho_{\min}} - \frac{1}{\rho_{\max}}\right)$$

$$\times\Pi\left(\arcsin\frac{(1 - \tau_1{}^2)^{1/2}}{k_1'}, \frac{k_1'^2}{\theta^2 - 1}, k_1'\right)$$

$$\left.\left. - K(k_1)\left[1 + \frac{R}{\rho_{\min}}\alpha^* - R\left(\frac{1}{\rho_{\min}} - \frac{1}{\rho_{\max}}\right)\alpha^{**}\right]\right\}\right) \tag{5.108}$$

In this formula

$$N_1{}^* = N_1 - \frac{2\delta}{\pi}\int_{k_1}^{\tau_1}\frac{\Lambda(\tau)\,d\tau}{(\tau^2 - k_1{}^2)^{1/2}} = N_1 - \frac{2\delta}{\pi}\lambda_{k_1}^{\tau_1}$$

$$N_2{}^* = N_2 - \frac{2\delta}{\pi}\int_{\tau_1}^{1}\frac{\Lambda(\tau)\,d\tau}{(\tau^2 - k_1{}^2)^{1/2}} = N_2 - \frac{2\delta}{\pi}\lambda_{\tau_1}^{1}$$

$$\lambda_0^{k_1} = \int_0^{k_1}\frac{\Lambda(\tau)\,d\tau}{(k_1{}^2 - \tau^2)^{1/2}}$$

$$F(\varphi, k) = \int_0^{\varphi}\frac{d\beta}{(1 - k^2\sin^2\beta)^{1/2}}$$ —incomplete elliptic integral of the first kind

$$K(k) = F\left(\frac{\pi}{2}, K\right)$$ —complete elliptic integral of the first kind

$$\Pi(\varphi, h, k) = \int_0^{\varphi}\frac{d\beta}{(1 + h\sin^2\beta)(1 - k^2\sin^2\beta)^{1/2}}$$ —elliptic integral of the third kind

$$k_1{}^2 + k_1'^2 = 1$$

$$\alpha^* = \frac{K(k_1')}{K(k_1)}, \quad \alpha^{**} = \frac{F\left[\arcsin\dfrac{(1 - \tau_1{}^2)^{1/2}}{k_1'}, k_1'\right]}{K(k_1)}$$

Equations (5.106) and (5.108) together determine the function $\Phi^1(x, y)$. Having calculated the derivative $\partial F^1/\partial n_0$ and introduced the result into the right-hand side of Eq. (5.97), we arrive at the integral equation for the unknown density μ^1. It must be added that Eq. (5.94) represents just the extra condition necessary for determination of the discontinuity line Σ_0.

An expression for the optimum value of the total current I is of primary interest for our investigation. We can readily obtain this expression on writing

$$I = \frac{z_+{}^1 - z_-{}^1}{R} = -\frac{4\delta}{\pi R}\int_0^{k_1}\frac{v_1(\tau, 0)}{(k_1{}^2 - \tau^2)^{1/2}}\,d\tau + \frac{1}{R}[\mathrm{P}^1(0, \delta) - \mathrm{P}^1(0, -\delta)]$$

Having performed the calculations (see Appendix), we obtain

$$I = \left\{\rho_{\min}\left[1 + \frac{R}{\rho_{\min}}\alpha^* - R\left(\frac{1}{\rho_{\min}} - \frac{1}{\rho_{\max}}\right)\alpha^{**}\right]\right\}^{-1}$$
$$\times\left\{2\left[N_1{}^* + N_2{}^*\frac{\rho_{\min}}{\rho_{\max}}\right] + \left[\mathrm{P}^1(0, \delta) - \mathrm{P}^1(0, -\delta) + \frac{4\delta}{\pi}\lambda_0^{k_1}\right]\right.$$
$$\left.\times\left[\alpha^* - \left(1 - \frac{\rho_{\min}}{\rho_{\max}}\right)\alpha^{**}\right] + \frac{4\delta}{\pi}\int_1^{\infty}\Sigma^*\left(\frac{x}{\lambda}\right)S(x, \delta)\,d\left(\frac{x}{\lambda}\right)\right\} \quad (5.109)$$

Here we have used the notation

$$\begin{aligned}
\Sigma^*\left(\frac{x}{\lambda}\right) &= \Sigma\left(\frac{x}{\lambda}\right) + \Delta\Sigma\left(\frac{x}{\lambda}\right)\\
\Sigma\left(\frac{x}{\lambda}\right) &= \frac{\lambda}{\delta}\,\theta\left(\frac{\theta^2 - k_1^{\,2}}{\theta^2 - 1}\right)^{1/2}\left[\Pi\left(\frac{\pi}{2}, \frac{k_1'^2}{\theta^2 - 1}, k_1'\right)\right.\\
&\quad \left. - \alpha^*\frac{\theta^2 - 1}{\theta^2}\,\Pi\left(\frac{\pi}{2}, -\frac{k_1^{\,2}}{\theta^2}, k_1\right)\right]\\
\Delta\Sigma\left(\frac{x}{\lambda}\right) &= \frac{\lambda}{\delta}\,\theta\left(\frac{\theta^2 - k_1^{\,2}}{\theta^2 - 1}\right)^{1/2}\left(1 - \frac{\rho_{\min}}{\rho_{\max}}\right)\\
&\quad \times\left[\alpha^{**}\frac{\theta^2 - 1}{\theta^2}\,\Pi\left(\frac{\pi}{2}, -\frac{k_1^{\,2}}{\theta^2}, k_1\right)\right.\\
&\quad \left. - \Pi\left(\arcsin\frac{(1 - \tau_1^{\,2})^{1/2}}{k_1'}, \frac{k_1'^2}{\theta^2 - 1}, k_1'\right)\right]\\
\theta &= k_1\cosh(\pi x/2\delta)
\end{aligned} \tag{5.110}$$

5.36 Some Limiting Cases

Let us consider in more detail the case of small values of the parameter p. If $p = 0$, then the conductivity of the working fluid is constant and fixed. Of course, no optimum problem can arise in this case. On the other hand, if the parameter p is sufficiently small compared with unity, then the angles $\arccos p$ and $(\pi - \arccos p)$ are quite close to $\pi/2$. By virtue of the Weierstrass condition (see theorem) we can easily indicate the limiting position of the (vanishing!) lines Σ_0 of discontinuity. It is readily observed that for this position we must take the locus Γ of those points where the vector lines **j** and grad ω_2, drawn for $\rho = \text{const}$, intersect each other in a right angle. (For the case when $B(x)$ vanishes for $|x| > \lambda$, we can easily draw these limiting curves if we lay Figs. 5a and 5b on one another. For three variants of the magnetic field graph $B(x)$ represented by Fig. 8, the corresponding curves Γ are drawn in Fig. 9.

For values of p not too different from zero, the lines Σ_0 of discontinuity do not differ very much from Γ, the Weierstrass conditions leading to the mutual disposition of regions with $\rho = \rho_{\max}$ or $\rho = \rho_{\min}$ just coinciding with that described in the preceding Section.

We are interested most of all in the value of the functional I due to optimization of the conductivity distribution as compared with that for conductivity equal to $\rho_{\min}^{-1}$ everywhere. The corresponding variation may be treated as

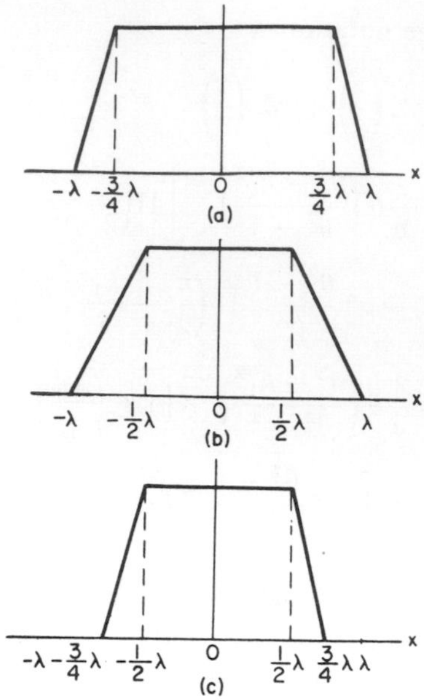

FIG. 8. Various shapes of the magnetic field graph.

consisting of the part (1) caused by decrease of conductivity to the value of $\rho_{\max}^{-1}$ in the regions $C'S'Q'P'C'$ and $CPQSC$ of the channel (Fig. 2), and of the variation (2) due to the subsequent transition from Γ to the line Σ_0 of discontinuity.

The latter variation, however, turns out to be of a higher order of magnitude. To demonstrate this, we may represent the function z^2 by means of Green's functions for the corresponding regions, and then pass to the variations (1) and (2). It will become obvious that the latter variation is combined from the terms containing products of the parameter p with quantities whose

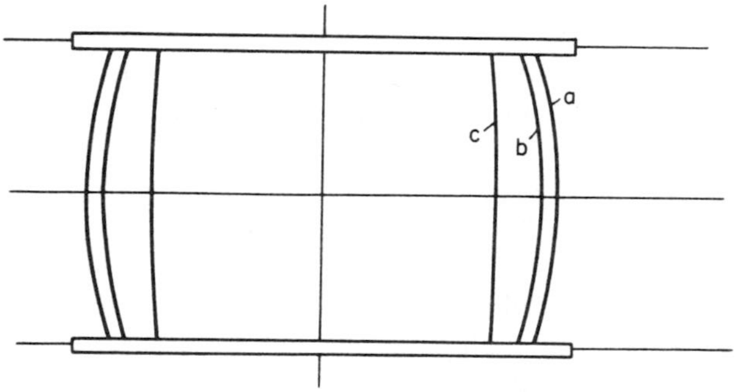

FIG. 9. Γ curves drawn for various profiles of external magnetic field.

order of magnitude is that of the variations of Green's functions caused by the transition from the boundary line Γ to that of Σ_0. The demonstration may be regarded as complete because the variations of Green's functions vanish together with p.

It is now obvious that we may calculate the variation of the total current I under the assumption that the line of discontinuity coincides with Γ. To do this, we must use Eq. (5.109), where it is sufficient to keep only terms of the same order of magnitude as p.

We must first of all calculate the density μ^1 to the same approximation; from Eq. (5.97) we infer that

$$\mu_1{}^1 = \frac{p}{\pi}\frac{\partial z^1}{\partial n_0}\bigg|_0 + \frac{p}{\pi}\frac{VB}{c}\, x t_0\bigg|_0 = \frac{p}{\pi}\,\rho_{\min}\frac{\partial z^2}{\partial t_0}\bigg|_0 = -\frac{p}{\pi}\,\rho_{\min}\, j_{n0}\bigg|_0 \tag{5.111}$$

The right-hand terms are calculated along the curve Γ. The directions $\mathbf{n}_0$ and $\mathbf{t}_0$ are normal and tangential, respectively, to Γ; the subscript zero denotes that the corresponding term is taken for $p = 0$ ($\rho_{\max} = \rho_{\min}$).

Having eliminated the density $\mu_1{}^1$ from Eq. (5.109) by virtue of Eq. (5.111), we obtain the following expression for the variation of the total current I (where the terms $O(p^2)$ are dropped):

$$\Delta I = \frac{R(1/\rho_{\min} - 1/\rho_{\max})\alpha^{**}}{1 + (R/\rho_{\min})\alpha^*}\, I_{\lambda_c} + 2\left[\rho_{\min}\left(1 + \frac{R}{\rho_{\min}}\alpha^*\right)\right]^{-1}$$
$$\times\left\{\left[\frac{4\delta}{\pi}\lambda_0^{k_1} + \mathrm{P}^1(0,\delta) - \mathrm{P}^1(0,-\delta)\right]\frac{\alpha^*}{2} + \frac{2\delta}{\pi}\int_1^\infty \Sigma\left(\frac{x}{\lambda}\right) S(x,\delta)\, d\left(\frac{x}{\lambda}\right)\right.$$
$$\left. + \int_0^\lambda S(x,\delta)\,dx - \frac{2\delta}{\pi}\int_{k_1}^1 \frac{\Lambda(\tau)\,d\tau}{(\tau^2 - k_1{}^2)^{1/2}} - \left(1 - \frac{\rho_{\min}}{\rho_{\max}}\right)\frac{V}{c}\int_{x_1}^\lambda B(x)\,dx\right\} \tag{5.112}$$

We have denoted by I_{λ_c} the value of total current for ρ everywhere equal to $\rho_{\min}$, this value being given by

$$I_{\lambda_c} = \frac{1}{\rho_{\min} + R\alpha^*}\frac{V}{c}\int_{-\lambda}^{\lambda} B(x)\,dx \tag{5.113}$$

In Table I we present the values of the ratio $\Delta I/pI_{\lambda_c}$ calculated according to Eq. (5.112) for three variants of the magnetic field distribution $B(x)$ indicated on Fig. 8. The parameter λ/δ is chosen equal to 1 and 2. It is obvious from this table that optimization of the conductivity distribution can provide a considerable increase in the total current.

An analogous investigation can also be conducted for the case when the magnetic field zone spreads beyond the limits of the electrode zone. It should be expected, however, that the effect of conductivity optimization should then be less than that in the preceding case, for now the vortex currents would be

TABLE I

VALUES OF CHARACTERISTIC RATIO $\Delta I/pI_{\lambda_c}$

Case	λ/δ	
	1	2
a	0.375	0.228
b	0.474	0.253
c	0.583	0.263

withdrawn from the electrode zone. Thus, we should consider the disposition of the magnetic field abatement region outside of the electrode zone as the optimization factor itself.[32]

Let us now proceed to the particular case $\rho_{\max} = \infty$. For this case, the parameter p is equal to unity. In the region where $\rho = \rho_{\max}$ there can be no current, whereas in the region $\rho = \rho_{\min}$, the Weierstrass condition (theorem) requires that the vector lines $\mathbf{j}$ and grad ω_2 be parallel with each other.

It is easy to verify that these requirements are met in certain circumstances by the following conductivity distribution:

$$\rho(x, y) = \begin{cases} \rho_{\max} = \infty & |x| > l \\ \rho_{\min} & |x| < l \end{cases} \qquad l \leq \lambda \tag{5.114}$$

The components of the current density are now expressed by

$$\zeta^1 = 0$$

$$\zeta^2 = \begin{cases} \dfrac{V}{c\rho_{\min}}\left[B(x) - \dfrac{Rl/\delta}{\rho_{\min} + Rl/\delta}\dfrac{1}{2l}\displaystyle\int_{-l}^{l} B(x)\,dx\right] & |x| < l \\ 0 & |x| > l \end{cases} \tag{5.115}$$

The functional I is equal to

$$I_l = \frac{G_l}{\rho_{\min} + Rl/\delta}, \qquad G_l = \frac{V}{c}\int_{-l}^{l} B(x)\,dx \tag{5.116}$$

The electric field is homogeneous, its only y component being $-I_l R/2\delta$. We can see that under these circumstances, the problem is unidimensional; from this it follows that the vector grad ω_2 now has only its y component different from zero, this component being constant and negative. Equation (5.94) provides a restriction imposed on the values of the abscissas $\pm l$ of the vertical lines of the conductivity jump. It follows now from this equation that these lines should be critical; in other words, the current density should vanish along them

$$\zeta^2(\pm l) = 0 \tag{5.117}$$

This latest equation, (5.117), together with Eq. (5.115), determines the unknown parameter l. Provided the least root of this equation does not exceed λ, this root gives just the abscissa to be determined. The very existence of such a root (or, equivalently, the existence of an optimal regime expressed by Eq. (5.114)) is essentially determined by the profile of the external magnetic field $B(x)$. It follows particularly from Eq. (5.115) that for the realization of

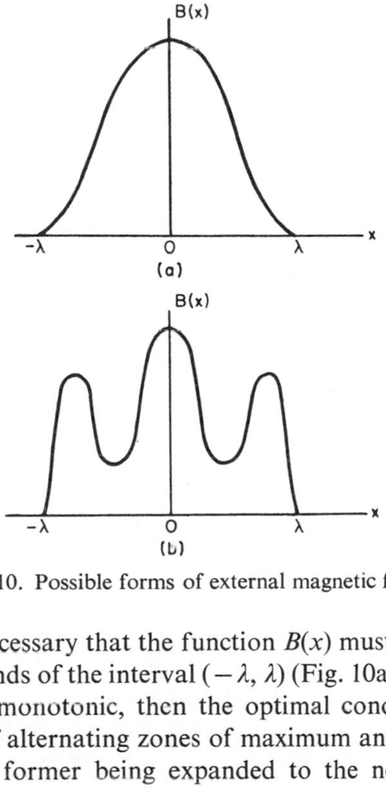

FIG. 10. Possible forms of external magnetic field.

regime (5.114) it is necessary that the function $B(x)$ must decrease sufficiently rapidly towards the ends of the interval $(-\lambda, \lambda)$ (Fig. 10a); if, presumably, the function $B(x)$ is nonmonotonic, then the optimal conductivity distribution may take the form of alternating zones of maximum and vanishing conductivity (Fig. 10b), the former being expanded to the neighborhoods of the maxima of the function $B(x)$.

It can be immediately demonstrated that in optimal regime (5.114) the total current I_l exceeds, for instance, that obtained for constant conductivity of the fluid, equal to $\rho_{\min}^{-1}$. In the latter case we get (see Sec. 5.34 for notation)

$$I_{\lambda_c} = \frac{2G_\lambda}{2\rho_{\min} + R\alpha}, \qquad G_\lambda = \frac{V}{c}\int_{-\lambda}^{\lambda} B(x)\,dx$$

For the profile of a magnetic field of the type presented in Fig. 10a, the following inequality is valid:

$$I_l \geq I_\lambda = \frac{G_\lambda}{\rho_{\min} + R\lambda/\delta}$$

This inequality follows from the fact that along the intervals (λ, l), $(-l, -\lambda)$ electric currents flow in the negative direction [cf. Eqs. (5.115) and (5.117)].

The inequality

$$\frac{\alpha\delta}{2\lambda} = -\frac{\pi K(1-k^2)^{1/2}}{2 \ln k\, K(k)} > 1, \qquad k = \exp(-\pi\lambda/\delta)$$

valid for any $0 < k < 1$, indicates that $I_\lambda > I_{\lambda_c}$, or according to what has already been stated, $I_l > I_{\lambda_c}$.

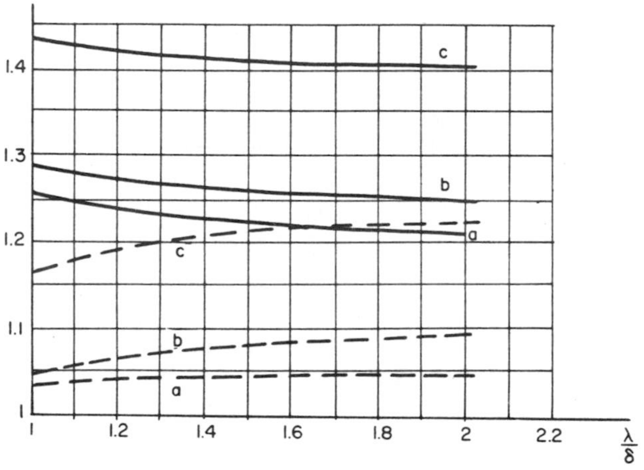

FIG. 11. Characteristic graphs of the ratios I_l/I_{λ_c} and I_l/I_λ as functions of λ/δ (Sec. 5.36).

Figure 11 presents the graphs I_l/I_{λ_c} and I_l/I_λ as functions of the parameter λ/δ for three variants of external magnetic field and the ratio $R/\rho_{\min}$ equal to unity. The first of these functions characterizes the effectiveness of the conductivity optimization as compared with the case when conductivity is everywhere constant and equal to $\rho_{\min}^{-1}$. In both cases the external magnetic field is concentrated in the electrode zone (the variants *a–c*, Fig. 8). It is obvious from the graphs (continuous curves) that the effectiveness of the optimization increases rapidly with transition from variant *a* to *c* or, equivalently, together with extension of the region of the magnetic field decrease towards the ends of the electrode zone. For any variant, the effectiveness of the optimization decreases slowly when the characteristic ratio λ/δ grows, because the relative part of the end losses is then being reduced. We have already observed an analogous situation in the case of small values of p (Table I).

The ratio I_l/I_λ (dashed curves on Fig. 11) characterizes the effectiveness of the conductivity optimization as compared to the case when conductivity vanishes outside the electrode zone.

It may be thought that in the latter case a sort of partial optimization of the conductivity distribution is accomplished, for now there is no longer the possibility of the current lines' departure from the electrode zone. From this it naturally follows that the effectiveness of the optimization decreases as compared with the preceding case (the dashed curves on Fig. 11 show lower values than the continuous ones). As before, however, the effectiveness decreases quite rapidly during the transition from a to c. On the other hand, the effectiveness increases together with the ratio λ/δ, the influence of the partial optimization now being decreased.

APPENDIX

The constant parameter γ is determined from the last Eq. (5.104). Having substituted Eq. (5.107) for $v_1(\tau, 0)$ into Eq. (5.104), we write the latter in the following form (for notation see Sec. 5.35):

$$-\frac{2\delta}{\pi}\int_0^{k_1}\frac{v_1{}^*(\tau,0)}{(k_1{}^2-\tau^2)^{1/2}}\,d\tau+\frac{2\delta}{\pi}\gamma\int_0^{k_1}\frac{d\tau}{[(1-\tau^2)(k_1{}^2-\tau^2)]^{1/2}}+\frac{2\delta}{\pi}\lambda_0^{k_1}$$
$$-R\frac{2\delta}{\pi}\left[\frac{1}{\rho_{\min}}\int_{k_1}^{\tau_1}\frac{v_1(\tau,0)}{(\tau^2-k_1{}^2)^{1/2}}\,d\tau\right.$$
$$\left.+\frac{1}{\rho_{\max}}\int_{\tau_1}^{1}\frac{v_1(\tau,0)}{(\tau^2-k_1{}^2)^{1/2}}\,d\tau\right]+R\left[\frac{N_1}{\rho_{\min}}+\frac{N_2}{\rho_{\max}}\right]$$
$$-\tfrac{1}{2}[\mathrm{P}^1(0,\delta)-\mathrm{P}^1(0,-\delta)] \tag{5.118}$$

The left-hand side of this equation can be rewritten as follows [see Eq. (107)]:

$$-\frac{2\delta}{\pi^2}\int_0^{k_1}\frac{d\tau}{(k_1{}^2-\tau^2)^{1/2}}\left(\frac{1+\tau}{1-\tau}\right)^{1/2}\left\{\int_{-\infty}^{-1}\frac{1}{\rho-\tau}\left(\frac{|\rho|+1}{|\rho|-1}\right)^{1/2}S_1(\rho)\,d\rho\right.$$
$$\left.+\int_1^{\infty}\frac{1}{\rho-\tau}\left(\frac{\rho-1}{\rho+1}\right)^{1/2}S_1(\rho)\,d\rho\right\}+\frac{2\delta}{\pi}\gamma K(k_1)+\frac{2\delta}{\pi}\lambda_0^{k_1}$$
$$=-\frac{2\delta}{\pi^2}\int_0^{k_1}\frac{d\tau}{(k_1{}^2-\tau^2)^{1/2}}\left(\frac{1+\tau}{1-\tau}\right)^{1/2}\left\{\int_1^{\infty}\left[\frac{1}{\rho-\tau}\left(\frac{\rho-1}{\rho+1}\right)^{1/2}\right.\right.$$
$$\left.\left.-\frac{1}{\rho+\tau}\frac{\rho+1}{\rho-1}\right]S_1(\rho)\,d\rho\right\}+\frac{2\delta}{\pi}\left[\gamma K(k_1)+\lambda_0^{k_1}\right]$$

Furthermore, we have

$$\int_0^{k_1} \frac{d\tau}{(k_1{}^2 - \tau^2)^{1/2}} \left(\frac{1+\tau}{1-\tau}\right)^{1/2} \int_1^{\infty} \left[\frac{1}{\rho - \tau}\left(\frac{\rho - 1}{\rho + 1}\right)^{1/2} - \frac{1}{\rho + \tau}\left(\frac{\rho + 1}{\rho - \tau}\right)^{1/2}\right] S_1(\rho)\, d\rho$$

$$= -2\int_0^{k_1} \frac{d\tau}{(k_1{}^2 - \tau^2)^{1/2}} \left(\frac{1+\tau}{1-\tau}\right)^{1/2} (1-\tau) \int_1^{\infty} \frac{\rho S_1(\rho)}{(\rho^2 - 1)^{1/2}} \frac{d\rho}{\rho^2 - \tau^2}$$

$$= -2\int_0^{k_1} \frac{d\tau}{[(1-\tau^2)(k_1{}^2 - \tau^2)]^{1/2}} \int_1^{\infty} \frac{\rho}{(\rho^2 - 1)^{1/2}} S_1(\rho)\, d\rho$$

$$+ 2\int_0^{k_1} \frac{d\tau}{(k_1{}^2 - \tau^2)^{1/2}} \frac{1}{(1-\tau^2)^{1/2}} \int_1^{\infty} \frac{\rho}{(\rho^2 - 1)^{1/2}} \frac{\rho^2 - 1}{\rho^2 - \tau^2} S_1(\rho)\, d\rho$$

$$= 2\int_1^{\infty} \frac{\rho}{(\rho^2 - 1)^{1/2}} S_1(\rho)\, d\rho \times \left[- K(k_1) + (\rho^2 - 1) \int_0^{k_1} \frac{d\tau}{(\rho^2 - \tau^2)[(k_1{}^2 - \tau^2)(1 - \tau^2)]^{1/2}} \right]$$

$$= 2\int_1^{\infty} \frac{\rho}{(\rho^2 - 1)^{1/2}} S_1(\rho)\, d\rho \left[\frac{\rho^2 - 1}{\rho^2} \Pi\left(\frac{\pi}{2}, -\frac{k_1{}^2}{\rho^2}, k_1\right) - K(k_1)\right]$$

The left-hand side of Eq. (5.118) is now equal to

$$-\frac{4\delta}{\pi^2}\int_1^{\infty} \frac{\rho}{(\rho^2 - 1)^{1/2}} S_1(\rho)\, d\rho \left[\frac{\rho^2 - 1}{\rho^2} \Pi\left(\frac{\pi}{2}, -\frac{k_1{}^2}{\rho^2}, k_1\right) - K(k_1)\right]$$
$$+ \frac{2\delta}{\pi} [\gamma K(k_1) + \lambda_0^{k_1}] \tag{5.119}$$

Consider now the right-hand side of Eq. (5.118). We write (for notation see Sec. 5.35):

$$\int_{k_1}^{\tau_1} \frac{v_1(\tau, 0)}{(\tau^2 - k_1{}^2)^{1/2}}\, d\tau$$

$$= \frac{1}{\pi}\int_{k_1}^{\tau_1} \frac{d\tau}{(\tau^2 - k_1{}^2)^{1/2}} \left(\frac{1+\tau}{1-\tau}\right)^{1/2}$$
$$\times \left\{\int_{-\infty}^{-1} \frac{1}{\rho - \tau}\left(\frac{|\rho| + 1}{|\rho| - 1}\right)^{1/2} S_1(\rho)\, d\rho + \int_1^{\infty} \frac{1}{\rho - \tau}\left(\frac{\rho - 1}{\rho + 1}\right)^{1/2} S_1(\rho)\, d\rho\right\}$$
$$-\gamma \int_{k_1}^{\tau_1} \frac{d\tau}{[(1-\tau^2)(\tau^2 - k_1{}^2)]^{1/2}} - \lambda_{k_1}^{\tau_1}$$

$$\int_{k_1}^{\tau_1} \frac{d\tau}{(\tau^2 - k_1{}^2)^{1/2}} \left(\frac{1+\tau}{1-\tau}\right)^{1/2} \left\{\int_{-\infty}^{-1} \dots d\rho + \int_1^{\infty} \dots d\rho\right\}$$

$$= -2\int_{k_1}^{\tau_1} \frac{d\tau}{[(1-\tau^2)(\tau^2 - k_1{}^2)^{1/2}} \int_1^{\infty} \frac{\rho}{(\rho^2-1)^{1/2}} S_1(\rho)\, d\rho$$

$$+ 2\int_1^{\infty} \frac{\rho}{(\rho^2-1)^{1/2}} (\rho^2 - 1) S_1(\rho)\Omega(\rho)\, d\rho$$

$$\Omega(\rho) = \int_{k_1}^{\tau_1} \frac{d\tau}{(\rho^2 - \tau^2)[(1-\tau^2)(\tau^2 - k_1{}^2)]^{1/2}}$$

The latter integral can be transformed by virtue of the substitution

$$\tau = (1 - k_1'^2\xi^2)^{1/2}, \qquad k_1{}^2 + k_1'^2 = 1$$

into the form

$$\Omega = -\frac{1}{\rho^2 - 1}\int_1^{\varepsilon} \frac{d\xi}{(1 + n'\xi^2)[(1-\xi^2)(1 - k_1{}'\xi^2)]^{1/2}}, \qquad \varepsilon = \left(\frac{1-\tau_1{}^2}{k_1{}'}\right)^{1/2}$$

Here we let $n' = k_1'^2/(\rho^2 - 1)$. The integral Ω is now equal to

$$\Omega = -\frac{1}{\rho^2 - 1}\left[\Pi\left(\arcsin\frac{1-\tau_1{}^2}{k_1{}'}, \frac{k_1'^2}{\rho^2-1}, k_1{}'\right) - \Pi\left(\frac{\pi}{2}, \frac{k_1'^2}{\rho^2-1}, k_1{}'\right)\right]$$

Now we can easily write down the resulting expression for the right-hand side of Eq. (5.118); namely,

$$-\frac{4\delta}{\pi^2} R\int_1^{\infty} \frac{\rho}{(\rho^2-1)^{1/2}} S_1(\rho)\, d\rho \left\{\frac{1}{\rho_{\min}}\left[F\left(\frac{\pi}{2}, k_1{}'\right)\right.\right.$$

$$\left.- F\left(\arcsin\frac{(1-\tau_1{}^2)^{1/2}}{k_1{}'}, k_1{}'\right)\right] + \frac{1}{\rho_{\max}} F\left(\arcsin\frac{(1-\tau_1{}^2)^{1/2}}{k_1{}'}, k_1{}'\right)$$

$$+ \frac{1}{\rho_{\min}}\left[\Pi\left(\arcsin\frac{(1-\tau_1{}^2)^{1/2}}{k_1{}'}, \frac{k_1'^2}{\rho^2-1}, k_1{}'\right) - \Pi\left(\frac{\pi}{2}, \frac{k_1'^2}{\rho^2-1}, k_1{}'\right)\right]$$

$$\left.- \frac{1}{\rho_{\max}} \Pi\left(\arcsin\frac{(1-\tau_1{}^2)^{1/2}}{k_1{}'}, \frac{k_1'^2}{\rho^2-1}, k_1{}'\right)\right\} \tag{5.120}$$

$$+ R\left[\frac{N_1{}^*}{\rho_{\min}} + \frac{N_2{}^*}{\rho_{\max}}\right] - \frac{1}{2}[\mathrm{P}^1(0, \delta) - \mathrm{P}^1(0, -\delta)]$$

$$-\frac{2\delta}{\pi} R\gamma\left\{\frac{1}{\rho_{\min}}\left[F\left(\frac{\pi}{2}, k_1{}'\right) - F\left(\arcsin\frac{(1-\tau_1{}^2)^{1/2}}{k_1{}'}, k_1{}'\right)\right]\right.$$

$$\left.+ \frac{1}{\rho_{\max}} F\left(\arcsin\frac{(1-\tau_1{}^2)^{1/2}}{k_1{}'}, k_1{}'\right)\right\}$$

The parameter γ can now be determined on setting expressions (5.119) and (5.120) equal to each other [see Eq. (5.108)].

The total current I is given by

$$I = -\frac{4\delta}{\pi R}\int_0^{k_1}\frac{v_1(\tau, 0)}{(k_1{}^2-\tau^2)^{1/2}}\,dt + \frac{1}{R}[\mathrm{P}^1(0, \delta) - \mathrm{P}^1(0, -\delta)]$$

Making use of the preceding equations, we find

$$\begin{aligned}
I = &-\frac{8\delta}{\pi^2 R}\int_1^{\infty}\frac{\rho}{(\rho^2-1)^{1/2}}\,S_1(\rho)\,d\rho\left[\frac{\rho^2-1}{\rho}\,\Pi\left(\frac{\pi}{2}, -\frac{k_1{}^2}{\rho^2}, k_1\right) - K(k_1)\right]\\
&+\frac{4\delta}{\pi R}K(k_1)\frac{\pi}{2\delta}\left[K(k_1) + \frac{R}{\rho_{\min}}K(k_1{}')\right.\\
&\left.-R\left(\frac{1}{\rho_{\min}} - \frac{1}{\rho_{\max}}\right)F\left(\arcsin\frac{(1-\tau_1{}^2)^{1/2}}{k_1{}'}, k_1{}'\right)\right]^{-1}\\
&\times\left\{\frac{4\delta}{\pi^2}\int_1^{\infty}\frac{\rho}{(\rho^2-1)^{1/2}}\,S_1(\rho)\,d\rho\left[\frac{\rho^2-1}{\rho^2}\,\Pi\left(\frac{\pi}{2}, -\frac{k_1{}^2}{\rho^2}, k_1\right)\right.\right.\\
&+\frac{R}{\rho_{\min}}\,\Pi\left(\frac{\pi}{2}, \frac{k_1'^2}{\rho^2-1}, k_1{}'\right) - R\left(\frac{1}{\rho_{\min}} - \frac{1}{\rho_{\max}}\right)\\
&\times\Pi\left(\arcsin\frac{(1-\tau_1{}^2)^{1/2}}{k_1{}'}, \frac{k_1'^2}{\rho^2-1}, k_1{}'\right) - K(k_1) - \frac{R}{\rho_{\min}}K(k_1{}')\\
&\left.+R\left(\frac{1}{\rho_{\min}} - \frac{1}{\rho_{\max}}\right)F\left(\arcsin\frac{(1-\tau_1{}^2)^{1/2}}{k_1{}'}\right)\right] + R\left[\frac{N_1{}^*}{\rho_{\min}} + \frac{N_2{}^*}{\rho_{\max}}\right]\\
&\left.-\tfrac{1}{2}[\mathrm{P}^1(0, \delta) - \mathrm{P}^1(0, -\delta)]\right\} + \frac{1}{R}[\mathrm{P}^1(0, \delta) - \mathrm{P}^1(0, -\delta)] + \frac{4\delta}{\pi R}\lambda_0^{k_1}
\end{aligned}$$

This expression can be immediately transformed to the form of Eq. (5.109).

References

1. R. Bellman and R. Kalaba, *J. Basic Eng.* **83** (1961).
2. A. I. Egorov, *Prikl. Mat. Mekh.* **27**, 688–696 (1963).
3. A. G. Butkovsky, A. Ya. Lerner, and S. A. Malii, *Dokl. Akad. Nauk SSSR* **153**, 772–775 (1963).
4. T. K. Sirazetdinov, *Izv. Vysshikh Uchebn. Zavedenii, Aviats. Tekhn.* **2**, 11–21 (1961).
5. R. Bellman and H. Osborn, *J. Math. Mech.*, **7**, 1 (1958).
6. A. G. Butkovsky and A. Ya. Lerner, *Dokl. Akad. Nauk SSSR* **134**, 778–781 (1960).
7. A. G. Butkovsky, *Avtomat. Telemekh.* (*Automat. Remote Control*) **22**, 17–26 (1961).
8. A. G. Butkovsky, *Avtomat. Telemekh.* **22**, 1288–1301 (1961).
9. Yu. V. Egorov, *Dokl. Akad. Nauk SSSR* **150**, 241–244 (1963).
10. K. G. Guderley and E. Hantsch, *Z. Flugwiss.* **3**, H. 9, S. 305–313 (1955).

11. G. V. B. Rao, *Jet Propulsion* **28**, 377–382 (1958).
12. Yu. D. Shmiglevsky, *Prikl. Mat. Mekh.* **21**, 195–206 (1957).
13. Yu. D. Shmiglevsky, *Prikl. Mat. Mekh.* **26**, 110–125 (1962).
14. K. G. Guderley and J. V. Armitage, Paper presented at the Symposium on Extremal Problems in Aerodynamics, Boeing Scientific Research Laboratories, Flight Sciences Laboratory, Seattle, Washington, December 3–4, 1962.
15. A. N. Kraiko, *Prikl. Mat. Mekh.* **28**, 285–295 (1964).
16. K. A. Lurie, *Prikl. Mat. Mekh.* **27**, 842–853 (1963).
17. P. K. Rashevsky, "Geometricheskaya Teoria Uravnenii s Tchastnimi Proisvodnimi." ("Geometrical Theory of Partial Differential Equations"), p. 323–324. Gostekhizdat, Moscow, 1947.
18. A. Miele, *in* "Optimization Techniques With Applications to Aerospace Systems" (G. Leitmann, ed.), p. 112. Academic Press, New York, 1962.
19. V. Volterra, *Att. Accad. Nazl. Lincei Rend.* **4**, 6^1 (1890).
20. R. E. Kopp, *in* "Optimization Techniques With Applications to Aerospace Systems" (G. Leitmann, ed.), pp. 255–279. Academic Press, New York, 1962.
21. G. W. Sutton, *Vistas Astron.* **3**, 53–64 (1960).
22. J. H. Drake, *AIAA J.* **1**, 2053–2057 (1963).
23. A. E. Sheindlin, A. V. Gubarev, V. I. Kovbasijuk, and V. A. Prokudin, *Izv. Akad. Nauk SSSR, Otd. Tekh. Nauk Energ. i Avtomat.* **6**, 34–38 (1962).
24. T. G. Cowling, "Magnetohydrodynamics." Wiley (Interscience), New York, 1957.
25. A. B. Vatazhin and S. A. Regirer, *Prikl. Mat. Mekh.* **26** (1962).
26. G. G. Cloutier and A. I. Carswell, *Phys. Rev. Letters* **10**, 327–329 (1963).
27. K. A. Lurie, *Prikl. Mat. Mekh.* **28**, 258–267 (1964).
28. L. I. Rozonoer, *Avtomat. Telemekh.* (*Automat. Remote Control*), **20**, 1320–1334, 1441–1458, 1561–1578 (1959).
29. A. B. Vatazhin, *Prikl. Mat. Mekh.* **25**, 965–968 (1961).
30. K. A. Lurie, *Zh. Prikl. Mekh. i Tekhn. Fiz.* No. 2 (1964).
31. O. D. Kellog, "Foundations of Potential Theory." Springer, Berlin, 1929.
32. A. B. Vatazhin, *Izv. Akad. Nauk SSSR, Otd. Tekhn. Nauk Mekh. i Mashinostr.* No. 1 (1962).
33. M. A. Lavrentjev and B. V. Shabat, "Methods of the Theory of Functions of the Complex Variable." Gostekhizdat, Moscow, 1951.

Part 2

A Geometric Approach

6

Mathematical Foundations of System Optimization

HUBERT HALKIN†

BELL TELEPHONE LABORATORIES,
WHIPPANY, NEW JERSEY

† *Present address*: Department of Mathematics, University of California, La Jolla, California.

6.0 Introduction

This chapter is devoted to a mathematical analysis of some of the problems encountered in the optimal control of deterministic systems described by nonlinear differential equations. It contains very few results which are not yet common tools for the growing number of engineers interested in control theory. The main purpose of this chapter is to give a rigorous but still easily understandable derivation of some of the most important of these results. The method developed here is the same as the method which we have introduced in earlier publications devoted to more complex versions of similar problems (Halkin[22,24]).

Many engineers, who were successful practitioners of the operational calculus of Heaviside long before Laurent Schwartz gave it mathematical respectability, could dispute the necessity of adding mathematical rigor to the proof of those results in optimal control which have been accepted for many years. From a purely utilitarian standpoint such an attitude would be acceptable if these results, even if not fully understood, would be applied correctly and successfully. Unfortunately, this is not the case: a great majority of the papers on optimal control in the American engineering literature is there to testify that these results are more often misused than not. Another shortcoming of engineering applications of optimal control is the present state of the art in computing techniques. Even after the pioneering work of Bryson and Denham,[8] Kelley,[33] Neustadt,[40] and Paiewonsky and Woodrow,[42] we must admit that computing techniques for optimization problems are still way behind the wishful manipulations of formulas that we find in so many engineering papers. We seriously believe that a sound understanding of the theory of optimal control would be of considerable help in applying it correctly and devising efficient computational methods.

The pièce de résistance in any mathematical treatment of the theory of optimal control is always the proof of the maximum principle. There have been some remarkable proofs of the maximum principle in the case of linear systems (Bellman *et al.*,[4] LaSalle,[34] and Neustadt[40] but very few rigorous proofs of the maximum principle in the case of nonlinear systems (Pontryagin *et al.*,[43] Warga,[48] Berkovitz,[5] and Halkin[24]).

The proof given by Pontryagin and his associates is often obscure and incomplete. The proof of Warga is short and precise but applies only to problems which have been "relaxed" by a proper convexification. The proof of Berkovitz is based on McShane's proof of the multiplier rule for the abnormal case of the problem of Bolza and presupposes an extensive knowledge of the classical calculus of variations.

The proof of Pontryagin *et al.*[43] is based on the construction of special variations which have been developed initially by McShane.[38] The special variations of McShane lead to the construction of some *convex cones*. The proof of Halkin[24] is also based on special variations which are different from the variations of McShane and which lead to the construction of some *convex sets*. The *convex cones* of McShane are the cones spanned by these *convex sets*. The properties of a convex cone spanned by a convex set are determined completely by this convex set. However, the reverse is not true: there are many properties of a convex set which are not recoverable from the knowledge of the properties of the convex cone spanned by this convex set. It is to be expected, and it is in fact the case, that from considerations of convex sets, we have been able (Halkin[24]) to derive all the results obtained from convex cones. Indeed, we have been able to derive some new results which are particularly useful when it comes to computational methods (Halkin[29]).

In addition to the preceding proofs, there are a great number of heuristic derivations of the maximum principle (Desoer,[12] Dreyfus,[13] Flügge-Lotz and Halkin,[15] and Kalman[32]). All these heuristic† derivations follow the pattern of Carathéodory's Method of "Geodätisches Gefälle,"[10] or equivalently of Bellman's "Dynamic Programming."[3] These derivations are excellent mnemonic devices to check the correctness of the final formulas.

In this chapter we shall present a simple and complete proof of the maximum principle.

† It should be added that these papers, especially Kalman,[32] give proofs which are rigorous for some special cases.

Our proof of the maximum principle proceeds in three steps. We are first interested in open loop systems, i.e., systems which are described by differential equations independent of the state variables or equivalently such that the output can be represented by the integral of a function depending on the input only. From there we go to time varying linear systems and finally to a general type of nonlinear systems. In so doing we are not only solving three separate problems of increasing difficulty but we build up a single proof in three steps each step closely related to one of the three types of systems mentioned above.

If, in the case of linear systems, we follow the guiding lines of the proof of McShane or Pontryagin, we obtain a proof which is only slightly simpler than the general proof for nonlinear systems. But if, in the case of linear systems, we follow the approach given in this chapter, we obtain the simple proof which has been developed specifically for linear systems by LaSalle.

The mathematical prerequisites for the present chapter are very elementary: calculus, matrix theory, finite dimensional Euclidean space, etc. The reader will find numerous footnotes to refresh his memory of these prerequisites. Moreover, we have collected in Appendix A all prerequisites related to the theory of ordinary differential equations and in Appendix B all prerequisites related to convexity in finite dimensional Euclidean spaces. The only nonelementary mathematical result quoted without proof in this chapter is the fixed point theorem of Brouwer for closed convex subsets of finite dimensional Euclidean spaces. Even if the proof of this theorem is not elementary its statement uses only elementary mathematical concepts and its content can be visualized easily. This chapter does not contain a single one of those measure theoretical concepts which have been for too long a necessary evil in the mathematical theory of optimal control. The end of this paragraph is intended only for the reader familiar with measure theory. An important step in the proof of the maximum principle given in Halkin[24] is based on a well-known theorem in measure theory which states that: if $\mathbf{f}$ is a Lebesgue integrable function from $[0, 1]$ into E^n and if $\mathscr{B}$ is the class of all Borel subsets of $[0, 1]$ then the set $\left\{\int_E \mathbf{f}(t)\, dt : E \in \mathscr{B}\right\}$ is convex. In Halkin[27] we have proved a new result of the same type: if $\mathbf{f}$ is a piecewise continuous function from $[0, 1]$ into E^n and if $\mathscr{A}$ is the class of all subsets of $[0, 1]$ which are the union of a finite number of disjoint intervals, then the set $\left\{\int_E \mathbf{f}(t)\, dt : E \in \mathscr{A}\right\}$ is convex. This new result allows us to take full advantage of the geometrical content of the proof given in Halkin[24] without using any measure theoretical results and, correspondingly, without introducing measurable control functions which are mathematical artifacts completely out of place in control theory.

Geometry is at the center of this chapter. The first step in this direction is the principle of optimal evolution (Halkin[23]) which states that: "Every event of an optimal process belongs to the boundary of the set of possible events." The principle of optimal evolution transforms the given optimization problem into a purely topological (geometrical) problem. We have solved this topological problem by proving that every trajectory belonging to the boundary of the set of possible events satisfies a maximum principle of the Pontryagin's type (Halkin[24]).

6.1 Dynamical Polysystem

6.11 System Evolution

We shall consider a system whose state is described by a vector $\mathbf{x} = (x_1, x_2, \ldots, x_n)$ of an n-dimensional Euclidean space E^n and whose evolution is given by the differential equation

$$\dot{\mathbf{x}} = \mathbf{f}(\mathbf{x}, \mathbf{u}, t) \qquad (\dot{\mathbf{x}} = d\mathbf{x}/dt) \tag{6.1}$$

where $\mathbf{u} = (u_1, \ldots, u_m)$ is an m-dimensional control vector of a Euclidean space E^m and $\mathbf{f}(\mathbf{x}, \mathbf{u}, t) = (f_1(\mathbf{x}, \mathbf{u}, t), f_2(\mathbf{x}, \mathbf{u}, t), \ldots, f_n(\mathbf{x}, \mathbf{u}, t))$ is a given n-dimensional vector valued function of $\mathbf{x}$, $\mathbf{u}$, and of the time t.

In this chapter we shall assume that we have selected an orthonormal base in E^n and that the Euclidean length of a vector $\mathbf{x} = (x_1, x_2, \ldots, x_n)$ is given by $|\mathbf{x}| = (\sum_{i=1}^{n} (x_i)^2)^{1/2}$. Similarly, we assume that we have selected an orthonormal base in E^m and that the Euclidean length of a vector $\mathbf{u} = (u_1, u_2, \ldots, u_m)$ is given by $|\mathbf{u}| = (\sum_{i=1}^{m} (u_i)^2)^{1/2}$.

We assume that the vector valued function $\mathbf{f}(\mathbf{x}, \mathbf{u}, t)$ is defined for all† $\mathbf{x} \in E^n$, all $\mathbf{u} \in E^m$ and all‡ $t \in [0, 1]$. Moreover, we assume that the function $\mathbf{f}(\mathbf{x}, \mathbf{u}, t)$ is twice§ continuously differentiable with respect to $\mathbf{x}$, continuous with respect to $\mathbf{u}$, and piecewise continuous with respect to t. More precisely, we assume that there exists a finite set¶ $\{t_0, t_1, \ldots, t_k\} \subset [0, 1]$ with $t_0 = 0 < t_1 < < t_k \cdots = 1$, a finite collection of vector valued functions $\{\mathbf{f}_1(\mathbf{x}, \mathbf{u}, t), \mathbf{f}_2(\mathbf{x}, \mathbf{u}, t), \ldots, \mathbf{f}_k(\mathbf{x}, \mathbf{u}, t)\}$ such that for each $i = 1, 2, \ldots, k$

† If A is a set then "$a \in A$" means "a is an element of A" and "$B \subset A$" means "B is a subset of A."

‡ If a and b are two real numbers with $a \leq b$ then $[a, b]$ denotes the closed interval from a to b, i.e., the set of all real numbers t such that $a \leq t \leq b$. Similarly, (a, b) denotes the open interval from a to b, i.e., the set of all real numbers t such that $a < t < b$.

§ Most of the results of the theory of optimal control, for instance the maximum principle of Pontryagin, can be proved by assuming only that $\mathbf{f}(\mathbf{x}, \mathbf{u}, t)$ is once continuously differentiable with respect to $\mathbf{x}$ instead of twice (see Halkin[24]). However, these proofs are greatly simplified by making the present assumption which is valid for all known practical applications.

¶ The set denoted by $\{t_0, t_1, \ldots, t_k\}$ is the set whose elements are $t_0, t_1, \ldots,$ and t_k.

(i) the vector valued function $\mathbf{f}_i(\mathbf{x}, \mathbf{u}, t)$ and all its first and second partial derivatives with respect to $\mathbf{x}$ are defined and continuous with respect to $\mathbf{x}$, $\mathbf{u}$ and t for all $\mathbf{x} \in E^n$, all $\mathbf{u} \in E^m$, and all $t \in [t_{i-1}, t_i]$;

(ii) $\mathbf{f}(\mathbf{x}, \mathbf{u}, t) = \mathbf{f}_i(\mathbf{x}, \mathbf{u}, t)$ for all $\mathbf{x} \in E^n$, all $\mathbf{u} \in E^m$, and all $t \in (t_{i-1}, t_i)$.

6.12 Control Functions

A bounded† subset Ω of E^m is given. This set Ω is called the set of admissible control vectors. Let F be the class of all piecewise continuous functions from $[0, 1]$ into Ω. This means that each function in the class F is continuous at every point $(0, 1)$ with the exception of at most a finite number of points where it has finite right‡ and left limits and has a finite right limit at the point 0 and a finite left limit at the point 1. The preceding definition implies, in particular, that every function in the class F is bounded. The class F is called the class (or the set) of admissible control functions.

We shall use script letters $\mathscr{U}$, $\mathscr{V}$, $\mathscr{W}$, to denote functions in the class F. It is understood that the function $\mathscr{U}$ is the function whose value at the time t is $\mathbf{u}(t)$; similarly, the function $\mathscr{V}$ is the function whose value at the time t is $\mathbf{v}(t)$, etc. We shall reserve the symbols $\mathbf{u}$, $\mathbf{v}$, $\mathbf{w}$, to denote vectors in the space E^m.

From the definition given above we see immediately that the class F of control functions has the following two fundamental properties:

(1) if $\mathbf{v} \in \Omega$ then the function $\mathscr{V}$ defined by $\mathbf{v}(t) = \mathbf{v}$ for all $t \in [0, 1]$ belongs to the class F;

† A subset Ω of E^m is bounded if there exists a constant k such that for all $\mathbf{u} \in \Omega$ we have $|\mathbf{u}| \leq k$.

‡ Let $f(t)$ be a function defined on some open interval (a, b). The right limit of the function $f(t)$ at the point a is, whenever it exists,

$$\lim_{\substack{\varepsilon \to 0 \\ \varepsilon > 0}} f(a + \varepsilon)$$

Similarly, the left limit of the function $f(t)$ at the point b is, whenever it exists,

$$\lim_{\substack{\varepsilon \to 0 \\ \varepsilon < 0}} f(b + \varepsilon)$$

The function $f(t)$ is continuous at a point $\tau \in (a, b)$ if its right and left limits exist and are finite and equal at the point τ. The function $f(t)$ has a jump of the first kind at a point $\tau \in (a, b)$ if its right and left limits exist and are finite but not equal at the point τ. If the function $f(t)$ has a finite right limit at the point τ which is equal to the value of the function $f(t)$ at the point τ, we say that the function $f(t)$ assumes its right limit at the point τ. A similar convention holds for a left limit.

(2) if $\mathscr{U}_1$ and $\mathscr{U}_2 \in F$, $\tau \in (0, 1)$ then the function $\mathscr{V}$ satisfying the relations†

$$\mathbf{v}(t) = \mathbf{u}_1(t) \quad \text{for all} \quad t \in [0, \tau)$$

$$\mathbf{v}(\tau) \in \Omega$$

$$\mathbf{v}(t) = \mathbf{u}_2(t) \quad \text{for all} \quad t \in (\tau, 1]$$

belongs also to the class F.

With the help of the second of these properties we may prove easily that if $\mathscr{U}_1$ and $\mathscr{U}_2 \in F$ and if A is a subset of $[0, 1]$ which is the union of a finite number of disjoint intervals then the function $\mathscr{V}$ satisfying relations‡

$$\mathbf{v}(t) = \mathbf{u}_1(t) \qquad \text{for all} \quad t \in [0, 1] \sim A$$

$$\mathbf{v}(t) = \mathbf{u}_2(t) \qquad \text{for all} \quad t \in A$$

belongs also to the class F.

If $\mathscr{U} \in F$ then the set $\Theta(\mathscr{U})$ will be defined as the set of points in $(0, 1)$ at which the function $\mathscr{U}$ and the function $\mathbf{f}(\mathbf{x}, \mathbf{u}, t)$ are continuous with respect to t. Since, by definition, every function $\mathscr{U}$ in the class F and the function $\mathbf{f}(\mathbf{x}, \mathbf{u}, t)$ are piecewise continuous with respect to t, it follows immediately that there is only a finite number of points on the interval $[0, 1]$ which do not belong also to the set $\Theta(\mathscr{U})$ and that the set $\Theta(\mathscr{U})$ is open.§

6.13 Trajectories

If $\mathscr{U}$ is a control function in the class F we shall denote by $\mathbf{x}(t; \mathscr{U})$ a continuous function of t differentiable over $\Theta(\mathscr{U})$ and such that¶

$$\text{(i)} \quad \dot{\mathbf{x}}(t; \mathscr{U}) = \mathbf{f}(\mathbf{x}(t; \mathscr{U}), \mathbf{u}(t), t) \qquad \text{for all} \quad t \in \Theta(\mathscr{U}) \tag{6.2}$$

$$\text{(ii)} \quad \mathbf{x}(0; \mathscr{U}) = \mathbf{o} \tag{6.3}$$

From the theory of ordinary differential equations we know that for every $\mathscr{U} \in F$ we have one and only one of the following two possibilities:

(i) the function $\mathbf{x}(t; \mathscr{U})$ exists and is unique and bounded over the interval $[0, 1]$;

† The set $[0, \tau)$ is the set of all t such that $0 \leq t < \tau$. Similarly, the set $(\tau, 1]$ is the set of all t such that $\tau < t \leq 1$. The set $[0, \tau)$ is sometimes called the left-closed right-open interval from 0 to τ. Similarly, $(\tau, 1]$ is called the left-open right-closed interval from τ to 1.

‡ If A and B are two sets than $A \sim B$ denotes the set of all points of A which do not belong to B.

§ A subset of A of the real line is open if for every $a \in A$ there is an $\varepsilon > 0$ such that any real number b with $|a - b| < \varepsilon$ belongs also to the set A.

¶ There is no loss of generality by assuming that the initial value of the state vector $\mathbf{x}$ is zero. This assumption greatly simplifies the notations and can always be made after an appropriate translation of the coordinate system.

with respect to t we may add a new artificial state variable and transform the problem corresponding to this time varying system into the problem treated by Pontryagin and his associates. However, in the more general case of a time varying system which is only piecewise continuous with respect to t, this transformation cannot be performed, Pontryagin's results do not apply, and the new results contained in this chapter are needed.

6.23 Remarks on the Evolution Interval

In this chapter we assume that $t = 0$ is the initial time and that $t = 1$ is the terminal time. Any problem with fixed initial and terminal times can be easily transformed in a problem of the type treated in this chapter.

6.3 The Principle of Optimal Evolution

6.31 Reachable Sets

In this section we introduce some geometrical concepts which are of fundamental importance to the theory of optimal control.

If $t \in [0, 1]$ and if $\mathbf{x}$ is a state such that there exists a control function $\mathscr{U}$ in the class F with $\mathbf{x}(t; \mathscr{U}) = \mathbf{x}$, we shall say that the state $\mathbf{x}$ is reachable at the time t. For every $t \in [0, 1]$ we define the set $W(t)$ as the set of all states which are reachable at the time t, i.e.,

$$W(t) = \{\mathbf{x}(t; \mathscr{U}) : \mathscr{U} \in F\} \tag{6.9}$$

We shall show here that the study of the sets $W(t)$ and of their boundaries† $\partial W(t)$ is closely related to the solution of the optimization problem stated in Sec. 6.2. Let us first consider the intersection‡ $S \cap W(1)$ of the terminal set S with $W(1)$, the reachable set at the time $t = 1$. If $S \cap W(1)$ is empty, which is denoted $S \cap W(1) = \varnothing$, the problem has no feasible solution and *a fortiori* no optimal solution. If $S \cap W(1)$ is not empty and if there is a point $\bar{\mathbf{x}}$ of $S \cap W(1)$ for which $\bar{x}_n$ takes the greatest value,§ then our problem has an

† If A is a certain subset of the n-dimensional Euclidean space E^n then ∂A, the boundary of the set A, is the set of all points $\mathbf{a}$ in E^n such that for every $\varepsilon > 0$ there exist a point $\mathbf{b}$ in A and a point $\mathbf{c}$ not in A such that $|\mathbf{a} - \mathbf{b}|$ and $|\mathbf{a} - \mathbf{c}| < \varepsilon$. Note that in general a boundary point of a set is not necessarily an element of that set. A closed set, however, contains all its boundary points. This last property is sometimes used to define a closed set.

‡ If A and B are sets then $A \cap B$ is the intersection of the sets A and B, i.e., the set $A \cap B$ is the set of all elements which belong to both sets A and B. Similarly, $A \cup B$ is the union of the sets A and B, i.e., the set $A \cup B$ is the set of all elements which belong to at least one of the sets A and B.

§ From the assumptions of Sec. 6.1 we know that the set $W(1)$ is bounded. The set $S \cap W(1)$ is *a fortiori* bounded. However, the reader should realize that a bounded set

optimal solution, and there is a control function $\mathscr{V}$ in the class F such that $\mathbf{x}(1 : \mathscr{V}) = \bar{\mathbf{x}}$. From now on, in this chapter we shall assume that such an optimal solution exists and we shall try to derive as many of its properties as possible.

We shall first note that $\mathbf{x}(1; \mathscr{V})$ is a boundary point of $W(1)$ since otherwise there would exist a point $\mathbf{x}^*$ in $W(1) \cap S$ with $x_n^* > x_n(1; \mathscr{V})$ which would contradict the optimality of the control function $\mathscr{V}$. Moreover, if† $N(\mathbf{x}(t_1; \mathscr{V}), \varepsilon_1) \subset W(t_1)$ for some $t_1 \in [0, 1]$ and $\varepsilon_1 > 0$, then for every $t_2 \in [t_1, 1]$ there exists an $\varepsilon_2 > 0$ with $N(\mathbf{x}(t_2; \mathscr{V}), \varepsilon_2) \subset W(t_2)$ since, from the smoothness of $\mathbf{f}(\mathbf{x}, \mathbf{u}, t)$ assumed in Sec. 6.1, the point $\mathbf{x}(t_2; \mathscr{V})$ is an interior‡ point of the set of all points reachable at the time t_2 with the *same* control function $\mathscr{V}$ from the points in $N(\mathbf{x}(t_1; \mathscr{V}), \varepsilon_1)$ at the time t_1. The preceding results can be summarized as follows (Flügge-Lotz and Halkin,[15] and Halkin[23]):

Principle of Optimal Evolution. If $\mathscr{V}$ is an optimal control function, then for every $t \in [0, 1]$ the state $\mathbf{x}(t; \mathscr{V})$ belongs to the boundary of the set $W(t)$.

6.32 Propagation Analogy

If we drop a pebble on the surface of a lake, we create a certain perturbation which will propagate with time. The boundary of the time varying set $W(t)$ is very similar to the wavefront associated with that propagation. In the remainder of this section we shall assume that for every $t \in (0, 1]$ the sets $W(t)$ have smooth boundaries§ and, in particular, have tangent hyperplanes at

---

$S \cap W(1)$ has not necessarily a point $\bar{\mathbf{x}}$ for which $\bar{x}_n$ takes the greatest value. This would be the case if the set S would be closed. The very important question of the closure of the sets S will not be considered in this chapter. The reader is referred to Filippov,[14], Roxin,[44] Warga,[47] LaSalle,[31] Neustadt,[40] and Halkin.[25]

† The set $N(\mathbf{x}(t_1; \mathscr{V}), \varepsilon_1)$ is the set of all points with a distance to $\mathbf{x}(t_1; \mathscr{V})$ less than ε_1.

‡ By definition the point $\mathbf{a}$ is interior to a set A if there is an $\varepsilon > 0$ with $N(\mathbf{a}, \varepsilon) \subset A$. A precise justification of the property stated in the text is given in Proposition A.8 of Appendix A.

§ For many classical problems in the calculus of variations this assumption is indeed valid. (The proof of that fact follows easily from the classical theory of Hamilton-Jacobi partial differential equations.) However, this assumption is *not* valid for a large class of problems in optimal control. In the case of the system

$$\dot{x}_1 = u_1, \qquad \dot{x}_2 = u_2$$

with the initial condition

$$x_1(0) = x_2(0) = 0$$

and the set of admissible control

$$\Omega = \{\mathbf{u} = (u_1, u_2) : |u_1| \quad \text{and} \quad |u_2| \leq 1\}$$

we have immediately

$$W(t) = \{\mathbf{x} = (x_1, x_2) : |x_1| \quad \text{and} \quad |x_2| \leq t\}$$

We see that the set $W(t)$ is a square and hence has a boundary which is not smooth.

each of their boundary points. This assumption allows us to state and prove in a very natural way some fundamental properties of optimal solutions. In later sections the same results will be derived without making these assumptions but this more general derivation will be longer as one could expect.

Let $\mathscr{V}$ be an optimal control function and let $\mathbf{x}(t; \mathscr{V})$ be the corresponding optimal trajectory. By the principle of optimal evolution we have

$$\mathbf{x}(t; \mathscr{V}) \in \partial W(t) \qquad \text{for all} \quad t \in [0, 1] \tag{6.10}$$

Let $\boldsymbol{\lambda}(t)$ be a nonzero outward normal to the set $\partial W(t)$ at the point $\mathbf{x}(t; \mathscr{V})$. The length of the vector $\boldsymbol{\lambda}(t)$ which is not yet defined will be determined later up to a multiplicative factor. This means that later we shall add some restrictions on the vector function $\boldsymbol{\lambda}(t)$ such that the knowledge of the length of $\boldsymbol{\lambda}(\tau)$ for some $\tau \in [0, 1]$ will be sufficient to derive the length of $\boldsymbol{\lambda}(t)$ for all $t \in [0, 1]$.

As in geometrical optics we can define the velocity of the wavefront $\partial W(t)$ at the point $\mathbf{x}(t; \mathscr{V})$. This wavefront velocity is parallel to the vector $\boldsymbol{\lambda}(t)$. We shall denote by $s(t)$ the wavefront speed, i.e., the length of the wavefront velocity.

We now have two important results†:

(1) For every propagation issued from $\mathbf{x}(t; \mathscr{V})$ at the time t the projection on the normal vector $\boldsymbol{\lambda}(t)$ of the propagation velocity is at most the wavefront speed $s(t)$, i.e.,

$$\frac{\mathbf{f}(\mathbf{x}(t; \mathscr{V}), \mathbf{u}, t) \cdot \boldsymbol{\lambda}(t)}{|\boldsymbol{\lambda}(t)|} \le s(t) \qquad \text{for all} \qquad \mathbf{u} \in \Omega \quad \text{and all} \quad t \in \Theta(\mathscr{V}) \tag{6.11}$$

(2) The propagation issued from $\mathbf{x}(t; \mathscr{V})$ at the time t and corresponding to the optimal trajectory must "keep up" with the wavefront $\partial W(t)$ (see the principle of optimal evolution), hence we have

$$\frac{\mathbf{f}(\mathbf{x}(t; \mathscr{V}), \mathbf{v}(t), t) \cdot \boldsymbol{\lambda}(t)}{|\boldsymbol{\lambda}(t)|} = s(t) \qquad \text{for all} \quad t \in \Theta(\mathscr{V}) \tag{6.12}$$

6.33 A Preview of the Maximum Principle

We define a function $H(\mathbf{x}, \mathbf{u}, t, \boldsymbol{\lambda})$ by the relation

$$H(\mathbf{x}, \mathbf{u}, t, \boldsymbol{\lambda}) = \mathbf{f}(\mathbf{x}, \mathbf{u}, t) \cdot \boldsymbol{\lambda} \tag{6.13}$$

† We recall that the scalar product of two vectors α and β is denoted by $\alpha \cdot \beta$ and that the norm, or Euclidean length, of the vector λ is denoted $|\boldsymbol{\lambda}|$, i.e., $|\boldsymbol{\lambda}| = (\sum_{i=1}^{n} (\lambda_i)^2)^{1/2}$, where $\lambda_1, \lambda_2, \ldots, \lambda_n$ are the components of the vector λ.

From the relations (6.11) and (6.12) we conclude that along the optimal trajectory $\mathbf{x}(t; \mathscr{V})$ we have

$$H(\mathbf{x}(t; \mathscr{V}), \mathbf{v}(t), t, \boldsymbol{\lambda}(t)) \geq H(\mathbf{x}(t; \mathscr{V}), \mathbf{u}, t, \boldsymbol{\lambda}(t)) \quad \text{for all} \quad \mathbf{u} \in \Omega \quad \text{and all} \quad t \in \Theta(\mathscr{V}) \tag{6.14}$$

The inequality (6.14) is a preview of the maximum principle which we shall state in detail in the next section.

6.4 Statement of the Maximum Principle

In this section we shall state the maximum principle of Pontryagin corresponding to the optimization problem defined in Sec. 6.2.

We first define the function

$$H(\mathbf{x}, \mathbf{u}, t, \boldsymbol{\lambda}) = \mathbf{f}(\mathbf{x}, \mathbf{u}, t) \cdot \boldsymbol{\lambda} \tag{6.15}$$

where $\mathbf{x}$, $\mathbf{u}$, and t are the variables introduced in Sec. 6.1 and where $\boldsymbol{\lambda} = (\lambda_1, \lambda_2, \ldots, \lambda_n)$ is an element of the n-dimensional space E^n. By $\mathbf{f}(\mathbf{x}, \mathbf{u}, t) \cdot \boldsymbol{\lambda}$ we mean the scalar product of the vectors $\mathbf{f}(\mathbf{x}, \mathbf{u}, t)$ and $\boldsymbol{\lambda}$, i.e., $\mathbf{f}(\mathbf{x}, \mathbf{u}, t) \cdot \boldsymbol{\lambda} = \sum_{i=1}^{n} f_i(\mathbf{x}, \mathbf{u}, t)\lambda_i$. The function $H(\mathbf{x}, \mathbf{u}, t, \boldsymbol{\lambda})$ is called a Hamiltonian. To the vector $\boldsymbol{\lambda}$ and the vector valued function $\boldsymbol{\lambda}(t)$, defined later, are associated many different names: adjoint vector, momentum vector, costate vector, Lagrange multipliers, sensitivity parameters, Green functions, influence functions, etc.

Pontryagin Maximum Principle. If $\mathscr{V}$ is an optimal control function, then there exists a vector valued function $\boldsymbol{\lambda}(t)$ defined and continuous over [0, 1] differentiable over $\Theta(\mathscr{V})$, and nonidentically zero such that:

(i) $$H(\mathbf{x}(t; \mathscr{V}), \mathbf{v}(t), t, \boldsymbol{\lambda}(t)) \geq H(\mathbf{x}(t; \mathscr{V}), \mathbf{u}, t, \boldsymbol{\lambda}(t)) \quad \text{for all} \quad t \in \Theta(\mathscr{V}) \quad \text{and all} \quad \mathbf{u} \in \Omega \tag{6.16}$$

(ii) $$\dot{\boldsymbol{\lambda}}(t) = -\left.\frac{\partial H(\mathbf{x}, \mathbf{v}(t), t, \boldsymbol{\lambda}(t))}{\partial \mathbf{x}}\right|_{\mathbf{x}=\mathbf{x}(t;\mathscr{V})} \quad \text{for all} \quad t \in \Theta(\mathscr{V}) \tag{6.17}$$

(iii) $$\lambda_i(1) = 0 \qquad \text{for} \quad i = r+1, \ldots, n-1 \tag{6.18}$$

(iv) $$\lambda_n(1) \geq 0 \tag{6.19}$$

In relation (6.17) we denote by $\partial H(\mathbf{x}, \mathbf{u}, t, \boldsymbol{\lambda})/\partial \mathbf{x}$ the vector whose ith component is $\partial H(\mathbf{x}, \mathbf{u}, t, \boldsymbol{\lambda})/\partial x_i$. By $\partial H(\mathbf{x}, \mathbf{v}(t), t, \boldsymbol{\lambda}(t))/\partial \mathbf{x}|_{\mathbf{x}=\mathbf{x}(t;\mathscr{V})}$ we mean the vector $\partial H(\mathbf{x}, \mathbf{u}, t, \boldsymbol{\lambda})/\partial \mathbf{x}$ evaluated at the point $\mathbf{x} = \mathbf{x}(t; \mathscr{V})$.

The condition (6.18) is sometimes called the transversality condition.

We have stated above the usual form of the maximum principle corresponding to the optimization problem given in Sec. 6.2. It is sometimes interesting to consider a purely geometrical form of the maximum principle in terms of some properties of the set $W(1)$ defined in Sec. 6.3 (see Halkin[24]).

Geometrical Maximum Principle. If $\mathbf{x}(1; \mathscr{V})$ is a boundary point of the set $W(1)$ then there exists a vector valued function $\lambda(t)$ defined and continuous over $[0, 1]$, differentiable over $\Theta(\mathscr{V})$, and not identically zero such that the relations (6.16) and (6.17) are satisfied.

6.5 Proof of the Maximum Principle for an Elementary Dynamical Polysystem

6.51 An Elementary Dynamical Polysystem

In this section we shall assume that the vector valued function $\mathbf{f}(\mathbf{x}, \mathbf{u}, t)$ is independent of the state vector $\mathbf{x}$ and takes the form $\boldsymbol{\varphi}(\mathbf{u}, t)$, i.e., we assume that the evolution of the dynamical polysystem under consideration is described by the equation

$$\dot{\mathbf{x}} = \boldsymbol{\varphi}(\mathbf{u}, t) \tag{6.20}$$

In conformity with the assumptions made in Sec. 6.1 for the vector valued function $\mathbf{f}(\mathbf{x}, \mathbf{u}, t)$ we shall assume in the present section that the vector valued function $\boldsymbol{\varphi}(\mathbf{u}, t)$ is continuous with respect to $\mathbf{u}$, and piecewise continuous with respect to t. In other words, we assume that there exists a finite set $\{t_0, t_1, \ldots, t_k\} \subset [0, 1]$ with $t_2 = 0 < t_1 \cdots < t_k = 1$, a finite collection of vector valued functions $\{\boldsymbol{\varphi}_1(\mathbf{u}, t), \boldsymbol{\varphi}_2(\mathbf{u}, t), \ldots, \boldsymbol{\varphi}_k(\mathbf{u}, t)\}$ such that for each $i = 1, 2, \ldots, k$.

(i) the vector valued function $\boldsymbol{\varphi}_i(\mathbf{u}, t)$ is defined and continuous with respect to $\mathbf{u}$ and t for all $\mathbf{u} \in E^m$ and all $t \in [t_{i-1}, t_i]$,

(ii) $\boldsymbol{\varphi}(\mathbf{u}, t) = \boldsymbol{\varphi}_i(\mathbf{u}, t)$ for all $\mathbf{u} \in E^m$ and all $t \in (t_{i-1}, t_i)$.

We shall also assume that the vector valued function $\boldsymbol{\varphi}(\mathbf{u}, t)$ is uniformly bounded over $[0, 1]$ for all $\mathbf{u} \in \Omega$, i.e., that there exists an $M < +\infty$ such that

$$|\boldsymbol{\varphi}(\mathbf{u}, t)| \leq M \qquad \text{for all} \quad \mathbf{u} \in \Omega \quad \text{and all} \quad t \in [0, 1] \tag{6.21}$$

The relation (6.21) is a particular case of the relation (6.4).

Under these assumptions the trajectory $\mathbf{x}(t; \mathscr{U})$ takes the simple form

$$\mathbf{x}(t; \mathscr{U}) = \int_0^t \boldsymbol{\varphi}(\mathbf{u}(\tau), \tau)\, d\tau$$

and we have immediately

$$|\mathbf{x}(t; \mathscr{U})| \leq M \qquad \text{for all} \quad \mathscr{U} \in F \quad \text{and all} \quad t \in [0, 1]$$

where M is the real number introduced in relation (6.21).

6.52 Reachable Set

We define† the set W of all states which can be reached at the time $t = 1$ from the initial state $\mathbf{x} = 0$ at the time $t = 0$ with some control function in the class F. In other words we have

$$W = \{\mathbf{x}(1; \mathscr{U}) : \mathscr{U} \in F\} \tag{6.22}$$

or equivalently

$$W = \left\{\int_0^1 \boldsymbol{\varphi}(\mathbf{u}(t), t)\, dt : \mathscr{U} \in F\right\} \tag{6.23}$$

Let $\mathscr{V}$ be an optimal control function. We shall define the set S^+ of all states in S with an nth coordinate greater than $x_n(1; \mathscr{V})$. In other words

$$S^+ = \{\mathbf{x} : \mathbf{x} \in S,\, x_n > x_n(1; \mathscr{V})\} \tag{6.24}$$

The sets S^+ and W would have no point in common since the existence of such a point would contradict the optimality of the control function $\mathscr{V}$. Moreover, the set S^+ and W are convex. We recall that a set A is convex if for every $\mathbf{a}$ and $\mathbf{b} \in A$ and every $\mu \in [0, 1]$ we have $\mu\mathbf{a} + (1 - \mu)\mathbf{b} \in A$. The convexity of the set S^+ is easy to verify. The proof of the convexity of the set W will be given later. Since the sets S^+ and W are convex and have no point in common then there is at least one hyperplane separating them. This means that there exists a unit vector $\boldsymbol{\lambda}$, the normal to this supporting hyperplane, and a real number h, the distance from the origin to this supporting hyperplane, such that:

$$\mathbf{x} \cdot \boldsymbol{\lambda} \le h \qquad \text{for every} \quad \mathbf{x} \in W \tag{6.25}$$

$$\mathbf{x} \cdot \boldsymbol{\lambda} \ge h \qquad \text{for every} \quad \mathbf{x} \in S^+ \tag{6.26}$$

If we denote by $\bar{S}^+$ the closure‡ of the set S^+, then the relation (6.26) may be strengthened to

$$\mathbf{x} \cdot \boldsymbol{\lambda} \ge h \qquad \text{for every} \quad \mathbf{x} \in \bar{S}^+ \tag{6.27}$$

By construction the point $\mathbf{x}(1; \mathscr{V})$ belongs to both sets W and $\bar{S}^+$, hence we have

$$\mathbf{x}(1; \mathscr{V}) \cdot \boldsymbol{\lambda} \le h \le \mathbf{x}(1; \mathscr{V}) \cdot \boldsymbol{\lambda} \tag{6.28}$$

† The set W is identical with the set $W(1)$ introduced in Sec. 6.3. In the present section we prefer to use the simpler notation W instead of $W(1)$, since we shall not consider $W(t)$ for any t besides $t = 1$.

‡ The closure of a set is the smallest closed set containing it. In this particular case

$$\bar{S}^+ = \{\mathbf{x} : \mathbf{x} \in S, \quad x_n \ge x_n(1; \mathscr{V})\}$$

The most useful property of a closed set B is the following: if $\mathbf{a} \in E_n$ and if $\mathbf{a}_1, \mathbf{a}_2, \ldots$ is a sequence in B such that $\lim_{i\to\infty} |\mathbf{a}_i - \mathbf{a}| = 0$ then $\mathbf{a} \in B$.

which implies

$$\mathbf{x}(1;\mathscr{V})\cdot\boldsymbol{\lambda}=h \tag{6.29}$$

We have then finally

$$\mathbf{x}\cdot\boldsymbol{\lambda}\leq\mathbf{x}(1;\mathscr{V})\cdot\boldsymbol{\lambda}\qquad\text{for every}\quad \mathbf{x}\in W \tag{6.30}$$

and

$$\mathbf{x}\cdot\boldsymbol{\lambda}\geq\mathbf{x}(1;\mathscr{V})\cdot\boldsymbol{\lambda}\qquad\text{for every}\quad \mathbf{x}\in \bar{S}^{+} \tag{6.31}$$

6.53 Maximum Principle

We shall prove that the constant nonzero vector $\boldsymbol{\lambda}$ satisfies the four conditions of the maximum principle.

We shall first prove by contradiction that condition (6.16) is satisfied, i.e., that

$$\begin{gathered}\boldsymbol{\varphi}(\mathbf{v}(t),t)\cdot\boldsymbol{\lambda}\geq\boldsymbol{\varphi}(\mathbf{u},t)\cdot\boldsymbol{\lambda}\\ \text{for all}\quad t\in\Theta(\mathscr{V})\quad\text{and all}\quad \mathbf{u}\in\Omega\end{gathered} \tag{6.32}$$

The relation (6.32) expresses the following simple fact: since the control function $\mathscr{V}$ is chosen such that $\mathbf{x}(1;\mathscr{V})$ is as far as possible in the direction $\boldsymbol{\lambda}$, then the projection of the derivative of $\mathbf{x}(t;\mathscr{V})$ on the vector $\boldsymbol{\lambda}$ must be as large as possible for all t for which this derivative is defined, i.e., for all $t\in\Theta(\mathscr{V})$.

If relation (6.32) does not hold, then there is a $\mathbf{u}\in\Omega$, a $t\in\Theta(\mathscr{V})$, and an $\boldsymbol{\eta}>0$ such that

$$\boldsymbol{\varphi}(\mathbf{v}(t),t)\cdot\boldsymbol{\lambda}<\boldsymbol{\varphi}(\mathbf{u},t)\cdot\boldsymbol{\lambda}-2\eta \tag{6.33}$$

We shall show that relation (6.33) leads to a contradiction. The set $\Theta(\mathscr{V})$ is open hence if $t\in\Theta(\mathscr{V})$ then there is an $\bar{\varepsilon}>0$ such that $\tau\in\Theta(\mathscr{V})$ for all τ with $|\tau-t|\leq\bar{\varepsilon}$. By definition the functions $\boldsymbol{\varphi}(\mathbf{v}(\tau),\tau)$ and $\boldsymbol{\varphi}(\mathbf{u},\tau)$ are continuous functions of τ over the interval $[t-\bar{\varepsilon},t+\bar{\varepsilon}]$, hence, from relation (6.33), there exists an ε with $0<\varepsilon\leq\bar{\varepsilon}$ such that

$$\begin{gathered}\boldsymbol{\varphi}(\mathbf{v}(\tau),\tau)\cdot\boldsymbol{\lambda}<\boldsymbol{\varphi}(\mathbf{u},\tau)\cdot\boldsymbol{\lambda}-\eta\\ \text{for all}\quad\tau\quad\text{with}\quad|\tau-t|\leq\varepsilon\end{gathered} \tag{6.34}$$

If we define a function $\mathscr{V}^*\in F$ by the relations

$$\begin{aligned}\mathbf{v}^*(\tau)&=\mathbf{v}(\tau)\qquad&&\text{if}\quad\tau\in[0,1]\sim(t-\varepsilon,t+\varepsilon)\\ \mathbf{v}^*(\tau)&=\mathbf{u}&&\text{if}\quad\tau\in[t-\varepsilon,t+\varepsilon]\end{aligned}$$

then we obtain the relation

$$\left(\int_0^1\boldsymbol{\varphi}(\mathbf{v}^*(t),t)\,dt\right)\cdot\boldsymbol{\lambda}\geq\left(\int_0^1\boldsymbol{\varphi}(\mathbf{v}(t),t)\,dt\right)\cdot\boldsymbol{\lambda}+2\eta\varepsilon \tag{6.35}$$

i.e.,

$$\mathbf{x}(1;\mathscr{V}^*)\cdot\boldsymbol{\lambda}\geq\mathbf{x}(1;\mathscr{V})\cdot\boldsymbol{\lambda}+2\eta\varepsilon \tag{6.36}$$

By construction we have $\mathbf{x}(1; \mathscr{V}^*) \in W$, hence the relation (6.36) contradicts the relation (6.30).

The condition (6.17) is trivially satisfied in the case of the elementary problem considered in this section.

Let $\mathbf{e}_i$ be the unit vector parallel to the ith axis. For every $i = r + 1, \ldots, n - 1$ we have

$$\mathbf{x}(1; \mathscr{V}) + \mathbf{e}_i \quad \text{and} \quad \mathbf{x}(1; \mathscr{V}) - \mathbf{e}_i \in \bar{S}^+ \tag{6.37}$$

which implies

$$(\mathbf{x}(1; \mathscr{V}) + \mathbf{e}_i) \cdot \boldsymbol{\lambda} \geq \mathbf{x}(1; \mathscr{V}) \cdot \boldsymbol{\lambda} \tag{6.38}$$

and

$$(\mathbf{x}(1; \mathscr{V}) - \mathbf{e}_i) \cdot \boldsymbol{\lambda} \geq \mathbf{x}(1; \mathscr{V}) \cdot \boldsymbol{\lambda} \tag{6.39}$$

i.e.,

$$\mathbf{e}_i \cdot \boldsymbol{\lambda} = 0 \tag{6.40}$$

or

$$\lambda_i = 0 \quad \text{for} \quad i = r + 1, \ldots, n - 1 \tag{6.41}$$

The last relation proves condition (6.18). We have also

$$\mathbf{x}(1; \mathscr{V}) + \mathbf{e}_n \in \bar{S}^+ \tag{6.42}$$

hence

$$(\mathbf{x}(1; \mathscr{V}) + \mathbf{e}_n) \cdot \boldsymbol{\lambda} \geq \mathbf{x}(1; \mathscr{V}) \cdot \boldsymbol{\lambda} \tag{6.43}$$

i.e.,

$$\mathbf{e}_n \cdot \boldsymbol{\lambda} \geq 0 \tag{6.44}$$

or

$$\lambda_n \geq 0 \tag{6.45}$$

The last relation proves condition (6.19).

6.54 Proof of the Convexity of the Set W

In Sec. 6.10 we shall prove the following result.

Proposition 10.2 *If* $\mathbf{f}(t)$ *is a piecewise continuous vector valued function defined over* [0, 1] *and if* $\mathscr{A}$ *is the class of all subsets of* [0, 1] *which are the union of a finite number of disjoint intervals, then the set*

$$\left\{\int_0^1 \mathbf{f}(t)\, \chi(E)\, dt : E \in \mathscr{A}\right\} \tag{6.46}$$

is convex. In the last relation $\chi(E)$ denotes the characteristic function of the set E, i.e., a function† which is one for all t in E and 0 for all t not in E.

† The reader should realize immediately that for every set E in the class $\mathscr{A}$ the characteristic function $\chi(E)$ is piecewise continuous.

We shall now prove the convexity of the set W with the help of Proposition 10.2. Let $\mathbf{a}$ and $\mathbf{b} \in W$ and $\mu \in [0, 1]$. We shall prove that $\mu\mathbf{a} + (1 - \mu)\mathbf{b} \in W$. If $\mathbf{a}$ and $\mathbf{b} \in W$ then there are functions $\mathscr{U}_{\mathbf{a}}$ and $\mathscr{U}_{\mathbf{b}}$ in F such that

$$\mathbf{a} = \int_0^1 \boldsymbol{\varphi}(\mathbf{u}_{\mathbf{a}}(t), t)\, dt \tag{6.47}$$

and

$$\mathbf{b} = \int_0^1 \boldsymbol{\varphi}(\mathbf{u}_{\mathbf{b}}(t), t)\, dt \tag{6.48}$$

Let L be the set

$$L = \left\{\int_0^1 (\boldsymbol{\varphi}(\mathbf{u}_{\mathbf{b}}(t), t) - \boldsymbol{\varphi}(\mathbf{u}_{\mathbf{a}}(t), t))\, \chi(E)\, dt : E \in \mathscr{A}\right\} \tag{6.49}$$

and L^* be the set

$$L^* = \left\{\int_0^1 \boldsymbol{\varphi}(\mathbf{u}_{\mathbf{a}}(t), t)\, dt + \mathbf{x} : \mathbf{x} \in L\right\} \tag{6.50}$$

The set L is convex by proposition 10.2 which implies immediately the convexity of the set L^*. For every $E \in \mathscr{A}$ the function $\mathscr{U}_E$ defined by the relations

$$\begin{aligned} \mathbf{u}_E(t) &= \mathbf{u}_{\mathbf{a}}(t) \qquad \text{if} \quad t \in [0, 1] \sim E \\ \mathbf{u}_E(t) &= \mathbf{u}_{\mathbf{b}}(t) \qquad \text{if} \quad t \in E \end{aligned}$$

belongs also to the class F. Moreover, for every $E \in \mathscr{A}$ we have

$$\boldsymbol{\varphi}(\mathbf{u}_E(t), t) = \boldsymbol{\varphi}(\mathbf{u}_{\mathbf{a}}(t), t) + (\boldsymbol{\varphi}(\mathbf{u}_{\mathbf{b}}(t), t) - \boldsymbol{\varphi}(\mathbf{u}_{\mathbf{a}}(t), t))\, \chi(E) \tag{6.51}$$

which implies

$$\begin{aligned} \int_0^1 \boldsymbol{\varphi}(\mathbf{u}_E(t), t)\, dt &= \int_0^1 \boldsymbol{\varphi}(\mathbf{u}_{\mathbf{a}}(t), t)\, dt \\ &\quad + \int_0^1 (\boldsymbol{\varphi}(\mathbf{u}_{\mathbf{b}}(t), t) - \boldsymbol{\varphi}(\mathbf{u}_{\mathbf{a}}(t), t))\, \chi(E)\, dt \end{aligned} \tag{6.52}$$

We have then $L^* \subset W$. For $E = \varnothing$, we have $\mathscr{U}_E = \mathscr{U}_{\mathbf{a}}$ and for $E = [0, 1]$ we have $\mathscr{U}_E = \mathscr{U}_{\mathbf{b}}$. The points $\mathbf{a}$ and $\mathbf{b}$ belong then to a convex subset L^* of W. Hence $\mu\mathbf{a} + (1 - \mu)\,\mathbf{b} \in W$.

6.6 Proof of the Maximum Principle for a Linear Dynamical Polysystem

6.61 A Linear Dynamical Polysystem

In this section we shall assume that the function $\mathbf{f}(\mathbf{x}, \mathbf{u}, t)$ has the particular form

$$\mathbf{f}(\mathbf{x}, \mathbf{u}, t) = A(t)\mathbf{x} + \boldsymbol{\varphi}(\mathbf{u}, t) \tag{6.53}$$

In conformity with the assumptions made in Sec. 6.1 for the function $\mathbf{f}(\mathbf{x}, \mathbf{u}, t)$ we shall assume in the present section that the matrix valued function $A(t)$ is piecewise continuous with respect to t and that the vector valued function $\boldsymbol{\varphi}(\mathbf{u}, t)$ is continuous with respect to $\mathbf{u}$ and piecewise continuous with respect to t. In other words, we assume that there exists a finite set $\{t_0, t_1, \ldots, t_k\} \subset [0, 1]$ with $t_0 = 0 < t_1 < \cdots < t_k = 1$, a finite collection of matrix valued functions $\{A_1(t), A_2(t), \ldots, A_k(t)\}$ and a finite collection of vector valued functions $\{\boldsymbol{\varphi}_1(\mathbf{u}, t), \boldsymbol{\varphi}_2(\mathbf{u}, t), \ldots, \boldsymbol{\varphi}_k(\mathbf{u}, t)\}$ such that for each $i = 1, 2, \ldots, k$

(i) the matrix valued function $A_i(t)$ is defined and continuous with respect to t for all $t \in [t_{i-1}, t_i]$;

(ii) the vector valued function $\boldsymbol{\varphi}_i(\mathbf{u}, t)$ is defined and continuous with respect to $\mathbf{u}$ and t for all $\mathbf{u} \in E^m$ and all $t \in (t_{i-1} - \varepsilon, t_i + \varepsilon)$;

(iii) $A(t) = A_i(t)$ for all $t \in (t_{i-1}, t_i)$;

(iv) $\boldsymbol{\varphi}(\mathbf{u}, t) = \boldsymbol{\varphi}_i(\mathbf{u}, t)$ for all $\mathbf{u} \in E^m$ and all $t \in (t_{i-1}, t_i)$.

6.62 Fundamental Matrix

Let $G(t)$ be the *fundamental matrix* associated to the linear system

$$\dot{\mathbf{x}} = A(t)\mathbf{x} \tag{6.54}$$

By this we mean that $G(t)$ is a matrix valued function defined and continuous for all $t \in [0, 1]$, continuously differentiable for all $t \in [0, 1]$ for which the matrix $A(t)$ is continuous and such that†

$$\dot{G}(t) = -G(t)\, A(t) \qquad \text{for all} \quad t \in [0, 1] \sim \{t_0, t_1, \ldots, t_k\} \tag{6.55}$$

and

$$G(1) = I \tag{6.56}$$

where I is the identity $n \times n$ matrix. It is a trivial matter to prove that the matrix valued function $G(t)$ exists, is unique, and has a continuous inverse $G^{-1}(t)$. This inverse matrix $G^{-1}(t)$ satisfies the differential equation

$$\frac{d}{dt} G^{-1}(t) = A(t)\, G^{-1}(t) \qquad \text{for all} \quad t \in [0, 1] \sim \{t_0, t_1, \ldots, t_k\} \tag{6.57}$$

and the terminal condition

$$G^{-1}(1) = I \tag{6.58}$$

† If the (i, j) element of $A(t)$ is $a_{ij}(t)$ and if the (i, j) element of $G(t)$ is $g_{ij}(t)$ then relation (6.55) stands for

$$\frac{d}{dt} g_{ij}(t) = -\sum_{h=1}^{n} g_{ih}(t)\, a_{hj}(t)$$

for all $i = 1, 2, \ldots, n$, all $j = 1, 2, \ldots, n$, and all $t \in [0, 1] - \{t_0, t_1, \ldots, t_k\}$.

An easy way to verify the compatibility of the relations (6.55) through (6.58) is to see that we have

$$G(1)\,G^{-1}(1) = II = I \tag{6.59}$$

and that for all $t \in [0, 1] \sim \{t_0, t_1, \ldots, t_k\}$ we have

$$\begin{aligned}\frac{d}{dt}(G(t)\,G^{-1}(t)) &= \left(\frac{d}{dt}G(t)\right)G^{-1}(t) + G(t)\frac{d}{dt}G^{-1}(t)\\ &= -G(t)\,A(t)\,G^{-1}(t) + G(t)\,A(t)\,G^{-1}(t) = 0\end{aligned} \tag{6.60}$$

We shall show below that for every $\mathscr{U} \in F$ the vector valued function $\mathbf{x}(t; \mathscr{U})$ takes the form

$$\mathbf{x}(t; \mathscr{U}) = G^{-1}(t)\int_0^t G(\tau)\,\boldsymbol{\varphi}(\mathbf{u}(\tau), \tau)\,d\tau \qquad \text{for every} \quad t \in [0, 1] \tag{6.61}$$

Since we know already that the function $\mathbf{x}(t; \mathscr{U})$ exists and is unique, we have only to verify that the form given in relation (6.61) satisfies the differential equation

$$\frac{d}{dt}\mathbf{x}(t; \mathscr{U}) = A(t)\,\mathbf{x}(t; \mathscr{U}) + \boldsymbol{\varphi}(\mathbf{u}(t), t) \tag{6.62}$$

for all $t \in \Theta(\mathscr{U})$ and the boundary condition

$$\mathbf{x}(0; \mathscr{U}) = 0 \tag{6.63}$$

Indeed, for all $t \in \Theta(\mathscr{U})$ we have

$$\begin{aligned}\frac{d}{dt}\mathbf{x}(t; \mathscr{U}) &= \left(\frac{d}{dt}G^{-1}(t)\right)\int_0^t G(\tau)\,\boldsymbol{\varphi}(\mathbf{u}(\tau), \tau)\,d\tau\\ &\quad + G^{-1}(t)\frac{d}{dt}\int_0^t G(\tau)\,\boldsymbol{\varphi}(\mathbf{u}(\tau), \tau)\,d\tau\\ &= A(t)\,G^{-1}(t)\int_0^t G(\tau)\,\boldsymbol{\varphi}(\mathbf{u}(\tau), \tau)\,d\tau\\ &\quad + G^{-1}(t)\,G(t)\,\boldsymbol{\varphi}(\mathbf{u}(t), t)\\ &= A(t)\,\mathbf{x}(t; \mathscr{U}) + \boldsymbol{\varphi}(\mathbf{u}(t), t)\end{aligned} \tag{6.64}$$

and the boundary condition (6.63) follows from the definition (6.61). We have then

$$\mathbf{x}(1; \mathscr{U}) = \int_0^1 G(t)\,\boldsymbol{\varphi}(\mathbf{u}(t), t)\,dt \tag{6.65}$$

6.63 Reachable Set

As in Sec. 6.4 we shall define the set W of all states which can be reached at the time $t = 1$ from the initial state $\mathbf{x} = \mathbf{0}$ at the time $t = 0$ with some control function in the class F. In other words we have

$$W = \{\mathbf{x}(1; \mathscr{U}) : \mathscr{U} \in F\} \tag{6.66}$$

or equivalently,

$$W = \left\{\int_0^1 G(t)\, \boldsymbol{\varphi}(\mathbf{u}(t), t)\, dt : \mathscr{U} \in F\right\} \tag{6.67}$$

Let us compare the two formulas (6.23) and (6.67). We see immediately that they have a similar structure the only difference being that the piecewise continuous vector valued function $\boldsymbol{\varphi}(\mathbf{u}(t), t)$ is now replaced by the piecewise continuous vector valued function $G(t)\, \boldsymbol{\varphi}(\mathbf{u}(t), t)$.

By repeating word for word what has been stated in Sec. 6.5, we can prove that for every optimal control function $\mathscr{V}$ there exists a nonzero constant vector $\boldsymbol{\lambda}$ such that

$$\text{(i)}\quad (G(t)\, \boldsymbol{\varphi}(\mathbf{v}(t), t)) \cdot \boldsymbol{\lambda} \geq (G(t)\, \boldsymbol{\varphi}(\mathbf{u}, t)) \cdot \boldsymbol{\lambda} \quad \text{for all} \quad t \in \Theta(\mathscr{V}) \quad \text{and all} \quad \mathbf{u} \in \Omega; \tag{6.68}$$

$$\text{(ii)}\quad \lambda_i = 0 \qquad \text{for} \quad i = r + 1, \ldots, n - 1; \tag{6.69}$$

$$\text{(iii)}\quad \lambda_n \geq 0. \tag{6.70}$$

6.64 Maximum Principle

We shall now define a vector valued function $\boldsymbol{\lambda}(t)$ by the following relation

$$\boldsymbol{\lambda}(t) = G^T(t)\boldsymbol{\lambda} \qquad \text{for all} \quad t \in [0, 1] \tag{6.71}$$

where $G^T(t)$ is the transpose of the matrix $G(t)$. Since the constant vector $\boldsymbol{\lambda}$ is different from zero and since the matrix valued function $G(t)$ is continuous and piecewise differentiable over $[0, 1]$ and has an inverse it follows that the vector valued function $\boldsymbol{\lambda}(t)$ is continuous, piecewise differentiable, and non-identically zero on the interval $[0, 1]$.

We shall prove that the vector valued function $\boldsymbol{\lambda}(t)$ satisfies the four conditions of the maximum principle. The relation (6.68) can be written in the form

$$\boldsymbol{\varphi}(\mathbf{v}(t), t) \cdot (G^T(t)\boldsymbol{\lambda}) \geq \boldsymbol{\varphi}(\mathbf{u}, t) \cdot (G^T)t)\boldsymbol{\lambda})$$

i.e.,

$$\boldsymbol{\varphi}(\mathbf{v}(t), t) \cdot \boldsymbol{\lambda}(t) \geq \boldsymbol{\varphi})\mathbf{u}, t) \cdot \boldsymbol{\lambda}(t) \tag{6.72}$$

which implies

$$(A(t)\,\mathbf{x}(t;\mathscr{V}) + \boldsymbol{\varphi}(\mathbf{v}(t),t))\cdot\boldsymbol{\lambda}(t) \geq (A(t)\,\mathbf{x}(t;\mathscr{V}) + \boldsymbol{\varphi}(\mathbf{u},t))\cdot\boldsymbol{\lambda}(t) \quad \text{for all} \quad t\in\Theta(\mathscr{V}) \quad \text{and all} \quad \mathbf{u}\in\Omega \tag{6.73}$$

For the linear problem considered in this section the relation (6.73) is equivalent to relation (6.16). From the relations (6.71) and (6.55) we obtain

$$\frac{d}{dt}\boldsymbol{\lambda}(t) = \left(\frac{d}{dt}\,G(t)\right)^{T}\boldsymbol{\lambda} = (-G(t)\,A(t))^{T}\boldsymbol{\lambda} \tag{6.74}$$

$$= -A^{T}(t)\,G^{T}(t)\boldsymbol{\lambda} = -A^{T}(t)\,\boldsymbol{\lambda}(t) \tag{6.75}$$

This last relation is equivalent to relation (6.17). Finally, we note that relations (6.69) and (6.70) are equivalent to relations (6.18) and (6.19). This concludes the proof of the maximum principle in the case of a linear dynamical polysystem.

6.65 Remarks on Convexity

Many early papers in the theory of optimal control were devoted to the study of systems whose evolutions are described by equations of the form

$$\dot{\mathbf{x}} = A(t)\mathbf{x} + B(t)\mathbf{u} \tag{6.76}$$

where $A(t)$ is a piecewise continuous $n \times n$ matrix valued function and $B(t)$ is a piecewise continuous $n \times m$ matrix valued function.

In these early papers it was always assumed that the set Ω of admissible control vectors is convex.† This assumption is very convenient in order to obtain the following direct proof of the convexity of the set W, i.e., a proof of the convexity of the set W which does not depend on Proposition 10.2.

In the case of Eq. (6.76) the relation (6.67) takes the form

$$W = \left\{\int_0^1 G(t)\,B(t)\,\mathbf{u}(t)\,dt : \mathscr{U}\in F\right\} \tag{6.77}$$

† In many practical applications Ω is either some hypercube or the vertices of some hypercube. In the first case Ω is convex and each component of the control vector may take any value between its minimum and maximum values. In the second case Ω is not convex and each component of the control vector may take only its minimum or maximum values. The theory of the first case is easy but the apparatus (rheostats, function generators, etc.) is costly. The theory of the second case is not so easy but the apparatus (contactors, relays, etc.) is inexpensive. It has been proved that a system of the second type can always do what a system of the first type can do. (See LaSalle,[34] and Halkin.[25])

Let **a** and **b** $\in W$ and $\mu \in [0, 1]$. We shall prove that $\mathbf{c} = \mu\mathbf{a} + (1 - \mu)\,\mathbf{b} \in W$. If **a** and **b** $\in W$, then there are control functions $\mathscr{U}_{\mathbf{a}}$ and $\mathscr{U}_{\mathbf{b}}$ in the class F such that

$$\mathbf{a} = \int_0^1 G(t)\, B(t)\, \mathbf{u}_{\mathbf{a}}(t)\, dt \tag{6.78}$$

and

$$\mathbf{b} = \int_0^1 G(t)\, B(t)\, \mathbf{u}_{\mathbf{b}}(t)\, dt \tag{6.79}$$

Let $\mathscr{U}_{\mathbf{c}}$ be the control function defined by the relation

$$\mathbf{u}_{\mathbf{c}}(t) = \mu\mathbf{u}_{\mathbf{a}}(t) + (1 - \mu)\, \mathbf{u}_{\mathbf{b}}(t) \tag{6.80}$$

Since the set Ω is convex it follows that $\mathscr{U}_{\mathbf{c}} \in F$, hence there is a vector **c** in the set W such that

$$\mathbf{c} = \int_0^1 G(t)\, B(t)\, \mathbf{u}_{\mathbf{c}}(t)\, dt \tag{6.81}$$

6.66 Comoving Space along a Trajectory

This paragraph does not contain any new results but gives a geometrical interpretation of some results obtained earlier in this section.

We shall show that for every trajectory $\mathbf{x}(t; \mathscr{V})$ we can introduce a new state variable $\mathbf{y} = (y_1, y_2, \ldots, y_n)$ and a certain *time varying* transformation from the old state variable **x** into the new state variable **y** in such a way that the differential equation in **y** corresponding to the differential equation in **x** given by relation (6.15) is of the type given by relation (6.20).

We have defined earlier the continuous and piecewise differentiable $n \times n$ matrix valued function $G(t)$ over the interval [0, 1] by the relations

$$\dot{G}(t) = -G(t)A(t) \qquad \text{for all} \quad t \in [0, 1] \sim \{t_2, t_1, \ldots, t_k\} \tag{6.82}$$

and

$$G(1) = I \tag{6.83}$$

For every $t \in [0, 1]$ and every $\mathbf{x} \in E^n$ the new state variable **y** is defined by

$$\mathbf{y} = G(t)(\mathbf{x} - \mathbf{x}(t; \mathscr{V})) \tag{6.84}$$

We have then

$$\begin{aligned}\mathbf{y} &= \dot{G}(t)(\mathbf{x} - \mathbf{x}(t; \mathscr{V})) + G(t)(\dot{\mathbf{x}} - \dot{\mathbf{x}}(t; \mathscr{V})) = -G(t)A(t)(x - x(t; \mathscr{V}))\\ &\quad + G(t)(A(t)\mathbf{x} + \boldsymbol{\varphi}(\mathbf{u}, t) - A(t)\mathbf{x}(t; \mathscr{V}) - \boldsymbol{\varphi}(\mathbf{v}(t), t))\\ &= G(t)(\boldsymbol{\varphi}(\mathbf{u}, t) - \boldsymbol{\varphi}(\mathbf{v}(t), t))\end{aligned} \tag{6.85}$$

and we see that the last equation is of the type given in relation (6.20). The system of coordinates corresponding to the new state variable **y** is called the comoving space along the trajectory $\mathbf{x}(t; \mathscr{V})$. It follows then that a linear dynamical polysystem can always be considered as an open loop system if we look at it from the comoving space along a trajectory.

The trajectory $\mathbf{x}(t; \mathscr{V})$ can be expressed in the comoving space by the relation

$$\mathbf{y} \equiv 0 \tag{6.86}$$

and any trajectory corresponding to the *same* control function $\mathscr{V}$ but with different initial condition can be expressed in the comoving space by the relation

$$\mathbf{y} = \text{const} \tag{6.87}$$

In other words the time varying transformation from the state variable **x** into the state variable **y** is a transformation which stretches and twists the field of all trajectories with the same control function $\mathscr{V}$ into a nice field of parallel rectilinear trajectories.

6.7 Proof of the Maximum Principle for a General Dynamical Polysystem

6.71 Fundamental Matrix along an Optimal Trajectory

In this section we shall assume that $\mathscr{V}$ is an optimal control function for the optimization problem stated in Sec. 6.2. We have already defined the trajectory $\mathbf{x}(t; \mathscr{V})$ corresponding to the control function $\mathscr{V}$. Let $A(t)$ be the $n \times n$ matrix valued function of the time t whose (i, j) element is

$$\left. \frac{\partial f_i(\mathbf{x}, \mathbf{v}(t), t)}{\partial x_j} \right|_{\mathbf{x} = \mathbf{x}(t; \mathscr{V})} \tag{6.88}$$

From the assumptions made in Sec. 6.1 it follows that the matrix valued function $A(t)$ is well defined and piecewise continuous over the interval [0, 1]. More precisely, the function $A(t)$ is continuous at every point t in $\Theta(\mathscr{V})$.

As in Sec. 6.6 we define a matrix valued function† $G(t)$ continuous with respect to t over [0, 1] and differentiable with respect to t over $\Theta(\mathscr{V})$ by the relations:

$$\dot{G}(t) = -G(t)A(t) \qquad \text{for all} \quad t \in \Theta(\mathscr{V}) \tag{6.89}$$

and

$$G(1) = I \tag{6.90}$$

† Compare the content of this paragraph with Appendix A. You will note that the matrix $G(t)$ defined here corresponds to the inverse matrix $K^{-1}(t; \bar{t}, \bar{\mathbf{x}})$ defined in Appendix A with the boundary condition $\bar{t} = 1$ and $\bar{\mathbf{x}} = \mathbf{x}(1; \mathscr{V})$.

The reader should realize that the matrices $A(t)$ and $G(t)$ have been defined for the particular control function $\mathscr{V}$. Similar but different matrices could be defined for the other control functions in the class F. The characteristic property of the linear system considered in Sec. 6.6 is that the matrices $A(t)$ and $G(t)$ are the same for every control function in the class F. This last property *does not hold* for the general nonlinear system considered in the present section. In this section we shall not have to consider matrices $A(t)$ and $G(t)$ corresponding to other control functions besides the optimal control function $\mathscr{V}$. This is fortunate, since it enables us to avoid clumsy notations of the form $A(t; \mathscr{V})$, $A(t; \mathscr{U})$, $G(t; \mathscr{V})$, and $G(t; \mathscr{U})$.

6.72 Variational Trajectory

For every control function $\mathscr{U}$ in the class F we define the vector valued function $\mathbf{y}(t; \mathscr{U})$ by the relation:

$$\mathbf{y}(t; \mathscr{U}) = \mathbf{x}(t; \mathscr{U}) - \mathbf{x}(t; \mathscr{V}) \qquad \text{for all} \quad t \in [0, 1] \tag{6.91}$$

The vector valued function $\mathbf{y}(t; \mathscr{U})$ is called the variational trajectory for the control function $\mathscr{U}$ with respect to the control function $\mathscr{V}$.

Let†

$$\Theta^*(\mathscr{U}) = \Theta(\mathscr{U}) \cap \Theta(\mathscr{V}) \tag{6.92}$$

By construction the vector valued function $\mathbf{y}(t; \mathscr{U})$ is continuous with respect to t for all $t \in [0, 1]$, differentiable with respect to t for all $t \in \Theta^*(\mathscr{U})$ and we have

$$\dot{\mathbf{y}}(t; \mathscr{U}) = \mathbf{f}(\mathbf{x}(t; \mathscr{U}), \mathbf{u}(t), t) - \mathbf{f}(\mathbf{x}(t; \mathscr{V}), \mathbf{v}(t), t)$$
$$\text{for every} \quad t \in \Theta^*(\mathscr{U}) \tag{6.93}$$

Let $\boldsymbol{\varphi}(\mathbf{u}, t)$ and $\mathbf{k}(t; \mathscr{U})$ be vector valued functions defined by the following relations:

$$\boldsymbol{\varphi}(\mathbf{u}, t) = \mathbf{f}(\mathbf{x}(t; \mathscr{V}), \mathbf{u}, t) - \mathbf{f}(\mathbf{x}(t; \mathscr{V}), \mathbf{v}(t), t) \tag{6.94}$$

$$\mathbf{k}(t; \mathscr{U}) = \mathbf{f}(\mathbf{x}(t; \mathscr{U}), \mathbf{u}(t), t) - \mathbf{f}(\mathbf{x}(t; \mathscr{V}), \mathbf{v}(t), t)$$
$$- \boldsymbol{\varphi}(\mathbf{u}(t), t) - A(t)(\mathbf{x}(t; \mathscr{U}) - \mathbf{x}(t; \mathscr{V})) \tag{6.95}$$

The vector valued function $\boldsymbol{\varphi}(\mathbf{u}, t)$ is continuous with respect to $\mathbf{u}$ and piecewise continuous with respect to t. For every $\mathscr{U} \in F$ the vector valued function $\mathbf{k}(t; \mathscr{U})$ is piecewise continuous with respect to t.

† If A and B are sets then $A \cap B$ is the intersection of the sets A and B, i.e., the set $A \cap B$ is the set of all elements which belong to both sets A and B. Similarly, $A \cup B$ is the union of the sets A and B, i.e., the set $A \cup B$ is the set of all elements which belong to at least one of the sets A and B.

We can then write

$$\dot{\mathbf{y}}(t; \mathscr{U}) = A(t)\mathbf{y}(t; \mathscr{U}) + \boldsymbol{\varphi}(\mathbf{u}(t), t) + \mathbf{k}(t; \mathscr{U}) \quad \text{for all} \quad t \in \Theta^*(\mathscr{U}) \tag{6.96}$$

and

$$\mathbf{y}(t; \mathscr{U}) = G^{-1}(t) \int_0^t G(\tau)(\boldsymbol{\varphi}(\mathbf{u}(\tau), \tau) + \mathbf{k}(\tau; \mathscr{U}))\, d\tau \quad \text{for all} \quad t \in [0, 1] \tag{6.97}$$

The vector valued function $\mathbf{k}(t; \mathscr{U})$ is identically zero for the linear problem considered in Sec. 6.6. Although $\mathbf{k}(t; \mathscr{U})$ is not identically zero for the non-linear problem considered in this section, it has nevertheless two interesting properties:

(i) there exists a $K_1 < +\infty$ such that for all $\mathscr{U} \in F$, we have

$$|\mathbf{k}(t; \mathscr{U})| \leq K_1 \, |\mathbf{y}(t; \mathscr{U})|^2 \qquad \text{for all} \quad t \in [0, 1] \tag{6.98}$$

such that $\mathbf{u}(t) = \mathbf{v}(t)$;

(ii) there exists a $K_2 < +\infty$ such that for all $\mathscr{U} \in F$ and all $t \in [0, 1]$ we have

$$|\mathbf{k}(t; \mathscr{U})| \leq K_2 \, |\mathbf{y}(t; \mathscr{U})| \tag{6.99}$$

These two properties are direct consequences of the definitions (6.91), (6.94), and (6.95) and of the assumptions made in Sec. 6.1. An explicit derivation of these two properties is given in the last paragraph of this section.

6.73 Approximation Trajectory

For every $\mathscr{U} \in F$ let $\mathbf{z}(t; \mathscr{U})$ be a vector valued function of t defined and continuous over [0, 1], differentiable over $\Theta^*(\mathscr{U})$ and such that

(i) $\dot{\mathbf{z}}(t; \mathscr{U}) = A(t)\mathbf{z}(t; \mathscr{U}) + \boldsymbol{\varphi}(\mathbf{u}(t), t) \qquad \text{for all} \quad t \in \Theta^*(\mathscr{U})$ (6.100)

(ii) $\mathbf{z}(0; \mathscr{U}) = \mathbf{0}$ (6.101)

or, equivalently, such that

$$\mathbf{z}(t; \mathscr{U}) = G^{-1}(t) \int_0^t G(\tau)\boldsymbol{\varphi}(\mathbf{u}(\tau), \tau)\, d\tau \quad \text{for all} \quad t \in [0, 1] \tag{6.102}$$

We have then

$$\mathbf{y}(t; \mathscr{U}) - \mathbf{z}(t; \mathscr{U}) = G^{-1}(t) \int_0^t G(\tau)\mathbf{k}(\tau; \mathscr{U})\, d\tau \quad \text{for all} \quad t \in [0, 1] \tag{6.103}$$

The vector valued function $\mathbf{z}(t; \mathscr{U})$ is called the approximation trajectory for the variational trajectory $\mathbf{y}(t; \mathscr{U})$. The name "approximation trajectory" is well justified, since the difference $\mathbf{y}(t; \mathscr{U}) - \mathbf{z}(t; \mathscr{U})$ is small, whenever $\mathbf{k}(t; \mathscr{U})$ is small (relation (6.103)) i.e., whenever $\mathbf{y}(t; \mathscr{U})$ is small (relations (6.98) and (6.99)), i.e., whenever the comparison trajectory $\mathbf{x}(t; \mathscr{U})$ is close to the optimal trajectory $\mathbf{x}(t; \mathscr{V})$.

6.74 Remarks on Linearization Techniques

All the formulas listed above are familiar to everyone interested in the optimal control of nonlinear systems. We have taken great care to write down all these definitions because we have found a great lack of precision and rigor in most of the available expositions of these questions.

Many authors replace the basic differential equation by the first two terms of its Taylor expansion plus a remainder term which corresponds here to the functions $\mathbf{k}(t; \mathscr{U})$. At various stages of the reasoning they state, without proof, that the effect of this remainder term can be neglected. Such derivations are, in our opinion, very unsatisfactory, since they are strictly equivalent to replacing, from the very start, the nonlinear system by its linear approximation around the comparison trajectory.

In our approach we give a precise definition of the linear approximation. Moreover, in the whole development we maintain a clear distinction between the nonlinear system and its linear approximation and when an interesting property of the linear approximation could be fruitfully and legitimately applied to the nonlinear system we *prove* that this application is wholly justified.

6.75 Statement of the Fundamental Lemma

Let us define the sets W and $\tilde{W}$ by the following relations

$$W = \{\mathbf{x}(1; \mathscr{V}) + \mathbf{y}(1; \mathscr{U}) : \mathscr{U} \in F\} \tag{6.104}$$

$$\tilde{W} = \{\mathbf{x}(1; \mathscr{V}) + \mathbf{z}(1; \mathscr{U}) : \mathscr{U} \in F\} \tag{6.105}$$

Equivalently, the set W could be written under the form

$$W = \{\mathbf{x}(1; \mathscr{U}) : \mathscr{U} \in F\} \tag{6.106}$$

and the set $\tilde{W}$ could be written under the form

$$\tilde{W} = \{\mathbf{x}(1; \mathscr{V}) + \mathbf{z} : \mathbf{z} \in Z\} \tag{6.107}$$

where Z is the set

$$Z = \{\mathbf{z}(1; \mathscr{U}) : \mathscr{U} \in F\} \tag{6.108}$$

From the results of Sec. 6.6 we know that the set Z is convex, hence that the set $\tilde{W}$ is convex. As in Sec. 6.5 we define the set S^+ by the relation

$$S^+ = \{\mathbf{x} : \mathbf{x} \in S, x_n > x_n(1; \mathscr{V})\} \tag{6.109}$$

where S is the terminal set introduced in Sec. 6.2. The set S^+ is convex.

Since the function $\mathbf{z}(t; \mathscr{U})$ is a certain approximation of the function $\mathbf{y}(t; \mathscr{U})$, it is natural to expect that the set $\tilde{W}$ is a certain approximation of the set W (compare relations (6.104) and (6.105)). We have indeed the following important result:

Fundamental Lemma. *If there is no hyperplane separating the convex sets S^+ and $\tilde{W}$ then the sets S^+ and W have at least one point in common.*

The proof of the fundamental lemma is given in Sec. 6.11. We see immediately that the fundamental lemma is a tautology in the case of a linear system, since for a linear system we have $W = \tilde{W}$.

An immediate corollary of the fundamental lemma states that:

If the sets S^+ and W have no point in common then there is a hyperplane which separates the convex sets S^+ and $\tilde{W}$.

6.76 Maximum Principle

The sets S^+ and W cannot have a point in common since the existence of such a point would contradict the optimality of the control function $\mathscr{V}$. If the sets S^+ and W have no point in common then, from the corollary of the fundamental lemma, we conclude that there is a hyperplane separating the convex sets S^+ and $\tilde{W}$. Hence, according to Sec. 6.6 there exists a vector valued function $\boldsymbol{\lambda}(t)$, defined, continuous, piecewise differentiable, and non-identically zero on [0, 1] such that

$$\text{(i)}\quad \boldsymbol{\varphi}(\mathbf{v}(t), t) \cdot \boldsymbol{\lambda}(t) \geq \boldsymbol{\varphi}(\mathbf{u}, t) \cdot \boldsymbol{\lambda}(t) \quad \text{for all} \quad t \in \Theta(\mathscr{V}) \quad \text{and all} \quad \mathbf{u} \in \Omega \tag{6.110}$$

$$\text{(ii)}\quad \frac{d}{dt}\boldsymbol{\lambda}(t) = -A^T(t)\boldsymbol{\lambda}(t) \qquad \text{for all} \quad t \in \Theta(\mathscr{V}) \tag{6.111}$$

$$\text{(iii)}\quad \lambda_i(1) = 0 \qquad \text{for} \quad i = r+1, \ldots, n-1 \tag{6.112}$$

$$\text{(iv)}\quad \lambda_n(1) \geq 0 \tag{6.113}$$

With the help of definitions (6.88) and (6.94) these relations can be transformed immediately into the four conditions of the maximum principle.

6.77 Derivation of the Properties of the Function $\mathbf{k}(t; \mathscr{U})$

In this paragraph we give an explicit derivation of the inequalities (6.98) and (6.99) mentioned earlier.

From the assumptions of Sec. 6.1 and from relation (6.91) we know that there exists a $K < +\infty$ such that

$$|\mathbf{y}(t; \mathscr{U})| \leq K \qquad \text{for all} \quad t \in [0, 1] \quad \text{and all} \quad \mathscr{U} \in F \tag{6.114}$$

From the relations (6.94) and (6.95) we have

$$\mathbf{k}(t; \mathscr{U}) = \mathbf{f}(\mathbf{x}(t; \mathscr{U}), \mathbf{u}(t), t) - \mathbf{f}(\mathbf{x}(t; \mathscr{V}), \mathbf{u}(t), t) - A(t)(\mathbf{x}(t; \mathscr{U}) - \mathbf{x}(t; \mathscr{V})) \tag{6.115}$$

Hence, for all $t \in [0, 1]$ such that $\mathbf{u}(t) = \mathbf{v}(t)$ we have

$$\mathbf{k}(t; \mathscr{U}) = \mathbf{f}(\mathbf{x}(t; \mathscr{U}), \mathbf{v}(t), t) - \mathbf{f}(\mathbf{x}(t; \mathscr{V}), \mathbf{v}(t), t) - A(t)(\mathbf{x}(t; \mathscr{U}) - \mathbf{x}(t; \mathscr{V})) \tag{6.116}$$

i.e., from relation (6.91),

$$\mathbf{k}(t; \mathscr{U}) = \mathbf{f}(\mathbf{x}(t; \mathscr{V}) + \mathbf{y}(t; \mathscr{U}), \mathbf{v}(t), t) - \mathbf{f}(\mathbf{x}(t; \mathscr{V}), \mathbf{v}(t), t) - A(t)\mathbf{y}(t; \mathscr{U}) \tag{6.117}$$

Let us denote by $\boldsymbol{\psi}(t; \mathbf{y})$ the vector valued function

$$\mathbf{f}(\mathbf{x}(t; \mathscr{V}) + \mathbf{y}, \mathbf{v}(t), t) - \mathbf{f}(\mathbf{x}(t; \mathscr{V}), \mathbf{v}(t), t) - A(t)\mathbf{y} \tag{6.118}$$

We see immediately that $\boldsymbol{\psi}(t; \mathbf{0}) = \mathbf{0}$. From the assumptions of Sec. 6.1 we know that all the second partial derivatives with respect to $\mathbf{y}$ of $\boldsymbol{\psi}(t; \mathbf{y})$ exist, are continuous with respect to $\mathbf{y}$ and piecewise continuous with respect to t. We have then

$$\boldsymbol{\psi}(t; \mathbf{y}) = \left(\left.\frac{\partial \boldsymbol{\psi}(t; \mathbf{y})}{\partial \mathbf{y}}\right|_{\mathbf{y}=0}\right)\mathbf{y} + \boldsymbol{\rho}(t; \mathbf{y}) \tag{6.119}$$

and there exists a $K_1 < \infty$ such that

$$|\boldsymbol{\rho}(t; \mathbf{y})| \leq K_1 \, |\mathbf{y}|^2 \tag{6.120}$$

for all $t \in [0, 1]$ and for all $\mathbf{y}$ with $|\mathbf{y}| \leq K$. From the definition of the matrix $A(t)$ we have

$$\left(\left.\frac{\partial \boldsymbol{\psi}(t; \mathbf{y})}{\partial \mathbf{y}}\right|_{\mathbf{y}=0}\right) = 0 \tag{6.121}$$

We obtain finally

$$|\boldsymbol{\psi}(t; \mathbf{y})| \leq K_1 |\mathbf{y}|^2 \tag{6.122}$$

for all $t \in [0, 1]$ and for all $\mathbf{y}$ with $|\mathbf{y}| \le K$, i.e.,

$$|\mathbf{k}(t, \mathscr{U})| \le K_1 |\mathbf{y}(t; \mathscr{U})|^2 \tag{6.123}$$

for all $\mathscr{U} \in F$ and all $t \in [0, 1]$ such that $\mathbf{u}(t) = \mathbf{v}(t)$. This concludes the derivation of inequality (6.98).

The relation (6.115) may be written

$$\mathbf{k}(t; \mathscr{U}) = \mathbf{f}(\mathbf{x}(t; \mathscr{V}) + \mathbf{y}(t; \mathscr{U}), \mathbf{u}(t), t) - \mathbf{f}(\mathbf{x}(t; \mathscr{V}), \mathbf{u}(t), t) - A(t)\mathbf{y}(t; \mathscr{U}) \tag{6.124}$$

Let us define the vector valued function $\boldsymbol{\mu}(t; \mathbf{y}, \mathbf{u})$ by the relation

$$\boldsymbol{\mu}(t; \mathbf{y}, \mathbf{u}) = \mathbf{f}(\mathbf{x}(t; \mathscr{V}) + \mathbf{y}, \mathbf{u}, t) - \mathbf{f}(\mathbf{x}(t; \mathscr{V}), \mathbf{u}, t) - A(t)\mathbf{y} \tag{6.125}$$

For every $t \in [0, 1]$ and every $\mathbf{u} \in \Omega$ we have $\boldsymbol{\mu}(t; \mathbf{0}, \mathbf{u})$, and from the assumptions made in Sec. 6.1 we know that $\boldsymbol{\mu}(t; \mathbf{y}, \mathbf{u})$ has a derivative with respect to $\mathbf{y}$ which is bounded for all $t \in [0, 1]$, all $\mathbf{u} \in \Omega$ and all $\mathbf{y}$ such that $|\mathbf{y}| \le K$. Hence, there is a constant $K_2 < \infty$ such that

$$|\boldsymbol{\mu}(t; \mathbf{y}, \mathbf{u})| \le K_2 |\mathbf{y}| \tag{6.126}$$

for all $t \in [0, 1]$, all $\mathbf{u} \in \Omega$ and all $\mathbf{y}$ with $|\mathbf{y}| \le K$. In other words, there is a constant $K_2 < \infty$ such that

$$|\mathbf{k}(t; \mathscr{U})| \le K_2 |\mathbf{y}(t; \mathscr{U})| \tag{6.127}$$

for all $t \in [0, 1]$ and all $\mathscr{U} \in F$. This concludes the proof of inequality (6.99).

6.8 Uniformly Continuous Dependence of Trajectories with Respect to Variations of the Control Functions

6.81 Distance between Two Control Functions

In Sec. 6.1 we defined a vector valued function $\mathbf{x}(t; \mathscr{U})$, called a trajectory, for each control function $\mathscr{U}$ in the class F. The purpose of the present section is to state and prove a result which we could colloquially express as follows: if the change from the control function $\mathscr{U}_1$ to the control function $\mathscr{U}_2$ is "small" then the change from the trajectory $\mathbf{x}(t; \mathscr{U}_1)$ to the trajectory $\mathbf{x}(t; \mathscr{U}_2)$ will also be "small."

We shall first state precisely what we mean by a "small" change from a control function $\mathscr{U}_1$ to a control function $\mathscr{U}_2$. In Sec. 6.4 we defined $\mathscr{A}$ as the class of all subsets of [0, 1] which are the union of a finite number of disjoint intervals. For each set E in the collection $\mathscr{A}$ let $\mu(E)$ be the length of the set E, i.e., the sum of the lengths of the finite number of disjoint intervals constituting the set E. We shall say that the distance† between two control functions $\mathscr{U}_1$ and $\mathscr{U}_2$ is at most the nonnegative number α if there exists a set E in the collection $\mathscr{A}$ such that $\mu(E) \leq \alpha$, and such that the two control functions $\mathscr{U}_1$ and $\mathscr{U}_2$ differ at most on the set E, i.e., such that $\mathbf{u}_1(t) = \mathbf{u}_2(t)$ for all $t \in [0, 1] \sim E$.

Remark. There are many possible definitions of the distance between two control functions: for instance one could have defined the distance between the two functions $\mathscr{U}_1$ and $\mathscr{U}_2$ as the supremum of $|\mathbf{u}_1(t) - \mathbf{u}_2(t)|$ for all $t \in [0, 1]$. For many readers this second definition could seem more "natural" than the first definition. However, we have chosen the first given definition not for its "naturalness" but for its convenience in the derivation of further results. The reader who is well acquainted with classical calculus of variations will realize immediately that the first definition corresponds to the concept of strong variations and that the second definition corresponds to the concept of weak variations.

6.82 Uniform Boundedness of Variational Trajectories

This paragraph will be devoted to the proof of the following result:

Proposition 8.1. *There exists an $N < +\infty$ such that for all $\mathscr{U}_1$ and $\mathscr{U}_2 \in F$ and all $E \in \mathscr{A}$ with $\mathbf{u}_1(t) = \mathbf{u}_2(t)$ for all $t \in [0, 1] \sim E$ we have*

$$|\mathbf{x}(\tau; \mathscr{U}_1) - \mathbf{x}(\tau; \mathscr{U}_2)| \leq N\mu(E) \qquad \text{for all} \quad \tau \in [0, 1] \tag{6.128}$$

PROOF. The scalar valued function $|\mathbf{x}(t; \mathscr{U}_1) - \mathbf{x}(t; \mathscr{U}_2)|$ is continuous over $[0, 1]$ and differentiable over $\Theta(\mathscr{U}_1) \cap \Theta(\mathscr{U}_2)$. We have immediately

$$\frac{d}{dt}|\mathbf{x}(t; \mathscr{U}_1) - \mathbf{x}(t; \mathscr{U}_2)| \leq |\dot{\mathbf{x}}(t; \mathscr{U}_1) - \dot{\mathbf{x}}(t; \mathscr{U}_2)| \tag{6.129}$$

† This footnote is intended only for the reader familiar with measure theory. As we said in the introduction we want to avoid any measure theoretical consideration in this chapter. Without such a stringent restriction we would have naturally defined the distance between two control functions $\mathscr{U}_1$ and $\mathscr{U}_2$ as the measure of the set of points where these two functions differ. If $\mathscr{U}_1$ and $\mathscr{U}_2 \in F$ the set

$$S = \{t : t \in [0, 1], \quad \mathbf{u}_1(t) \neq \mathbf{u}_2(t)\}$$

is not necessarily in the class $\mathscr{A}$. If in Sec. 6.1 we would have required all functions in the class F to be piecewise analytic, then the set S would, indeed, be in the class $\mathscr{A}$ and the writing of the present section would have been somewhat simplified. However, we have decided that this simplification was not worth such a supplementary requirement on the class F.

i.e.,

$$\frac{d}{dt}|\mathbf{x}(t;\mathscr{U}_1)-\mathbf{x}(t;\mathscr{U}_2)| \leq |\mathbf{f}(\mathbf{x}(t;\mathscr{U}_1),\mathbf{u}_1(t),t)-\mathbf{f}(\mathbf{x}(t;\mathscr{U}_2),\mathbf{u}_2(t),t)| \tag{6.130}$$

i.e.,

$$\frac{d}{dt}|\mathbf{x}(t;\mathscr{U}_1)-\mathbf{x}(t;\mathscr{U}_2)| \leq |\mathbf{f}(\mathbf{x}(t;\mathscr{U}_1),\mathbf{u}_2(t),t)-\mathbf{f}(\mathbf{x}(t;\mathscr{U}_2),\mathbf{u}_2(t),t)| + |\mathbf{f}(\mathbf{x}(t;\mathscr{U}_1),\mathbf{u}_1(t),t)-\mathbf{f}(\mathbf{x}(t;\mathscr{U}_1),\mathbf{u}_2(t),t)| \tag{6.131}$$

for all t in $\Theta(\mathscr{U}_1)\cap\Theta(\mathscr{U}_2)$.

We have seen in Sec. 6.1 that $\mathbf{x}(t;\mathscr{U})$ is uniformly bounded over [0, 1] for all $\mathscr{U}$ in F. Hence, from the assumptions stated in Sec. 6.1 for the function $\mathbf{f}(\mathbf{x},\mathbf{u},t)$ we know that there are constants L_1 and $L_2 < +\infty$ such that

$$|\mathbf{f}(\mathbf{x}(t;\mathscr{U}_2),\mathbf{u}_2(t),t)-\mathbf{f}(\mathbf{x}(t;\mathscr{U}_1),\mathbf{u}_2(t),t)| \leq L_1\,|\mathbf{x}(t;\mathscr{U}_2)-\mathbf{x}(t;\mathscr{U}_1)| \tag{6.132}$$

and

$$|\mathbf{f}(\mathbf{x}(t;\mathscr{U}_1(t),t)-\mathbf{f}(\mathbf{x}(t;\mathscr{U}_1),\mathbf{u}_2(t),t)| \leq L_2 \tag{6.133}$$

for all $\mathscr{U}_1$ and $\mathscr{U}_2 \in F$ and all $t \in [0, 1]$.

We have then for all $t\in\Theta(\mathscr{U}_1)\cap\Theta(\mathscr{U}_2)$

$$\frac{d}{dt}|\mathbf{x}(t;\mathscr{U}_1)-\mathbf{x}(t;\mathscr{U}_2)| \leq L_1\,|\mathbf{x}(t;\mathscr{U}_1)-\mathbf{x}(t;\mathscr{U}_2)| + L_2\,\chi(E) \tag{6.134}$$

where $\chi(E)$ is the characteristic function of the set E, i.e., a function equal to one when $t\in E$ and equal to zero when $t\in[0,1]\sim E$.

From a generalization of Gronwall's inequality proved in Proposition A.1 of Appendix A we obtain

$$|\mathbf{x}(\tau;\mathscr{U}_1)-\mathbf{x}(\tau;\mathscr{U}_2)| \leq L_2\,e^{L_1}\int_0^\tau \chi(E)\,dt \tag{6.135}$$

for all $\tau\in[0,1]$, i.e.,

$$|\mathbf{x}(\tau;\mathscr{U}_1)-\mathbf{x}(\tau;\mathscr{U}_2)| \leq N\mu(E) \tag{6.136}$$

where $N = L_2\,e^{L_1}$. This concludes the proof of Proposition 7.1.

6.9 Some Uniform Estimates for the Approximation $z(t; \mathscr{U})$ of the Variational Trajectory $y(t; \mathscr{U})$

In Scc. 6.7 we have assumed that the control function $\mathscr{V}$ was an optimal control function for the optimization problem stated in Sec. 6.2. To this optimal control function $\mathscr{V}$ is associated an optimal trajectory $\mathbf{x}(t; \mathscr{V})$. For every control function $\mathscr{U}$ in the class F we have also a trajectory $\mathbf{x}(t; \mathscr{U})$ and in Sec. 6.7 we have defined $\mathbf{y}(t; \mathscr{U})$ as the difference between $\mathbf{x}(t; \mathscr{U})$ and $\mathbf{x}(t; \mathscr{V})$. The vector valued function $\mathbf{y}(t; \mathscr{U})$ is called the variational trajectory for the control function $\mathscr{U}$ with respect to the control function $\mathscr{V}$. In Sec. 6.7 we have also defined an approximation $\mathbf{z}(t; \mathscr{U})$ for the variational trajectory $\mathbf{y}(t; \mathscr{U})$. The aim of the present section is to state and prove some results which characterize how well the trajectory $\mathbf{z}(t; \mathscr{U})$ approximates the variational trajectory $\mathbf{y}(t; \mathscr{U})$.

More precisely, the remainder of this section will be devoted to the proof of the following result:

Proposition 9.1. *There exists a* $K < +\infty$ *such that for all* $\mathscr{U} \in F$ *and all* $E \in \mathscr{A}$ *with* $\mathbf{u}(t) = \mathbf{v}(t)$ *for all* $t \in [0, 1] \sim E$ *we have*

$$|\mathbf{y}(\tau, \mathscr{U}) - \mathbf{z}(\tau; \mathscr{U})| \leq K(\mu(E))^2 \qquad \text{for all} \quad \tau \in [0, 1] \tag{6.137}$$

We have seen in Sec. 6.8 that

$$|\mathbf{x}(t; \mathscr{U}) - \mathbf{x}(t; \mathscr{V})| \leq N\mu(E) \qquad \text{for all} \quad t \in [0, 1] \tag{6.138}$$

i.e.,

$$|\mathbf{y}(t; \mathscr{U})| \leq N\mu(E) \qquad \text{for all} \quad t \in [0, 1] \tag{6.139}$$

We have seen in Sec. 6.7 that

$$\dot{\mathbf{y}}(t; \mathscr{U}) - \dot{\mathbf{z}}(t; \mathscr{U}) = \mathbf{k}(t; \mathscr{U}) \qquad \text{for all} \quad t \in \Theta(\mathscr{U}) \tag{6.140}$$

and

$$|\mathbf{y}(0; \mathscr{U}) - \mathbf{z}(0; \mathscr{U})| = 0 \tag{6.141}$$

It follows then that

$$|\mathbf{y}(\tau, \mathscr{U}) - \mathbf{z}(\tau; \mathscr{U})| \leq \int_0^1 |\mathbf{k}(t; \mathscr{U})| \, dt \qquad \text{for all} \quad \tau \in [0, 1] \tag{6.142}$$

We may write

$$\int_0^1 |\mathbf{k}(t; \mathscr{U})| \, dt = \int_E |\mathbf{k}(t; \mathscr{U})| \, dt + \int_{[0,1]\sim E} \mathbf{k}(t; \mathscr{U})| \, dt \tag{6.143}$$

We have seen in Sec. 6.7 that there is a $K_1 < +\infty$ such that

$$|\mathbf{k}(t;\mathscr{U})| \le K_1 \,|\mathbf{y}(t;\mathscr{U})|^2 \qquad \text{for all} \quad t \in [0,1] \sim E \tag{6.144}$$

i.e.,

$$|\mathbf{k}(t;\mathscr{U})| \le K_1 N^2(\mu(E))^2 \qquad \text{for all} \quad t \in [0,1] \sim E \tag{6.145}$$

which implies

$$\int_{[0,1]\sim E} |\mathbf{k}(t;\mathscr{U})|\,dt \le K_1 N^2(\mu(E))^2 \tag{6.146}$$

We have also seen in Sec. 6.7 that there is a $K_2 < +\infty$ such that

$$|\mathbf{k}(t;\mathscr{U})| \le K_2 \,|\mathbf{y}(t;\mathscr{U})| \qquad \text{for all} \quad t \in E \tag{6.147}$$

i.e.,

$$|\mathbf{k}(t;\mathscr{U})| \le K_2 N \mu(E) \qquad \text{for all} \quad t \in E \tag{6.148}$$

which implies

$$\int_E |\mathbf{k}(t;\mathscr{U})|\,dt \le K_2 N(\mu(E))^2 \tag{6.149}$$

Combining relations (6.142), (6.143), (6.146), and (6.149) we obtain

$$\begin{aligned} |\mathbf{y}(\tau;\mathscr{U}) - \mathbf{z}(\tau;\mathscr{U})| &\le (K_1 N^2 + K_2 N)(\mu(E))^2 \\ &\text{for all} \quad \tau \in [0,1] \end{aligned} \tag{6.150}$$

We may write $K = K_1 N^2 + K_2 N$ and so obtain relation (6.137). This concludes the proof of Proposition 9.1.

6.10 Convexity of the Range of a Vector Integral over the Class $\mathscr{A}$ of Subsets of [0, 1]

6.101 Multiple Balayage of Vector Integrals

In this section we shall prove two theorems which have been used repeatebly throughout this chapter. Both theorems are somewhat related to a well-known theorem of Lyapounov on the range of a vector integral.

We shall denote by $\mathbf{f}(t)$ some given piecewise continuous† function from

† A vector valued function $\mathbf{f}(t)$ defined over [0, 1] is piecewise continuous over [0, 1] if it is continuous at all points of (0, 1), with the exception of a finite number of points where it has finite right and left limits and if, moreover, it has a finite right limit at the point 0 and a finite left limit at the point 1. From this definition it follows that a piecewise continuous function $\mathbf{f}(t)$ is bounded, i.e., there exists a $K < +\infty$ such that

$$|\mathbf{f}(t)| \le K \qquad \text{for all} \quad t \in [0,1]$$

where $|\mathbf{f}(t)|$ is the Euclidean norm (or length) of the vector $\mathbf{f}(t)$.

[0, 1] into an n-dimensional Euclidean space E^n. The vector $I = \int_0^1 \mathbf{f}(t)\,dt$ represents the average of the function $\mathbf{f}(t)$ on the interval [0, 1]. The vector I is also the value at $t = 1$ of the function $\mathbf{g}(t) = \int_0^t \mathbf{f}(\tau)\,d\tau$. If we consider the estimation of the average I as a continuous process then the vector $\mathbf{g}(t)$ may be regarded as a certain approximation of the fraction tI of the average vector I. This continuous estimation process is not very accurate if the function $\mathbf{f}(t)$ fluctuates greatly. Instead of basing our estimation on a single balayage† of the interval [0, 1] we could consider a simultaneous balayage of each of the intervals $[0, \frac{1}{2}]$ and $[\frac{1}{2}, 1]$ and introduce a function $\mathbf{g}_1(t)$ defined over [0, 1] by the relation

$$\mathbf{g}_1(t) = \int_0^{t/2} \mathbf{f}(\tau)\,d\tau + \int_{1/2}^{1/2+t/2} \mathbf{f}(\tau)\,d\tau \tag{6.151}$$

as an approximation of the fraction tI of the average vector I. Intuitively, we could hope that the fluctuations of the function $\mathbf{f}(t)$ on the intervals $[0, \frac{1}{2}]$ and $[\frac{1}{2}, 1]$ will compensate each other and that $\mathbf{g}_1(t)$ will be a better approximation of tI than $\mathbf{g}(t)$. This process may be refined further: for each integer k we partition the interval [0, 1] into 2^k consecutive intervals of equal length $1/2^k$ and we define a function $\mathbf{g}_k(t)$ over [0, 1] by the relation

$$\mathbf{g}_k(t) = \sum_{i=1}^{2^k} \int_{(i-1)/2^k}^{(i-1+t)/2^k} \mathbf{f}(\tau)\,d\tau \tag{6.152}$$

or, equivalently, by the relation

$$\mathbf{g}_k(t) = \int_{D_t^k} \mathbf{f}(\tau)\,d\tau \tag{6.153}$$

where the sets D_{t^k} are defined by the relation‡

$$D_t^k = \bigcup_{i=1}^{2^k} \left[\frac{i-1}{2^k}, \frac{i-1+t}{2^k}\right) \tag{6.154}$$

In other words, the set D_t^k is obtained by dividing the interval [0, 1] into 2^k consecutive and equal intervals and by taking the union of the first fraction t of each of these 2^k intervals. In Proposition 10.1 we prove that the functions $\mathbf{g}_1(t), \mathbf{g}_2(t), \ldots, \mathbf{g}_k(t), \ldots$ are becoming more and more accurate approximations of the function tI as k increases. More precisely, we shall prove the following result:

† The mathematical term "balayage," which comes from the French, means literally: "The act of sweeping."

‡ We recall that if $a \leq b$ then $[a, b)$ is the set of all t such that $a \leq t \leq b$. If $A_1, A_2, \ldots, A_k$ is a finite collection of sets then $\cup_{i=1}^k A_i$ is the set of all points which belong to at least one of the sets $A_1, A_2, \ldots, A_k$. Similarly, $\cap_{i=1}^k A_i$ is the set of all points which belong to each of the sets $A_1, A_2, \ldots, A_k$.

Proposition 10.1 *If* $\mathbf{f}(t)$ *is a piecewise continuous function from* [0, 1] *into an n-dimensional Euclidean space and if* $\varepsilon > 0$, *then there exists an integer K such that*

$$\left| \int_{D_\alpha{}^k} \mathbf{f}(t)\, dt - \alpha \int_0^1 \mathbf{f}(t)\, dt \right| \leq \varepsilon \quad \text{for all} \quad \alpha \in [0, 1] \quad \text{and all} \quad k \geq K \tag{6.155}$$

PROOF. We shall first assume that $n = 1$, i.e., that the function $\mathbf{f}(t)$ is real valued. Since a piecewise continuous function on [0, 1] is *a fortiori* bounded, there exists a real number $M < +\infty$ such that

$$|f(t)| \leq M \qquad \text{for all} \quad t \in [0, 1] \tag{6.156}$$

We have then

$$\int_0^1 |f(t)|^2\, dt \leq M^2 < +\infty \tag{6.157}$$

and from the theory of Fourier series we know that there exists a sequence of real numbers $a_0, a_1, a_{-1}, a_2, a_{-2}, \ldots$ such that

$$|a_0|^2 + \sum_{i=1}^{\infty} (|a_i|^2 + |a_{-i}|^2) < +\infty \tag{6.158}$$

$$f(t) \approx a_2 + \sum_{i=1}^{\infty} (a_i \cos 2\pi i t + a_{-i} \sin 2\pi i t) \tag{6.159}$$

and

$$a_0 = \int_0^1 f(t)\, dt \tag{6.160}$$

where " $\approx$ " in the relation (6.159) means that

$$\lim_{k \to \infty} \int_1^0 \left| a_0 + \sum_{i=0}^{k} (a_i \cos 2\pi i t + a_{-i} \sin 2\pi i t) - f(t) \right|^2 dt = 0 \tag{6.161}$$

Let $f_1(t), f_2(t), \ldots$ be real valued functions defined over [0, 1] by the relations

$$f_1(t) = \frac{1}{2}\left(f\left(\frac{t}{2}\right) + f\left(\frac{1}{2} + \frac{t}{2}\right) \right) \tag{6.162}$$

$$f_{k+1}(t) = \frac{1}{2}\left(f_k\left(\frac{t}{2}\right) + f_k\left(\frac{1}{2} + \frac{t}{2}\right) \right) \qquad \text{for} \quad k = 1, 2, \ldots \tag{6.163}$$

We have then

$$f_1(t) \approx a_0 + \sum_{i=1}^{\infty} a_i(\tfrac{1}{2}\cos i\pi t + \tfrac{1}{2}\cos i\pi(1+t)) + \sum_{i=1}^{\infty} a_{-i}(\tfrac{1}{2}\sin i\pi t + \tfrac{1}{2}\sin i\pi(1+t)) \tag{6.164}$$

We know that for an even integer i we have

$$\cos i\pi t = \cos i\pi(t+1) \tag{6.165}$$

$$\sin i\pi t = \sin i\pi(t+1) \tag{6.166}$$

and that for an odd integer i we have

$$\cos i\pi t = -\cos i\pi(t+1) \tag{6.167}$$

$$\sin i\pi t = -\sin i\pi(t+1) \tag{6.168}$$

Relation (6.164) may then be written

$$f_1(t) \approx a_0 + \sum_{i=2,4,6,\ldots}^{\infty} (a_i \cos i\pi t + a_{-i}\sin i\pi t) \tag{6.169}$$

i.e.,

$$f_1(t) \approx a_0 + \sum_{i=1,2,3,\ldots}^{\infty} (a_{2i}\cos 2i\pi t + a_{-2i}\sin 2i\pi t) \tag{6.170}$$

By repeating the same procedure we could prove easily that

$$f_k(t) \approx a_0 + \sum_{i=1,2,3,\ldots}^{\infty} (a_{i2^k}\cos 2i\pi t + a_{-i2^k}\sin 2i\pi t) \tag{6.171}$$

It follows then that

$$\int_0^1 |f_k(t) - a_0|^2\, dt \leq \sum_{i=2^k}^{\infty} (|a_i|^2 + |a_{-i}|^2) \tag{6.172}$$

i.e.,

$$\lim_{k\to 0}\int_0^1 |f_k(t) - a_0|^2\, dt = 0 \tag{6.173}$$

since

$$\sum_{i=1}^{\infty} (|a_i|^2 + |a_{-i}|^2) < +\infty \tag{6.174}$$

From relation (6.173) we know that there exists an integer K such that

$$\left(\int_0^1 |f_k(t) - a_0|^2\, dt\right)^{1/2} \leq \varepsilon \qquad \text{for all} \quad k \geq K \tag{6.175}$$

It is a trivial matter† to verify that

$$\int_{D_\alpha{}^k} f(t)\,dt = \int_0^\alpha f_k(t)\,dt \tag{6.176}$$

We have then

$$\left| \int_{D_\alpha{}^k} f(t)\,dt - \alpha \int_0^1 f(t)\,dt \right| = \left| \int_0^\alpha f_k(t)\,dt - \int_0^\alpha a_0\,dt \right|$$

$$\leq \int_0^\alpha |f_k(t) - a_0|\,dt \leq \int_0^1 |f_k(t) - a_0|\,dt \tag{6.177}$$

By Cauchy-Schwartz inequality‡ we have

$$\int_0^1 |f_k(t) - a_0|\,dt \leq \left(\int_0^1 |f_k(t) - a_0|^2\,dt \right)^{1/2} \tag{6.178}$$

We have already proved (see relation (6.175)) that the right side of the previous inequality is not larger than ε when $k \geq K$. Hence we have

$$\left| \int_{D_\alpha{}^k} f(t)\,dt - \alpha \int_0^1 f(t)\,dt \right| \leq \varepsilon \qquad \text{for all} \quad \alpha \in [0, 1] \qquad \text{and all} \quad k \geq K \tag{6.179}$$

This concludes the proof of Proposition 6.10 in the case of a real valued piecewise continuous function $f(t)$.

† We have immediately

$$\int_{D_\alpha{}^k} f(t)\,dt = \int_0^\alpha f_1(t)\,dt$$

since

$$\int_{D_\alpha{}^1} f(t)\,dt = \int_0^{\alpha/2} f(t)\,dt + \int_{1/2}^{1/2+\alpha/2} f(t)\,dt$$

$$= \int_0^{\alpha/2} (f(t) + f(t + \tfrac{1}{2}))\,dt$$

$$= \int_0^\alpha \frac{1}{2} \left(f\left(\frac{t}{2}\right) + f\left(\frac{t}{2} + \frac{1}{2}\right) \right) dt$$

$$= \int_0^\alpha f_1(t)\,dt$$

By repeating the same procedure we obtain easily relation (10.26) for $k = 2, 3, 4, \ldots$.

‡ We recall Cauchy-Schwartz inequality for Riemann integrals (see Courant and Hilbert,[11] Vol. I, p. 49). If $g(t)$ and $h(t)$ are two real valued piecewise continuous functions over [0, 1] then

$$\int_0^1 |g(t)h(t)|\,dt \leq \left(\int_0^1 |g(t)|^2\,dt \right)^{1/2} \left(\int_0^1 |h(t)|^2\,dt \right)^{1/2}$$

Here we let $g(t) = f_k(t) - a_0$ and $h(t) = 1$.

In the case of an n-dimensional vector valued piecewise continuous function $\mathbf{f}(t) = (f^1(t), f^2(t), \ldots, f^n(t))$ the previous result can be applied to each component: for each $i = 1, \ldots, n$ there exists an integer K_i such that†

$$\left| \int_0^\alpha f_k^i(t)\, dt - \alpha \int_0^1 f^i(t)\, dt \right| \leq \frac{\varepsilon}{n} \qquad (6.180)$$

$$\text{for all} \quad \alpha \in [0, 1] \quad \text{and all} \quad k \geq K_i$$

Let $K = \max_{i=1,\ldots,n} K_i$. We have immediately

$$\left| \int_0^\alpha \mathbf{f}_k(t)\, dt - \alpha \int_0^1 \mathbf{f}(t)\, dt \right| \leq \varepsilon \qquad (6.181)$$

$$\text{for all} \quad \alpha \in [0, 1] \quad \text{and all} \quad k \geq K$$

This concludes the proof of Proposition 10.1.

6.102 Convexity of the Range of a Vector Integral

Before introducing the statement of Proposition 10.2 we define $\mathscr{A}$ as the class of all subsets of [0, 1] which are the union of a finite number of intervals. The sets $D_\alpha{}^k$ defined earlier are examples of sets in the class $\mathscr{A}$. The class $\mathscr{A}$ is an *algebra* of sets. This fact could be colloquially expressed as follows: after a finite number of operations on sets in the class $\mathscr{A}$, one obtains sets which are also in $\mathscr{A}$. More precisely, we have the following properties‡:

(i) $\varnothing \in \mathscr{A}$;
(ii) $[0, 1] \in \mathscr{A}$;
(iii) if A and $B \in \mathscr{A}$ then $A \cap B \in \mathscr{A}$;
(iv) if A and $B \in \mathscr{A}$ then $A \cup B \in \mathscr{A}$;
(v) if $A \in \mathscr{A}$ then $([0, 1] \sim A) \in \mathscr{A}$.

† For each $i = 1, 2, \ldots, n$ and each $k = 1, 2, 3, \ldots$ the function $f_k{}^i(t)$ is defined in a way similar to (6.163), i.e.,

$$f_{k=1}^i(t) = \frac{1}{2}\left(f_k{}^i\left(\frac{t}{2}\right) + f_k{}^i\left(\frac{1}{2} + \frac{t}{2}\right)\right)$$

and the vector valued function $(f_k{}^1(t), f_k{}^2(t), \ldots, f_k{}^n(t))$ is denoted by $\mathbf{f}_k(t)$.

‡ We do not need these five properties to define an algebra of sets: the reader may verify for instance that properties (ii) and (iii) can be derived from properties (i), (iv), and (v). We recall that $\varnothing$ denotes the empty set, i.e., the set with no element, that $A \cap B$ denotes the intersection of the sets A and B, i.e., the set of elements which belong to both A and B, that $A \cup B$ denotes the union of the sets A and B, i.e., the set of elements which belong either to A, or to B, or to A and B, and that $[0, 1] \sim A$ denotes the complement of A, i.e., the set of elements of [0, 1] which do not belong to A.

Let $\mathbf{f}(t)$ be a piecewise continuous function from [0, 1] into an n-dimensional Euclidean space. For each set A in the class $\mathscr{A}$ there exists a vector $\int_A f(t)\,dt$. Let us consider the set $L(f)$ of all these vectors corresponding to all the sets in the class $\mathscr{A}$. Formally we have then

$$L(\mathbf{f}) = \left\{\int_A \mathbf{f}(t)\,dt : A \in \mathscr{A}\right\} \tag{6.182}$$

We shall prove that

Proposition 10.2. *If the vector valued function* $\mathbf{f}(t)$ *is piecewise continuous then the set* $L(\mathbf{f})$ *is convex.*†

The proof of Proposition 6.10 will proceed in three steps. In Lemma 1 we shall prove that $\bar{L}(\mathbf{f})$, the closure‡ of $L(\mathbf{f})$, is convex. This result is relatively easy to prove, using Proposition 10.1, and is already a good indication of the plausibility of Proposition 10.2. However, we must note immediately that Lemma 1 is not yet as strong as Proposition 10.1, since it is quite possible for a set A to have a closure $\bar{A}$ which is convex without being itself convex.§

In Lemma 2 we shall prove that any point interior¶ to the convex hull†† of $L(f)$ belongs also to $L(f)$. The proof of this result is based on Lemma 1 and on Brouwer's fixed point theorem.‡‡ Again we note that Lemma 2 is stronger than Lemma 1 but not yet as strong as Proposition 10.2, since it is quite

† We recall that a set A is convex if for any pair of points $\mathbf{a}$ and $\mathbf{b}$ in A and any real number μ with $0 < \mu < 1$ there exists a point $\mathbf{c}$ in A with $\mathbf{c} = \mu\mathbf{a} + (1 - \mu)\mathbf{b}$.

‡ If A is a set in an n-dimensional Euclidean space then $\bar{A}$ is the closure of the set A defined as follows: $\bar{A}$ is the smallest closed set containing A or equivalently $\bar{A}$ is the union of A and of the set of the accumulation points of A. We recall that a point $\mathbf{a}$, not necessarily in A, is an accumulation point of A if for every $\varepsilon > 0$ there exists a point $\mathbf{b}$ in A with $\mathbf{b} \neq \mathbf{a}$ and $|\mathbf{a} - \mathbf{b}| \leq \varepsilon$.

§ The set $A = \{\mathbf{x} : \mathbf{x} \in E^n, |\mathbf{x}| \leq 1, |\mathbf{x}| \neq 0\}$ is not convex but the set $\bar{A} = \{\mathbf{x} : \mathbf{x} \in E^n$ $|\mathbf{x}| \leq 1\}$ is convex.

¶ We recall that a point $\mathbf{a}$ is interior to a set A in an n-dimensional Euclidean space if there exists an $\varepsilon > 0$ such that for all $\mathbf{b}$ with $|\mathbf{a} - \mathbf{b}| < \varepsilon$ we have $\mathbf{b} \in A$. We shall denote by int A the set of points which are interior to A and by $N(\mathbf{a}, \varepsilon)$ the set of all points $\mathbf{b}$ such that $|\mathbf{a} - \mathbf{b}| < \varepsilon$.

†† If A is a set in an n-dimensional Euclidean space, then co A denotes the convex hull of the set A, i.e., the smallest convex set containing A. The fundamental property of co A is the following: if $\mathbf{a} \in \text{co } A$ then there exists $n+1$ points $\mathbf{a}_1, \mathbf{a}_2, \ldots, \mathbf{a}_{n+1}$ in A and $n+1$ non-negative real numbers $\mu_1, \mu_2, \ldots, \mu_{n+1}$ such that

$$\sum_{i=1}^{n+1} \mu_i = 1 \qquad \text{and} \qquad \mathbf{a} = \sum_{i=1}^{n+1} \mu_i \mathbf{a}_i .$$

‡‡ Lemma 2 could also be proved using some generalizations of the implicit function theorem or using Peano's theorem, a theorem establishing the existence, but not necessarily the uniqueness, of the solution of some type of systems of ordinary differential equations.

possible to construct† a set A which is not convex and such that any point interior to co A, the convex hull of A, belongs also to the set A. In Lemma 3 we prove finally that the set $L(f)$ is convex. The proof of Lemma 3 is a proof by induction based on the fact that for a space of dimension one Lemma 2 and 3 are equivalent.

Lemma 1. *The set* $\bar{L}(\mathbf{f})$ *is convex.*

PROOF. Let $\mathbf{a}^*$ and $\mathbf{b}^* \in \bar{L}(\mathbf{f})$ and $\mu \in [0, 1]$ we have to prove that $\mathbf{c}^* = \mu\mathbf{a}^* + (1-\mu)\mathbf{b}^* \in \bar{L}(\mathbf{f})$, i.e., that for any $\varepsilon > 0$ there exists a $\mathbf{c} \in L(\mathbf{f})$ such that $|\mathbf{c}^* - \mathbf{c}| \leq \varepsilon$. There exist an $\mathbf{a}$ and a $\mathbf{b} \in L(\mathbf{f})$ such that $|\mathbf{a} - \mathbf{a}^*|$ and $|\mathbf{b} - \mathbf{b}^*| < \varepsilon/4$. Let A and $B \in \mathscr{A}$ with $\mathbf{a} = \int_A \mathbf{f}(t)\,dt$ and $\mathbf{b} = \int_B \mathbf{f}(t)\,dt$. From Proposition 10.1 there exists an integer k_A such that‡

$$\left| \int_{D_\mu{}^k} \mathbf{f}(t)\,\chi(A)\,dt - \mu \int_0^1 \mathbf{f}(t)\,\chi(A)\,dt \right| \leq \frac{\varepsilon}{8} \tag{6.183}$$

for all $k \geq k_\mathbf{a}$ and an integer $k_\mathbf{b}$ such that

$$\left| \int_{D_\mu{}^k} \mathbf{f}(t)\,\chi(B)\,dt - \mu \int_0^1 \mathbf{f}(t)\,\chi(B)\,dt \right| \leq \frac{\varepsilon}{8} \tag{6.184}$$

for all $k \geq k_\mathbf{b}$. Let $K = \max\{k_\mathbf{a}, k_\mathbf{b}\}$. We have then

$$\left| \int_{D_\mu{}^k} \mathbf{f}(t)\,\chi(A)\,dt - \mu \int_0^1 \mathbf{f}(t)\,\chi(A)\,dt \right| \leq \frac{\varepsilon}{8} \tag{6.185}$$

and

$$\left| \int_{D_\mu{}^K} \mathbf{f}(t)\,\chi(B)\,dt - \mu \int_0^1 \mathbf{f}(t)\,\chi(B)\,dt \right| \leq \frac{\varepsilon}{8} \tag{6.186}$$

From relation (6.186) we have immediately

$$\left| \int_{[0,1]\sim D_\mu{}^K} \mathbf{f}(t)\,\chi(B)\,dt - (1-\mu) \int_0^1 \mathbf{f}(t)\,\chi(B)\,dt \right| \leq \frac{\varepsilon}{8} \tag{6.187}$$

† Let B be the closed unit square in the plane, i.e.,

$$B = \{\mathbf{x} = (x_1, x_2) : |x_1| \leq 1, |x_2| \leq 1\}$$

and let $A = B \sim \{(0, 1)\}$. In other words, the set A is a closed square with one point missing in the middle of one of its sides. The set A is not convex but every point interior to the convex hull of A belongs to A.

‡ The characteristic function of the set A is denoted $\chi(A)$, i.e., $\chi(A)$ is a function whose value is 1 for all $t \in A$ and 0 for all $t \in [0, 1] \sim A$.

Let

$$C = (A \cap D\mu^K) \cup (B \cap ([0, 1] \sim D\mu^K)) \tag{6.188}$$

We have then from (6.185) and (6.187)

$$\left| \int_C \mathbf{f}(t)\, dt - \mu \int_A \mathbf{f}(t)\, dt - (1 - \mu) \int_B \mathbf{f}(t)\, dt \right| \leq \frac{\varepsilon}{4} \tag{6.189}$$

i.e.,

$$|\mathbf{c} - \mu \mathbf{a} - (1 - \mu)\mathbf{b}| \leq \frac{\varepsilon}{4} \tag{6.190}$$

We have now

$$\begin{aligned} |c - c^*| &= |c - \mu \mathbf{a}^* - (1 - \mu)\mathbf{b}^*| \\ &\leq |c - \mu \mathbf{a} - (1 - \mu)\mathbf{b}| + |\mathbf{a} - \mathbf{a}^*| + |\mathbf{b} - \mathbf{b}^*| \\ &\leq \varepsilon/4 + \varepsilon/4 + \varepsilon/4 < \varepsilon \end{aligned} \tag{6.191}$$

This concludes the proof of Lemma 1.

Lemma 2. *The set* into co $L(\mathbf{f})$ *is a subset of* $L(\mathbf{f})$.

PROOF. Let $\mathbf{a} \in \text{int co } L(\mathbf{f})$. We shall prove that $\mathbf{a} \in L(\mathbf{f})$. There is an $\varepsilon > 0$ and a set $S^* = \{\mathbf{a}_i^* : i = 1, \ldots, n + 1\} \subset \text{int co } L(\mathbf{f})$ such that $N(\mathbf{a}, 2\varepsilon) \subset$ co S^*. We have int co $L(\mathbf{f}) \subset$ int co $\bar{L}(\mathbf{f})$ and from Lemma 1 we have co$\bar{L}(\mathbf{f}) = \bar{L}(\mathbf{f})$ it follows then that into co $L(\mathbf{f}) \subset$ int $\bar{L}(\mathbf{f})$ and that $S^* \subset$ int $\bar{L}(\mathbf{f})$. Hence, there exists† a set $S = \{\mathbf{a}_i : i = 1, \ldots, n + 1\} \subset L(\mathbf{f})$ such that $N(\mathbf{a}, \varepsilon) \subset$ co S.

For every $\mathbf{a}_i \in S$ there exists a set $A_i \in \mathscr{A}$ with $\int_{A_i} \mathbf{f}(t)\, dt = \mathbf{a}_i$. For each $i = 1, \ldots, n + 1$ we know by Proposition 10.1 that there exists a positive integer K_i such that

$$\left| \int_{D_\alpha{}^k \cap A_i} \mathbf{f}(t)\, dt - \alpha \int_{A_i} \mathbf{f}(t)\, dt \right| \leq \frac{\varepsilon}{4(n + 1)} \tag{6.192}$$

for all integer $k \geq K_i$ and all $\alpha \in [0, 1]$. Let $K = \max_{i=1,2,\ldots,n+1} K_i$. We have then

$$\left| \int_{D_\alpha{}^k \cap A_i} \mathbf{f}(t)\, dt - \alpha \int_{A_i} \mathbf{f}(t)\, dt \right| \leq \frac{\varepsilon}{4(n + 1)} \tag{6.193}$$

for all integer $k \geq K$, all $i = 1, 2, \ldots, n + 1$, and all $\alpha \in [0, 1]$.

† A rigorous proof of this intuitive fact follows: For each $\mathbf{a}_i^* \in \bar{L}(\mathbf{f})$ let $\mathbf{a}_{i1}^*, \mathbf{a}_{i2}^*, \mathbf{a}_{i3}^*, \ldots$ be a sequence in $L(\mathbf{f})$ converging to $\mathbf{a}_i^*$. Let $S_j^* = \{\mathbf{a}_{ij}^* : i = 1, 2, \ldots, n + 1\}$ and $\varepsilon_j = \max_{i=1,2,\ldots,n+1} |\mathbf{a}_{ij}^* - \mathbf{a}_i^*|$. We have co $S^* \subset N$ (co S_j^*, ε_j). We recall that if A is a set and $\varepsilon > 0$ then $N(A, \varepsilon)$ is the union of all the spheres of radius ε with centers in A. Since $\lim_{j=\infty} \varepsilon_j = 0$ there exists an integer m such that $\varepsilon_m \leq \varepsilon$. We have then $N(\mathbf{a}, 2\varepsilon) \subset$ co $S^* \subset N(\text{co } S_m^*, \varepsilon)$ and $N(\mathbf{a}, \varepsilon) \subset S_m^*$. We conclude by writing $\mathbf{a}_i = \mathbf{a}_{im}^*$ for $i = 1, 2, \ldots, n + 1$.

Let

$$\Lambda = \left\{\boldsymbol{\lambda} = (\lambda_1, \lambda_2, \ldots, \lambda_{n+1}) : \lambda_i \geq 0, \sum_{i=1}^{n+1} \lambda_i = 1\right\}$$

For each $\boldsymbol{\lambda} \in \Lambda$ we define a set $A(\boldsymbol{\lambda})$ by the following rules†:

$$M(i, \boldsymbol{\lambda}) = \sum_{i=1}^{i-1} \lambda_s \tag{6.194}$$

$$N(i, \boldsymbol{\lambda}) = M(i, \boldsymbol{\lambda}) + \lambda_i \tag{6.195}$$

$$A_i(\boldsymbol{\lambda}) = (D^K_{N(i,\lambda)} \sim D^K_{M(i,\lambda)}) \cap A_i \tag{6.196}$$

$$A(\boldsymbol{\lambda}) = \bigcup_{i=1}^{n+1} A_i(\boldsymbol{\lambda}) \tag{6.197}$$

We note immediately that for a given $\boldsymbol{\lambda} \in \Lambda$ the sets $A_1(\boldsymbol{\lambda}), A_2(\boldsymbol{\lambda}), \ldots, A_{n+1}(\boldsymbol{\lambda})$ are disjoint. From relation (6.193) and the fact that $\mathbf{a}_i = \int_{Ai} \mathbf{f}(t)\, dt$ we have

$$\left| \int_{D^K_{M(i,\lambda)} \cap A_i} \mathbf{f}(t)\, dt - M(i, \boldsymbol{\lambda})\, \mathbf{a}_i \right| \leq \frac{\varepsilon}{4(n+1)} \tag{6.198}$$

and

$$\left| \int_{D^K_{N(i,\lambda)} \cap A_i} \mathbf{f}(t)\, dt - N(i, \boldsymbol{\lambda})\, \mathbf{a}_i \right| \leq \frac{\varepsilon}{4(n+1)} \tag{6.199}$$

for all $i = 1, 2, \ldots, n+1$ and all $\boldsymbol{\lambda} \in \Lambda$. From relations (6.198) and (6.199) we obtain then

$$\left| \int_{A_i(\lambda)} \mathbf{f}(t)\, dt - \lambda_i \mathbf{a}_i \right| \leq \frac{\varepsilon}{2(n+1)} \tag{6.200}$$

for all $i = 1, 2, \ldots, n+1$ and all $\boldsymbol{\lambda} \in \Lambda$. We have then

$$\left| \int_{A(\lambda)} \mathbf{f}(t)\, dt - \sum_{i=1}^{n+1} \lambda_i \mathbf{a}_i \right| \leq \frac{\varepsilon}{2} \tag{6.201}$$

for every $\boldsymbol{\lambda} \in \Lambda$. Let us prove now that $\int_{A(\lambda)} \mathbf{f}(t)\, dt$ is a continuous function of $\boldsymbol{\lambda}$ on Λ.

† Let $A_1, A_2, \ldots, A_k$ be a finite collection of sets. The set $\cup_{i=1}^k A_i$ is defined as the set of all points which belongs to at least one of the sets $A_1, A_2, \ldots, A_k$. Similarly, the $\cap_{i=1}^k A_i$ is defined as the set of all points which belongs to each of the sets $A_1, A_2, \ldots, A_k$.

For any $i = 1, \ldots, n+1$ and any λ' and $\lambda'' \in \Lambda$ we have (see relations (6.194), (6.195) and (6.197))

$$|M(i, \boldsymbol{\lambda}') - M(i, \boldsymbol{\lambda}'')| \leq |\boldsymbol{\lambda}' - \boldsymbol{\lambda}''| \tag{6.202}$$

$$|N(i, \boldsymbol{\lambda}') - N(i, \boldsymbol{\lambda}'')| \leq |\boldsymbol{\lambda}' - \boldsymbol{\lambda}''| \tag{6.203}$$

$$|\lambda_i' - \lambda_i''| \leq |\boldsymbol{\lambda}' - \boldsymbol{\lambda}''| \tag{6.204}$$

and

$$\mu(A_i(\boldsymbol{\lambda}') \, \Delta A_i(\boldsymbol{\lambda}'')) \leq 3\,|\boldsymbol{\lambda}' - \boldsymbol{\lambda}''| \tag{6.205}$$

where $A \, \Delta B$ denotes the symmetric difference between the sets A and B, i.e., $A \, \Delta B = (A \sim B) \cup (B \sim A)$ and where $\mu(A)$ is the length of the set A, i.e., the sum of the lengths of the finite number of disjoint intervals constituting A. We have then, from relation (6.197),

$$\mu(A(\boldsymbol{\lambda}') \, \Delta A(\boldsymbol{\lambda}'')) \leq 3(n+1)\,|\boldsymbol{\lambda}' - \boldsymbol{\lambda}''| \tag{6.206}$$

which implies

$$\left| \int_{A(\boldsymbol{\lambda}')} \mathbf{f}(t)\, dt - \int_{A(\boldsymbol{\lambda}'')} \mathbf{f}(t)\, dt \right| \leq 3M(n+1)\,|\boldsymbol{\lambda}' - \boldsymbol{\lambda}''| \tag{6.207}$$

where M is an upper bound of $|\mathbf{f}(t)|$ over the interval $[0, 1]$. For every $\mathbf{x} \in \text{co } S$ let $\boldsymbol{\lambda}(\mathbf{x}) \in \Lambda$ be defined by

$$\mathbf{x} = \sum_{i=1}^{n+1} \lambda_i(\mathbf{x})\mathbf{a}_i \tag{6.208}$$

Let $\mathbf{h}(\mathbf{x})$ be the continuous function of $\mathbf{x}$ defined over co S by the relation

$$\mathbf{h}(\mathbf{x}) = \mathbf{a} - \int_{A(\boldsymbol{\lambda}(\mathbf{x}))} \mathbf{f}(t)\, dt + \mathbf{x} \tag{6.209}$$

We have then

$$|\mathbf{h}(\mathbf{x}) - \mathbf{a}| = \left| \int_{A(\boldsymbol{\lambda}(\mathbf{x}))} \mathbf{f}(t)\, dt - \sum_{i=1}^{n+1} \lambda_i(\mathbf{x})\mathbf{a}_i \right| \leq \frac{\varepsilon}{2} \tag{6.210}$$

which implies that $h(x)$ is a continuous function mapping co S into itself. By Brouwer's fixed point theorem† there exists an $\bar{\mathbf{x}} \in \text{co } S$ such that $\mathbf{h}(\bar{\mathbf{x}}) = \bar{\mathbf{x}}$, i.e., $\mathbf{a} = \int_{A(\boldsymbol{\lambda}(\bar{\mathbf{x}}))} \mathbf{f}(t)\, dt$ which implies $\mathbf{a} \in L(\mathbf{f})$. This concludes the proof of Lemma 2.

† The fixed point theorem is the only nonelementary mathematical result quoted without proof in the present chapter. This theorem states that if a continuous function maps a closed convex subset of an Euclidean space E^n into itself then it has a fixed point. In other words, if $\mathbf{h}(\mathbf{x})$ is a continuous function defined and continuous on the closed convex set A such that $\mathbf{h}(\mathbf{x}) \in A$ for all $\mathbf{x} \in A$ then there is an $\bar{\mathbf{x}} \in A$ such that $\mathbf{h}(\bar{\mathbf{x}}) = \bar{\mathbf{x}}$. The proof of the fixed point theorem can be found in most textbooks of topology.

Lemma 3. *The set $L(\mathbf{f})$ is convex.*

PROOF. The proof of Lemma 3 will proceed by induction. If $n = 1$ nothing needs to be proved since the statements of Lemmas 2 and 3 are equivalent for $n = 1$. Let us assume that Lemma 3 is true for $n = \nu$ and then prove it for $n = \nu + 1$.

Let $\mathbf{a}$ and $\mathbf{b} \in L(\mathbf{f})$. We have to prove that $\mathbf{a}\mu + \mathbf{b}(1 - \mu) \in L(\mathbf{f})$ for all $\mu \in (0, 1)$. If $\mathbf{a} = \mathbf{b}$ the previous statement is immediate. Let us assume that $\mathbf{a} \neq \mathbf{b}$. We have now two possibilities†

$$\text{(i)} \quad \mu\mathbf{a} + (1 - \mu)\mathbf{b} \in \partial \operatorname{co} L(\mathbf{f}) \qquad \text{for all} \quad \mu \in [0, 1]; \tag{6.211}$$

$$\text{(ii)} \quad \mu\mathbf{a} + (1 - \mu)\mathbf{b} \in \operatorname{int} \operatorname{co} L(\mathbf{f}) \qquad \text{for some} \quad \mu \in [0, 1]. \tag{6.212}$$

In case (ii) we have immediately‡

$$\mu\mathbf{a} + (1 - \mu)\mathbf{b} \in \operatorname{int} \operatorname{co} L(\mathbf{f}) \qquad \text{for all} \quad \mu \in (0, 1) \tag{6.213}$$

which, by Lemma 2, implies that

$$\mu\mathbf{a} + (1 - \mu)\mathbf{b} \in L(\mathbf{f}) \qquad \text{for all} \quad \mu \in (0, 1) \tag{6.214}$$

and hence proves Lemma 3 for case (ii).

In case (i) there exists a supporting hyperplane to the convex set $\operatorname{co} L(\mathbf{f})$ passing through the point $\frac{1}{2}\mathbf{a} + \frac{1}{2}\mathbf{b}$. Let $\mathbf{p}$ be a nonzero outward normal to this supporting hyperplane. We have immediately§

$$\mathbf{p} \cdot \mathbf{a} = \mathbf{p} \cdot \mathbf{b} = \mathbf{p} \cdot (\mu\mathbf{a} + (1 - \mu)\mathbf{b}) \tag{6.215}$$

for all $\mu \in [0, 1]$ and

$$\mathbf{p} \cdot \mathbf{a} \geq \mathbf{p} \cdot \mathbf{x} \qquad \text{for all} \quad \mathbf{x} \in \operatorname{co} L(\mathbf{f}) \tag{6.216}$$

We shall consider the sets

$$\tilde{L} = \left\{\int_D \mathbf{f}(t)\, dt : D \in \mathscr{A}, \quad D \subset (A \,\Delta B)\right\} \tag{6.217}$$

and

$$L^* = \left\{\int_{A \cap B} \mathbf{f}(t)\, dt + \mathbf{x} : \mathbf{x} \in \tilde{L}\right\} \tag{6.218}$$

† If A is a subset of E^n then ∂A denotes the set of boundary points of A. We recall that a point $\mathbf{a}$ is a boundary point of the set A if for every $\varepsilon > 0$ there is a $\mathbf{b} \in A$ and a $\mathbf{c} \notin A$ with $\mathbf{a} - \mathbf{b}|$ and $|\mathbf{a} - \mathbf{c}| < \varepsilon$.

‡ Suppose that there is a $\mu \in [0, 1]$ such that $\bar{\mu}\mathbf{a} + (1 - \bar{\mu})\mathbf{b} \in \operatorname{int} \operatorname{co} L(\mathbf{f})$. This implies that there is an $\bar{\varepsilon} > 0$ such that $N(\bar{\mu}\mathbf{a} + (1 - \bar{\mu})\mathbf{b}, \bar{\varepsilon}) \subset \operatorname{int} \operatorname{co} L(\mathbf{f})$. Then for all $\mu \in (0, 1)$ the point $\mu\mathbf{a} + (1 - \mu)\mathbf{b}$ belongs to the interior of the convex hull of the set $N(\bar{\mu}\mathbf{a} + (1 - \bar{\mu})\mathbf{b}, \bar{\varepsilon}) \cup \{\mathbf{a}\} \cup \{\mathbf{b}\}$ and *a fortiori* to the set $\operatorname{int} \operatorname{co} L(\mathbf{f})$. We recall that $\{\mathbf{a}\}$ denotes the set having a single element $\mathbf{a}$.

§ We denote by $\mathbf{p} \cdot \mathbf{a}$ the scalar product of the two vectors $\mathbf{p}$ and $\mathbf{a}$.

We have immediately $\mathbf{a}$ and $\mathbf{b} \in L^*$ and $L^* \subset L(\mathbf{f})$. We conclude by proving that the set L^* is convex or equivalently by proving that the set $\tilde{L}$ is convex.

We shall prove that for every $\mathbf{x} \in \tilde{L}$ we have $\mathbf{p} \cdot \mathbf{x} = 0$ which implies that the set $\tilde{L}$ has at most dimension v and hence is convex by the induction hypothesis.

Indeed, if there is an $\mathbf{x}^+ \in \tilde{L}$ with $\mathbf{p} \cdot \mathbf{x}^+ < 0$ let $D^+ \in \mathscr{A}$ such that $D^+ \subset (A^+ \Delta B)$ and $\int_{D^+} \mathbf{f}(t)\, dt = \mathbf{x}^+$. Let $\mathbf{x}_A{}^+ = \int_{D^+ \cap (A \sim B)} \mathbf{f}(t)\, dt$ and $\mathbf{x}_B{}^+ = \int_{D^+ \cap (B \sim A)} \mathbf{f}(t)\, dt$. We have then $\mathbf{x}_A{}^+ + \mathbf{x}_B{}^+ = \mathbf{x}^+$. We cannot have $\mathbf{p} \cdot \mathbf{x}_A{}^+ \geq 0$ and $\mathbf{p} \cdot \mathbf{x}_B{}^+ \geq 0$ because this would imply $\mathbf{p} \cdot \mathbf{x}^+ \geq 0$. Let us assume that $\mathbf{p} \cdot \mathbf{x}_A{}^+ < 0$ (a similar proof can be made for the case $\mathbf{p} \cdot \mathbf{x}_B{}^+ < 0$.). Let $\mathbf{x}^* = \int_{A \sim (D^+ \cap (A \sim B))} \mathbf{f}(t)\, dt$. We have then $\mathbf{x}^* \in L(\mathbf{f})$ and $\mathbf{a} = \mathbf{x}^* + \mathbf{x}_A{}^+$. We obtain then the contradiction $\mathbf{p} \cdot \mathbf{a} < \mathbf{p} \cdot \mathbf{x}^*$.

Similarly, if there is an $\mathbf{x}^+ \in \tilde{L}$ with $\mathbf{p} \cdot \mathbf{x}^+ > 0$ we define D^+, $\mathbf{x}_A{}^+$ and $\mathbf{x}_B{}^+$ as above. We cannot have $\mathbf{p} \cdot \mathbf{x}_A{}^+ \leq 0$ and $\mathbf{p} \cdot \mathbf{x}_B{}^+ \leq 0$ because this would imply $\mathbf{p} \cdot \mathbf{x}^+ \leq 0$. Let us assume that $\mathbf{p} \cdot \mathbf{x}_A{}^+ > 0$ (a similar proof can be made for the case $\mathbf{p} \cdot \mathbf{x}_B{}^+ > 0$). Let $\mathbf{x}^* = \int_{B \cup (D^+ \cap (A \sim B))} \mathbf{f}(t)\, dt$. We have then $\mathbf{x}^* \in L(\mathbf{f})$ and $\mathbf{x}^* = \mathbf{b} + \mathbf{x}_A{}^+$. We obtain then the contradiction $\mathbf{p} \cdot \mathbf{x}^* > \mathbf{p} \cdot \mathbf{b}$. This concludes the proof of Lemma 3.

6.11 Proof of the Fundamental Lemma

6.111 Proof of the Fundamental Lemma in the Case $r = n - 1$

In Sec. 6.7 we have stated the following result:

Fundamental Lemma. *If there is no hyperplane separating the convex sets S^+ and $\tilde{W}$ then the sets S^+ and W have at least one point in common.*

We recall the definition of the sets S^+, $\tilde{W}$, and W:

$$S^+ = \{\mathbf{x} : \mathbf{x} \in S,\, x_n > x_n(1\,; \mathscr{V})\} \tag{6.219}$$

$$\tilde{W} = \{\mathbf{x}(1\,; \mathscr{V}) + \mathbf{z}(1\,; \mathscr{U}) : \mathscr{U} \in F\} \tag{6.220}$$

$$W = \{\mathbf{x}(1\,; \mathscr{V}) + \mathbf{y}(1\,; \mathscr{U}) : \mathscr{U} \in F\} \tag{6.221}$$

It is convenient to introduce three new sets $S_*{}^+$, $\tilde{W}_*$, and W_* by the relations

$$S_*{}^+ = \{\mathbf{x} : \mathbf{x} + \mathbf{x}(1\,; \mathscr{V}) \in S^+\} \tag{6.222}$$

$$\tilde{W}_* = \{\mathbf{x} : \mathbf{x} + \mathbf{x}(1\,; \mathscr{V}) \in \tilde{W}\} \tag{6.223}$$

$$W_* = \{\mathbf{x} : \mathbf{x} + \mathbf{x}(1\,; \mathscr{V}) \in W\} \tag{6.224}$$

In other words, the sets S_*^+, $\tilde{W}_*$, and W_* are respective translations of the sets S^+, $\tilde{W}$, and W along the vector $\mathbf{x}(1; \mathscr{V})$. The sets S_*^+, $\tilde{W}_*$, and W_* can be equivalently expressed as follows:

$$S_*^+ = \{\mathbf{x} : x_i = 0 \quad \text{for} \quad i = 1, \ldots, r \quad \text{and} \quad x_n > 0\} \tag{6.225}$$

$$\tilde{W}_* = \{\mathbf{z}(1; \mathscr{U}) : \mathscr{U} \in F\} \tag{6.226}$$

$$W_* = \{\mathbf{y}(1; \mathscr{U}) : \mathscr{U} \in F\} \tag{6.227}$$

The fundamental lemma stated above is then equivalent to the following result:

Modified Fundamental Lemma. *If there is no hyperplane separating the convex sets S_*^+ and $\tilde{W}_*$ then the sets S_*^+ and W_* have at least one point in common.*

We shall first prove the modified fundamental lemma in the case $r = n - 1$. In a later paragraph we shall show how this proof can be extended to the general case. The proof given here is of some interest even when $r < n - 1$ since it is sufficient in order to prove the maximum principle without the transversality condition.

In the case $r = n - 1$ the set S_*^+ is of the form

$$S_*^+ = \{(0, 0, \ldots, 0, \alpha) : \alpha > 0\} \tag{6.228}$$

If there is no hyperplane separating the convex sets S_*^+ and $\tilde{W}_*$ then† there is an $\alpha_* > 0$ such that $x_* = (0, 0, \ldots, 0, \alpha_*) \in \text{int } \tilde{W}_*$. Hence, there is an $\eta > 0$ and a subset $\{\mathbf{e}_1, \mathbf{e}_2, \ldots, \mathbf{e}_n\}$ of $\tilde{W}_*$ such that $N(\mathbf{x}_*, \eta) \subset A = \text{co}\,\{\mathbf{0}, \mathbf{e}_1, \mathbf{e}_2, \ldots, \mathbf{e}_n\}$. Let

$$\Lambda = \left\{\boldsymbol{\lambda} : \boldsymbol{\lambda} \in E^n, \lambda_i \geq 0, \sum_{i=1}^{n} \lambda_i \leq 1\right\}.$$

For every $\mathbf{x} \in A$ there is a unique $\boldsymbol{\lambda}(\mathbf{x}) \in \Lambda$ such that

$$\mathbf{x} = \sum_{i=1}^{n} \lambda_i(\mathbf{x})\mathbf{e}_i \tag{6.229}$$

For every $\boldsymbol{\lambda} \in \Lambda$ there is a unique $\mathbf{x}(\boldsymbol{\lambda}) \in A$ such that

$$\mathbf{x}(\boldsymbol{\lambda}) = \sum_{i=1}^{n} \lambda_i \mathbf{e}_i \tag{6.230}$$

and there is a $L < +\infty$ such that

$$|\mathbf{x}(\boldsymbol{\lambda}') - \mathbf{x}(\mathbf{y}'')| \leq L\,|\boldsymbol{\lambda}' - \boldsymbol{\lambda}''| \quad \text{for all} \quad \boldsymbol{\lambda}' \quad \text{and} \quad \boldsymbol{\lambda}'' \in \Lambda \tag{6.231}$$

and

$$|\boldsymbol{\lambda}(\mathbf{x}') - \boldsymbol{\lambda}(\mathbf{x}'')| \leq L\,|\mathbf{x}' - \mathbf{x}''| \quad \text{for all} \quad \mathbf{x}' \quad \text{and} \quad \mathbf{x}'' \in A \tag{6.232}$$

† For a proof of that statement see Appendix B.

Let ε and γ be two positive numbers smaller than one such that

$$KL^2(\alpha_* + \eta)^2\gamma^2 + 2n\varepsilon \le \gamma\eta/2 \tag{6.233}$$

where K is the quantity introduced in Sec. 6.9. The reason for introducing ε and γ in the given form will become clear at the end of the proof.

For every $i = 1, 2, \ldots, n$ there is a control function $\mathscr{U}_i$ in the class F such that

$$\mathbf{e}_i = \mathbf{z}(1; \mathscr{U}_i) \tag{6.234}$$

We know also that

$$\mathbf{z}(1; \mathscr{U}_i) = \int_0^1 G(t)\boldsymbol{\varphi}(\mathbf{u}_i(t), t)\, dt \tag{6.235}$$

From the results of Sec. 6.10 we know that there is an integer k_i such that

$$\left|\alpha\mathbf{z}(1; \mathscr{U}_i) - \int_{D_\alpha{}^k} G(t)\,\boldsymbol{\varphi}(\mathbf{u}_i(t), t)\, dt\right| \le \varepsilon$$
$$\text{for all} \quad \alpha \in [0, 1] \quad \text{and all} \quad k \ge k_i \tag{6.236}$$

where

$$D = \bigcup_{i=1}^{2^k} \left[\frac{i-1}{2^k}, \frac{i-1+\alpha}{2^k}\right) \tag{6.237}$$

Let $\nu = \max_{i=1,\ldots,n} k_i$. For every $\mathbf{x} \in A$ and every $i = 1, 2, \ldots, n$, let

$$\alpha_i(\mathbf{x}) = \sum_{j=1}^{i-1} \lambda_i(\mathbf{x}) \tag{6.238}$$

$$M_i(\mathbf{x}) = D^\nu_{\alpha i+1(x)} \sim D^\nu_{\alpha i(x)} \tag{6.239}$$

and

$$M(\mathbf{x}) = \bigcup_{i=1}^{n} M_i(\mathbf{x}) \tag{6.240}$$

We have then

$$\mu(M(\mathbf{x})) = |\boldsymbol{\lambda}(\mathbf{x})| \tag{6.241}$$

For every $\mathbf{x} \in A$ let $\mathscr{U}_\mathbf{x}$ be a control function defined as follows:

$$\mathbf{u}_\mathbf{x}(t) = \mathbf{u}_i(t) \qquad \text{if} \quad t \in M_i(\mathbf{x}) \qquad \text{for some} \quad i = 1, \ldots, n$$
$$\mathbf{u}_\mathbf{x}(t) = \mathbf{v}(t) \qquad \text{otherwise}$$

The function $\mathscr{U}_\mathbf{x}$ is well defined since for every $\mathbf{x} \in A$ the sets $M_i(\mathbf{x})$ are disjoint. It follows then that $\mathscr{U}_\mathbf{x}$ is an admissible control function in the class F.

From the results of Sec. 6.9 we have then

$$|\mathbf{z}(1\,;\mathscr{U}_{\mathbf{x}}) - \mathbf{y}(1\,;\mathscr{U}_{\mathbf{x}})| \leq K(\mu(M(\mathbf{x})))^2 \tag{6.242}$$

i.e.,

$$|\mathbf{z}(1\,;\mathscr{U}_{\mathbf{x}}) - \mathbf{y}(1\,;\mathscr{U}_{\mathbf{x}})| \leq K\,|\boldsymbol{\lambda}(\mathbf{x})|^2 \leq KL^2\,|\mathbf{x}|^2 \tag{6.243}$$

It is a trivial matter† to verify that

$$|\mathbf{z}(1\,;\mathscr{U}_{\mathbf{x}}) - \mathbf{x}| \leq 2n\varepsilon \tag{6.244}$$

From the relations (6.241) and (6.242) it follows that

$$|\mathbf{x} - \mathbf{y}(1\,;\mathscr{U}_{\mathbf{x}})| \leq KL^2\,|\mathbf{x}|^2 + 2n\varepsilon \tag{6.245}$$

We define a set A^* by the following relation

$$A^* = \{\gamma\mathbf{x} : \mathbf{x} \in N(\mathbf{x}_*, \eta)\} \tag{6.246}$$

Since $N(\mathbf{x}_*, \eta) \subset A$, $\gamma \leq 1$ and A is the convex hull of a set containing the origin we have immediately $A^* \subset A$. We define a function $\mathbf{h}(\mathbf{x})$ on the set A^* by the relation

$$\mathbf{h}(\mathbf{x}) = \mathbf{x} - \mathbf{y}(1\,;\mathscr{U}_{\mathbf{x}}) + \gamma\mathbf{x}_* \tag{6.247}$$

From the results of Sec. 6.8 and the preceding definitions it follows that $\mathbf{y}(1\,;\mathscr{U}_{\mathbf{x}})$ is a continuous function of $\mathbf{x}$ over A^*. This implies that the function

† Indeed, we have

$$\mathbf{z}(1\,;\mathscr{U}_{\mathbf{x}}) - \mathbf{x}| = \left|\mathbf{z}(1\,;\mathscr{U}_{\mathbf{x}}) - \sum_{i=1}^{n} \lambda_i(\mathbf{x})\mathbf{z}(1\,;\mathscr{U}_i)\right|$$

and

$$\mathbf{z}(1\,;\mathscr{U}_{\mathbf{x}}) = \int_0^1 G(t)\boldsymbol{\varphi}(\mathbf{u}_{\mathbf{x}}(t), t)\,dt = \sum_{i=1}^{n} \int_{M_i(\mathbf{x})} G(t)\boldsymbol{\varphi}(\mathbf{u}_i(t), t)\,dt$$

We have then

$$|\mathbf{z}(1\,;\mathscr{U}_{\mathbf{x}}) - \mathbf{x}| \leq \left|\sum_{i=1} \int_{M_i(\mathbf{x})} G(t)\boldsymbol{\varphi}(\mathbf{u}_i(t), t)\,dt - \sum_{i=1}^{n} \lambda_i(\mathbf{x})\mathbf{z}(1\,;\mathscr{U}_i)\right|$$

$$\leq \sum_{i=1}^{n} \left|\int_{M_i(\mathbf{x})} G(t)\boldsymbol{\varphi}(\mathbf{u}_i(t), t)\,dt - \lambda_i(\mathbf{x})\mathbf{z}(1\,;\mathscr{U}_i)\right|$$

$$\leq \sum_{i=1}^{n} \left|\int_{D^{\nu}_{\alpha_{i+1}(\mathbf{x})}} G(t)\boldsymbol{\varphi}(\mathbf{u}_i(t), t)\,dt - \alpha_{i+1}(\mathbf{x})\mathbf{z}(1\,;\mathscr{U}_i)\right|$$

$$\leq \sum_{i=1}^{n} \left|\int_{D^{\nu}_{\alpha_i(\mathbf{x})}} G(t)\boldsymbol{\varphi}(\mathbf{u}_i(t), t)\,dt - \alpha_i(\mathbf{x})\mathbf{z}(1\,;\mathscr{U}_i)\right| \leq 2n\varepsilon$$

The last inequality implies then relation (6.244).

$\mathbf{h}(\mathbf{x})$ is also continuous with respect to $\mathbf{x}$ over A^*. We shall prove that the function $\mathbf{h}(\mathbf{x})$ maps the set A^* into itself.†

We have indeed

$$|\mathbf{h}(\mathbf{x}) - \gamma \mathbf{x}_*| \leq |\mathbf{x} - \mathbf{y}(1; \mathscr{U}_\mathbf{x})| \leq KL^2 |\mathbf{x}|^2 + 2\eta\varepsilon$$
$$\leq KL^2(\alpha_* + \eta)^2\gamma^2 + 2\eta\varepsilon \qquad \text{for all} \quad \mathbf{x} \in A^* \tag{6.248}$$

i.e., using finally relation (6.233)

$$|\mathbf{h}(\mathbf{x}) - \gamma x_*| \leq \gamma\eta/2 \tag{6.249}$$

which proves that $\mathbf{h}(\mathbf{x})$ maps the set S^* into itself. From Brouwer's fixed point theorem‡ it follows that there is an $\tilde{\mathbf{x}} \in A^*$ such that $\mathbf{h}(\tilde{\mathbf{x}}) = \tilde{\mathbf{x}}$ i.e., such that

$$\mathbf{y}(1; \mathscr{U}_\mathbf{x}) = \gamma \mathbf{x}_* \tag{6.250}$$

We have $\mathbf{y}(1; \mathscr{U}\tilde{\mathbf{x}}) \in W_*$ and $\gamma \mathbf{x}_* \in S_*{}^+$. This concludes the proof of the fundamental lemma in the case $r = n - 1$.

6.112 Extension of the Preceding Proof to the General Case

Let $S_\pi{}^+$, $\tilde{W}_\pi$, and W_π be the projection§ of the sets $S_*{}^+$, $\tilde{W}_*$, and W_* on the $(r + 1)$-dimensional Euclidean space E^{r+1} obtained by taking the dimensions $1, 2, \ldots, r$ and n of the original Euclidean space E^n. To prove the modified fundamental lemma in the general case it is sufficient to prove that:

Proposition 11.1. *If there is no hyperplane in E^{r+1} separating the convex sets $S_\pi{}^+$ and $\tilde{W}_\pi$ then the sets $S_\pi{}^+$ and W_π have at least one point in common.*

Let us prove that Proposition 11.1 implies the modified fundamental lemma in the general case. If there is no hyperplane in E^n separating the convex sets $S_*{}^+$ and $\tilde{W}_*$ then there is no hyperplane in E^{r+1} separating the convex sets $S_\pi{}^+$ and $\tilde{W}_\pi$. By Proposition 11.1 the last statement implies that the sets $S_\pi{}^+$ and W_π have at least one point $\mathbf{x}_\pi$ in common. There is some point $\mathbf{x}$ in W whose projection is $\mathbf{x}_\pi$. By definition of the set $S_*{}^+$ we know that $\mathbf{x}$ belongs also to $S_*{}^+$. This concludes the proof that Proposition 11.1 implies the modified fundamental lemma in the general case.

We note, finally, that Proposition 11.1 is identical with the modified fundamental lemma in the case $r = n - 1$.

† This means that for all $\mathbf{x} \in A^*$ we have $\mathbf{h}(\mathbf{x}) \in A^*$.

‡ The fixed point theorem is the only nonelementary mathematical result quoted without proof in the present chapter. This theorem states that if a continuous function maps a closed convex subset of an Euclidean space E^n into itself then it has a fixed point. In other words, if $\mathbf{f}$ is a continuous function defined and continuous on the closed convex set A such that $\mathbf{f}(\mathbf{x}) \in A$ for all $\mathbf{x} \in A$ then there is an $\tilde{\mathbf{x}} \in A$ such that $\mathbf{f}(\tilde{\mathbf{x}}) = \tilde{\mathbf{x}}$. The proof of the fixed point theorem can be found in most textbooks of topology.

§ This elegant procedure is due to Warga.[48]

6.12 An Intuitive Approach to the Maximum Principle

We shall conclude this chapter by a heuristic and intuitive description of the maximum principle. For every control function $\mathbf{u}(t)$ in the class F we have defined a trajectory and a matrix $G(t)$ along that trajectory. The basic property of the matrix $G(t)$ is that: a little variation $d\mathbf{x}$ of the state vector at the time t produces a little shift $G^{-1}(t)\, d\mathbf{x}$ of the state vector at the terminal time. One possible way to create at the time t a little variation $d\mathbf{x}$ of the state vector is to replace the control function $\mathbf{u}(t)$ for a time dt by some other admissible control vector $\mathbf{v}$. An optimal trajectory is characterized by the fact that it is impossible to find an admissible variation which will produce a shift of the terminal state vector in a defined direction (or group of defined directions) which we call "interesting" directions.

Since different shifts of the terminal state vector can be added linearly, we must also require that all possible shifts of the terminal state vector be located on one side of a certain hyperplane. Otherwise we could combine different "uninteresting" shifts to make a shift in an "interesting" direction. This terminal hyperplane is transformed by the matrix $G(t)$ into a corresponding hyperplane $\pi(t)$ at each time t. We must then require that at each time t all possible variations be on one side of this hyperplane $\pi(t)$. This is the maximum principle.

APPENDIX A
SOME RESULTS FROM THE THEORY OF ORDINARY DIFFERENTIAL EQUATIONS

In this appendix we shall state and prove some results from the theory of ordinary differential equations which are of particular interest in the study of optimization problems.

We consider a differential equation

$$\dot{\mathbf{x}} = \mathbf{f}(\mathbf{x}, t) \tag{6.251}$$

where the state variable $\mathbf{x} = (x_1, x_2, \ldots, x_n)$ is an element of an n-dimensional Euclidean space E^n, where the time t is an element of the closed interval† $[0, 1]$ and where the n-dimensional vector valued function $\mathbf{f}(\mathbf{x}, t) = (f_1(\mathbf{x}, t), f_2(\mathbf{x}, t), \ldots, f_n(\mathbf{x}, t))$ is given.

† If a and b are real numbers with $a \leq b$ we denote by $[a, b]$ the closed interval from a to b, i.e., the set of all real numbers t such that $a \leq t \leq b$. Similarly, we denote by (a, b) the open interval from a to b, i.e., the set of all real numbers t such that $a < t < b$.

We assume that the vector valued function $\mathbf{f}(\mathbf{x}, t)$ is defined for all† $\mathbf{x} \in E^n$ and all $t \in [0, 1]$, continuously differentiable with respect to $\mathbf{x}$ and piecewise continuous with respect to t. More precisely, we assume that there exists a finite set‡ $\{t_0, t_1, \dots, t_k\} \subset [0, 1]$ with $t_0 = 0 < t_1 \cdots < t_k = 1$, and a finite collection of vector valued functions $\{f_1(\mathbf{x}, t), \mathbf{f}_2(\mathbf{x}, t), \dots, \mathbf{f}_k(\mathbf{x}, t)\}$ such that for each $i = 1, 2, \dots, k$,

(i) the vector valued function $\mathbf{f}_i(\mathbf{x}, t)$ and all its first partial derivatives with respect to $\mathbf{x}$ are defined and continuous with respect to $\mathbf{x}$ and t for all $\mathbf{x} \in E^n$ and all $t \in [t_{i-1}, t_i]$;

(ii) $\mathbf{f}(\mathbf{x}, t) = \mathbf{f}_i(\mathbf{x}, t)$ for all $\mathbf{x} \in E^n$ and all $t \in (t_{i-1}, t_i)$.

Moreover, we shall assume that there is a positive real number $M < +\infty$ such that

$$\frac{|\mathbf{f}(\mathbf{x}, t)|}{1 + |\mathbf{x}|} \leq M \tag{6.252}$$

for all $\mathbf{x} \in E^n$ and all $t \in [0, 1]$. In the previous expression $|\mathbf{x}|$ stands for the Euclidean length of the vector $\mathbf{x}$, i.e.,

$$|\mathbf{x}| = \left(\sum_{i=1}^{n} (x_i)^2 \right)^{1/2} \tag{6.253}$$

Similarly,

$$|\mathbf{f}(\mathbf{x}, t)| = \left(\sum_{i=1}^{n} (f_i(\mathbf{x}, t))^2 \right)^{1/2} \tag{6.254}$$

Let Θ be the set§ $[0, 1] \sim \{t_0, t_1, \dots, t_k\}$.

Let $\bar{\mathbf{x}} \in E^n$ and $\bar{t} \in [0, 1]$. A solution of the Eq. 6.251 with the boundary condition $\mathbf{x} = \bar{\mathbf{x}}$ at $t = \bar{t}$ is a vector valued function $\boldsymbol{\varphi}(t : \bar{t}, \bar{\mathbf{x}})$ which satisfies the following conditions:

(i) $\boldsymbol{\varphi}(t; \bar{t}, \bar{\mathbf{x}})$ is continuous with respect to t over $[0, 1]$;

(ii) $\boldsymbol{\varphi}(t; \bar{t}, \bar{\mathbf{x}})$ is differentiable with respect to t over Θ;

(iii) $\dfrac{d}{dt} \boldsymbol{\varphi}(t; \bar{t}, \bar{\mathbf{x}}) = \mathbf{f}(\boldsymbol{\varphi}(t; \bar{t}, \bar{\mathbf{x}}), t)$ for all $t \in \Theta$;

(iv) $\boldsymbol{\varphi}(\bar{t}; \bar{t}, \bar{\mathbf{x}}) = \bar{\mathbf{x}}$.

We have then the following results:

Theorem 1. *For every $\bar{\mathbf{x}} \in E^n$ and every $\bar{t} \in [0, 1]$ there exists one and only one solution $\boldsymbol{\varphi}(t; \bar{t}, \bar{\mathbf{x}})$ with the boundary condition $\mathbf{x} = \bar{\mathbf{x}}$ at $t = \bar{t}$.*

† If A is a set then "$a \in A$" means "a is an element of A" and "$B \subset A$" means "B is a subset of A."

‡ The set denoted by $\{t_0, t_1, \dots, t_k\}$ is the set whose elements are $t_0, t_1, \dots$, and t_k.

§ If A and B are sets then $A \sim B$ is the set of all points in A which are not in B.

Theorem 2. *For every t and $\bar{t} \in [0, 1]$ the function $\boldsymbol{\varphi}(t; \bar{t}, \bar{\mathbf{x}})$ is continuously differentiable with respect to $\bar{\mathbf{x}}$.*

With the help of these two classical† theorems we shall prove some results which are very useful in the theory of optimization.

Proposition A.1.‡ *Suppose that $f(t)$ is a real-valued continuous and piecewise-differentiable function defined over $[0, 1]$, that $g(t)$ is a real-valued piecewise-continuous function defined over $[0, 1]$, and that L is a constant. We assume, moreover, that the following relation holds for all $t \in [0, 1]$ for which $f(t)$ is differentiable and $g(t)$ is continuous*

$$\dot{f}(t) \leq Lf(t) + g(t) \tag{6.255}$$

Then the following relation holds for all $t \in [0, 1]$

$$f(t) \leq e^{Lt}\left(f(0) + \int_0^t e^{-L\tau} g(\tau)\, d\tau\right) \tag{6.256}$$

PROOF. Let us denote by Θ the set of points t in $[0, 1]$ for which the function $f(t)$ is differentiable and the function $g(t)$ is continuous. We define a function $h(t)$ over the interval $[0, 1]$ as the continuous solution of the differential equation

$$\dot{h}(t) = Lh(t) + g(t) \qquad \text{for all} \quad t \in \Theta \tag{6.257}$$

with the initial condition

$$h(0) = f(0) \tag{6.258}$$

From Theorem 1 stated above we know that the function $h(t)$ exists and is unique. Moreover, we can easily verify that the function $h(t)$ has the following form

$$h(t) = e^{+Lt}\left(f(0) + \int_0^t e^{-L\tau} g(\tau)\, d\tau\right) \tag{6.259}$$

It remains to prove that for all $t \in [0, 1]$ we have

$$f(t) \leq h(t) \tag{6.260}$$

Let us consider the family of solutions of the differential equation (6.257) corresponding to varying initial conditions at $t = 0$. For increasing t the

† The proof of these two theorems can be found in any good text book on ordinary differential equations such as Coddington and Levinson's "Theory of Ordinary Differential Equations." McGraw-Hill, New York, 1955.

‡ Generalized Gronwall's inequality.

differential inequality (6.255) prevents the function $f(t)$ from crossing upward the family of solutions of the differential equality (6.257). Hence, the function $f(t)$ is always on or below the curve $h(t)$ passing through $f(0)$ at $t = 0$ and we obtain the inequality (6.260).

To the geometrical ideas stated above corresponds the following analytical proof. The previous argument is based entirely on the concept of relative motion of the point $f(t)$ with respect to the family of solutions

$$e^{Lt}\left(h_0 + \int_0^t e^{-L\tau}\, g(\tau)\, d\tau\right) \tag{6.261}$$

of the differential equation (6.257) for varying initial condition h_0 at time 0. This relative motion of the point $f(t)$ with respect to the family of solutions (6.261) is best described by introducing a function $k(t)$ in the following manner: $k(t)$ is the value at time 0 of the particular solution (6.261) which has the value $f(t)$ at time t. In other words, we define the function $k(t)$ by the relation

$$e^{Lt}\left(k(t) + \int_0^t e^{-L\tau}\, g(\tau)\, d\tau\right) = f(t) \tag{6.262}$$

which gives immediately

$$k(t) = e^{-Lt} f(t) - \int_0^t e^{-L\tau}\, g(\tau)\, d\tau \tag{6.263}$$

and

$$k(t) = e^{-Lt}(f(t) - h(t)) \tag{6.264}$$

We conclude this analytical proof by showing that

$$k(t) \leq 0 \qquad \text{implies} \qquad f(t) \leq h(t) \tag{6.265}$$

and

$$k(t) \leq 0 \qquad \text{for all} \quad t \in [0, 1] \tag{6.266}$$

The relation (6.265) follows immediately from relation (6.264). Let us now consider relation (6.266). From relation (6.263) we know that the function $k(t)$ is continuous over [0, 1] and we have immediately

$$k(0) = 0 \tag{6.267}$$

and

$$\begin{aligned} \dot{k}(t) &= -Le^{-Lt}f(t) + e^{-Lt}\dot{f}(t) - e^{-Lt}g(t) \\ &\leq -Le^{-Lt}f(t) + e^{-Lt}(Lf(t) + g(t)) - e^{-Lt}g(t) = 0 \end{aligned} \tag{6.268}$$

for all $t \in \Theta$. The relation (6.266) is then satisfied. This concludes the proof of Proposition A.1.

Proposition A.2. *For every* $\mathbf{x}_1 \in E^n$ *and every* t_1, t_2, *and* $t_3 \in [0, 1]$ *we have the identity*

$$\boldsymbol{\varphi}(t_3\,;\,t_2\,,\,\boldsymbol{\varphi}(t_2\,;\,t_1,\,\mathbf{x}_1)) = \boldsymbol{\varphi}(t_3\,;\,t_1,\,\mathbf{x}_1) \tag{6.269}$$

PROOF. This proposition could be colloquially expressed as follows: if we integrate the system (6.251) from the state $\mathbf{x}_1$ at the time t_1 to the time t_2 and then integrate the system (6.251) from the new state $\boldsymbol{\varphi}(t_2\,;\,t_1,\,\mathbf{x}_1)$ at the time t_2 to the time t_3, we obtain a final state identical to the state which we would have obtained by integrating directly the system (6.251) from the state $\mathbf{x}_1$ at the time t_1 to the time t_3. The proof of this proposition is a direct consequence of Theorem 1. By definition we know that

(i) the functions $\boldsymbol{\varphi}(t;\,t_2\,,\,\boldsymbol{\varphi}(t_2\,;\,t_1,\,\mathbf{x}_1))$ and $\boldsymbol{\varphi}(t;\,t_1,\,\mathbf{x}_1)$ are both solutions of the system (6.251);

(ii) $\boldsymbol{\varphi}(t;\,t_2\,,\,\boldsymbol{\varphi}(t_2\,;\,t_1,\,\mathbf{x}_1)) = \boldsymbol{\varphi}(t;\,t_1,\,\mathbf{x}_1)$ for $t = t_2$.

Hence, from Theorem 1, we have

$$\boldsymbol{\varphi}(t;\,t_2\,,\,\boldsymbol{\varphi}(t_2\,;\,t_1,\,\mathbf{x}_1)) = \boldsymbol{\varphi}(t;\,t_1,\,\mathbf{x}_1) \qquad \text{for all} \quad t \in [0, 1]$$

and in particular,

$$\boldsymbol{\varphi}(t_3\,;\,t_2\,,\,\boldsymbol{\varphi}(t_2\,;\,t_1,\,\mathbf{x}_1)) = \boldsymbol{\varphi}(t_3\,;\,t_1,\,\mathbf{x}_1)$$

This concludes the proof of Proposition A.2.

Proposition A.3. *For every* $\bar{\mathbf{x}} \in E^n$ *and every* t *and* $\bar{t} \in [0, 1]$ *we have*

$$|\boldsymbol{\varphi}(t;\,t,\,\mathbf{x})| \leq (|\bar{\mathbf{x}}| + 1)\, e^{M|t-\bar{t}|}. \tag{6.270}$$

PROOF. Let $r(t) = |\boldsymbol{\varphi}(t;\,\bar{t},\,\bar{\mathbf{x}})|$. The function $r(t)$ is continuous over $[0, 1]$ and differentiable over Θ. For every $t \in \Theta$ we have immediately

$$r(t) \leq |\mathbf{f}(\boldsymbol{\psi}(t\,,\,\bar{t},\,\bar{\mathbf{x}}),\,t)| \tag{6.271}$$

From relation (6.252) we have

$$|\mathbf{f}(\boldsymbol{\varphi}(t;\,\bar{t},\,\bar{\mathbf{x}}),\,t)| \leq M(1 + |\boldsymbol{\varphi}(t;\,\bar{t},\,\bar{\mathbf{x}})|)$$

i.e.,

$$|\mathbf{f}(\boldsymbol{\varphi}(t;\,\bar{t},\,\bar{\mathbf{x}}),\,t)| \leq M(1 + r(t)) \tag{6.272}$$

We have then

$$\dot{r}(t) \leq M(1 + r(t))$$

and also

$$r(\bar{t}) = |\bar{\mathbf{x}}|$$

From Proposition (A.1) we obtain then

$$r(t) \leq (|\bar{\mathbf{x}}| + 1)\, e^{M(t-\bar{t})}. \qquad \text{for all} \quad t \in [\bar{t}, 1]$$

A similar argument would lead to the relation

$$r(t) \leq (|\bar{\mathbf{x}}| + 1)\, e^{M(\bar{t}-t)}. \qquad \text{for all} \quad t \in [0, \bar{t}]$$

By combining the last two relations we obtain the desired result:

$$r(t) \leq (|\mathbf{x}| + 1)\, e^{M|t-t|}. \qquad \text{for all} \quad t \in [0, 1] \tag{6.273}$$

This concludes the proof of Proposition A.3.

We shall denote by $K(t; \bar{t}, \bar{\mathbf{x}})$ the matrix whose (i, j) element is $\partial \varphi_i(t; \bar{t}, \bar{\mathbf{x}})/\partial \bar{\mathbf{x}}_j$ and by $D(t; \bar{t}, \bar{\mathbf{x}})$ the matrix whose (i, j) element is $\partial f_i(\mathbf{x}, t)/\partial \mathbf{x}_j|_{x=\varphi(t;\bar{t},\bar{\mathbf{x}})}$, i.e., the function $\partial f_i(\mathbf{x}, t)/\partial x_j$ evaluated at the point $\mathbf{x} = \varphi(t; \bar{t}, \bar{\mathbf{x}})$.

From Theorem 2 we know that for every t and $\bar{t} \in [0, 1]$ and every $\mathbf{x} \in E^n$ the matrix $K(t; \bar{t}, \mathbf{x})$ exists and is continuous with respect to $\bar{\mathbf{x}}$.

Proposition A.4. *The matrix $K(t; \bar{t}, \bar{\mathbf{x}})$ is continuous with respect to t over* [0, 1], *differentiable with respect to t over Θ and satisfies the following matrix differential equation*†

$$\dot{K}(t; t, \mathbf{x}) = D(t; \bar{t}, \bar{\mathbf{x}})\, K(t; \bar{t}, \bar{\mathbf{x}}) \qquad \text{for all} \quad t \in \Theta \tag{6.274}$$

with the boundary condition

$$K(\bar{t}; \bar{t}, \bar{\mathbf{x}}) = I \tag{6.275}$$

where I is the $n \times n$ identity matrix.

Proof. The boundary condition (6.275) is immediately satisfied. From the definition of $\varphi(t; \bar{t}, \bar{\mathbf{x}})$ we have immediately

$$\varphi(t; \bar{t}, \bar{\mathbf{x}}) = \bar{\mathbf{x}} + \int_{\bar{t}}^{t} \mathbf{f}(\varphi(\tau; \bar{t}, \bar{\mathbf{x}}), \tau)\, d\tau \qquad \text{for all} \quad t \in [0, 1] \tag{6.276}$$

We may take the partial derivative with respect to $\mathbf{x}$ of both sides of relation (6.276). This operation is justified by Theorem 2 and by our assumptions concerning the function $\mathbf{f}(\mathbf{x}, t)$. We obtain

$$\frac{\partial \varphi(t; \bar{t}, \bar{\mathbf{x}})}{\partial \bar{\mathbf{x}}} = I + \int_{\bar{t}}^{t} \left(\left. \frac{\partial \mathbf{f}(\mathbf{x}, \tau)}{\partial \mathbf{x}} \right|_{\mathbf{x}=\varphi(\tau;\bar{t},\bar{\mathbf{x}})} \right) \frac{\partial \varphi(\tau; \bar{t}, \bar{\mathbf{x}})}{\partial \bar{x}}\, d\tau \qquad \text{for all} \quad t \in [0, 1] \tag{6.277}$$

† If we denote by $K_{ij}(t; \bar{t}, \bar{\mathbf{x}})$ the (i, j) element of the matrix $K(t; \bar{t}, \bar{\mathbf{x}})$ and by $D_{ij}(t; \bar{t}, \bar{\mathbf{x}})$ the (i, j) element of the matrix $D(t; \bar{t}, \bar{\mathbf{x}})$ then the relation (6.274) could be explicitly written as follows

$$\dot{K}_{ij}(t; \bar{t}, \bar{\mathbf{x}}) = \sum_{l=1}^{n} D_{il}(t; \bar{t}, \bar{\mathbf{x}}) K_{lj}(t; \bar{t}, \bar{\mathbf{x}})$$

for all $i = 1, 2, \ldots, n$, all $j = 1, 2, \ldots, n$, and all $t \in \Theta$.

i.e.,

$$K(t; \bar{t}, \bar{\mathbf{x}}) = I + \int_{\bar{t}}^{t} D(\tau; \bar{t}, \bar{\mathbf{x}}) K(\tau; \bar{t}, \bar{\mathbf{x}}) d\tau \quad \text{for all} \quad \tau \in [0, 1] \tag{6.278}$$

The elements of the matrix $D(t; \bar{t}, \bar{\mathbf{x}})$ are uniformly bounded for all $t \in [0, 1]$ and hence, from Theorem 1, the differential system (6.274) with boundary condition (6.275) admits a unique solution which must coincide with the solution given by relation (6.278).

This concludes the proof of Proposition A.4.

Proposition A.5. *The matrix* $K(t; \bar{t}, \bar{\mathbf{x}})$ *has an inverse* $K^{-1}(t; \bar{t}, \bar{\mathbf{x}})$ *which is continuous with respect to t over* $[0, 1]$, *differentiable with respect to t over* Θ *and satisfies the following matrix differentiable equation:*

$$\dot{K}^{-1}(t; \bar{t}, \bar{\mathbf{x}}) = -K^{-1}(t; \bar{t}, \bar{\mathbf{x}}) D(t; \bar{t}, \bar{\mathbf{x}}) \quad \text{for all} \quad t \in \Theta \tag{6.279}$$

with the boundary condition

$$K^{-1}(\bar{t}; \bar{t}, \bar{\mathbf{x}}) = I \tag{6.280}$$

where I is the $n \times n$ *identity matrix.*

PROOF. The differential system (6.279) with the boundary condition (6.280) has a unique solution $K^{-1}(t; \bar{t}, \bar{\mathbf{x}})$. It remains to prove that

$$K^{-1}(t; \bar{t}, \bar{\mathbf{x}}) K(t; \bar{t}, \bar{\mathbf{x}}) = I \tag{6.281}$$

for all $t \in [0, 1]$. Indeed we have

$$K^{-1}(\bar{t}, \bar{t}, \bar{\mathbf{x}}) K(\bar{t}; \bar{t}, \bar{\mathbf{x}}) = I \tag{6.282}$$

and

$$\frac{d}{dt}(K^{-1}(t; t, \mathbf{x}) K(t; t, \mathbf{x})) = 0 \qquad \text{for all} \quad t \in \Theta \tag{6.283}$$

since

$$\begin{aligned} &\dot{K}^{-1}(t; \bar{t}, \bar{\mathbf{x}}) K(t; \bar{t}, \bar{\mathbf{x}}) + K^{-1}(t; \bar{t}, \bar{\mathbf{x}}) \dot{K}(t; \bar{t}, \bar{\mathbf{x}}) \\ &\quad = -K^{-1}(t; \bar{t}, \bar{\mathbf{x}}) D(t; t, \mathbf{x}) K(t; \bar{t}, \bar{\mathbf{x}}) \\ &\qquad + K^{-1}(t; \bar{t}, \bar{\mathbf{x}}) D(t; \bar{t}, \bar{\mathbf{x}}) K(t; \bar{t}, \bar{\mathbf{x}}) = 0 \end{aligned} \tag{6.284}$$

This concludes the proof of Proposition A.5.

Proposition A.6. *For every* $\mathbf{x}_1 \in E^n$ *and every* t_1, t_2, *and* $t_3 \in [0, 1]$ *we have*

$$K(t_3 ; t_2, \boldsymbol{\varphi}(t_2 ; t_1, \mathbf{x}_1))K(t_2 ; t_1, \mathbf{x}_1) = K(t_3 ; t_1, \mathbf{x}_1) \tag{6.285}$$

PROOF. Let us take the partial derivative with respect to $\mathbf{x}$ of the relation (6.260). This operation is justified by Theorem 2 and from the definition of the matrix $K(t; \bar{t}, \bar{\mathbf{x}})$ we obtain immediately relation (6.285). This concludes the proof of Proposition A.6.

In the particular case $t_3 = t_1$ the identity (6.285) becomes

$$K(t_1 ; t_2, \boldsymbol{\varphi}(t_2 ; t_1, \mathbf{x}_1)) = K^{-1}(t_2 ; t_1, \mathbf{x}_1) \tag{6.286}$$

Proposition A.7. *We assume that*

(i) $\mathbf{y}(t)$ *is a vector valued function, continuous over* $[0, 1]$, *differentiable over* Θ, *and such that*

$$(\alpha) \qquad \dot{\mathbf{y}}(t) = D(t; \bar{t}, \bar{\mathbf{x}})\mathbf{y}(t) \qquad \text{for all} \quad t \in \Theta \tag{6.287}$$

$$(\beta) \qquad \mathbf{y}(\bar{t}) = \bar{\mathbf{y}} \tag{6.288}$$

(ii) $\mathbf{p}(t)$ *is a vector valued function continuous over* $[0, 1]$, *differentiable over* Θ, *and such that*†

$$(\alpha) \qquad \dot{\mathbf{p}}(t) = - D^T(t; \bar{t}, \bar{\mathbf{x}})\mathbf{p}(t) \qquad \text{for all} \quad t \in \Theta \tag{6.289}$$

$$(\beta) \qquad \mathbf{p}(\bar{t}) = \bar{\mathbf{p}} \tag{6.290}$$

Then

$$\text{(i)} \qquad \mathbf{y}(t) = K(t; \bar{t}, \bar{\mathbf{x}})\bar{\mathbf{y}} \qquad \text{for all} \quad t \in [0, 1] \tag{6.291}$$

$$\text{(ii)} \qquad \mathbf{p}(t) = (K^{-1}(t; \bar{t}, \bar{\mathbf{x}}))^T\bar{\mathbf{p}} \qquad \text{for all} \quad t \in [0, 1] \tag{6.292}$$

$$\text{(iii)} \qquad \mathbf{y}(t) \cdot \mathbf{p}(t) = \bar{\mathbf{y}} \cdot \bar{\mathbf{p}} \qquad \text{for all} \quad t \in [0, 1] \tag{6.293}$$

PROOF. The matrix $D(t; \bar{t}, \bar{\mathbf{x}})$ is uniformly bounded for $t \in [0, 1]$. Hence the vector valued functions $\mathbf{y}(t)$ and $\mathbf{p}(t)$ exist and are unique. It remains to verify that relations (6.287) and (6.288) hold for the function $\mathbf{y}(t)$ defined by relation (6.291) and that relations (6.289) and (6.290) hold for the function $\mathbf{p}(t)$ defined by relation (6.292). We note first that $K(\bar{t}; \bar{t}, \bar{\mathbf{x}}) = K^{-1}(\bar{t}; \bar{t}, \bar{\mathbf{x}}) = I$, and hence that relations (6.288) and (6.290) are verified. From relations (6.274) and (6.291) we obtain for all $t \in \Theta$

$$\begin{aligned} \dot{\mathbf{y}}(t) &= (\dot{K}t; \bar{t}, \bar{\mathbf{x}})\bar{\mathbf{y}} = D(t; \bar{t}, \bar{\mathbf{x}})K(t; \bar{t}, \bar{\mathbf{x}})\bar{\mathbf{y}} \\ &= D(t; \bar{t}, \bar{\mathbf{x}})\mathbf{y}(t) \end{aligned} \tag{6.294}$$

† The transpose of the matrix $D(t, \bar{t}, \bar{\mathbf{x}})$ is denoted $(D(t; \bar{t}, \bar{\mathbf{x}}))^T$ or more simply $D^T(t; \bar{t}, \bar{\mathbf{x}})$ when no confusion is possible. Accordingly, $(K^{-1}(t; \bar{t}, \bar{\mathbf{x}}))^T$ is the transpose of the matrix $K^{-1}(t; \bar{t}, \bar{\mathbf{x}})$.

and from relations (6.279) and (6.292) we obtain for all $t \in \Theta$

$$\mathbf{p}(t) = \frac{d}{dt}(K^{-1}(t; \bar{t}, \bar{\mathbf{x}}))^T\bar{\mathbf{p}} = (-K^{-1}(t; \bar{t}, \bar{\mathbf{x}})D(t; \bar{t}, \bar{\mathbf{x}}))^T\bar{\mathbf{p}}$$

$$= -D^T(t; \bar{t}, \bar{\mathbf{x}})(K^{-1}(t; \bar{t}, \bar{\mathbf{x}}))^T\bar{\mathbf{p}} = -D^T(t; \bar{t}, \bar{\mathbf{x}})\mathbf{p}(t) \qquad (6.295)$$

We have, finally, for all $t \in [0, 1]$

$$\mathbf{y}(t) \cdot \mathbf{p}(t) = (K(t; \bar{t}, \bar{\mathbf{x}})\bar{\mathbf{y}}) \cdot ((K^{-1}(t; t, x))^T\bar{\mathbf{p}})$$
$$= (K^{-1}(t; \bar{t}, \bar{\mathbf{x}})K(t; \bar{t}, \bar{\mathbf{x}})\mathbf{y}) \cdot \bar{\mathbf{p}} = \bar{\mathbf{y}} \cdot \bar{\mathbf{p}} \qquad (6.296)$$

Proposition A.8. *If $t_1 \in [0, 1]$ and $\mathbf{x}_1 \in \text{int}\, A$ then for all $t_2 \in [0, 1]$ the state $\boldsymbol{\varphi}(t_2 ; \mathbf{x}_1, t_1)$ is interior to the set† $\{\boldsymbol{\varphi}(t_2 ; \mathbf{x}_1, t_1) : \mathbf{x}_1 \subset A\}$.*

PROOF. The vector $\boldsymbol{\varphi}(t_2 ; \mathbf{x}_1, t_1)$ is continuously differentiable with respect to $\mathbf{x}_1$ and $K(t_2 ; \mathbf{x}_1, t_1)$, the matrix of partial derivatives with respect to $\mathbf{x}_1$, has a nonzero determinant (since it has an inverse $K^{-1}(t_2 ; \mathbf{x}_1, t_1)$). The proof of Proposition A.8 follows then immediately from the inverse function theorem.‡

Proposition A.9. *Suppose that $t \in [0, 1]$, that $\mathbf{z}(\varepsilon)$ is a continuously differentiable function over $[0, \sigma]$ for some $\sigma > 0$. For every $t \in [0, 1]$ and every $\varepsilon \in [0, \sigma]$ define $\mathbf{z}(t; \varepsilon) = \boldsymbol{\varphi}(t; \bar{t}, \mathbf{z}(\varepsilon))$. Then for every $t \in [0, 1]$ the function $\mathbf{z}(t; \varepsilon)$ is continuously differentiable with respect to ε. Define $\mathbf{y}(t)$ as the derivative $d/d\varepsilon\, \mathbf{z}(t; \varepsilon)$ evaluated at $\varepsilon = 0$. The function $\mathbf{y}(t)$ satisfies then the following conditions:*

(i) $\mathbf{y}(t)$ is continuous for all $t \in [0, 1]$;
(ii) $\mathbf{y}(t)$ is differentiable for all $t \in \Theta$;
(iii) $\dot{\mathbf{y}}(t) = D(t; \bar{t}, \mathbf{z}(0))\mathbf{y}(t)$ for all $t \in \Theta$.

PROOF. By taking the total derivative with respect to ε of the relation

$$\mathbf{z}(t; \varepsilon) = \boldsymbol{\varphi}(t; \bar{t}, \bar{\mathbf{z}}(\varepsilon)) \qquad (6.297)$$

we obtain

$$\frac{d}{d\varepsilon}\mathbf{z}(t; \varepsilon) = \left(\frac{\partial \boldsymbol{\varphi}(t; \bar{t}, \mathbf{x})}{\partial x}\bigg|_{\mathbf{x} = \bar{\mathbf{z}}(\varepsilon)}\right)\frac{d}{d\varepsilon}\bar{\mathbf{z}}(\varepsilon) \qquad (6.298)$$

† The notation $\{\boldsymbol{\varphi}(t_2 ; \mathbf{x}_1, t_1) : \mathbf{x}_1 \in A\}$ stands for "the set of all vectors $\boldsymbol{\varphi}(t_2 ; \mathbf{x}_1, t_1)$ such that $\mathbf{x}_1 \in A$." We recall that a point $\mathbf{a}$ is interior to a set A if there exists an $\varepsilon > 0$ such that for all $\mathbf{b}$ with $|\mathbf{a} - \mathbf{b}| \leq \varepsilon$ we have $\mathbf{b} \in A$. The notation "$\mathbf{a} \in \text{int}\, A$" means "$\mathbf{a}$ is interior to the set A."

‡ See T. M. Apostol, "Mathematical Analysis," p. 144. Addison-Wesley, Reading, Massachusetts, 1957.

and for $\varepsilon = 0$

$$\mathbf{y}(t) = \left(\frac{\partial \boldsymbol{\varphi}(t;\, t,\, \mathbf{x})}{\partial \mathbf{x}} \bigg|_{\mathbf{x} = \bar{\mathbf{z}}(0)} \right) \mathbf{y}(\bar{t}) \tag{6.299}$$

i.e.,

$$\mathbf{y}(t) = K(t;\, \bar{t},\, \bar{\mathbf{z}}(0))\mathbf{y}(\bar{t}) \tag{6.300}$$

From relation (6.300) and the properties of the matrix $K(t;\, \bar{t},\, \bar{\mathbf{z}}(0))$ listed in Proposition A.4, we obtain, immediately, the required properties of the vector $\mathbf{y}(t)$. This concludes the proof of Proposition A.9.

APPENDIX B
THE GEOMETRY OF CONVEX SETS

In this appendix we shall state and prove some results about convex sets.† These results are needed at various stages of the theory of optimal control.

For any positive integer n the n-dimensional Euclidean space will be denoted by E^n. The length of a vector $\mathbf{a}$ in E^n will be denoted by $|\mathbf{a}|$. The scalar product of two vectors $\mathbf{a}$ and $\mathbf{b}$ in E^n will be denoted by $\mathbf{a} \cdot \mathbf{b}$. We have obviously $\mathbf{a} \cdot \mathbf{a} = |\mathbf{a}|^2$ for all $\mathbf{a} \in E^n$.

We write "$\mathbf{a} \in A$" to mean "$\mathbf{a}$ is an element of the set A" and "$A \subset B$" to mean "the set A is a subset of the set B". Similarly, "$\mathbf{a} \notin A$" means "$\mathbf{a}$ is not an element of the set A." If A and B are sets then $A \cap B$, the intersection of A and B, is the set of all elements belonging to both sets A and B; $A \cup B$, the union of A and B, is the set of all elements belonging to at least one of the sets A and B; $A \sim B$ is the set of all elements of A which do not belong to B.

We start by recalling some definitions concerning the topology of Euclidean spaces:

(i) a point $\mathbf{a}$ is interior to a subset A of E^n if there exists an $\varepsilon > 0$ such that for all $\mathbf{b} \in E^n$ with $|\mathbf{a} - \mathbf{b}| \le \varepsilon$ we have $\mathbf{b} \in A$;

(ii) the interior of a set A is the set of all interior points of A. The interior of a set A is denoted by int A;

(iii) a point $\mathbf{a}$ is a boundary point of a subset A of E^n if for every $\varepsilon > 0$ there exists a $\mathbf{b} \in A$ and a $\mathbf{c} \notin A$ such that $|\mathbf{a} - \mathbf{b}|$ and $|\mathbf{a} - \mathbf{c}| \le \varepsilon$;

(iv) the boundary of a set A is the set of all its boundary points. The boundary of a set A is denoted by ∂A;

(v) a set A in E^n is open if all points are interior points of A;

(vi) a set A in E^n is closed if the set $E^n \sim A$ is open;

(vii) the closure of a set A is the smallest closed set containing A. The closure of a set A is denoted by $\bar{A}$.

† For a more balanced study of convex sets see H. G. Eggleston, "Convexity." Cambridge Univ. Press, London and New York, 1948.

We introduce now the definition of convex set. A set A in E^n is convex if for any $\mathbf{a}$ and $\mathbf{b} \in A$ and any $\mu \in [0, 1]$ we have $\mu\mathbf{a} + (1 - \mu)\mathbf{b} \in A$. In other words a set A is convex if any line segment connecting two points of A is entirely contained in A.

Proposition B.1. *If the set A is convex and if $\mathbf{a} \notin \bar{A}$ then there exists a nonzero vector $\mathbf{p}$ such that*

$$\mathbf{p} \cdot \mathbf{x} \leq \mathbf{p} \cdot \mathbf{a} \qquad \text{for all} \quad \mathbf{x} \in A \tag{6.301}$$

PROOF. Let $\mathbf{b}$ be a point of $\bar{A}$ which is closest to $\mathbf{a}$, i.e., such that

$$|\mathbf{a} - \mathbf{b}| \leq |\mathbf{a} - \mathbf{x}| \qquad \text{for all} \quad \mathbf{x} \in \bar{A} \tag{6.302}$$

We have $\mathbf{a} \neq \mathbf{b}$. Let $\mathbf{p} = \mathbf{a} - \mathbf{b}$. It remains to prove that

$$(\mathbf{a} - \mathbf{b}) \cdot \mathbf{x} \leq (\mathbf{a} - \mathbf{b}) \cdot \mathbf{a} \qquad \text{for all} \quad \mathbf{x} \in A \tag{6.303}$$

Indeed, for all $\mathbf{x} \in A$ and all $\mu \in [0, 1]$ we have $\mu\mathbf{b} + (1 - \mu)\mathbf{x} \in \bar{A}$ which implies

$$|\mathbf{b} - \mathbf{a}|^2 \leq |(1 - \mu)\mathbf{b} + \mu\mathbf{x} - \mathbf{a}|^2 \tag{6.304}$$

i.e.,

$$2\mu((\mathbf{x} - \mathbf{b}) \cdot (\mathbf{b} - \mathbf{a})) + \mu^2((\mathbf{x} - \mathbf{b}) \cdot (\mathbf{x} - \mathbf{b})) \geq 0 \tag{6.305}$$

Since relation (6.305) holds for all $\mu \in [0, 1]$, we have

$$(\mathbf{x} - \mathbf{b}) \cdot (\mathbf{b} - \mathbf{a}) \geq 0 \tag{6.306}$$

i.e.,

$$(\mathbf{a} - \mathbf{b}) \cdot \mathbf{x} < (\mathbf{a} - \mathbf{b}) \cdot \mathbf{a} \tag{6.307}$$

This concludes the proof of Proposition B.1.

Proposition B.2. *If the set A is convex and if $\mathbf{a} \in \partial A$ then there exists a nonzero vector $\mathbf{p}$ such that*

$$\mathbf{p} \cdot \mathbf{x} \leq \mathbf{p} \cdot \mathbf{a} \qquad \text{for all} \quad \mathbf{x} \in A \tag{6.308}$$

PROOF. Let $\mathbf{a}_1, \mathbf{a}_2, \ldots$ be a sequence of points converging to the point $\mathbf{a}$ and such that $\mathbf{a}_i \notin \bar{A}$ for $i = 1, 2, \ldots$. For each $\mathbf{a}_i$ let $\mathbf{p}_i$ be the nonzero vector given by Proposition B.1 such that

$$\mathbf{p}_i \cdot \mathbf{x} \leq \mathbf{p}_i \cdot \mathbf{a}_i \qquad \text{for all} \quad \mathbf{x} \in A \tag{6.309}$$

We may assume that $|\mathbf{p}_i| = 1$ for all $i = 1, 2, \ldots$. There exists a vector $\mathbf{p}$ with $|\mathbf{p}| = 1$ such that some subsequence $\mathbf{p}_{k_1}, \mathbf{p}_{k_2}, \ldots$ of $\mathbf{p}_1, \mathbf{p}_2, \ldots$ converges to $\mathbf{p}$.

We have then for any $\mathbf{x} \in A$

$$\mathbf{p} \cdot \mathbf{x} = \lim_{i=\infty} (\mathbf{p}_{k_i} \cdot \mathbf{x}) \leq \lim_{i=\infty} (\mathbf{p}_{k_i} \cdot \mathbf{a}_{k_i}) = \mathbf{p} \cdot \mathbf{a} \tag{6.310}$$

This concludes the proof of Proposition B.2.

Let us introduce another definition. Two convex sets A and B are separated if there exists a nonzero vector $\mathbf{p}$ and a scalar α such that

$$\begin{aligned} \mathbf{x} \cdot \mathbf{p} \leq \alpha \quad & \text{for all} \quad \mathbf{x} \in A \\ \mathbf{x} \cdot \mathbf{p} \geq \alpha \quad & \text{for all} \quad \mathbf{x} \in B \end{aligned} \tag{6.311}$$

Colloquially speaking we could say that two convex sets A and B are separated if there exists an hyperplane P such that the set A is on one side of P and the set B is on the other side of P. An hyperplane P is completely determined by a nonzero vector $\mathbf{p}$, normal to P, and a real number α. In that case the hyperplane P is the set of all vectors $\mathbf{x}$ such that

$$\mathbf{x} \cdot \mathbf{p} = \alpha \tag{6.312}$$

Proposition B.3. *Let A be a convex set in E^n. Let* $\mathbf{a} \in A$ and $\mathbf{b} \in E^n$ with $\mathbf{a} \neq \mathbf{b}$. *The set $\{\mathbf{a} + \lambda(\mathbf{b} - \mathbf{a}) : \lambda > 0\}$ is denoted by B. Suppose that the convex sets A and B are not separated. Then there exists an $\alpha > 0$ such that* $\mathbf{a} + \alpha(\mathbf{b} - \mathbf{a}) \in \operatorname{int} A$.

PROOF. The set $\bar{A}$, closure of the convex set A, is also convex. There are three possibilities

(i) $\mathbf{a} + \lambda(\mathbf{b} - \mathbf{a}) \notin \bar{A}$ for all $\lambda > 0$;
(ii) there exists a $\bar{\lambda} > 0$ such that $\mathbf{a} + \lambda(\mathbf{b} - \mathbf{a}) \in \partial A$ for all $\lambda \in (0, \bar{\lambda})$;
(iii) there exists a $\bar{\lambda} > 0$ such that $\mathbf{a} + \lambda(\mathbf{b} - \mathbf{a}) \in \operatorname{int} A$ for all $\lambda \in (0, \bar{\lambda})$.

Possibility (iii) leads immediately to the required result. We shall show now that possibilities (i) and (ii) lead to contradictions.

First we consider possibility (i). For every $i = 1, 2, 3, \ldots$ let $\mathbf{p}_i$ be the nonzero vector given by Proposition B.1 such that

$$\mathbf{p}_i \cdot \mathbf{x} \leq \mathbf{p}_i \cdot \left(\mathbf{a} + \frac{1}{i}(\mathbf{b} - \mathbf{a})\right) \qquad \text{for all} \quad \mathbf{x} \in A \tag{6.313}$$

We may assume that $|\mathbf{p}_i| = 1$ for all $i = 1, 2, \ldots$. There exists a vector $\mathbf{p}$ with $|\mathbf{p}| = 1$ such that some subsequence $\mathbf{p}_{k_1}, \mathbf{p}_{k_2}, \ldots$ of the sequence $\mathbf{p}_1, \mathbf{p}_2, \ldots$ converges to $\mathbf{p}$.

For every $i = 1, 2, \ldots$ we have then

$$\mathbf{p}_{k_i} \cdot (\mathbf{a} + k_i^{-1}(\mathbf{b} - \mathbf{a})) \geq \mathbf{p}_{k_i} \cdot \mathbf{a} \tag{6.314}$$

Hence, for every $\lambda > k_i^{-1}$ we have

$$\mathbf{p}_{k_i} \cdot (\mathbf{a} + \lambda(\mathbf{b} - \mathbf{a})) \geq \mathbf{p}_{i_k} \cdot \mathbf{a} \tag{6.315}$$

For any $\mathbf{x} \in A$ we have

$$\mathbf{p} \cdot \mathbf{x} = \lim_{i=\infty} (\mathbf{p}_{k_i} \cdot \mathbf{x}) \leq \lim_{i=\infty} (\mathbf{p}_{k_i} \cdot (\mathbf{a} + k)_i^{-1}(\mathbf{b} - \mathbf{a})) = \mathbf{p} \cdot \mathbf{a} \tag{6.316}$$

and for any $\lambda > 0$ we have

$$\begin{aligned} \mathbf{p} \cdot (\mathbf{a} + \lambda(\mathbf{b} - \mathbf{a})) &= \lim_{i=\infty} (\mathbf{p}_{k_i} \cdot (\mathbf{a} + \lambda(\mathbf{b} - \mathbf{a}))) \\ &\geq \lim_{i=\infty} (\mathbf{p}_{k_i} \cdot \mathbf{a}) = \mathbf{p} \cdot \mathbf{a} \end{aligned} \tag{6.317}$$

From relations (6.316) and (6.317) we conclude that the sets A and B are separated which contradicts our assumption.

Now we shall consider possibility (ii). Let $\mathbf{p}$ be the nonzero vector given by Proposition B.2 such that

$$\mathbf{p} \cdot \mathbf{x} \leq \mathbf{p} \cdot (\mathbf{a} + (\bar{\lambda}/2)(\mathbf{b} - \mathbf{a})) \qquad \text{for all} \quad \mathbf{x} \in \bar{A} \tag{6.318}$$

In particular, we have

$$\mathbf{p} \cdot \mathbf{a} \leq \mathbf{p} \cdot (\mathbf{a} + (\bar{\lambda}/2)(\mathbf{b} - \mathbf{a})) \tag{6.319}$$

and

$$\mathbf{p} \cdot (\mathbf{a} + \lambda(\mathbf{b} - \mathbf{a})) \leq \mathbf{p} \cdot (\mathbf{a} + (\bar{\lambda}/2)(\mathbf{b} - \mathbf{a})) \tag{.6320}$$

Relations (6.319) and (6.320) imply that

$$\mathbf{p} \cdot (\mathbf{a} + \lambda(\mathbf{b} - \mathbf{a})) = 0 \qquad \text{for any} \quad \lambda > 0 \tag{6.321}$$

From relations (6.318) and (6.321) we conclude that the sets A and B are separated which contradicts our assumption.

Let us introduce a last definition. If A is a set in E'', we define the convex hull of A as the smallest convex set containing A. The convex hull of A is denoted co A.

Proposition B.4. *If A is a set in E'' and if $\mathbf{a} \in$ co A then $\mathbf{a}$ is the convex combination of $n + 1$ vectors in A, i.e., there exists $n + 1$ vectors $\mathbf{a}_1, \mathbf{a}_2, \ldots, \mathbf{a}_{n+1}$ in A and $n + 1$ nonnegative numbers $\mu_1, \mu_2, \ldots, \mu_{n+1}$ such that $\mathbf{a} = \sum_{i=1}^{n+1} \mu_i \mathbf{a}_i$ and $1 = \sum_{i=1}^{n+1} \mu_i$.*

PROOF. Let A^* be the set of all points of the form $\sum_{i=1}^{k} \mu_i a_i$ where $\mathbf{a}_1, \mathbf{a}_2, \ldots, \mathbf{a}_k \in A$, $\mu_1, \mu_2, \ldots, \mu_k \geq 0$ and $\sum_{i=1}^{k} \mu_i = 1$. The set A^* is convex and hence co $A \subset A^*$. If $\mathbf{a} \subset A^*$ we may construct the sequence $\mathbf{a}_1{}^*, \mathbf{a}_2{}^*, \ldots, \mathbf{a}_{k-1}$ by the following rules:

$$\mathbf{a}_1{}^* = \left(\frac{\mu_1}{\mu_1 + \mu_2}\right)\mathbf{a}_1^* + \left(\frac{\mu_2}{\mu_1 + \mu_2}\right)\mathbf{a}_2 \tag{6.322}$$

$$\mathbf{a}_i{}^* = \left(\frac{\mu_1 + \cdots + \mu_i}{\mu_1 + \cdots + \mu_{i+1}}\right)\mathbf{a}_{i-1}^* + \left(\frac{\mu_{i+1}}{\mu_1 + \cdots + \mu_{i+1}}\right)\mathbf{a}_{i+1}, \qquad i = 2, \ldots, k-1 \tag{6.323}$$

We have then $\mathbf{a}_i^* \in \text{co } A$ for all $i = 1, 2, \ldots, k-1$ and $\mathbf{a}_{k-1}^* = a$. This proves that $A^* \subset \text{co } A$ and hence, $A^* = \text{co } A$.

Now we shall prove by contradiction that any $\mathbf{a} \in A^*$ can be expressed as a convex combination of $n + 1$ vectors in A. Let k be the smallest integer such that there exists vectors $\mathbf{a}_1, \mathbf{a}_2, \ldots, \mathbf{a}_k$ in A and real numbers $\mu_1, \mu_2, \ldots, \mu_k > 0$ with $\sum_{i=1}^k \mu_i = 1$ and $\sum_{i=1}^k \mu_i \mathbf{a}_i = \mathbf{a}$. If $k \leq n + 1$ then nothing remains to prove. We shall show that $k > n + 1$ leads to a contradiction. If $k > n + 1$ then the vectors $\mathbf{a}_1, \mathbf{a}_2, \ldots, \mathbf{a}_k$ are linearly dependent and there exist real numbers $\alpha_1, \alpha_2, \ldots, \alpha_k$, one of them at least being different from zero, such that $\sum_{i=1}^k \alpha_i = 0$ and $\alpha_1 \mathbf{a}_1 + \alpha_2 \mathbf{a}_2 + \alpha_3 \mathbf{a}_3 + \cdots + \alpha_k \mathbf{a}_k = 0$. Let Θ be the set of real numbers θ such that $\theta \alpha_i \geq -\mu_i$ for $i = 1, 2, \ldots, k$. The set Θ is closed, nonempty (since it contains the number zero), and does not contain the entire real line (since one at least of the α_i is different from zero). Let θ_0 be a boundary point of the set Θ. We have $\theta_0 \alpha_j = -\mu_j$ for some j among the integers $1, 2, \ldots, k$. We have then $\mathbf{a} = \sum_{i=1}^k (\mu_i + \theta_0 \alpha_j) \mathbf{a}_i$, i.e.,

$$\mathbf{a} = \sum_{\substack{i=1 \\ i \neq j}}^{k} (\mu_i + \theta_0 \alpha_i) \mathbf{a}_i$$

Since $\mu_i + \theta_0 \alpha_i \geq 0$ and

$$\sum_{\substack{i=1 \\ i \neq j}}^{k} (\mu_i + \theta_0 \alpha_i) = 1$$

we obtain a contradiction. This concludes the proof of Proposition B.4.

Acknowledgments

I am very grateful to my wife Carolyn Halkin and to Messrs. A. A. Fredericks, J. W. Holtzman, S. Horing, R. A. Horn, J. C. Hsu, A. G. Lubowe, and V. O. Mowery for their valuable comments on this paper.

During the Fall of 1964 I gave a series of lectures on the mathematical theory of optimal control at the Bell Telephone Laboratories. The "textbook" for these lectures was an earlier version of the present chapter. At that occasion I was most fortunate to receive many pertinent suggestions for which I thank S. B. Alterman, H. G. Ansell, P. J. Buxbaum, and W. L. Nelson.

References

1. M. Aoki, Mimimal Effort Control Systems with an Upper Bound of the Control Time, *IEEE Trans. Automat. Control* No **1**, 60–61 (1963).
2. R. Bellman, "Adaptive Control Processes, a Guided Tour." Princeton Univ. Press, Princeton, New Jersey, 1961.
3. R. Bellman, "Dynamic Programming." Princeton Univ. Press, Princeton, New Jersey, 1957.

4. R. Bellman, I. Glicksberg and O. Gross, On the "Bang-Bang" control problems, *Quart. Appl. Math.* **14**, 11–18 (1956).
5. L. D. Berkovitz, Variational Methods in Problems of Control and Programming, *J. Math. Anal. Appl.* **3**, 145-169 (1961).
6. A. Blaquière and G. Leitmann, On the Geometry of Optimal Processes, Div. Appl. Mech. Univ. California, Berkeley, Tech. Rept. 64–10 (1964).
7. J. V. Breakwell, The Optimizations of Trajectories, *J. Soc. Indust. Appl. Math.* **7**, No 2, 215–247 (1959).
8. A. E. Bryson and W. R. Denham, A Steepest-Ascent Method for Solving Optimum Programming Problems, Raytheon Company. Tech. Rept. BR-1303 (1961).
9. D. Bushaw, Dynamical Polysystems and Optimization, *Contributions to Differential Equations* **2**, No 3, 351–365 (1963).
10. C. Carathéodory, Variationsrechnung, *in* "Die Differential und Integralgleichungen der Mechanik und Physik" (Ph. Frank and R. v. Mises, eds.), pp. 227–279. Vieweg, Braunschweig, Germany, 1930.
11. R. Courant and D. Hilbert, "Methoden der Mathematischen Physik," Springer, Berlin, 1937.
12. C. A. Desoer, Pontryagin's Maximum Principle and the Principle of Optimality, *J. Franklin Inst.* **271**, 413–426 (1961).
13. S. Dreyfus, Dynamic Programming and the Calculus of Variations, *J. Math. Anal. Appl.* **1**, 228–239 (1960).
14. A. F. Filippov, On Certain Questions in the Theory of Optimal Control, *Vestn. Mosk. Univ. Ser. Mat. Mekhan. Astron. Fiz. Khim*, No. 2, 25–32 (1959). [Engl. Transl.: *J. Soc. Ind. Appl. Math. Ser. A* pp. 76–84 (1962).]
15. I. Flügge-Lotz and H. Halkin, Pontryagin's Maximum Principle and Optimal Control, Stanford Univ., Stanford, California, Tech. Rept. 130 (1961).
16. I. Flügge-Lotz and R. Marbach, The Optimal Control of Some Altitude Control Systems for Different Performance Criteria, *ASME J. Basic Eng. Ser. D* **85**, 165–176 (1963).
17. I. Flügge-Lotz and M. Maltz, Analysis of Chatter in Contractor Control Systems, with Applications to Dual-Input Plans, Stanford University, Stanford, California, Tech. Rept. SUDAER 155 (1963).
18. B. Fraejis de Veubeke, Méthodes variationnelles et performances optimales en aéronautique, *Bull. Soc. Math. Belg.* **8**, 136–157 (1956).
19. A. T. Fuller, Bibliography of Optimum Nonlinear Control of Determinate and Stochastic-Definite Systems, *J. Electronics Control* **13**, 589–611 (1962).
20. A. T. Fuller, Bibliography of Pontryagin's Maximum Principle, *J. Electronics Control* **15**, 513–517 (1963).
21. R. V. Gamkrelidze, Optimal Sliding States, *Dokl. Akad. Nauk SSSR* **143**, 1243–1245 (1962). (In Russian.)
22. H. Halkin, Lyapounov's Theorem on the Range of a Vector Measure and Pontryagin's Maximum Principle, *Arch. Rational Mech. Anal.* **10**, 296–304 (1962).
23. H. Halkin, The Principle of Optimal Evolution, *in* "Nonlinear Differential Equations and Nonlinear Mechanics" (J. P. LaSalle and S. Lefschetz, eds.), pp. 284–302. Academic Press, New York, 1963.
24. H. Halkin, On the Necessary Condition for Optimal Control of Nonlinear Systems, *J. Anal. Math.* **12**, 1–82 (1964).
25. H. Halkin, A Generalization of LaSalle's "Bang-Bang" Principle, *SIAM J. Control* **2**, 199–203 (1965).
26. H. Halkin, On a Generalization of a Theorem of Lyapounov, *J. Math. Anal. Appl.* **10**, 325–329 (1965).

27. H. Halkin, Some Further Generalizations of a Theorem of Lyapounov, *Arch. Rational Mech. Anal.* **17**, 272–277 (1964).
28. H. Halkin, Topological Aspects of Optimal Control of Dynamical Polysystems, *Contributions to Differential Equations* **3**, 377–385 (1964).
29. H. Halkin, Method of Convex Ascent, *in* "Computing Methods in Optimization Problems," pp. 211–239, (A. V. Balakrishnan and Lucien W. Neustadt, eds.). Academic Press, New York, 1964.
30. H. Halkin, Optimal Control for Systems Described by Difference Equations, *Advan. Control Systems* 173–196 (1964).
31. T. J. Higgins, A Résumé of the Basic Literature of State-Space Techniques in Automatic Control Theory, *JACC* (1962).
32. R. E. Kalman, The Theory of Optimal Control and the Calculus of Variations, RIAS Report 61–3 (1961).
33. H. J. Kelley, Methods of Gradients, *in* "Optimization Techniques" (G. Leitmann, ed.). Academic Press, New York, 1962.
34. J. P. LaSalle, The Time Optimal Control Problem, *in* "Contributions to the Theory of Nonlinear Oscillations," Vol. V, pp. 1–24. Princeton Univ. Press, Princeton, New Jersey, 1960.
35. G. Leitmann, "Necessary Conditions for Optimal Control and Applications," parts I and II, *Div. Appl. Mech.*, Univ. California, Berkeley, California, Tech. Rept. 64-3 (1964).
36. G. Leitmann, On a Class of Variational Problems in Rocket Flight, *J. Aerospace Sci.* **26**, No. 9, 586–591 (1959).
37. A. Lyapounov, Sur les fonctions vecteurs complètement additives, *Bull. Acad. Sci. USSR Phys. Ser.* **4**, 465–478 (1940). (In Russian with a French résumé.)
38. E. J. McShane, On Multipliers for Lagrange Problems, *Amer. J. Math.* **61**, 809–819 (1939).
39. A. Miele, A Survey of the Problem of Optimizing Flight Paths of Aircraft and Missiles, Boeing Scientific Research Laboratories, Tech. Rep. No. 27, July 1960.
40. L. W. Neustadt, The Existence of Optimal Controls in the Absence of Convexity Conditions, *J. Math. Anal. Appl.* **7**, 110–117 (1963).
41. J. J. O'Donnell, Bounds on Limit Cycles in Two-Dimensional Bang-Bang Control Systems with an Almost Time Optimal Switching Curve. *Proc. JACC* (1964).
42. B. Paiewonsky and P. J. Woodrow, The Synthesis of Optimal Controls for a Class of Rocket Steering Problems, AIAA Summer Meeting 1963.
43. L. S. Pontryagin, V. G. Boltyanskii, R. V. Gamkrelidze, and E. F. Mishchenko, "The mathematical theory of optimal processes" [Engl. Transl.] (L. W. Neustadt, ed.). Wiley (Interscience), New York, 1962.
44. E. Roxin, The Existence of Optimal Controls, *Michigan Math. J.* **9**, 109–119 (1962).
45. J. A. Stiles, Time Optimal Control of a Two Variable System (Ph. D. dissertation), Cambridge Univ., Cambridge, 1964.
46. L. G. Stoleru, A Quantitative Model of Growth of the Algerian Economy, Inst. Math. Studies Soc. Sci., Stanford University, Stanford, California, Tech. Rept. 124 (1963).
47. J. Warga, Relaxed Variational Problems, *J. Math. Anal. Appl.* **4**, 111–128 (1962).
48. J. Warga, Necessary Conditions for Minimum in Relaxed Variational Problems, *J. Math. Annal. Appl.* **4**, 129–145 (1962).

7

On the Geometry of Optimal Processes†

A. BLAQUIÈRE

FACULTY OF SCIENCES,
UNIVERSITY OF PARIS,
PARIS, FRANCE

G. LEITMANN

DEPARTMENT OF MECHANICAL ENGINEERING,
UNIVERSITY OF CALIFORNIA,
BERKELEY, CALIFORNIA,

† This work was supported by the U.S. Office of Naval Research under Contract Nonr-3656(31).

7.0 Introduction

This chapter contains an investigation of the geometry in state space of a dynamical system which behaves in an optimal fashion. The general notion of a *dynamical system* is introduced in terms of a *set of admissible rules* which determine the motion of the system in its state space. A *cost* is associated with the transfer of the system by means of an admissible rule. *Optimality* is then defined by the requirement that an admissible rule render the *minimum value of the cost* associated with transfer between prescribed end states.

Under the sole assumption that the cost obeys an additivity property, the existence of so-called *limiting surfaces* in cost-augmented state space is exhibited. Each member of the one-parameter family of limiting surface is the locus of all optimal trajectories whose initial points belong to it. Furthermore, each such surface belongs to the boundary of the region which contains all trajectories emanating from that surface. These global properties of a limiting surface are of fundamental importance to a discussion of optimal processes.

Under various assumptions concerning the geometry of limiting surfaces, local properties of these surfaces are deduced. In particular, for systems described by the usual set of differential state equations and for integral cost, additional geometric aspects of limiting surfaces are discussed. While it is not the primary purpose of the investigation reported here to present a derivation of the maximum principle, this principle is found to be a consequence of the global and local properties of limiting surfaces. Finally, the relation between the maximum principle and dynamic programming is established from the geometric point of view.

A word concerning notation and nomenclature may be in order. Unless specifically stated, they are the ones in common use. New symbols are defined, usually in a footnote, where they are first introduced.

7.1 Dynamical System

7.11 Transfer of System

We shall consider a dynamical system whose *state* is defined by n real numbers $x_1, x_2, \ldots, x_n$. We may think of a state as a point in an n-dimensional Euclidean space E^n, termed the *state space*. In state space we select a rectangular coordinate system so that we may define a point by the *state vector* $\mathbf{x} = (x_1, x_2, \ldots, x_n)$.

We shall suppose that the behavior of the dynamical system—that is, the evolution in time t of the system's states—is governed by any one in a *prescribed set of rules*. A rule which belongs to the prescribed set will be termed an *admissible rule*. Given an initial state of the system and an admissible rule, the state vector is a function† of time, $\mathbf{x}(t)$, which is defined on the time interval during which the rule is operative. In other words, given a point $\mathbf{x}^0$ and an admissible rule r, the point $\mathbf{x}(t)$ moves along a *path* p in E^n.‡

† We shall use the same symbol to represent a function of time and its value at a given time. The intended meaning should be evident from the context.

‡ If $\mathbf{x}(t)$ is defined on $[t_0, t_1]$, then the corresponding path p is the image of $[t_0, t_1]$ under graph $\{(t, \mathbf{x}): t \in [t_0, t_1], \mathbf{x} = \mathbf{x}(t)\}$.

In the subsequent discussion we shall be concerned with the paths generated by all admissible rules. In particular, we shall be interested in transferring the system from an initial point $\mathbf{x}^0$ to a *prescribed terminal point* $\mathbf{x}^1$. In general, some admissible rules generate paths from $\mathbf{x}^0$ which terminate at the prescribed point $\mathbf{x}^1$, while other admissible rules generate paths from $\mathbf{x}^0$ which terminate at some point $\bar{\mathbf{x}}^1 \neq \mathbf{x}^1$.

7.12 Performance Index and Optimality

Next let us adopt a rule, or functional, which assigns a unique real number to each transfer† effected by an admissible rule governing the behavior of the dynamical system. Such a rule will be termed a *performance index*. The number which it assigns to a transfer will be called the *cost* of the transfer. We shall admit a performance index such that the cost of transfer from $\mathbf{x}^0$ to $\mathbf{x}^f$, where $\mathbf{x}^f = \mathbf{x}^1$ or $\bar{\mathbf{x}}^1$, depends on the generating rule r and the corresponding path p. We shall denote the cost of such a transfer by $V(\mathbf{x}^0, \mathbf{x}^f; r, p)$.

We shall call a rule *optimal* for a transfer from $\mathbf{x}^0$ to $\mathbf{x}^1$, and denote it by r^* and the corresponding path by p^*, if the *cost takes on its minimum value*; that is,

$$V(\mathbf{x}^0, \mathbf{x}^1; r^*, p^*) \leq V(\mathbf{x}^0, \mathbf{x}^1; r, p) \tag{7.1}$$

for all admissible rules. While there may exist more than one optimal rule, the definition of optimality expressed by inequality (7.1) implies that the *minimum cost is unique*. Thus, for prescribed terminal point $\mathbf{x}^1$, the minimum cost depends only on the initial point $\mathbf{x}^0$. To emphasize this fact, we write

$$V^*(\mathbf{x}^0; \mathbf{x}^1) \triangleq V(\mathbf{x}^0, \mathbf{x}^1; r^*, p^*), \qquad \forall r^* \tag{7.2}$$

7.13 Additivity Property; Union of Paths

Rather than specify at the outset the set of rules which govern the behavior of the dynamical system and the rule or performance index which assigns a cost to a transfer, we shall make certain assumptions concerning these rules.

Regarding the performance index, we shall *assume that the cost obeys an additivity property*; in particular,

$$\begin{gathered} V(\mathbf{x}^0, \mathbf{x}^f; r, p) = V(\mathbf{x}^0, \mathbf{x}^i; r, p^i) + V(\mathbf{x}^i, \mathbf{x}^f; r, p_i) \\ \forall \mathbf{x}^i \in p, \qquad p = p^i \cup p_i \end{gathered} \tag{7.3}$$

where

$$\lim_{\mathbf{x}^i \to \mathbf{x}^f} V(\mathbf{x}^i, \mathbf{x}^f; r, p_i) = 0$$

† The term transfer is to be understood as a change of the system's state from one given state to another.

Note that rule r, which generates a transfer from $\mathbf{x}^0$ to $\mathbf{x}^f$ along p, also generates a transfer from $\mathbf{x}^0$ to $\mathbf{x}^i$ along p^i and then from $\mathbf{x}^i$ to $\mathbf{x}^f$ along p_i.

We shall also assume that the union of paths, or of portions of paths, is generated by an admissible rule.

7.2 Augmented State Space and Trajectories

We shall find it convenient to introduce another variable, x_0, and to consider an $(n+1)$-dimensional Euclidean space E^{n+1} of points $\mathbf{x}$, where $\mathbf{x} = (x_0, \mathbf{x}) = (x_0, x_1, \ldots, x_n)$ is the vector which defines a point relative to a rectangular coordinate system in E^{n+1}, the *augmented state space*.

Next let us define a *trajectory* Γ in E^{n+1}; namely,

$$\Gamma \triangleq \{\mathbf{x}^i : x_0{}^i + V(\mathbf{x}^i, \mathbf{x}^f; r, p_i) = C, \quad p_i \subset p\} \tag{7.4}$$

where p is a path from $\mathbf{x}^0$ to $\mathbf{x}^f$ generated by rule r, and C is a constant parameter. Thus, path p is the projection on E^n of a trajectory Γ in E^{n+1}.

If a rule is optimal, the corresponding trajectory will be called an *optimal trajectory* and denoted by Γ^*; that is,

$$\Gamma^* \triangleq \{\mathbf{x}^i : x_0{}^i + V(\mathbf{x}^i, \mathbf{x}^1; r^*, p_i) = C, \quad p_i \subset p^*\} \tag{7.5}$$

where r^* is an optimal rule for a transfer from $\mathbf{x}^0$ to $\mathbf{x}^1$, and p^* is the corresponding path.

Let $\mathbf{x}^0$ and $\mathbf{x}^f$ denote the initial and terminal points, respectively, of a trajectory Γ. Then

$$x_0{}^0 = C - V(\mathbf{x}^0, \mathbf{x}^f; r, p)$$
$$x_0{}^f = C$$

so that $x_0{}^f - x_0{}^0$ is equal to the cost of transfer from $\mathbf{x}^0$ to $\mathbf{x}^f$. Thus, if $x_0{}^0 = 0$, then C is equal to the cost of this transfer. If Γ is a trajectory whose projection on E^n is a path p which terminates at the prescribed terminal point $\mathbf{x}^1$, then Γ terminates at a point $\mathbf{x}^1$ on a line X^1 which is parallel to the x_0-axis and intersects E^n in $\mathbf{x}^1$. Hence, an optimal trajectory Γ^* from $\mathbf{x}^0$ is one for which the value of $x_0{}^1$ is minimum with respect to all other trajectories from $\mathbf{x}^0$.

7.3 Limiting Surfaces and Optimal Isocost Surfaces

Let us now consider two subsets of state space E^n:

(i) the set E of all initial points, $\mathbf{x}^0$, for which there exist admissible rules transferring the system to the prescribed terminal point $\mathbf{x}^1$, that is,

$$E \triangleq \{\mathbf{x}^0 : \exists p \quad \text{from} \quad \mathbf{x}^0 \quad \text{to} \quad \mathbf{x}^1\}$$

(ii) the set E^* of all initial points, $\mathfrak{x}^0$, for which there exist optimal rules, that is,

$$E^* \triangleq \{\mathfrak{x}^0 : \exists p^* \quad \text{from} \quad \mathfrak{x}^0 \quad \text{to} \quad \mathfrak{x}^1\}$$

Of course, $E^* \subseteq E \subseteq E''$, so that E^* and E may possess boundary points.

Since $V^*(\mathfrak{x}^0; \mathfrak{x}^1)$ is defined for all $\mathfrak{x}^0 \in E^*$, the equation

$$x_0 + V^*(\mathfrak{x}; \mathfrak{x}^1) = C \tag{7.6}$$

where C is a constant parameter, defines a single-sheeted surface Σ in $\mathscr{E}^* \triangleq E^* \times x_0$. In other words, Σ is a set of points which are in one-to-one correspondence with the points of E^*.

The function

$$x_0 = C - V^*(\mathfrak{x}; \mathfrak{x}^1) \ .$$

is defined on E^* and, in general,† vanishes on a surface S whose equation is

$$V^*(\mathfrak{x}; \mathfrak{x}^1) = C \tag{7.7}$$

As the value of parameter C is varied, equations (7.6) and (7.7) define two one-parameter families of surfaces, namely, $\{\Sigma\}$ in $\mathscr{E}^*$ and $\{S\}$ in E^*. We shall call the former *limiting surfaces* and the latter *optimal isocost surfaces*. The first of these names is motivated by a property of Σ to be discussed in Sec. 7.5. The second name follows from the definitions of minimum cost $V^*(\mathfrak{x}; \mathfrak{x}^1)$ and surface S; namely, a given S surface is the locus of all initial points from which the system can be transferred to the given terminal point with the *same minimum cost*.

7.4 Some Properties of Optimal Isocost Surfaces

The function $V^*(\mathfrak{x}; \mathfrak{x}^1)$ is termed *sign-definite* in E^* if

(i) it is sign-invariant for all $\mathfrak{x} \in E^*$;
(ii) it is zero only at $\mathfrak{x} = \mathfrak{x}^1$;
(iii) partial derivatives $\partial V^*(\mathfrak{x}; \mathfrak{x}^1)/\partial x_j$, $j = 1, 2, \dots, n$, are defined and continuous on $\mathring{E}^*$.‡

If $V^*(\mathfrak{x}; \mathfrak{x}^1)$ is sign-definite, then it possesses the following properties:

(i) If $\mathfrak{x}^1$ is an interior point of E^*, then there exists a region $D \subseteq E^*$ such that $\mathfrak{x}^1$ is an interior point of D, and such that every S surface in D is a closed surface which surrounds $\mathfrak{x}^1$.

† In the exceptional case of $V^*(\mathfrak{x}; \mathfrak{x}^1)$ independent of $\mathfrak{x}$, it can be shown that $V^*(\mathfrak{x}; \mathfrak{x}^1) \equiv 0$. In that case surface S is not defined.

‡ $\mathring{E}^*$ is the set of all interior points of E^*.

(ii) Furthermore, the optimal isocost surfaces contract towards $\mathbf{x}^1$ as $|C| \to 0$. Here we distinguish between (a) $V^*(\mathbf{x}; \mathbf{x}^1)$ positive definite, i.e., $C > 0$, in which case S contracts towards $\mathbf{x}^1$ as C *decreases* to zero; and (b) $V^*(\mathbf{x}; \mathbf{x}^1)$ negative definite, i.e., $C < 0$, in which case C *increases* to zero.

(iii) If $E^* \subset E^n$, and $\mathbf{x}^1$ belongs to the boundary of E^*, the optimal isocost surfaces are no longer closed surfaces. However, a connected curve which starts at $\mathbf{x}^1$, lies in E^* and terminates at a point $\mathbf{x}'$ for which $V^*(\mathbf{x}'; \mathbf{x}^1) = C'$, intersects every S surface corresponding to $C \leq C'$ if $V^*(\mathbf{x}; \mathbf{x}^1)$ is positive definite, and to $C \geq C'$ if $V^*(\mathbf{x}; \mathbf{x}^1)$ is negative definite. Here also the optimal isocost surfaces contract towards $\mathbf{x}^1$ as $|C| \to 0$.

Finally, we note that optimal isocost surfaces, corresponding to different values of parameter C, do not intersect each other.

7.5 Some Global Properties of Limiting Surfaces

Here we shall deduce some preliminary lemmas concerning trajectories in augmented state space. Based on these lemmas we shall then prove a fundamental theorem which embodies some global properties of limiting surfaces.

7.51 Lemma 1

First among the preliminary lemmas is

Lemma 1.† *Any optimal trajectory* Γ^* *which intersects line* X^1 *at point* $\mathbf{x}^1$ *lies entirely in the* Σ *surface passing through* $\mathbf{x}^1$.

To prove this lemma we shall invoke additivity property (7.3). From this property it follows that $V^*(\mathbf{x}^1; \mathbf{x}^1) = 0$, so that definition (7.6) implies that one and only one Σ surface passes through point $\mathbf{x}^1$. Furthermore, we need show that

$$V(\mathbf{x}^i, \mathbf{x}^1; r^*, p_i) = V^*(\mathbf{x}^i; \mathbf{x}^1), \qquad p_i \subset p^* \tag{7.8}$$

so that, in view of (7.5) and (7.6), the values of $x_0{}^i$ on Γ^* and on Σ, respectively, passing through $\mathbf{x}^1$, coincide for every point $\mathbf{x}^i$ on the corresponding optimal path p^* from $\mathbf{x}^0$ to $\mathbf{x}^1$.

From additivity property (7.3) we have

$$\begin{aligned} V^*(\mathbf{x}^0; \mathbf{x}^1) &\triangleq V(\mathbf{x}^0, \mathbf{x}^1; r^*, p^*) \\ &= V(\mathbf{x}^0, \mathbf{x}^i; r^*, p^i) + V(\mathbf{x}^i, \mathbf{x}^1; r^*, p_i) \end{aligned}$$

† If $\mathbf{x}^1 \notin E^*$, it belongs to the boundary of E^*; in that case it is the closure of Σ in E^{n+1}, which contains $\mathbf{x}^1$.

for all $\boldsymbol{x}^i \in p^*$, where $p^* = p^i \cup p_i$. Suppose now that (7.8) is false, namely.

$$V^*(\boldsymbol{x}^i; \boldsymbol{x}^1) \triangleq V(\boldsymbol{x}^i, \boldsymbol{x}^1; r_i^*, p_i^*) < V(\boldsymbol{x}^i, \boldsymbol{x}^1; r^*, p_i)$$

where r_i^* is an optimal rule for a transfer from $\boldsymbol{x}^i$ to $\boldsymbol{x}^1$, and p_i^* is the corresponding path. Then we may transfer the system from $\boldsymbol{x}^0$ to $\boldsymbol{x}^i$ along path p^i using rule r^*, and then from $\boldsymbol{x}^i$ to $\boldsymbol{x}^1$ along path p_i^* using rule r_i^*. However, invoking again (7.3), it follows that

$$V(\boldsymbol{x}^0, \boldsymbol{x}^1; r, p) = V(\boldsymbol{x}^0, \boldsymbol{x}^i; r^*, p^i) + V(\boldsymbol{x}^i, \boldsymbol{x}^1; r_i^*, p_i^*)$$

where rule r is made up of r^* from $\boldsymbol{x}^0$ to $\boldsymbol{x}^i$ and of r_i^* from $\boldsymbol{x}^i$ to $\boldsymbol{x}^1$, and $p = p^i \cup p_i$. Thus, we arrive at

$$V(\boldsymbol{x}^0, \boldsymbol{x}^1; r, p) < V(\boldsymbol{x}^0, \boldsymbol{x}^1; r^*, p^*)$$

which contradicts the optimality of rule r^*. And so (7.8), and hence the lemma, is established.

7.52 Lemma 2

The second preliminary lemma is

Lemma 2. *An optimal trajectory* Γ^* *with one point on a limiting surface* Σ *lies entirely on* Σ; *that is. limiting surfaces* $\{\Sigma\}$ *are the loci of all optimal trajectories.*

In view of definition (7.6), the members of the one-parameter family of limiting surfaces can be deduced from one another by translation parallel to the x_0-axis. Furthermore, these surfaces are ordered along the x_0-axis in the same way as the value of parameter C. Clearly, one and only one Σ surface passes through a given point in $\mathscr{E}^*$. This latter property and Lemma 1 lead at once to Lemma 2.

7.53 *A*- and *B*-Points

Before deducing the next lemma let us introduce a bit more nomenclature. It is quite obvious from definition (7.6) that a given Σ surface separates $\mathscr{E}^*$ into two disjoint regions. We shall denote these regions by A/Σ ("above" Σ) and B/Σ ("below" Σ), respectively.

For a limiting surface Σ, corresponding to parameter value C, we have

$$A/\Sigma \triangleq \{\mathbf{x} : x_0 > C - V^*(\boldsymbol{x}; \boldsymbol{x}^1) \quad \forall \boldsymbol{x} \in E^*\} \tag{7.9}$$

and

$$B/\Sigma \triangleq \{\mathbf{x} : x_0 < C - V^*(\boldsymbol{x}; \boldsymbol{x}^1) \quad \forall \boldsymbol{x} \in E^*\} \tag{7.10}$$

A point $\mathbf{x} \in A/\Sigma$ will be called an A-point relative to Σ, and a point $\mathbf{x} \in B/\Sigma$ a B-point relative to Σ.

7.54 Lemma 3

We can now proceed with the proof of

Lemma 3. *There exists no trajectory which starts on a given limiting surface* Σ *and intersects line* X^1 *at a B-point relative to* Σ.

Consider a limiting surface Σ corresponding to parameter value C; a point $\mathbf{x}^0 \in \Sigma$, whose projection on E^n is $\boldsymbol{x}^0$; and a non-optimal trajectory Γ, corresponding to parameter value C', which emanates from point $\mathbf{x}^0$ and terminates at point $\mathbf{x}^1$ on X^1.

The equation of surface Σ is

$$x_0 + V^*(\boldsymbol{x}; \boldsymbol{x}^1) = C$$

whereas the x_0-coordinate of Γ is given by

$$x_0{}^i + V(\boldsymbol{x}^i, \boldsymbol{x}^1; r, p_i) = C', \qquad p_i \subset p$$

where r is a non-optimal rule which generates path p, the projection of Γ on E^n. Since r is a non-optimal rule, it follows that

$$V^*(\boldsymbol{x}^0; \boldsymbol{x}^1) < V(\boldsymbol{x}^0, \boldsymbol{x}^1; r, p)$$

so that

$$C' > C$$

Consequently, a non-optimal trajectory which reaches line X^1 intersects it at an A-point relative to the limiting surface on which it starts. This conclusion and Lemma 2 result in Lemma 3.

7.55 Theorem 1 and Corollary 1

We shall now utilize the preliminary lemmas to establish

Theorem 1. *A trajectory (optimal or non-optimal) whose initial point belongs to a given limiting surface* Σ *has no B-point relative to* Σ.

And

Corollary 1. *A trajectory whose initial point is an A-point relative to a given limiting surface* Σ *has no B-point relative to* Σ*, nor, indeed, a point on it.*

Consider a limiting surface, say Σ_1, corresponding to a parameter value C_1, and non-optimal trajectory Γ which emanates from a point $\mathbf{x}^0$ on Σ_1. Suppose now that a point, say $\mathbf{x}'$, of Γ is a B-point relative to Σ_1. Let Σ_0 denote the limiting surface which passes through $\mathbf{x}'$, and let C_0 be the corresponding parameter value. Equation (7.6) and the definition of a B-point lead at once to

$$C_0 < C_1$$

Consequently, the intersection of Σ_0 and line X^1, that is, point $(C_0, \mathfrak{x}^1)$, is a B-point relative to Σ_1.

Let us now postulate a trajectory which consists of the portion of non-optimal trajectory Γ from $\mathbf{x}^0$ to $\mathbf{x}'$, followed by an *optimal* trajectory from $\mathbf{x}'$ to line X^1. According to Lemma 2, the optimal trajectory which starts at $\mathbf{x}'$ lies entirely in Σ_0, and hence intersects X^1 at a B-point relative to Σ_1. However, in view of Lemma 3, a trajectory which starts on Σ_1 does not intersect line X^1 at a B-point relative to Σ_1.

We conclude that a non-optimal trajectory which issues from a point on a given limiting surface Σ has no B-point relative to Σ. This result and Lemma 2 establish Theorem 1. Corollary 1 follows from an analogous argument in which we consider the limiting surface passing through the initial point of the trajectory.

Theorem 1 embodies the *limiting* property of surfaces $\{\Sigma\}$; namely, a given Σ surface belongs to the boundary of the region which contains *all* trajectories emanating from that surface.

7.6 Some Local Properties of Limiting Surfaces

In the last section we deduced some *global* properties of limiting surfaces, global in the sense that they pertain to the behavior of trajectories relative to limiting surfaces as a whole. In this section we shall investigate some *local* properties of limiting surfaces, local in the sense that they pertain to neighborhoods of points on a given Σ surface.

In the following discussion we shall find it convenient to refer to regions

$$\widetilde{A/\Sigma} \triangleq (A/\Sigma) \cup \Sigma \tag{7.11}$$

and

$$\widetilde{B/\Sigma} \triangleq (B/\Sigma) \cup \Sigma \tag{7.12}$$

namely, the complements in $\mathscr{E}^*$ of regions B/Σ and A/Σ, respectively. In other words, we have

$$(\widetilde{A/\Sigma}) \cup (B/\Sigma) = \mathscr{E}^*, \qquad (\widetilde{A/\Sigma}) \cap (B/\Sigma) = \phi$$

and alternately

$$(\widetilde{B/\Sigma}) \cup (A/\Sigma) = \mathscr{E}^*, \qquad (\widetilde{B/\Sigma}) \cap (A/\Sigma) = \phi$$

7.61 First Basic Assumption

Henceforth we shall make a basic assumption concerning the way a given limiting surface Σ separates $\mathscr{E}^*$ into the two disjoint regions $\widetilde{A/\Sigma}$ and B/Σ.

Let $\boldsymbol{\eta}$ be any bound vector at an *interior*† point $\mathbf{x}$ of a given limiting surface Σ. We shall *assume* that for every vector $\boldsymbol{\eta}$ there exists a scalar $\delta > 0$ such that for every ε, $0 < \varepsilon < \delta$, the point $\mathbf{x} + \varepsilon\boldsymbol{\eta}$ belongs either to region $\widetilde{A/\Sigma}$ or to region B/Σ.

This assumption will be understood to apply hereafter as, for example, in the definitions introduced in the next section.

7.62 Definitions of Local Cones $\mathscr{C}_A(\mathbf{x})$ and $\mathscr{C}_B(\mathbf{x})$

Next let us define two cones associated with every interior point of a limiting surface. Again let $\boldsymbol{\eta}$ be a bound vector at an interior point $\mathbf{x}$ of a given limiting surface Σ. Then we let

$$\mathscr{C}_A(\mathbf{x}) \triangleq \{\mathbf{x} + \boldsymbol{\eta} : \exists\alpha > 0 \quad \text{such that} \quad \forall\varepsilon, \quad 0 < \varepsilon < \alpha, \quad \mathbf{x} + \varepsilon\boldsymbol{\eta} \in \widetilde{A/\Sigma}\} \tag{7.13}$$

Similarly, we let

$$\mathscr{C}_B(\mathbf{x}) \triangleq \{\mathbf{x} + \boldsymbol{\eta} : \exists\beta > 0 \quad \text{such that} \quad \forall\varepsilon, \quad 0 < \varepsilon < \beta, \quad \mathbf{x} + \varepsilon\boldsymbol{\eta} \in B/\Sigma\} \tag{7.14}$$

Note that $\mathscr{C}_A(\mathbf{x})$ and $\mathscr{C}_B(\mathbf{x})$ are local *cones* with vertex at point $\mathbf{x}$.

7.63 Interior Points of $\mathscr{C}_A(\mathbf{x})$ and $\mathscr{C}_B(\mathbf{x})$; A Second Basic Assumption; Lemma 4

Before introducing a second basic assumption concerning the way a limiting surface separates $\mathscr{E}^*$, let us define an *interior point of a local cone* $\mathscr{C}_A(\mathbf{x})$ or $\mathscr{C}_B(\mathbf{x})$.

We shall say that $\mathbf{x} + \boldsymbol{\eta}$ is an interior point of $\mathscr{C}_A(\mathbf{x})$ (or $\mathscr{C}_B(\mathbf{x})$), if

(i) $\mathbf{x} + \boldsymbol{\eta} \in \mathscr{C}_A(\mathbf{x})$ (or $\mathscr{C}_B(\mathbf{x})$); and

(ii) there exists an open ball $B(\mathbf{x} + \boldsymbol{\eta})$ in E^{n+1} with center at $\mathbf{x} + \boldsymbol{\eta}$ such that all points of $B(\mathbf{x} + \boldsymbol{\eta})$ belong to $\mathscr{C}_A(\mathbf{x})$ (or $\mathscr{C}_B(\mathbf{x})$).

The definition of the *open* local cones, $\mathring{\mathscr{C}}_A(\mathbf{x})$ and $\mathring{\mathscr{C}}_B(\mathbf{x})$, follows at once; namely,

$$\mathring{\mathscr{C}}_A(\mathbf{x}) \triangleq \{\mathbf{x} + \boldsymbol{\eta} : \mathbf{x} + \boldsymbol{\eta} \text{ is interior point of } \mathscr{C}_A(\mathbf{x})\}$$
$$\mathring{\mathscr{C}}_B(\mathbf{x}) \triangleq \{\mathbf{x} + \boldsymbol{\eta} : \mathbf{x} + \boldsymbol{\eta} \text{ is interior point of } \mathscr{C}_B(\mathbf{x})\}$$

† By "interior point of Σ" we shall always mean a point which belongs to Σ and is an interior point of $\mathscr{E}^*$.

Our *second basic assumption* is the following: Let $\mathbf{x}+\boldsymbol{\eta}'$ be an interior point of $\mathscr{C}_A(\mathbf{x})$ (or $\mathscr{C}_B(\mathbf{x})$); namely, there exists an open ball $B(\mathbf{x}+\boldsymbol{\eta}')$ in E^{n+1} which belongs to $\mathscr{C}_A(\mathbf{x})$ (or $\mathscr{C}_B(\mathbf{x})$). Then there exists an open ball $B'(\mathbf{x}+\boldsymbol{\eta}')$ in E^{n+1} which belongs to $\mathscr{C}_A(\mathbf{x})$ (or $\mathscr{C}_B(\mathbf{x})$) and which has the property that for every point $\mathbf{x}+\boldsymbol{\eta}$ in $B'(\mathbf{x}+\boldsymbol{\eta}')$ there exists a positive number α (*independent of* $\boldsymbol{\eta}$) such that for all ε, $0<\varepsilon\leq\alpha$, point $\mathbf{x}+\varepsilon\boldsymbol{\eta}$ belongs to $\widetilde{A/\Sigma}$ (or B/Σ).†

With the aid of this assumption we shall now prove

Lemma 4. *Consider an interior point* $\mathbf{x}$ *of a limiting surface* Σ, *and a point* $\mathbf{x}+\boldsymbol{\eta}'\in\mathring{\mathscr{C}}_A(\mathbf{x})$. *Then there exists an open ball* $B'(\mathbf{x}+\boldsymbol{\eta}')\subset\mathscr{C}_A(\mathbf{x})$ *and a positive number* β *such that for all* $\mathbf{x}+\boldsymbol{\eta}\in B'(\mathbf{x}+\boldsymbol{\eta}')$ *and all* ε, $0<\varepsilon<\beta$, $\mathbf{x}+\varepsilon\boldsymbol{\eta}\in A/\Sigma$.

According to our second basic assumption, there exists an $\alpha>0$ such that for all ε, $0<\varepsilon\leq\alpha$, and for all $\mathbf{x}+\boldsymbol{\eta}$ in some open ball $B'(\mathbf{x}+\boldsymbol{\eta}')$, $\mathbf{x}+\varepsilon\boldsymbol{\eta}\in\widetilde{A/\Sigma}$.

Consider now a *conic neighborhood*

$$N(\mathbf{x})\triangleq\{\mathbf{x}+k\boldsymbol{\eta}:k>0,\quad \mathbf{x}+\boldsymbol{\eta}\in B'(\mathbf{x}+\boldsymbol{\eta}')\}\tag{7.15}$$

and an open ball‡

$$B(\mathbf{x})\triangleq\{\mathbf{x}+\varepsilon\boldsymbol{\rho}\mathbin{\mathring{:}}|\boldsymbol{\rho}|=1,\quad 0<\varepsilon<\alpha\}$$

In view of our second basic assumption, we have

$$N(\mathbf{x})\cap B(\mathbf{x})\subset\widetilde{A/\Sigma}$$

But $N(\mathbf{x})$ and $B(\mathbf{x})$ are open sets, so that

$$\mathbf{x}+\varepsilon\boldsymbol{\eta}\text{ is an interior point of }N(\mathbf{x}),\qquad \varepsilon>0$$

and

$$\mathbf{x}+\varepsilon\boldsymbol{\eta}\text{ is an interior point of }B(\mathbf{x}),\qquad 0<\varepsilon<\alpha/|\boldsymbol{\eta}|$$

Now let $\beta\triangleq\alpha/|\boldsymbol{\eta}|_{\max}$, where $|\boldsymbol{\eta}|_{\max}$ denotes the maximum value of $|\boldsymbol{\eta}|$ for all $\mathbf{x}+\boldsymbol{\eta}\in B'(\mathbf{x}+\boldsymbol{\eta}')$. Then we conclude that for all ε, $0<\varepsilon<\beta$,

$$\mathbf{x}+\varepsilon\boldsymbol{\eta}\in A/\Sigma$$

which establishes Lemma 4.

7.64 Local Cone $\mathscr{S}(\mathbf{x})$

Local cones $\mathscr{C}_A(\mathbf{x})$ and $\mathscr{C}_B(\mathbf{x})$ may be neither open nor closed, depending on the local properties of the corresponding limiting surface. Let us now

† Note that here, as in the definitions of $\mathscr{C}_A(\mathbf{x})$ and $\mathscr{C}_B(\mathbf{x})$, we have $\widetilde{A/\Sigma}$ but B/Σ.

‡ $|(\ )|$ denotes the norm (Euclidean length) of vector ( ).

consider the closed† local cones $\bar{\mathscr{C}}_A(\mathbf{x})$ and $\bar{\mathscr{C}}_B(\mathbf{x})$, and *define* another local cone at $\mathbf{x}$. We shall denote by $\mathscr{S}(\mathbf{x})$ the intersection of $\bar{\mathscr{C}}_A(\mathbf{x})$ and $\bar{\mathscr{C}}_B(\mathbf{x})$; that is,

$$\mathscr{S}(\mathbf{x}) \triangleq \bar{\mathscr{C}}_A(\mathbf{x}) \cap \bar{\mathscr{C}}_B(\mathbf{x}) \tag{7.16}$$

In the next section we shall show that $\mathscr{S}(\mathbf{x})$ is not empty; in fact, that it is the common boundary of $\mathscr{C}_A(\mathbf{x})$ and $\mathscr{C}_B(\mathbf{x})$.

7.7 Some Properties of Local Cones

7.71 A Partition of E^{n+1}; Lemma 5; Corollaries 2 and 3

We shall now prove

Lemma 5. *If* $\mathbf{x}$ *is an interior point of a limiting surface* Σ, *then local cones* $\mathscr{C}_A(\mathbf{x})$ *and* $\mathscr{C}_B(\mathbf{x})$ *constitute a partition of augmented state space* E^{n+1}; *in other words*‡

$$\mathscr{C}_A(\mathbf{x}) = \text{comp}\, \mathscr{C}_B(\mathbf{x}) \qquad \text{and} \qquad \mathscr{C}_B(\mathbf{x}) = \text{comp}\, \mathscr{C}_A(\mathbf{x})$$

Let us note first of all that definitions (7.13) and (7.14) of $\mathscr{C}_A(\mathbf{x})$ and $\mathscr{C}_B(\mathbf{x})$ lead at once to

$$\mathscr{C}_A(\mathbf{x}) \cup \mathscr{C}_B(\mathbf{x}) = E^{n+1} \tag{7.17}$$

To prove Lemma 5, we need only show that neither cone is empty, and that their intersection is empty.

Consider two open rays, L_- and L_+, which emanate from point $\mathbf{x}$, are parallel to the x_0-axis and point into the negative and positive x_0-directions, respectively. As a consequence of definitions (7.9), (7.10), and (7.11) of A/Σ, B/Σ, and $\widetilde{A/\Sigma}$, we have

$$\mathbf{x} + \varepsilon\boldsymbol{\eta} \in L_+ \Rightarrow \mathbf{x} + \varepsilon\boldsymbol{\eta} \in \widetilde{A/\Sigma}$$

$$\mathbf{x} + \varepsilon\boldsymbol{\eta} \in L_- \Rightarrow \mathbf{x} + \varepsilon\boldsymbol{\eta} \in B/\Sigma$$

Thus, it follows from the definitions of $\mathscr{C}_A(\mathbf{x})$ and $\mathscr{C}_B(\mathbf{x})$ that

$$\mathscr{C}_A(\mathbf{x}) \neq \phi, \qquad \mathscr{C}_B(\mathbf{x}) \neq \phi \tag{7.18}$$

Next we shall show that

$$\mathscr{C}_A(\mathbf{x}) \cap \mathscr{C}_B(\mathbf{x}) = \phi \tag{7.19}$$

† Unless otherwise specified, $\overline{(\ )}$ denotes the topological closure in E^{n+1} of ( ).
‡ Notation comp ( ) denotes the complement of ( ) in E^{n+1}.

To prove this property, suppose that it is incorrect; namely,

$$\mathscr{C}_A(\mathbf{x}) \cap \mathscr{C}_B(\mathbf{x}) \neq \phi$$

and consider a point $\mathbf{x} + \boldsymbol{\eta}$ such that

$$\mathbf{x} + \boldsymbol{\eta} \in \mathscr{C}_A(\mathbf{x}) \qquad \text{and} \qquad \mathbf{x} + \boldsymbol{\eta} \in \mathscr{C}_B(\mathbf{x})$$

Then

$$\exists \alpha > 0 \quad \text{such that} \quad \forall \varepsilon, \quad 0 < \varepsilon < \alpha, \quad \mathbf{x} + \varepsilon\boldsymbol{\eta} \in \widetilde{A/\Sigma}$$

$$\exists \beta > 0 \quad \text{such that} \quad \forall \varepsilon, \quad 0 < \varepsilon < \beta, \quad \mathbf{x} + \varepsilon\boldsymbol{\eta} \in B/\Sigma$$

Suppose, for instance, that $\alpha < \beta$; then

$$\forall \varepsilon, \quad 0 < \varepsilon < \alpha, \quad \mathbf{x} + \varepsilon\boldsymbol{\eta} \in \widetilde{A/\Sigma}, \quad \text{and} \quad \mathbf{x} + \varepsilon\boldsymbol{\eta} \in B/\Sigma$$

which implies that

$$(\widetilde{A/\Sigma}) \cap (B/\Sigma) \neq \phi$$

This is not the case, and so (7.19) is valid. Conditions (7.17)–(7.19) establish Lemma 5.

Corollary 2. *Local cone $\mathscr{S}(\mathbf{x}) \triangleq \bar{\mathscr{C}}_A(\mathbf{x}) \cap \bar{\mathscr{C}}_B(\mathbf{x})$ is the common boundary of local cones $\mathscr{C}_A(\mathbf{x})$ and $\mathscr{C}_B(\mathbf{x})$.*

It is well known that†

$$\partial\mathscr{C}_A(\mathbf{x}) = \bar{\mathscr{C}}_A(\mathbf{x}) \cap \overline{\text{comp}\,\mathscr{C}_A(\mathbf{x})}, \qquad \partial\mathscr{C}_B(\mathbf{x}) = \bar{\mathscr{C}}_B(\mathbf{x}) \cap \overline{\text{comp}\,\mathscr{C}_B(\mathbf{x})}$$

These relations together with Lemma 5 result in Corollary 2.

Furthermore, we have

Corollary 3. *The following relations are valid for local cones $\mathscr{C}_A(\mathbf{x})$ and $\mathscr{C}_B(\mathbf{x})$:*

$$\text{comp}\,\mathring{\mathscr{C}}_A(\mathbf{x}) = \bar{\mathscr{C}}_B(\mathbf{x}), \qquad \text{comp}\,\mathring{\mathscr{C}}_B(\mathbf{x}) = \bar{\mathscr{C}}_A(\mathbf{x})$$

This corollary is a consequence of Lemma 5 with

$$\overline{\text{comp}\,\mathscr{C}_A(\mathbf{x})} = \text{comp}\,\mathring{\mathscr{C}}_A(\mathbf{x}), \qquad \overline{\text{comp}\,\mathscr{C}_B(\mathbf{x})} = \text{comp}\,\mathring{\mathscr{C}}_B(\mathbf{x})$$

7.72 Lemmas 6 and 7; Corollary 4

Next we shall deduce two lemmas which will be useful during the subsequent discussion. The first of these is

† Notation $\partial(\ )$ denotes the boundary of ( ).

Lemma 6. *Let* $\boldsymbol{\eta}$ *be a bound vector at an interior point* $\mathbf{x}$ *of a limiting surface* Σ. *If* $\boldsymbol{\eta} = \boldsymbol{\eta}(\varepsilon)$ *is a function of a parameter* ε *with the following properties*:

(i) $\boldsymbol{\eta}(\varepsilon) \to \mathbf{l}$ as $\varepsilon \to 0$

(ii) $\exists \gamma > 0$ such that $\forall \varepsilon$, $0 < \varepsilon < \gamma$, $\mathbf{x} + \varepsilon\boldsymbol{\eta}(\varepsilon) \in \widetilde{A/\Sigma}$

then

$$\mathbf{x} + \mathbf{l} \in \overline{\mathscr{C}}_A(\mathbf{x})$$

To prove this lemma let us suppose that it is incorrect†; namely,

$$\mathbf{x} + \mathbf{l} \notin \overline{\mathscr{C}}_A(\mathbf{x})$$

so that, by Corollary 3, we have

$$\mathbf{x} + \mathbf{l} \in \mathring{\mathscr{C}}_B(\mathbf{x})$$

Then, according to our second basic assumption, there exists an open ball $B'(\mathbf{x} + \mathbf{l})$ and a positive number α such that for every point $\mathbf{x} + \boldsymbol{\eta}$ in $B'(\mathbf{x} + \mathbf{l})$ and all ε, $0 < \varepsilon < \alpha$, the point $\mathbf{x} + \varepsilon\boldsymbol{\eta}$ belongs to B/Σ.

However, since $\boldsymbol{\eta}(\varepsilon) \to \mathbf{l}$ as $\varepsilon \to 0$, there exists a positive number $\delta < \gamma$ such that for ε, $0 < \varepsilon < \delta$, the point $\mathbf{x} + \boldsymbol{\eta}(\varepsilon)$ belongs to $B'(\mathbf{x} + \mathbf{l})$. Consequently, there exists a positive number β such that for all ε, $0 < \varepsilon < \beta$, $\mathbf{x} + \varepsilon\boldsymbol{\eta}(\varepsilon) \in B/\Sigma$

$$\mathbf{x} + \varepsilon\boldsymbol{\eta}(\varepsilon) \in B/\Sigma$$

which contradicts (ii) of Lemma 6, and so establishes the lemma.

Conversely, we have

Lemma 7. *Let* $\boldsymbol{\eta}$ *be a bound vector at an interior point* $\mathbf{x}$ *of a limiting surface* Σ. *If* $\boldsymbol{\eta} = \boldsymbol{\eta}(\varepsilon)$ *is a function of a parameter* ε *with the following properties*:

(i) $\boldsymbol{\eta}(\varepsilon) \to \mathbf{l}$ as $\varepsilon \to 0$

(ii) $\exists \gamma > 0$ such that $\forall \varepsilon$, $0 < \varepsilon < \gamma$, $\mathbf{x} + \varepsilon\boldsymbol{\eta}(\varepsilon) \in \widetilde{B/\Sigma}$

then

$$\mathbf{x} + \mathbf{l} \in \overline{\mathscr{C}}_B(\mathbf{x})$$

Suppose again that the lemma is incorrect,‡ that is,

$$\mathbf{x} + \mathbf{l} \notin \overline{\mathscr{C}}_B(\mathbf{x})$$

so that, according to Corollary 3,

$$\mathbf{x} + \mathbf{l} \in \mathring{\mathscr{C}}_A(\mathbf{x})$$

† Note that the lemma is immediately valid if $\mathring{\mathscr{C}}_B(\mathbf{x}) = \phi$.

‡ Again, the lemma is clearly valid if $\mathring{\mathscr{C}}_A(\mathbf{x}) = \phi$.

Then, as in the proof of Lemma 6, we can state that there exists a positive number $\delta < \gamma$ such that for all ε, $0 < \varepsilon < \delta$,

$$\mathbf{x} + \boldsymbol{\eta}(\varepsilon) \in \mathring{\mathscr{C}}_A(\mathbf{x})$$

But then Lemma 4 allows us to conclude that there exists a positive number $\beta < \delta < \gamma$ such that for all ε, $0 < \varepsilon < \beta$, $\mathbf{x} + \varepsilon\boldsymbol{\eta}(\varepsilon) \in A/\Sigma$ which contradicts hypothesis (ii) of Lemma 7 and so establishes the lemma.

As an immediate consequence of these lemmas we have

Corollary 4. *Let* $\boldsymbol{\eta}$ *be a bound vector at an interior point* $\mathbf{x}$ *of a limiting surface* Σ. *If* $\boldsymbol{\eta} = \boldsymbol{\eta}(\varepsilon)$ *is a function of a parameter* ε *with the following properties*:

(i) $\boldsymbol{\eta}(\varepsilon) \to \mathbf{l}$ as $\varepsilon \to 0$

(ii) $\exists \gamma > 0$ such that $\forall \varepsilon$, $0 < \varepsilon < \gamma$, $\mathbf{x} + \varepsilon\boldsymbol{\eta}(\varepsilon) \in \Sigma$

then

$$\mathbf{x} + \mathbf{l} \in \mathscr{S}(\mathbf{x})$$

Since

$$\Sigma = (\widetilde{A/\Sigma}) \cap (\widetilde{B/\Sigma})$$

we have

$$\mathbf{x} + \varepsilon\boldsymbol{\eta}(\varepsilon) \in \widetilde{A/\Sigma} \qquad \text{and} \qquad \mathbf{x} + \varepsilon\boldsymbol{\eta}(\varepsilon) \in \widetilde{B/\Sigma}$$

In view of Lemmas 6 and 7, respectively, it follows that

$$\mathbf{x} + \mathbf{l} \in \overline{\mathscr{C}}_A(\mathbf{x}) \qquad \text{and} \qquad \mathbf{x} + \mathbf{l} \in \overline{\mathscr{C}}_B(\mathbf{x})$$

so that

$$\mathbf{x} + \mathbf{l} \subset \overline{\mathscr{C}}_A(\mathbf{x}) \cap \overline{\mathscr{C}}_B(\mathbf{x}) = \mathscr{S}(\mathbf{x})$$

7.73 Lemma 8

Consider now any conic neighborhood

$$N(\mathbf{x}) \triangleq \{\mathbf{x} + k\boldsymbol{\eta} : k > 0, \quad \mathbf{x} + \boldsymbol{\eta} \in B(\mathbf{x} + \mathbf{l})\}$$

where $B(\mathbf{x} + \mathbf{l})$ is an open ball in E^{n+1} with center at $\mathbf{x} + \mathbf{l}$. We shall prove

Lemma 8. *Let* $\mathbf{l}$ *be a bound vector at an interior point* $\mathbf{x}$ *of a limiting surface* Σ. *If* $\mathbf{x} + \mathbf{l} \in \mathscr{S}(\mathbf{x})$ *and* $N(\mathbf{x})$ *is a conic neighborhood, then*

$$N(\mathbf{x}) \cap \mathscr{C}_A(\mathbf{x}) \neq \phi$$

and

$$N(\mathbf{x}) \cap \mathscr{C}_B(\mathbf{x}) \neq \phi$$

Moreover

$$N(\mathbf{x}) \cap \mathring{\mathscr{C}}_A(\mathbf{x}) \neq \phi \qquad \text{provided} \quad \mathring{\mathscr{C}}_B(\mathbf{x}) = \mathring{\overline{\mathscr{C}}}_B(\mathbf{x})$$

and

$$N(\mathbf{x}) \cap \mathring{\mathscr{C}}_B(\mathbf{x}) \neq \phi \qquad \text{provided} \quad \mathring{\mathscr{C}}_A(\mathbf{x}) = \mathring{\overline{\mathscr{C}}}_A(\mathbf{x})$$

Suppose that the lemma is false; in particular, that

$$N(\mathbf{x}) \cap \mathscr{C}_A(\mathbf{x}) = \phi$$

Then it follows from Lemma 5 that

$$N(\mathbf{x}) \subset \mathscr{C}_B(\mathbf{x})$$

In view of the definitions of a conic neighborhood and of $\mathring{\mathscr{C}}_B(\mathbf{x})$, the last relation implies that

$$\mathbf{x} + \mathbf{l} \in \mathring{\mathscr{C}}_B(\mathbf{x})$$

This, in turn, contradicts the hypothesis of the lemma that $\mathbf{x} + \mathbf{l} \in \mathscr{S}(\mathbf{x})$. Similarly by supposing that

$$N(\mathbf{x}) \cap \mathscr{C}_B(\mathbf{x}) = \phi$$

we arrive at a contradiction.

Now suppose that

$$N(\mathbf{x}) \cap \mathring{\mathscr{C}}_A(\mathbf{x}) = \phi$$

Then it follows from Corollary 3 that

$$N(\mathbf{x}) \subset \overline{\mathscr{C}}_B(\mathbf{x})$$

and, since $N(\mathbf{x})$ is open, we have

$$\mathring{N}(\mathbf{x}) = N(\mathbf{x}) \qquad \text{and} \quad N(\mathbf{x}) \subset \mathring{\overline{\mathscr{C}}}_B(\mathbf{x})$$

Furthermore, from the assumption $\mathring{\mathscr{C}}_B(\mathbf{x}) = \mathring{\overline{\mathscr{C}}}_B(\mathbf{x})$, it follows that

$$N(\mathbf{x}) \subset \mathring{\mathscr{C}}_B(\mathbf{x}) \subset \mathscr{C}_B(\mathbf{x})$$

which leads to a contradiction, as discussed above. Similarly, by supposing that

$$N(\mathbf{x}) \cap \mathring{\mathscr{C}}_B(\mathbf{x}) = \phi$$

we arrive at a contradiction. Hence, Lemma 8 is proved.

7.74 Lemma 9

Next we shall prove

Lemma 9. *Let* $\mathbf{x}'$ *be an interior point of a limiting surface* Σ, *and let* L *be a connected curve which joins* $\mathbf{x}_A \in \bar{\mathscr{C}}_A(\mathbf{x}')$ *and* $\mathbf{x}_B \in \bar{\mathscr{C}}_B(\mathbf{x}')$. *Then* L *intersects* $\mathscr{S}(\mathbf{x}')$, *that is,*

$$L \cap \mathscr{S}(\mathbf{x}') \neq \phi$$

The lemma is clearly valid if either $\mathring{\mathscr{C}}_A(\mathbf{x}') = \phi$ or $\mathring{\mathscr{C}}_B(\mathbf{x}') = \phi$, since

$$\mathring{\mathscr{C}}_A(\mathbf{x}') = \phi \Rightarrow \mathbf{x}_A \in \mathscr{S}(\mathbf{x}'), \qquad \mathring{\mathscr{C}}_B(\mathbf{x}') = \phi \Rightarrow \mathbf{x}_B \in \mathscr{S}(\mathbf{x}')$$

If neither $\mathring{\mathscr{C}}_A(\mathbf{x}')$ nor $\mathring{\mathscr{C}}_B(\mathbf{x}')$ is empty, and the lemma is false, that is,

$$L \cap \mathscr{S}(\mathbf{x}') = \phi$$

then

$$\mathbf{x}_A \in \mathring{\mathscr{C}}_A(\mathbf{x}') \qquad \text{and} \qquad \mathbf{x}_B \in \mathring{\mathscr{C}}_B(\mathbf{x}')$$

However, according to Lemma 5 and Corollary 2,

$$\mathring{\mathscr{C}}_A(\mathbf{x}') \cup \mathring{\mathscr{C}}_B(\mathbf{x}') \cup \mathscr{S}(\mathbf{x}') = E^{n+1}$$

so that a point of L belongs to one of the two sets

$$\Delta_A \triangleq L \cap \mathring{\mathscr{C}}_A(\mathbf{x}'), \qquad \Delta_B \triangleq L \cap \mathring{\mathscr{C}}_B(\mathbf{x}')$$

so that

$$\Delta_A \cup \Delta_B - L$$

We shall denote by $d(\mathbf{x}_i, \mathbf{x}_j)$ the *curvilinear* distance between $\mathbf{x}_i \in L$ and $\mathbf{x}_j \in L$, that is, the distance along curve L (properly parametrized). Consider now two sets of points

$$\{\mathbf{x} : \mathbf{x} = \mathbf{x}_i^A \in \Delta_A, \quad i = 1, 2, \ldots, k\}$$

and

$$\{\mathbf{x} : \mathbf{x} = \mathbf{x}_i^B \in \Delta_B, \quad i = 1, 2, \ldots, k\}$$

constructed in the following manner: Consider the midpoint of L; it belongs either to Δ_A or to Δ_B. If it belongs to Δ_A, we shall denote it by $\mathbf{x}_1^A$ and let $\mathbf{x}_1^B = \mathbf{x}_B$. If it belongs to Δ_B, we shall denote it by $\mathbf{x}_1^B$ and let $\mathbf{x}_1^A = \mathbf{x}_A$. Then we consider the midpoint of the segment of L between $\mathbf{x}_1^A$ and $\mathbf{x}_1^B$. If this point belongs to Δ_A, we shall denote it by $\mathbf{x}_2^A$ and let $\mathbf{x}_2^B = \mathbf{x}_1^B$. If it belongs to Δ_B, we shall denote it by $\mathbf{x}_2{}^B$ and let $\mathbf{x}_2{}^A = \mathbf{x}_1{}^A$. By repeating this process, we obtain two sets of points having the following properties:

$$d(\mathbf{x}_A, \mathbf{x}_1{}^A) \le d(\mathbf{x}_A, \mathbf{x}_2{}^A) \le \cdots \le d(\mathbf{x}_A, \mathbf{x}_k{}^A)$$
$$d(\mathbf{x}_B, \mathbf{x}_1{}^B) \le d(\mathbf{x}_B, \mathbf{x}_2{}^B) \le \cdots \le d(\mathbf{x}_B, \mathbf{x}_k{}^B)$$
$$d(\mathbf{x}_1{}^A, \mathbf{x}_1{}^B) > d(\mathbf{x}_2{}^A, \mathbf{x}_2{}^B) > \cdots > d(\mathbf{x}_k{}^A, \mathbf{x}_k{}^B)$$

Furthermore, since L is connected

$$d(\mathbf{x}_k{}^A, \mathbf{x}_k{}^B) \to 0 \qquad \text{as} \quad k \to \infty$$

so that $\mathbf{x}_k{}^A$ and $\mathbf{x}_k{}^B$ tend to the same limit, $\mathbf{x}_L$, as k increases; that is,

$$\left.\begin{array}{l}\mathbf{x}_k{}^A \to \mathbf{x}_L \\ \mathbf{x}_k{}^B \to \mathbf{x}_L\end{array}\right. \qquad \text{as} \quad k \to \infty$$

According to our supposition, $\mathbf{x}_L$ belongs either to Δ_A or to Δ_B. Suppose, for instance, that $\mathbf{x}_L \in \Delta_A$ and hence $\mathbf{x}_L \in \mathring{\mathscr{C}}_A(\mathbf{x}')$. Then there exists a $\delta > 0$ such that an open ball $B(\mathbf{x}_L)$ with center at $\mathbf{x}_L$ and radius ρ, $0 < \rho < \delta$, belongs to $\mathring{\mathscr{C}}_A(\mathbf{x}')$. But this contradicts the fact that

$$\mathbf{x}_k{}^B \to \mathbf{x}_L \qquad \text{as} \quad k \to \infty$$

By the same token we arrive at a contradiction, if $\mathbf{x}_L \in \Delta_B$. Consequently, our supposition is incorrect and, in fact, we have

$$L \cap \mathscr{S}(\mathbf{x}') \ne \phi$$

7.8 Tangent Cone $\mathscr{C}_\Sigma(\mathbf{x})$

7.81 Definition of $\mathscr{C}_\Sigma(\mathbf{x})$

We shall say that a *unit vector* $\mathbf{t}_\Sigma$ *is tangent to a limiting surface* Σ at a point $\mathbf{x}$ in $\bar{\Sigma}$, if the following conditions are fulfilled:

(i) There exists a vector function $\boldsymbol{\eta}(\varepsilon)$ and a positive scalar function $m(\varepsilon)$, both of the same parameter ε, such that

$$|\boldsymbol{\eta}(\varepsilon)| = 1 \qquad \text{and} \qquad \left.\begin{array}{l}\boldsymbol{\eta}(\varepsilon) \to \mathbf{t}_\Sigma \\ m(\varepsilon) \to 0\end{array}\right. \qquad \text{as} \quad \varepsilon \to 0$$

(ii) There exists an infinite sequence

$$S_\Sigma \triangleq \{\varepsilon : \varepsilon = \varepsilon_i, \quad i = 1, 2, \ldots, k, \quad \text{and} \quad \varepsilon_k \to 0 \quad \text{as} \quad k \to \infty\}$$

and a positive number α such that, for all $\varepsilon \in S_\Sigma$ and $0 < \varepsilon < \alpha$, the point

$$\mathbf{x} + m(\varepsilon)\boldsymbol{\eta}(\varepsilon) \in \Sigma$$

We define now the tangent cone $\mathscr{C}_\Sigma(\mathbf{x})$ of Σ at $\mathbf{x}$; namely,

$$\mathscr{C}_\Sigma(\mathbf{x}) \triangleq \{\mathbf{x} + k\mathbf{t}_\Sigma : k > 0, \quad \forall \mathbf{t}_\Sigma\} \tag{7.20}$$

Obviously, we can extend this definition to apply for a subset† (open, closed, or neither) of Σ. For instance, let Σ_ν denote a subset of Σ. In defining a unit vector $\mathbf{t}_{\Sigma_\nu}$ tangent to Σ_ν at a point $\mathbf{x}$ in $\overline{\Sigma}_\nu$, we retain condition (i) with $\mathbf{t}_\Sigma = \mathbf{t}_{\Sigma_\nu}$. In condition (ii) we require the existence of an infinite sequence S_{Σ_ν} and of a positive number α such that for all $\varepsilon \in S_{\Sigma_\nu}$, $0 < \varepsilon < \alpha$, the point $\mathbf{x} + m(\varepsilon)\boldsymbol{\eta}(\varepsilon) \in \Sigma_\nu$. The tangent cone of Σ_ν at $\mathbf{x}$ is given by

$$\mathscr{C}_{\Sigma_\nu}(\mathbf{x}) \triangleq \{\mathbf{x} + k\mathbf{t}_{\Sigma_\nu} : k > 0, \quad \forall \mathbf{t}_{\Sigma_\nu}\}$$

Clearly, the definition applies to the closure of Σ_ν; thus, the tangent cone of $\overline{\Sigma}_\nu$ is defined by

$$\mathscr{C}_{\overline{\Sigma}_\nu}(\mathbf{x}) \triangleq \{\mathbf{x} + k\mathbf{t}_{\overline{\Sigma}_\nu} : k > 0, \quad \forall \mathbf{t}_{\overline{\Sigma}_\nu}\}$$

7.82 Closure of a Subset of Σ

It is easily shown that

$$\mathscr{C}_{\Sigma_\nu}(\mathbf{x}) = \mathscr{C}_{\overline{\Sigma}_\nu}(\mathbf{x}) \tag{7.21}$$

If $\mathbf{t}_{\overline{\Sigma}_\nu} \in \mathscr{C}_{\overline{\Sigma}_\nu}(\mathbf{x})$, then conditions (i) and (ii) are satisfied. Let $\varepsilon \in S_{\overline{\Sigma}_\nu}$, $0 < \varepsilon < \alpha$, so that

$$\mathbf{x} + m(\varepsilon)\boldsymbol{\eta}(\varepsilon) \in \overline{\Sigma}_\nu$$

and consider a ball $B(\mathbf{x} + m(\varepsilon)\boldsymbol{\eta}(\varepsilon))$ with center at $\mathbf{x} + m(\varepsilon)\boldsymbol{\eta}(\varepsilon)$ and radius ρ. Since $\mathbf{x} + m(\varepsilon)\boldsymbol{\eta}(\varepsilon)$ is either a point of Σ_ν or a limit point of Σ_ν, a ball $B(\mathbf{x} + m(\varepsilon)\boldsymbol{\eta}(\varepsilon))$ contains a point of Σ_ν; let us denote such a point by

$$\mathbf{x} + m'(\varepsilon)\boldsymbol{\eta}'(\varepsilon) \in \begin{cases} \Sigma_\nu \\ B(\mathbf{x} + m(\varepsilon)\boldsymbol{\eta}(\varepsilon)) \end{cases} \tag{7.22}$$

where $|\boldsymbol{\eta}'(\varepsilon)| = 1$. Thus, we have

$$m'(\varepsilon)\boldsymbol{\eta}'(\varepsilon) = m(\varepsilon)\boldsymbol{\eta}(\varepsilon) + \boldsymbol{\rho}'(\varepsilon) \tag{7.23}$$

where

$$|\boldsymbol{\rho}'(\varepsilon)| \leq \rho$$

However,

$$\begin{aligned} |m'(\varepsilon)\boldsymbol{\eta}'(\varepsilon)| &= |m(\varepsilon)\boldsymbol{\eta}(\varepsilon) + \boldsymbol{\rho}'(\varepsilon)| \\ &\leq |m(\varepsilon)\boldsymbol{\eta}(\varepsilon)| + |\boldsymbol{\rho}'(\varepsilon)| \end{aligned}$$

† Note, however, that in this case a tangent vector might not be defined; e.g., if Σ_ν is a point.

so that, since $|\boldsymbol{\eta}(\varepsilon)| = |\boldsymbol{\eta}'(\varepsilon)| = 1$, we have

$$m'(\varepsilon) \leq m(\varepsilon) + |\boldsymbol{\rho}'(\varepsilon)|$$

Now let

$$m'(\varepsilon) = m(\varepsilon) + \rho'', \qquad 0 \leq \rho'' \leq |\boldsymbol{\rho}'(\varepsilon)| \tag{7.24}$$

and substitute in (7.23); that is,

$$m(\varepsilon)\,|\boldsymbol{\eta}'(\varepsilon) - \boldsymbol{\eta}(\varepsilon)| = \boldsymbol{\rho}'(\varepsilon) - \rho''\boldsymbol{\eta}'(\varepsilon)$$

so that

$$|\boldsymbol{\eta}'(\varepsilon) - \boldsymbol{\eta}(\varepsilon)| \leq \frac{|\boldsymbol{\rho}'(\varepsilon)| + \rho''}{m(\varepsilon)}$$

$$\leq 2\frac{|\boldsymbol{\rho}'(\varepsilon)|}{m(\varepsilon)}$$

Since radius ρ of $B(\mathbf{x} + m(\varepsilon)\boldsymbol{\eta}(\varepsilon))$ is arbitrary, let us choose

$$\rho = o(m(\varepsilon)), \qquad \frac{o(m(\varepsilon))}{m(\varepsilon)} \to 0 \quad \text{as} \quad \varepsilon \to 0$$

Consequently,

$$\boldsymbol{\eta}'(\varepsilon) \to \mathbf{t}_{\Sigma_\nu} \qquad \text{as} \quad \varepsilon \to 0 \tag{7.25}$$

and, in view of (7.24), also

$$m'(\varepsilon) \to 0 \qquad \text{as} \quad \varepsilon \to 0 \tag{7.26}$$

Thus, (7.22), (7.25), and (7.26) imply the satisfaction of conditions (i) and (ii); and so

$$\mathbf{t}_{\Sigma_\nu} \in \mathscr{C}_{\Sigma_\nu}(\mathbf{x})$$

Conversely, it is clear that

$$\mathbf{t}_{\Sigma_\nu} \in \mathscr{C}_{\Sigma_\nu}(\mathbf{x})$$

implies that

$$\mathbf{t}_{\Sigma_\nu} \in \mathscr{C}_{\Sigma_\nu}(\mathbf{x})$$

since

$$\mathbf{x} + m(\varepsilon)\boldsymbol{\eta}(\varepsilon) \in \Sigma_\nu$$

implies that

$$\mathbf{x} + m(\varepsilon)\boldsymbol{\eta}(\varepsilon) \in \overline{\Sigma}_\nu$$

This completes the proof of (7.21).

7.83 A Partition of Σ; Lemma 10

We shall now prove

Lemma 10. *Let* $\{\Sigma_1, \Sigma_2, \ldots, \Sigma_\mu\}$ *constitute a partition*† *of a limiting surface* Σ, *and consider a point* $\mathbf{x} \in \bigcap_{i=1}^{\gamma} \bar{\Sigma}_i$, *where the* Σ_i, $i = 1, 2, \ldots, \gamma \le \mu$, *belong to the partition and are all the subsets whose closures contain* $\mathbf{x}$.‡ *Then*

$$\mathscr{C}_\Sigma(\mathbf{x}) = \bigcup_{i=1}^{\gamma} \mathscr{C}_{\Sigma_i}(\mathbf{x})$$

To prove this lemma, consider a vector $\mathbf{t}_\Sigma$ such that

$$\mathbf{x} + \mathbf{t}_\Sigma \in \mathscr{C}_\Sigma(\mathbf{x})$$

so that conditions (i) and (ii), defining a tangent vector, are met. Condition (i) implies that for every ball $B(\mathbf{x} + \mathbf{t}_\Sigma)$ with center at $\mathbf{x} + \mathbf{t}_\Sigma$ there exists a $\beta > 0$ such that

$$\forall \varepsilon, \quad 0 < \varepsilon < \beta, \qquad \mathbf{x} + \boldsymbol{\eta}(\varepsilon) \in B(\mathbf{x} + \mathbf{t}_\Sigma) \tag{7.27}$$

Also, according to condition (ii), there exists a sequence S_Σ of ε, and a positive number α, such that

$$\forall \varepsilon, \quad 0 < \varepsilon < \alpha, \qquad \varepsilon \in S_\Sigma, \qquad \mathbf{x} + m(\varepsilon)\boldsymbol{\eta}(\varepsilon) \in \bigcup_{i=1}^{\gamma} \Sigma_i \tag{7.28}$$

Thus, there exists a positive number σ, $0 < \sigma \le \alpha$, such that (7.27) *and* (7.28) are met for all ε, $0 < \varepsilon < \sigma$. Condition (7.28) then implies that

$$\forall \varepsilon, \quad 0 < \varepsilon < \sigma, \qquad \varepsilon \in S_\Sigma, \qquad \mathbf{x} + m(\varepsilon)\boldsymbol{\eta}(\varepsilon) \in \Sigma_\nu$$

where

$$\Sigma_\nu \in \{\Sigma_1, \Sigma_2, \ldots, \Sigma_\gamma\}$$

We must now consider two possibilities:

(a) Let S_Σ' denote an infinite subsequence of S_Σ, and suppose that

$$\forall \varepsilon, \quad 0 < \varepsilon < \sigma, \qquad \varepsilon \in S_\Sigma', \qquad \mathbf{x} + m(\varepsilon)\boldsymbol{\eta}(\varepsilon) \in \Sigma_1 \tag{7.29}$$

Then

$$\mathbf{t}_\Sigma \in \mathscr{C}_{\Sigma_1}(\mathbf{x})$$

(b) Alternatively, there does not exist a S_Σ' for which (7.29) is fulfilled; for instance,

$$\mathbf{x} + m(\varepsilon)\boldsymbol{\eta}(\varepsilon) \notin \Sigma_1, \qquad \varepsilon < \sigma_1 \le \sigma$$

† That is, $\Sigma_i \subset \Sigma$ and $\Sigma_i \neq \phi$, $i = 1, 2, \ldots, \mu$; $\Sigma_i \cap \Sigma_j = \phi$, $i \neq j$; and $\bigcup_{i=1}^{\mu} \Sigma_i = \Sigma$.
‡ This can always be done by renumbering the members of the partition.

Then we replace (7.27) and (7.28), respectively, by the statement that there exists a σ_1, $0 < \sigma_1 \leq \sigma \leq \alpha$, such that

$$\forall \varepsilon, \quad 0 < \varepsilon < \sigma_1, \qquad \mathbf{x} + \boldsymbol{\eta}(\varepsilon) \in B(\mathbf{x} + \mathbf{t}_\Sigma)$$

and

$$\forall \varepsilon, \quad 0 < \varepsilon < \sigma_1, \quad \varepsilon \in S_\Sigma, \qquad \mathbf{x} + m(\varepsilon)\boldsymbol{\eta}(\varepsilon) \in \bigcup_{i=2}^{\gamma} \Sigma_i$$

We repeat this process at most $\gamma - 1$ times. Since conditions (i) and (ii), and hence (7.27) and (7.28), must be met, we conclude that case (a) must arise for at least one Σ_i, $i = 1, 2, \ldots, \gamma$. In other words,

$$\mathbf{t}_\Sigma \in \bigcup_{i=1}^{\gamma} \mathscr{C}_{\Sigma_i}(\mathbf{x})$$

which completes the proof of Lemma 10.

7.9 A Nice Limiting Surface

We shall say that a limiting surface Σ is *nice*, if it possesses the following properties:

(i) There exists a partition $\{\Sigma_1, \Sigma_2, \ldots, \Sigma_\mu\}$ of Σ such that at every point $\mathbf{x}$ in $\bar{\Sigma}_i$, $i = 1, 2, \ldots, \mu$, the tangent cone $\mathscr{C}_{\Sigma_i}(\mathbf{x})$ is defined and belongs to a k-dimensional plane $T_{\Sigma_i}(\mathbf{x})$, $k \leq n$, through point $\mathbf{x}$.

(ii) If $\mathbf{x}$ is an *interior* point of $\mathscr{E}^*$, consider a ball $B(\mathbf{x})$ with center at $\mathbf{x}$ and sufficiently small radius so that $B(\mathbf{x}) \subset \mathscr{E}^*$.

Consider also points†

$$\mathbf{x}_A \in B(\mathbf{x}) \cap A/\Sigma, \qquad \mathbf{x}_B \in B(\mathbf{x}) \cap B/\Sigma$$

Then there exists a positive number α such that, for every pair of points $\mathbf{x}_A$ and $\mathbf{x}_B$, the point

$$\alpha\mathbf{x}_A + (1 - \alpha)\mathbf{x}_B \in \Sigma$$

7.91 Closure of a Subset of a Nice Σ; Lemma 11

We shall now prove

Lemma 11. *Let Σ be a nice limiting surface, and consider a point $\mathbf{x} \in \bigcap_{i=1}^{\gamma} \bar{\Sigma}_i$, $\gamma \leq \mu$.‡ If $\mathbf{t}_\Sigma$ is a vector tangent to $\bigcap_{i=1}^{\gamma} \bar{\Sigma}_i$, at $\mathbf{x}$, then*

$$\mathbf{x} + \mathbf{t}_\Sigma \in \bigcap_{i=1}^{\gamma} T_{\Sigma_i}(\mathbf{x})$$

† This is always possible in view of definitions (7.9) and (7.10) of A/Σ and B/Σ, respectively.

‡ That is, the set $\{\Sigma_1, \Sigma_2, \ldots, \Sigma_\gamma\}$ belongs to $\{\Sigma_1, \Sigma_2, \ldots, \Sigma_\mu\}$ which is a partition of Σ satisfying property (i) of a nice limiting surface.

According to property (ii) of a tangent vector $\mathbf{t}_{\Sigma_i}$ of $\bar{\Sigma}_i$ at $\mathbf{x}$, there exist an infinite sequence S_{Σ_i} and a positive number α such that for $\varepsilon \in S_{\Sigma_i}$, $0 < \varepsilon < \alpha$, the point

$$\mathbf{x} + m(\varepsilon)\boldsymbol{\eta}(\varepsilon) \in \bar{\Sigma}_i, \qquad i = 1, 2, \ldots, \gamma$$

Hence,

$$\mathbf{x} + \mathbf{t}_\Sigma = \mathbf{x} + \mathbf{t}_{\Sigma_i} \in \mathscr{C}_{\Sigma_i}(\mathbf{x}), \qquad i = 1, 2, \ldots, \gamma$$

and so, by (7.21), we have

$$\mathbf{x} + \mathbf{t}_\Sigma \in \mathscr{C}_{\Sigma_i}(\mathbf{x}), \qquad i = 1, 2, \ldots, \gamma$$

But according to property (i) of a *nice* Σ surface,

$$\mathscr{C}_{\Sigma_i}(\mathbf{x}) \subset T_{\Sigma_i}(\mathbf{x}), \qquad i = 1, 2, \ldots, \gamma$$

Consequently,

$$\mathbf{x} + \mathbf{t}_\Sigma \in T_{\Sigma_i}(\mathbf{x}), \qquad i = 1, 2, \ldots, \gamma$$

whence follows Lemma 11.

7.92 Cones $\mathscr{S}(\mathbf{x})$ and $\mathscr{C}_\Sigma(\mathbf{x})$ of a Nice Σ; Lemma 12

Another salient property of a *nice* limiting surface is embodied in

Lemma 12. *Let* $\mathbf{x}$ *be an interior point of a nice limiting surface* Σ *with local cone* $\mathscr{S}(\mathbf{x})$ *and tangent cone* $\mathscr{C}_\Sigma(\mathbf{x})$. *Then*

$$\mathscr{C}_\Sigma(\mathbf{x}) = \mathscr{S}(\mathbf{x})$$

Consider a unit vector

$$\mathbf{l} \in \mathscr{S}(\mathbf{x}), \qquad \|\mathbf{l}\| = 1$$

and any conic neighborhood

$$N(\mathbf{x}) \triangleq \{\mathbf{x} + k\boldsymbol{\eta} : k > 0, \quad \mathbf{x} + \boldsymbol{\eta} \in B(\mathbf{x} + \mathbf{l})\}$$

where $B(\mathbf{x} + \mathbf{l})$ is an open ball in E^{n+1} with center at $\mathbf{x} + \mathbf{l}$ and radius ρ. Consider another open ball $B'(\mathbf{x})$ in E^{n+1} with center at $\mathbf{x}$ and the same radius ρ. Since $\mathbf{x}$ is an interior point of $\mathscr{E}^*$, there exists a $\delta > 0$ such that

$$\forall \rho, \quad 0 < \rho < \delta, \qquad B'(\mathbf{x}) \subset \mathscr{E}^*$$

We shall show that

$$N(\mathbf{x}) \cap B'(\mathbf{x}) \cap \Sigma \neq \phi \tag{7.30}$$

Suppose (7.30) is false, that is,

$$N(\mathbf{x}) \cap B'(\mathbf{x}) \cap \Sigma = \phi \tag{7.31}$$

We shall show first of all that (7.31) implies

$$N(\mathbf{x}) \cap B'(\mathbf{x}) \subset A/\Sigma \qquad \text{or} \qquad N(\mathbf{x}) \cap B'(\mathbf{x}) \subset B/\Sigma \tag{7.32}$$

Consider two points $\mathbf{x}_A$ and $\mathbf{x}_B$ in $N(\mathbf{x}) \cap B'(\mathbf{x})$, and assume that

$$\mathbf{x}_A \in A/\Sigma \qquad \text{and} \qquad \mathbf{x}_B \in B/\Sigma$$

Now, since $N(\mathbf{x})$ and $B'(\mathbf{x})$ are convex, $N(\mathbf{x}) \cap B'(\mathbf{x})$ is convex; that is, for all α and β, $\alpha \geq 0$, $\beta \geq 0$, and $\alpha + \beta = 1$,

$$\alpha \mathbf{x}_A + \beta \mathbf{x}_B \in N(\mathbf{x}) \cap B'(\mathbf{x})$$

But, since Σ is *nice*, there exist α and β, $\alpha > 0$, $\beta > 0$, $\alpha + \beta = 1$, such that

$$\alpha \mathbf{x}_A + \beta \mathbf{x}_B \in \Sigma$$

which contradicts (7.31), proving that (7.31) implies (7.32).

However, if (7.32) is valid, then it follows from the definitions of $\mathscr{C}_A(\mathbf{x})$ and $\mathscr{C}_B(\mathbf{x})$, and of interior points, that $\mathbf{x} + \mathbf{l}$ is an interior point of $\mathscr{C}_A(\mathbf{x})$ or of $\mathscr{C}_B(\mathbf{x})$. But that contradicts the assumption of the lemma that $\mathbf{x} + \mathbf{l}$ belongs to $\mathscr{S}(\mathbf{x})$ and hence establishes (7.30).

Since both $N(\mathbf{x})$ and $B'(\mathbf{x})$ are defined in terms of the same radius ρ, condition (7.30) implies that for all ρ there exist a number m, $0 < m < \rho$, and a vector $\boldsymbol{\eta}$, $|\boldsymbol{\eta}| = 1$, such that

$$\mathbf{x} + m\boldsymbol{\eta} \in N(\mathbf{x}) \cap B'(\mathbf{x}) \qquad \textit{and} \qquad \mathbf{x} + m\boldsymbol{\eta} \in \Sigma$$

Therefore, we can associate with every value of ρ a vector

$$\boldsymbol{\eta} \triangleq \boldsymbol{\eta}(\rho), \qquad |\boldsymbol{\eta}(\rho)| = 1$$

and a scalar

$$m \triangleq m(\rho)$$

such that

$$\left.\begin{aligned} \boldsymbol{\eta}(\rho) &\to \mathbf{l} \\ m(\rho) &\to 0 \end{aligned}\right\} \qquad \text{as} \quad \rho \to 0$$

Furthermore, since (7.30) is valid for all values of ρ, it follows that for any sequence of ρ

$$\rho_1, \rho_2, \ldots, \rho_k \ldots \qquad \text{where} \quad \rho_k \to 0 \qquad \text{as} \quad k \to \infty$$

we have

$$\mathbf{x} + m(\rho)\boldsymbol{\eta}(\rho) \in \Sigma$$

Thus, properties (i) and (ii) of a tangent vector to Σ at $\mathbf{x}$ are fulfilled; that is

$$\mathbf{x} + \mathbf{l} \in \mathscr{C}_\Sigma(\mathbf{x})$$

and so

$$\mathbf{x} + \mathbf{l} \in \mathscr{S}(\mathbf{x}) \Rightarrow \mathbf{x} + \mathbf{l} \in \mathscr{C}_\Sigma(\mathbf{x})$$

In other words,

$$\mathscr{S}(\mathbf{x}) \subset \mathscr{C}_\Sigma(\mathbf{x}) \tag{7.33}$$

However, a tangent vector to Σ at $\mathbf{x}$ satisfies conditions (i) and (ii) of Corollary 4; consequently,

$$\mathbf{x} + \mathbf{l} \in \mathscr{C}_\Sigma(\mathbf{x}) \Rightarrow \mathbf{x} + \mathbf{l} \in \mathscr{S}(\mathbf{x})$$

so that

$$\mathscr{C}_\Sigma(\mathbf{x}) \subset \mathscr{S}(\mathbf{x}) \tag{7.34}$$

Lemma 12 follows directly from (7.33) and (7.34).

7.93 Lemmas 13 and 14

Let $\{\Sigma_1, \Sigma_2, \ldots, \Sigma_\mu\}$ constitute a partition of a nice limiting surface Σ, which satisfies property (i) of such a surface. Consider a point

$$\mathbf{x} \subset \bigcap_{i-1}^{\gamma} \bar{\Sigma}_i, \qquad \gamma \leq \mu$$

where the Σ_i, $i = 1, 2, \ldots, \gamma \leq \mu$, belong to the partition, and are *all* the subsets of the partition whose closures contain $\mathbf{x}$. Furthermore, we shall suppose that $\mathbf{x}$ is an interior point of $\mathscr{E}^*$.

Then it follows from Lemma 10 that

$$\mathscr{C}_\Sigma(\mathbf{x}) = \bigcup_{i=1}^{\gamma} \mathscr{C}_{\Sigma_i}(\mathbf{x})$$

so that, in view of property (i) of a nice Σ,

$$\mathscr{C}_\Sigma(\mathbf{x}) \subset \bigcup_{i=1}^{\gamma} T_{\Sigma_i}(\mathbf{x})$$

Furthermore, according to Lemma 12,

$$\mathscr{S}(\mathbf{x}) = \mathscr{C}_\Sigma(\mathbf{x})$$

Consequently,

$$\mathscr{S}(\mathbf{x}) \subset \bigcup_{i=1}^{\gamma} T_{\Sigma_i}(\mathbf{x}) \tag{7.35}$$

Finally, consider a vector $\mathbf{t}_\Sigma$ which is tangent to $\bigcap_{i=1}^{\gamma}\Sigma_i$ at $\mathbf{x}$; then, by Lemma 11, we have

$$\mathbf{x} + \mathbf{t}_\Sigma \in \bigcap_{i=1}^{\gamma} T_{\Sigma_i}(\mathbf{x}) \tag{7.36}$$

Concerning the situation outlined above, we shall now prove

Lemma 13. *Provided $\mathring{\bar{\mathscr{C}}}_B(\mathbf{x}) = \mathring{\mathscr{C}}_B(\mathbf{x})$, then for all $\boldsymbol{\eta}$ such that*

$$\mathbf{x} + \boldsymbol{\eta} \in \bar{\mathscr{C}}_A(\mathbf{x})$$

and all $\alpha \geqq 0$

$$\mathbf{x} + \boldsymbol{\eta} + \alpha \mathbf{t}_\Sigma \in \bar{\mathscr{C}}_A(\mathbf{x})$$

Clearly, if $\mathring{\mathscr{C}}_B(\mathbf{x}) = \phi$ so that $\bar{\mathscr{C}}_A(\mathbf{x}) = E^{n+1}$, the lemma is correct. So let us consider

$$\mathring{\mathscr{C}}_B(\mathbf{x}) \neq \phi$$

and suppose the lemma is false; namely, there exists a value of α, say $\alpha = \alpha'$, such that

$$\mathbf{x} + \boldsymbol{\eta} + \alpha' \mathbf{t}_\Sigma \notin \bar{\mathscr{C}}_A(\mathbf{x}) \tag{7.37}$$

and hence

$$\mathbf{x} + \boldsymbol{\eta} + \alpha' \mathbf{t}_\Sigma \in \mathring{\mathscr{C}}_B(\mathbf{x}) \tag{7.38}$$

Then there exists an open ball with center at $\mathbf{x} + \boldsymbol{\eta} + \alpha' \mathbf{t}_\Sigma$ and belonging to $\mathring{\mathscr{C}}_B(\mathbf{x})$, say

$$B'(\mathbf{x} + \boldsymbol{\eta} + \alpha' \mathbf{t}_\Sigma) \subset \mathring{\mathscr{C}}_B(\mathbf{x})$$

Next consider an open ball $B(\mathbf{x} + \boldsymbol{\eta})$ with center at $\mathbf{x} + \boldsymbol{\eta}$ and radius ρ. Then no matter how small radius ρ, $\rho > 0$,

$$B(\mathbf{x} + \boldsymbol{\eta}) \cap \mathring{\mathscr{C}}_A(\mathbf{x}) \neq \phi \tag{7.39}$$

For, if

$$B(\mathbf{x} + \boldsymbol{\eta}) \cap \mathring{\mathscr{C}}_A(\mathbf{x}) = \phi$$

we have that

$$B(\mathbf{x} + \boldsymbol{\eta}) \subset \bar{\mathscr{C}}_B(\mathbf{x})$$

and, since $B(\mathbf{x} + \boldsymbol{\eta})$ is open, that

$$B(\mathbf{x} + \boldsymbol{\eta}) \subset \mathring{\bar{\mathscr{C}}}_B(\mathbf{x})$$

Since we have assumed that $\mathring{\bar{\mathscr{C}}}_B(\mathbf{x}) = \mathring{\mathscr{C}}_B(\mathbf{x})$, it follows that

$$B(\mathbf{x} + \boldsymbol{\eta}) \subset \mathscr{C}_B(\mathbf{x})$$

which contradicts the hypothesis of the lemma which implies that $\mathbf{x} + \boldsymbol{\eta}$ is not an interior point of $\mathscr{C}_B(\mathbf{x})$.

Now, in view of (7.39), we may consider a point $\mathbf{x} + \boldsymbol{\eta}'$ and an open ball $B''(\mathbf{x} + \boldsymbol{\eta}')$ centered at that point, such that

$$\mathbf{x} + \boldsymbol{\eta}' \in B(\mathbf{x} + \boldsymbol{\eta}) \cap \mathring{\mathscr{C}}_A(\mathbf{x})$$

and

$$B''(\mathbf{x} + \boldsymbol{\eta}') \subset B(\mathbf{x} + \boldsymbol{\eta}) \cap \mathring{\mathscr{C}}_A(\mathbf{x})$$

Thus, there exists a point $\mathbf{x} + \boldsymbol{\eta}''$ such that

(i) $\mathbf{x} + \boldsymbol{\eta}'' \in \mathring{\mathscr{C}}_A(\mathbf{x})$

(ii) $|\boldsymbol{\eta}'' - \boldsymbol{\eta}| < \rho, \quad \forall \rho$

(iii) $\mathbf{x} + \boldsymbol{\eta}'' \notin \bigcup_{i=1}^{\gamma} T_{\Sigma_i}(\mathbf{x})$

Indeed, $\mathbf{x} + \boldsymbol{\eta}''$ may be any point which belongs to ball $B''(\mathbf{x} + \boldsymbol{\eta}')$ *and* satisfies condition (iii) above.

Next consider the line L which passes through point $\mathbf{x} + \boldsymbol{\eta}''$ and is parallel to $\mathbf{t}_\Sigma$. Then line L is also parallel to line

$$L' \triangleq \{\mathbf{x} + \boldsymbol{\eta} + \alpha \mathbf{t}_\Sigma : \forall \alpha\}$$

Clearly the (minimum) distance between lines L and L' is less than radius ρ of ball $B(\mathbf{x} + \boldsymbol{\eta})$. Consequently, for sufficiently small ρ, line L intersects the ball $B'(\mathbf{x} + \boldsymbol{\eta} + \alpha' \mathbf{t}_\Sigma)$. This implies that, for sufficiently small ρ, there exist two points of L, say

$$\mathbf{x}_A = \mathbf{x} + \boldsymbol{\eta}''$$

and

$$\mathbf{x}_B \in B'(\mathbf{x} + \boldsymbol{\eta} + \alpha' \mathbf{t}_\Sigma)$$

such that

$$\mathbf{x}_A \in \mathring{\mathscr{C}}_A(\mathbf{x}), \qquad \mathbf{x}_B \in \mathring{\mathscr{C}}_B(\mathbf{x})$$

In that event, it follows from Lemma 9 that

$$L \cap \mathscr{S}(\mathbf{x}) \neq \phi$$

But this conclusion results in a contradiction. For, since L is parallel to $\mathbf{t}_\Sigma$, it follows from (7.36) that L is parallel to $T_{\Sigma_i}(\mathbf{x})$, $i = 1, 2, \ldots, \gamma$. Furthermore,

$$\mathbf{x}_A \in L$$

and

$$\mathbf{x}_A \notin \bigcup_{i=1}^{\gamma} T_{\Sigma_i}(\mathbf{x})$$

so that

$$L \cap T_{\Sigma_i}(\mathbf{x}) = \phi, \qquad i = 1, 2, \ldots, \gamma \tag{7.40}$$

But (7.40) with (7.35) implies that

$$L \cap \mathscr{S}(\mathbf{x}) = \phi$$

and so Lemma 13 is established.

By similar arguments one can prove

Lemma 14. *Provided* $\mathring{\bar{\mathscr{C}}}_A(\mathbf{x}) = \mathring{\mathscr{C}}_A(\mathbf{x})$, *then for all* $\boldsymbol{\eta}$ *such that*

$$\mathbf{x} + \boldsymbol{\eta} \in \bar{\mathscr{C}}_B(\mathbf{x})$$

and all $\alpha \gtrless 0$

$$\mathbf{x} + \boldsymbol{\eta} + \alpha \mathbf{t}_\Sigma \in \bar{\mathscr{C}}_B(\mathbf{x})$$

7.10 A Set of Admissible Rules

7.101 State Equations and Control

Thus far we have not specified the set of rules which govern the behavior of the system; rather, we have made certain assumptions regarding the system's behavior. Henceforth, we shall restrict the analysis to systems whose state variables are solutions of *state equations*

$$\dot{x}_j = f_j(x_1, x_2, \ldots, x_n; u_1, u_2, \ldots, u_m), \qquad j = 1, 2, \ldots, n \tag{7.41}†$$

where $u_1, u_2, \ldots, u_m$ are parameters.

The control vector, or simply the *control*

$$\mathbf{u} = (u_1, u_2, \ldots, u_m)$$

defines a point in an m-dimensional Euclidean space E^m. Given the control as a function of time

$$\mathbf{u} = \mathbf{u}(t), \qquad t_0 \le t \le t_1$$

the state equations provide a rule which governs the system's behavior during time interval $[t_0, t_1]$.

† $(\dot{\ })$ denotes differentiation of ( ) with respect to time t.

We shall assume that

(i) control $\mathbf{u}(t)$ is defined and piecewise continuous† on $[t_0, t_1]$;
(ii) $\mathbf{u}(t) \in \Omega, \qquad \forall t \in [t_0, t_1]$
where Ω is a given subset of E^m.

A control which satisfies both of these conditions will be termed an *admissible control.* Clearly, the set of admissible controls together with state equations (7.41) constitutes the set of admissible rules.

We shall assume that functions $f_j(\mathfrak{x}, \mathbf{u})$ and $\partial f_j(\mathfrak{x}, \mathbf{u})/\partial x_i$, $i, j = 1, 2, \ldots, n$, are continuous on $E^n \times \Omega$. Consequently, for a given admissible control $\mathbf{u}(t)$, $t_0 \leq t \leq t_1$, and prescribed initial condition

$$\mathfrak{x}(t_0) = \mathfrak{x}^0$$

the solution $\mathfrak{x}(t)$ of state equations (7.41) is unique and continuous on $[t_0, t_1]$.

7.102 An Integral Performance Index and the Trajectory Equation

Now we shall consider an integral performance index

$$\int_{t_0}^{t_1} f_0(\mathfrak{x}(t), \mathbf{u}(t))\, dt \tag{7.42}$$

where $\mathbf{u}(t)$, $t_0 \leq t \leq t_1$, is a control which transfers the system from given initial state $\mathfrak{x}^0$ at time t_0 to a terminal state $\mathfrak{x}^f$, $\mathfrak{x}^f = \bar{\mathfrak{x}}^1$ or $\mathfrak{x}^1$, at time t_1.

As in Sec. 7.2, we introduce a variable x_0 such that

$$x_0(t) + \int_t^{t_1} f_0(\mathfrak{x}(\tau), \mathbf{u}(\tau))\, d\tau = C$$

so that

$$\dot{x}_0 = f_0(\mathfrak{x}, \mathbf{u}) \tag{7.43}$$

We shall assume that $f_0(\mathfrak{x}, \mathbf{u})$ and $\partial f_0(\mathfrak{x}, \mathbf{u})/\partial x_j$, $j = 1, 2, \ldots, n$, are continuous on $E^n \times \Omega$.

Equations (7.41) and (7.43) constitute a set of $n + 1$ scalar equations which we shall write in vector form

$$\dot{\mathbf{x}} = \mathbf{f}(\mathbf{x}, \mathbf{u}) \tag{7.44}$$

where

$$\mathbf{f}(\mathbf{x}, \mathbf{u}) = (f_0(\mathfrak{x}, \mathbf{u}), f_1(\mathfrak{x}, \mathbf{u}), \ldots, f_n(\mathfrak{x}, \mathbf{u}))$$

† If $\mathbf{u}(t)$ is discontinuous at $t = t_c$, we shall take $\mathbf{u}(t_c) = \mathbf{u}(t_c - 0)$. Also, without loss of generality, we shall assume that $\mathbf{u}(t)$ is continuous at $t = t_0$ and $t = t_1$.

Equation (7.44) is the *trajectory equation*; namely, for given admissible control $\mathbf{u}(t)$, $t_0 \le t \le t_1$, and prescribed initial condition

$$\mathbf{x}(t_0) = \mathbf{x}^0$$

Equation (7.44) possesses a unique, continuous solution $\mathbf{x}(t)$ on $[t_0, t_1]$. This solution defines a trajectory Γ in E^{n+1}.

An *optimal control* $\mathbf{u}^*(t)$, $t_0 \le t \le t_1$, results in a transfer of the system from prescribed initial state $\mathfrak{x}^0$ to prescribed terminal state $\mathfrak{x}^1$ while rendering the minimum value of integral (7.42) or, equivalently, of $x_0(t_1) - x_0(t_0)$. Note that the value of integral (7.42) is independent of the initial value of x_0 so that we may choose $x_0(t_0) = 0$.

A solution of trajectory equation (7.44) with $\mathbf{u} = \mathbf{u}^*(t)$, $t_0 \le t \le t_1$, will be denoted by $\mathbf{x}^*(t)$; it defines an optimal trajectory Γ^* in E^{n+1}.

7.11 Velocity Vectors in Augmented State Space

Let us now consider the vector $\mathbf{f}(\mathbf{x}, \mathbf{u})$ in trajectory equation (7.44). Given a constant value $\mathbf{u}^b$ of admissible control, that is,

$$\mathbf{u}(t) = \mathbf{u}^b \in \Omega, \qquad -\infty < t < \infty$$

the vector function $\mathbf{f}(\mathbf{x}, \mathbf{u})$ defines a *field of velocity vectors* $\mathbf{f}(\mathbf{x}, \mathbf{u}^b)$, $\forall \mathbf{x} \in E^{n+1}$, which has the following properties:

(i) a *field line*—namely, the curve whose tangent at $\mathbf{x}$ is $\mathbf{f}(\mathbf{x}, \mathbf{u}^b)$—is an integral curve of (7.44), that is, a trajectory in E^{n+1}.

(ii) through every point of E^{n+1} there passes one and only one field line whose tangent is defined at that point.

7.111 Lemma 15

Consider now a field line, say L, defined parametrically by

$$\mathbf{x} = \mathbf{x}(t), \qquad t \in (-\infty, \infty) \tag{7.45}$$

and let

$$\boldsymbol{\eta}_+(\Delta t) \triangleq \frac{\Delta \mathbf{x}_+}{\Delta t}, \qquad \boldsymbol{\eta}_-(\Delta t) \triangleq \frac{\Delta \mathbf{x}_-}{\Delta t}$$

where

$$\Delta \mathbf{x}_+ \triangleq \mathbf{x}(t_i + \Delta t) - \mathbf{x}(t_i)$$

$$\Delta \mathbf{x}_- \triangleq \mathbf{x}(t_i - \Delta t) - \mathbf{x}(t_i)$$

$$\mathbf{x}(t_i) = \mathbf{x}, \quad \Delta t > 0$$

Clearly, by (7.45), we have

$$\mathbf{x} + \Delta\mathbf{x}_+ \in L, \qquad \mathbf{x} + \Delta\mathbf{x}_- \in L$$

Thus $\boldsymbol{\eta}_+(\Delta t)$ and $\boldsymbol{\eta}_-(\Delta t)$ are continuous functions of Δt, and

$$\left.\begin{aligned} \boldsymbol{\eta}_+(\Delta t) &\to \mathbf{f}(\mathbf{x}, \mathbf{u}^b) \\ \boldsymbol{\eta}_-(\Delta t) &\to -\mathbf{f}(\mathbf{x}, \mathbf{u}^b) \end{aligned}\right\} \quad \text{as} \quad \Delta t \to 0 \tag{7.46}$$

Suppose now that $\mathbf{x}$ is an *interior*† point of a limiting surface Σ; then it follows from Theorem 1 and Corollary 1, respectively, that

$$\begin{aligned} \mathbf{x} + \Delta\mathbf{x}_+ &= \mathbf{x} + \boldsymbol{\eta}_+(\Delta t)\,\Delta t \in \widetilde{A/\Sigma} \\ \mathbf{x} + \Delta\mathbf{x}_- &= \mathbf{x} + \boldsymbol{\eta}_-(\Delta t)\,\Delta t \in \widetilde{B/\Sigma} \end{aligned} \tag{7.47}$$

for sufficiently small Δt.

Conditions (7.46) and (7.47) together with Lemmas 6 and 7 result at once in

Lemma 15. *At an interior point* $\mathbf{x}$ *of a limiting surface* Σ

$$\mathbf{x} + \mathbf{f}(\mathbf{x}, \mathbf{u}) \in \bar{\mathscr{C}}_A(\mathbf{x}), \qquad \mathbf{x} - \mathbf{f}(\mathbf{x}, \mathbf{u}) \in \bar{\mathscr{C}}_B(\mathbf{x})$$

for all $\mathbf{u} \in \Omega$.

7.112 Lemma 16

Consider now an optimal trajectory Γ^* generated by $\mathbf{u}^*(t)$, $t_0 \le t \le t_1$, and given by $\mathbf{x}^*(t)$.

Here we distinguish between two cases:

(i) $\mathbf{x}^*(t) \neq$ const for a nonzero time interval, that is,

$$\mathbf{f}(\mathbf{x}^*(t), \mathbf{u}^*(t)) \neq 0, \qquad t' \le t \le t'', \quad t'' > t'$$

(ii) $\mathbf{x}^*(t) =$ const for a nonzero time interval, that is,

$$\mathbf{f}(\mathbf{x}^*(t), \mathbf{u}^*(t)) = 0, \qquad t' \le t \le t'', \quad t'' > t'$$

Now let

$$\boldsymbol{\eta}_+(\Delta t) \triangleq \frac{\Delta\mathbf{x}_+}{\Delta t}, \qquad \boldsymbol{\eta}_-(\Delta t) \triangleq \frac{\Delta\mathbf{x}_-}{\Delta t}$$

† That is, an interior point of $\mathscr{E}^*$.

where for case (i)

$$\Delta \mathbf{x}_+ \triangleq \mathbf{x}^*(t_c + \Delta t) - \mathbf{x}^*(t_c)$$
$$\Delta \mathbf{x}_- \triangleq \mathbf{x}^*(t_c - \Delta t) - \mathbf{x}^*(t_c)$$
$$\mathbf{x}^*(t_c) = \mathbf{x}, \quad t_c \in (t', t''), \quad \Delta t > 0$$
$$\mathbf{u}_+{}^* \triangleq \mathbf{u}^*(t_c + 0)$$
$$\mathbf{u}_-{}^* \triangleq \mathbf{u}^*(t_c - 0)$$

and for case (ii)

$$\Delta \mathbf{x}_+ \triangleq \mathbf{x}^*(t'' + \Delta t) - \mathbf{x}^*(t'')$$
$$\Delta \mathbf{x}_- \triangleq \mathbf{x}^*(t' - \Delta t) - \mathbf{x}^*(t')$$
$$\mathbf{x}^*(t') = \mathbf{x}^*(t'') = \mathbf{x}, \quad \Delta t > 0$$
$$\mathbf{u}_+{}^* \triangleq \mathbf{u}^*(t'' + 0)$$
$$\mathbf{u}_-{}^* \triangleq \mathbf{u}^*(t' - 0)$$

Thus, $\boldsymbol{\eta}_+(\Delta t)$ and $\boldsymbol{\eta}_-(\Delta t)$ are continuous functions of Δt, where

$$\left.\begin{aligned} \boldsymbol{\eta}_+(\Delta t) &\to \mathbf{f}_+{}^* \triangleq \mathbf{f}(\mathbf{x}, \mathbf{u}_+{}^*) \\ \boldsymbol{\eta}_-(\Delta t) &\to -\mathbf{f}_-{}^* \triangleq -\mathbf{f}(\mathbf{x}, \mathbf{u}_-{}^*) \end{aligned}\right\} \quad \text{as} \quad \Delta t \to 0 \tag{7.48}$$

Furthermore, if $\mathbf{x}$ is an interior point of $\mathscr{E}^*$ and Σ is the limiting surface on which Γ^* lies, we have from Lemma 2 that

$$\begin{aligned} \mathbf{x} + \Delta \mathbf{x}_+ &= \mathbf{x} + \boldsymbol{\eta}_+(\Delta t)\, \Delta t \in \Sigma \\ \mathbf{x} + \Delta \mathbf{x}_- &= \mathbf{x} + \boldsymbol{\eta}_-(\Delta t)\, \Delta t \in \Sigma \end{aligned} \tag{7.49}$$

for sufficiently small Δt.

Conditions (7.48) and (7.49) together with Corollary 4 result in

Lemma 16. *At an interior point* $\mathbf{x}$ *of a limiting surface* Σ

$$\mathbf{x} + \mathbf{f}_+{}^* \in \mathscr{S}(\mathbf{x}), \qquad \mathbf{x} - \mathbf{f}_-{}^* \in \mathscr{S}(\mathbf{x})$$

provided $\mathbf{f}_+{}^*$ *and* $\mathbf{f}_-{}^*$, *respectively, are defined.*†

Of course, if

$$\mathbf{u}_+{}^* = \mathbf{u}_-{}^*$$

then

$$\mathbf{f}_+{}^* = \mathbf{f}_-{}^* \triangleq \mathbf{f}^*$$

and

$$\mathbf{x} + \mathbf{f}^* \in \mathscr{S}(\mathbf{x}), \qquad \mathbf{x} - \mathbf{f}^* \in \mathscr{S}(\mathbf{x})$$

† Clearly, $\mathbf{f}_-{}^*$ is not defined if $\mathbf{x} = \mathbf{x}^*(t_0)$, and $\mathbf{f}_+{}^*$ is not defined if $\mathbf{x} = \mathbf{x}^*(t_1)$.

7.113 Lemmas 17 and 18; Corollary 5

We shall now prove

Lemma 17. *For every vector* $\boldsymbol{\eta}$ *at an interior point* $\mathbf{x}$ *of a limiting surface* Σ, *such that*

$$\mathbf{x} + \boldsymbol{\eta} \in \bar{\mathscr{C}}_A(\mathbf{x})$$

and for every α, $\alpha \geq 0$,

$$\mathbf{x} + \boldsymbol{\eta} + \alpha\mathbf{f}(\mathbf{x}, \mathbf{u}) \in \bar{\mathscr{C}}_A(\mathbf{x}), \qquad \forall \mathbf{u} \in \Omega$$

Let us first establish the lemma for

$$\mathbf{x} + \boldsymbol{\eta} \in \mathscr{C}_A(\mathbf{x}) \tag{7.50}$$

whence, according to definition (7.13) of $\mathscr{C}_A(\mathbf{x})$, there exists a $\sigma > 0$ such that for all ε, $0 < \varepsilon < \sigma$,

$$\mathbf{x} + \varepsilon\boldsymbol{\eta} \in \widetilde{A/\Sigma} \tag{7.51}$$

The subsequent arguments are similar to those employed in the proof of Lemma 15. Here we consider a trajectory, Γ, which passes through point $\mathbf{x} + \varepsilon\boldsymbol{\eta}$ at time t_i, and which is generated by a constant admissible control

$$\mathbf{u}(t) = \mathbf{u}^b \in \Omega, \qquad t \in (-\infty, \infty)$$

In other words, Γ is the integral curve of

$$\dot{\mathbf{x}} = \mathbf{f}(\mathbf{x}, \mathbf{u}^b)$$

passing through $\mathbf{x} + \varepsilon\boldsymbol{\eta}$.

Let $\mathbf{x}(t)$, $t \in (-\infty, \infty)$, be a point of Γ. We have

$$\left.\begin{aligned} \mathbf{x}(t_i) &= \mathbf{x} + \varepsilon\boldsymbol{\eta} \\ \mathbf{x}(t_i + \Delta t) &= \mathbf{x}(t_i) + \mathbf{f}(\mathbf{x} + \varepsilon\boldsymbol{\eta}, \mathbf{u}^b)\,\Delta t + \mathbf{o}(\Delta t), \qquad \Delta t > 0 \end{aligned}\right. \tag{7.52}$$

It follows from (7.51) with Theorem 1 and Corollary 1 that

$$\mathbf{x}(t_i + \Delta t) \in \widetilde{A/\Sigma}$$

for sufficiently small Δt. Thus, (7.52) leads to

$$\begin{aligned} &\mathbf{x} + \varepsilon\boldsymbol{\eta} + \mathbf{f}(\mathbf{x} + \varepsilon\boldsymbol{\eta}, \mathbf{u}^b)\,\Delta t + \mathbf{o}(\Delta t) \\ &= \mathbf{x} + \varepsilon\boldsymbol{\eta} + \mathbf{f}(\mathbf{x}, \mathbf{u}^b)\,\Delta t + \frac{\partial \mathbf{f}}{\partial \mathbf{x}}\varepsilon\boldsymbol{\eta}\,\Delta t + \mathbf{o}(\varepsilon)\,\Delta t + \mathbf{o}(\Delta t) \in \widetilde{A/\Sigma} \end{aligned} \tag{7.53†}$$

† Here $\partial\mathbf{f}/\partial\mathbf{x}$ denotes the $n+1 \times n+1$ matrix $[\partial f_j/\partial x_i]$, $i, j = 0, 1, \ldots, n$. evaluated at the point $(\mathbf{x}, \mathbf{u}^b)$ in $E^{n+1} \times E^m$.

Now we shall choose ε, $0 < \varepsilon < \sigma$, and Δt, $\Delta t > 0$, sufficiently small, such that

$$\Delta t/\varepsilon = \alpha$$

where α is any bounded positive scalar constant. Clearly, this is possible for α, $0 < \alpha < \infty$.

Rewriting (7.53), we have

$$\mathbf{x} + \varepsilon\left[\boldsymbol{\eta} + \alpha\mathbf{f}(\mathbf{x}, \mathbf{u}^b) + \frac{\partial \mathbf{f}}{\partial \mathbf{x}}\,\alpha\varepsilon\boldsymbol{\eta} + \alpha\mathbf{o}(\varepsilon) + \frac{\mathbf{o}(\varepsilon)}{\varepsilon}\right] \in \widetilde{A/\Sigma} \tag{7.54}$$

where the quantity in brackets is a continuous vector function, $\boldsymbol{\eta}(\varepsilon)$, of ε, such that

$$\boldsymbol{\eta}(\varepsilon) \to \boldsymbol{\eta} + \alpha\mathbf{f}(\mathbf{x}, \mathbf{u}^b) \qquad \text{as} \quad \varepsilon \to 0$$

Condition (7.54) together with Lemma 6 results at once in

$$\mathbf{x} + \boldsymbol{\eta} + \alpha\mathbf{f}(\mathbf{x}, \mathbf{u}^b) \in \overline{\mathscr{C}}_A(\mathbf{x}) \tag{7.55}$$

for all $\mathbf{u}^b \in \Omega$ and all $\alpha > 0$.

Now if $\mathscr{C}_A(\mathbf{x})$ is closed, then $\mathscr{C}_A(\mathbf{x}) = \overline{\mathscr{C}}_A(\mathbf{x})$, and Lemma 17 is established. On the other hand, if $\mathscr{C}_A(\mathbf{x})$ is not closed, there exist limit points of $\mathscr{C}_A(\mathbf{x})$ which do not belong to $\mathscr{C}_A(\mathbf{x})$; in that case, let us consider†

$$\mathbf{x} + \boldsymbol{\eta} \in \mathscr{S}(\mathbf{x})$$

Let $N(\mathbf{x})$ denote a conic neighborhood, that is,

$$N(\mathbf{x}) \triangleq \{\mathbf{x} + k\boldsymbol{\xi} : k > 0, \quad \mathbf{x} + \boldsymbol{\xi} \in B(\mathbf{x} + \boldsymbol{\eta})\}$$

where $B(\mathbf{x} + \boldsymbol{\eta})$ is an open ball in E^{n+1} with center at $\mathbf{x} + \boldsymbol{\eta}$ and radius ρ. As a consequence of Lemma 8, we have

$$N(\mathbf{x}) \cap \mathscr{C}_A(\mathbf{x}) \neq \phi, \qquad \forall \rho > 0 \tag{7.56}$$

Since ρ can be chosen arbitrarily small, it follows from (7.56) that there exists a sequence of vectors $\boldsymbol{\eta}_1, \boldsymbol{\eta}_2, \ldots, \boldsymbol{\eta}_\nu$, such that

$$\mathbf{x} + \boldsymbol{\eta}_i \in \mathscr{C}_A(\mathbf{x}), \qquad i = 1, 2, \ldots, \nu$$

$$\boldsymbol{\eta}_\nu \to \boldsymbol{\eta} \qquad \text{as} \quad \nu \to \infty$$

which implies, as shown earlier, that

$$\mathbf{x} + \boldsymbol{\eta}_\nu + \alpha\mathbf{f}(\mathbf{x}, \mathbf{u}^b) \in \overline{\mathscr{C}}_A(\mathbf{x}), \qquad \forall \mathbf{u}^b \in \Omega, \qquad \forall \alpha > 0$$

But

$$\mathbf{x} + \boldsymbol{\eta}_\nu + \alpha\mathbf{f}(\mathbf{x}, \mathbf{u}^b) \to \mathbf{x} + \boldsymbol{\eta} + \alpha\mathbf{f}(\mathbf{x}, \mathbf{u}^b) \tag{7.57}$$

† Note that $\overline{\mathscr{C}}_A(\mathbf{x}) = \mathring{\mathscr{C}}_A(\mathbf{x}) \cup \mathscr{S}(\mathbf{x})$ is the union of the set of all points of $\mathscr{C}_A(\mathbf{x})$ and the set of all limit points (accumulation points) of $\mathscr{C}_A(\mathbf{x})$, and $\mathring{\mathscr{C}}_A(\mathbf{x}) \subset \mathscr{C}_A(\mathbf{x})$. Thus, the limit points which do not belong to $\mathscr{C}_A(\mathbf{x})$ must belong to $\mathscr{S}(\mathbf{x})$.

as $\boldsymbol{\eta}_\nu \to \boldsymbol{\eta}$, that is, as $\nu \to \infty$. Thus, it is readily seen that

$$\mathbf{x} + \boldsymbol{\eta} + \alpha\mathbf{f}(\mathbf{x}, \mathbf{u}^b) \in \mathscr{C}_A(\mathbf{x})$$

for all $\mathbf{u}^h \in \Omega$ and all $\alpha > 0$. For, suppose this conclusion is false and

$$\mathbf{x} + \boldsymbol{\eta} + \alpha\mathbf{f}(\mathbf{x}, \mathbf{u}^b) \in \mathring{\mathscr{C}}_B(\mathbf{x})$$

Then it follows from (7.57) that there exists a positive number μ such that for $\nu > \mu$

$$\mathbf{x} + \boldsymbol{\eta}_\nu + \alpha\mathbf{f}(\mathbf{x}, \mathbf{u}^b) \in \mathring{\mathscr{C}}_B(\mathbf{x})$$

But this is in contradiction to the result of the first portion of the proof, since

$$\mathbf{x} + \boldsymbol{\eta}_\nu \in \mathscr{C}_A(\mathbf{x})$$

Finally, we note that Lemma 17 is trivially valid for $\alpha = 0$.

By arguments analogous to those employed above, one can prove

Lemma 18. *For every vector* $\boldsymbol{\eta}$ *at an interior point* $\mathbf{x}$ *of a limiting surface* Σ, *such that*

$$\mathbf{x} + \boldsymbol{\eta} \in \overline{\mathscr{C}}_B(\mathbf{x})$$

and for every α, $\alpha \geq 0$,

$$\mathbf{x} + \boldsymbol{\eta} - \alpha\mathbf{f}(\mathbf{x}, \mathbf{u}) \in \overline{\mathscr{C}}_B(\mathbf{x}), \qquad \forall \mathbf{u} \in \Omega$$

It is readily seen now that Lemma 15 is a direct consequence of Lemmas 17 and 18, obtained by setting $\boldsymbol{\eta} = 0$ and $\alpha = 1$.

Lemmas 17 and 18 lead at once to

Corollary 5. *If* $\mathbf{x}$ *is an interior point of a limiting surface* Σ, *and*

$$\sum_{\nu=1}^{r} \alpha_\nu \mathbf{f}(\mathbf{x}, \mathbf{u}^\nu)$$

is any linear combination of velocity vectors, where

$$\mathbf{u}^\nu \in \Omega, \qquad \alpha_\nu \geq 0, \quad \nu = 1, 2, \dots, r,$$

then

$$\mathbf{x} + \sum_{\nu=1}^{r} \alpha_\nu \mathbf{f}(\mathbf{x}, \mathbf{u}^\nu) \in \overline{\mathscr{C}}_A(\mathbf{x})$$

$$\mathbf{x} - \sum_{\nu=1}^{r} \alpha_\nu \mathbf{f}(\mathbf{x}, \mathbf{u}^\nu) \in \overline{\mathscr{C}}_B(\mathbf{x})$$

To prove this corollary, we invoke an argument by recursion. In view of Lemma 17, we have

$$\mathbf{x} + \alpha_1 \mathbf{f}(\mathbf{x}, \mathbf{u}^1) \in \bar{\mathscr{C}}_A(\mathbf{x})$$

Furthermore, suppose

$$\mathbf{x} + \boldsymbol{\eta} \triangleq \mathbf{x} + \sum_{\nu=1}^{s} \alpha_\nu \mathbf{f}(\mathbf{x}, \mathbf{u}^\nu) \in \bar{\mathscr{C}}_A(\mathbf{x})$$

Then it follows from Lemma 17 that

$$\mathbf{x} + \boldsymbol{\eta} + \alpha_{s+1} \mathbf{f}(\mathbf{x}, \mathbf{u}^{s+1}) = \mathbf{x} + \sum_{\nu=1}^{s+1} \alpha_\nu \mathbf{f}(\mathbf{x}, \mathbf{u}^\nu) \in \bar{\mathscr{C}}_A(\mathbf{x})$$

This establishes the first part of the corollary. The second part follows from analogous arguments invoking Lemma 18.

7.12 Separability of Local Cones

7.121 Separating Hyperplane

We shall now introduce some *definitions*. We shall say that an n-dimensional hyperplane $\mathscr{T}(\mathbf{x})$, containing an interior point $\mathbf{x}$ of a limiting surface Σ, is an *n-dimensional separating hyperplane* of closed cone $\bar{\mathscr{C}}_A(\mathbf{x})$ (or $\bar{\mathscr{C}}_B(\mathbf{x})$), if every point

$$\mathbf{x} + \boldsymbol{\eta} \in \bar{\mathscr{C}}_A(\mathbf{x}) \qquad (\text{or } \bar{\mathscr{C}}_B(\mathbf{x}))$$

lies in one of the closed half spaces determined by $\mathscr{T}(\mathbf{x})$.

The corresponding *closed* half space will be denoted by $\bar{R}_A$ (or $\bar{R}_B$), and the corresponding *open* half space by R_A (or R_B).

Then, if there exists an n-dimensional separating hyperplane of $\bar{\mathscr{C}}_A(\mathbf{x})$ (or $\bar{\mathscr{C}}_B(\mathbf{x})$), we shall say that cone $\bar{\mathscr{C}}_A(\mathbf{x})$ (or $\bar{\mathscr{C}}_B(\mathbf{x})$) is *separable*.

Indeed, if $\mathscr{T}(\mathbf{x})$ is an n-dimensional separating hyperplane of $\bar{\mathscr{C}}_A(\mathbf{x})$ or $\bar{\mathscr{C}}_B(\mathbf{x})$, respectively, then

$$\bar{\mathscr{C}}_A(\mathbf{x}) \subseteq \bar{R}_A \Rightarrow \begin{cases} \mathscr{C}_A(\mathbf{x}) \subseteq \bar{R}_A & (7.58) \\ \mathring{\mathscr{C}}_A(\mathbf{x}) \subseteq R_A & (7.59) \end{cases}$$

$$\bar{\mathscr{C}}_B(\mathbf{x}) \subseteq \bar{R}_B \Rightarrow \begin{cases} \mathscr{C}_B(\mathbf{x}) \subseteq \bar{R}_B & (7.60) \\ \mathring{\mathscr{C}}_B(\mathbf{x}) \subseteq R_B & (7.61) \end{cases}$$

7.122 Cone of Normals

If $\overline{\mathscr{C}}_A(\mathbf{x})$ (or $\overline{\mathscr{C}}_B(\mathbf{x})$) is separable, let us consider a separating hyperplane $\mathscr{T}(\mathbf{x})$ and, at point $\mathbf{x}$, a bound vector $\mathbf{n}(\mathbf{x})$, $|\mathbf{n}(\mathbf{x})| = 1$, which is normal to $\mathscr{T}(\mathbf{x})$. Furthermore

(i) if $\overline{\mathscr{C}}_A(\mathbf{x})$ is separable, we shall choose $\mathbf{n}(\mathbf{x})$ such that

$$\mathbf{x} + \mathbf{n}(\mathbf{x}) \in \text{comp } \bar{R}_A \tag{7.62}$$

(ii) if $\overline{\mathscr{C}}_B(\mathbf{x})$ is separable, we shall choose $\mathbf{n}(\mathbf{x})$ such that

$$\mathbf{x} + \mathbf{n}(\mathbf{x}) \in R_B \tag{7.63}$$

Note that (i) and (ii) are equivalent if both $\overline{\mathscr{C}}_A(\mathbf{x})$ and $\overline{\mathscr{C}}_B(\mathbf{x})$ are separable.

Finally, if $\overline{\mathscr{C}}_A(\mathbf{x})$ (or $\overline{\mathscr{C}}_B(\mathbf{x})$) is separable, we shall consider the set $\{\mathbf{n}(\mathbf{x})\}$ of vectors $\mathbf{n}(\mathbf{x})$ defined above—using (i) or (ii) as applicable—for all separating hyperplanes of $\overline{\mathscr{C}}_A(\mathbf{x})$ (or $\overline{\mathscr{C}}_B(\mathbf{x})$), and define the *cone of normals* at point $\mathbf{x}$ by

$$\mathscr{C}_n(\mathbf{x}) \triangleq \{\mathbf{x} + k\mathbf{n}(\mathbf{x}) : k > 0, \quad \mathbf{n}(\mathbf{x}) \in \{\mathbf{n}(\mathbf{x})\}\} \tag{7.64}$$

7.13 Regular and Nonregular Interior Points of a Limiting Surface

We shall say that an interior point $\mathbf{x}$ of $\mathscr{E}^*$ is a *regular* interior point of the limiting surface Σ which passes through $\mathbf{x}$, if both $\overline{\mathscr{C}}_A(\mathbf{x})$ and $\overline{\mathscr{C}}_B(\mathbf{x})$ are separable. In order to make this concept more precise, let us suppose that $\mathbf{x} \in \Sigma$ is a point of this kind and that $\mathscr{T}_A(\mathbf{x})$ is a separating plane of $\overline{\mathscr{C}}_A(\mathbf{x})$, for instance.

Accordingly, $\bar{R}_A$ is the closed half space determined by $\mathscr{T}_A(\mathbf{x})$ which contains $\overline{\mathscr{C}}_A(\mathbf{x})$. As pointed out in (7.58), we have

$$\mathscr{C}_A(\mathbf{x}) \subseteq \bar{R}_A$$

But

$$\mathscr{C}_B(\mathbf{x}) = \text{comp } \mathscr{C}_A(\mathbf{x})$$

so that

$$\mathscr{C}_A(\mathbf{x}) \subseteq \bar{R}_A \Rightarrow \begin{cases} \text{comp } \bar{R}_A \subseteq \mathscr{C}_B(\mathbf{x}) \\ \text{comp } R_A \subseteq \overline{\mathscr{C}}_B(\mathbf{x}) \end{cases} \tag{7.65}$$

Now let $\mathscr{T}_B(\mathbf{x})$ denote an n-dimensional separating hyperplane of $\overline{\mathscr{C}}_B(\mathbf{x})$, and $\bar{R}_B$ the closed half space which is determined by $\mathscr{T}_B(\mathbf{x})$ and contains $\overline{\mathscr{C}}_B(\mathbf{x})$. Then

$$\overline{\mathscr{C}}_B(\mathbf{x}) \subseteq \bar{R}_B \tag{7.66}$$

It follows from (7.65) and (7.66) that

$$\text{comp } R_A \subseteq \bar{\mathscr{C}}_B(\mathbf{x}) \subseteq \bar{R}_B \tag{7.67}$$

Since both planes $\mathscr{T}_A(\mathbf{x})$ and $\mathscr{T}_B(\mathbf{x})$, which bound closed half spaces comp R_A and $\bar{R}_B$, respectively, pass through point $\mathbf{x}$, (7.67) implies that

$$\text{comp } R_A = \bar{R}_B \tag{7.68}$$

which, in turn, implies that

$$\mathscr{T}_A(\mathbf{x}) = \mathscr{T}_B(\mathbf{x}) \triangleq \mathscr{T}(\mathbf{x}) \tag{7.69}$$

Furthermore, (7.67) implies that

$$\bar{\mathscr{C}}_B(\mathbf{x}) = \bar{R}_B \tag{7.70}$$

However, since

$$\mathring{\mathscr{C}}_A(\mathbf{x}) = \text{comp } \bar{\mathscr{C}}_B(\mathbf{x})$$

it follows from (7.68) and (7.70) that

$$\mathring{\mathscr{C}}_A(\mathbf{x}) = R_A$$

whence†

$$\bar{\mathscr{C}}_A(\mathbf{x}) = \bar{R}_A \tag{7.71}$$

Finally, from (7.70) and (7.71) we have

$$\mathscr{S}(\mathbf{x}) \triangleq \bar{\mathscr{C}}_A(\mathbf{x}) \cap \bar{\mathscr{C}}_B(\mathbf{x}) = \bar{R}_A \cap \bar{R}_B = \mathscr{T}(\mathbf{x}) \tag{7.72}$$

These conclusions are important since they show the special features of a *regular* interior point of Σ; namely, $\bar{\mathscr{C}}_A(\mathbf{x})$ and $\bar{\mathscr{C}}_B(\mathbf{x})$ possess the *same* separating hyperplane

$$\mathscr{T}(\mathbf{x}) = \mathscr{S}(\mathbf{x})$$

and, moreover, this separating hyperplane is *unique*, since $\mathscr{S}(\mathbf{x})$ is unique.

If Σ is a *nice* limiting surface, then

$$\mathscr{S}(\mathbf{x}) = \mathscr{C}_\Sigma(\mathbf{x})$$

Thus, at a regular interior point $\mathbf{x}$ of a *nice* limiting surface Σ, the tangent cone $\mathscr{C}_\Sigma(\mathbf{x})$ is an n-dimensional hyperplane, namely, the *tangent plane* $T_\Sigma(\mathbf{x})$ of Σ at point $\mathbf{x}$; that is,

$$\mathscr{C}_\Sigma(\mathbf{x}) = T_\Sigma(\mathbf{x}) \tag{7.73}$$

This tangent plane is the common separating hyperplane of $\bar{\mathscr{C}}_A(\mathbf{x})$ and $\bar{\mathscr{C}}_B(\mathbf{x})$; it is unique.

† Indeed $\bar{\mathring{\mathscr{C}}}_A(\mathbf{x}) = \bar{R}_A$ and $\bar{\mathring{\mathscr{C}}}_A(\mathbf{x}) \subseteq \bar{\mathscr{C}}_A(\mathbf{x})$. It follows that $\bar{R}_A \subseteq \bar{\mathscr{C}}_A(\mathbf{x})$, and since $\bar{\mathscr{C}}_A(\mathbf{x}) \subseteq \bar{R}_A$ we have (7.71).

On the other hand, if *not both* $\overline{\mathscr{C}}_A(\mathbf{x})$ and $\overline{\mathscr{C}}_B(\mathbf{x})$ are separable, then point $\mathbf{x}$ will be called a *nonregular* interior point of Σ.

We distinguish among three possibilities:

(i) $\overline{\mathscr{C}}_A(\mathbf{x})$ is separable, and $\overline{\mathscr{C}}_B(\mathbf{x})$ is not.
(ii) $\overline{\mathscr{C}}_B(\mathbf{x})$ is separable, and $\overline{\mathscr{C}}_A(\mathbf{x})$ is not.
(iii) Neither $\overline{\mathscr{C}}_A(\mathbf{x})$ nor $\overline{\mathscr{C}}_B(\mathbf{x})$ is separable; in that case, we shall call $\mathbf{x}$ an *antiregular* point of Σ.

7.14 Some Properties of a Linear Transformation

7.141 Variational Equations; Lemma 19

Consider a vector

$$\boldsymbol{\eta} = (\eta_0, \eta_1, \ldots, \eta_n)$$

at point $\mathbf{x}^*(t)$ of optimal trajectory Γ^* generated by control $\mathbf{u}^*(t)$, $t_0 \le t \le t_1$, whose components $\eta_j = \eta_j(t)$ comprise the solution of *variational equations*

$$\dot{\eta}_j = \sum_{i=0}^{n} \frac{\partial f_j(\mathbf{x}, \mathbf{u}^*(t))}{\partial x_i}\bigg|_{\mathbf{x}=\mathbf{x}^*(t)} \eta_i, \qquad j = 0, 1, \ldots, n \tag{7.74}$$

for given initial condition $\boldsymbol{\eta}(t') = \boldsymbol{\eta}'$, $t_0 \le t' \le t_1$.

The solution of Eqs. (7.74) defines a nonsingular linear transformation $A(t', t)$ such that

$$\boldsymbol{\eta}(t) = A(t', t)\boldsymbol{\eta}', \qquad t_0 \le t' \le t \le t_1 \tag{7.75}$$

For $t = t''$, we write $\boldsymbol{\eta}(t'') \triangleq \boldsymbol{\eta}''$, so that

$$\boldsymbol{\eta}'' = A(t', t'')\boldsymbol{\eta}', \qquad t_0 \le t' \le t'' \le t_1 \tag{7.76}$$

Since $A(t', t'')$ is a linear operator which transforms $\boldsymbol{\eta}'$ at time t' into $\boldsymbol{\eta}''$ at time t'', it may be written in matrix form. This amounts to representing $A(t', t'')$ by a set of coefficients $a_{ij}(t', t'')$, and the linear transformation by

$$\eta_i'' = \sum_{j=0}^{n} a_{ij}(t', t'')\eta_j', \qquad i = 0, 1, \ldots, n$$

Henceforth, we shall not distinguish between linear operator $A(t', t'')$ and its matrix representation.

Since transformation $A(t', t'')$ is *nonsingular*, an inverse transformation $A^{-1}(t', t'')$ is defined such that

$$\boldsymbol{\eta}' = A^{-1}(t', t'')\boldsymbol{\eta}'', \qquad t_0 \le t' \le t'' \le t_1 \tag{7.77}$$

Indeed, (7.77) is equivalent to (7.76). It is readily seen that (7.77) renders the solution $\eta_j(t)$ at time t' for initial conditions $\eta_j(t'') = \eta_j''$, $j = 0, 1, \ldots, n$.

In other words, (7.77) implies backward integration, whereas (7.76) implies forward integration. Accordingly, we shall put

$$A^{-1}(t', t'') = A(t'', t')$$

so that (7.77) reads

$$\boldsymbol{\eta}' = A(t'', t')\boldsymbol{\eta}'', \qquad t_0 \le t' \le t'' \le t_1$$

The remarks above allow us to extend the notation in (7.75) to cases in which $t_0 \le t \le t' \le t_1$. Thus, if $t_p, t_{p+1}, \dots, t_{q-1}, t_q$, is a sequence of points, *not necessarily ordered*, belonging to $[t_0, t_1]$, then it follows from the multiplication rule for linear operators that

$$A(t_p, t_q) = A(t_{q-1}, t_q)A(t_{q-2}, t_{q-1}) \cdots A(t_{p+1}, t_{p+2})A(t_p, t_{p+1}) \qquad (7.78)$$

so that

$$\begin{aligned}\boldsymbol{\eta}(t_q) &= A(t_p, t_q)\boldsymbol{\eta}(t_p) \\ &= A(t_{q-1}, t_q)[A(t_{q-2}, t_{q-1}) \cdots [A(t_{p+1}, t_{p+2})[A(t_p, t_{p+1})\boldsymbol{\eta}(t_p)]] \cdots]\end{aligned}$$

In other words,

$$\begin{aligned}\boldsymbol{\eta}(t_{p+1}) &= A(t_p, t_{p+1})\boldsymbol{\eta}(t_p) \\ \boldsymbol{\eta}(t_{p+2}) &= A(t_{p+1}, t_{p+2})\boldsymbol{\eta}(t_{p+1}) \\ &\;\vdots \\ \boldsymbol{\eta}(t_{q-1}) &= A(t_{q-2}, t_{q-1})\boldsymbol{\eta}(t_{q-2}) \\ \boldsymbol{\eta}(t_q) &= A(t_{q-1}, t_q)\boldsymbol{\eta}(t_{q-1})\end{aligned}$$

Moreover, we have the obvious relations

$$A(t_p, t_p) = 1$$

$$A(t_p, t_q)A(t_q, t_p) = 1$$

Finally, from the properties of linear transformation $A(t', t)$, $t_0 \le t' \le t_1$ and $t_0 \le t \le t_1$, we have

Lemma 19. *The transform $\Pi(\mathbf{x}^*(t))$ of a plane $\Pi(\mathbf{x}^*(t'))$ containing point $\mathbf{x}^*(t')$ of Γ^*, due to linear transformation $A(t', t)$, has the following properties:*

(i) *$\Pi(\mathbf{x}^*(t))$ is defined for all $t \in [t_0, t_1]$;*
(ii) *$\Pi(\mathbf{x}^*(t))$ is a plane of the same dimension as $\Pi(\mathbf{x}^*(t'))$;*
(iii) *the orientation of $\Pi(\mathbf{x}^*(t))$ is continuous on $[t_0, t_1]$.*

7.142 Adjoint Equations

Consider now the equations adjoint to variational Eqs. (7.74), namely,

$$\dot{\lambda}_j = - \sum_{i=0}^{n} \left. \frac{\partial f_i(\mathbf{x}, \mathbf{u}^*(t))}{\partial x_j} \right|_{\mathbf{x}=\mathbf{x}^*(t)} \lambda_i, \qquad j = 0, 1, \ldots, n \tag{7.79}$$

whose solution $\boldsymbol{\lambda}(t) = (\lambda_0(t), \lambda_1(t), \ldots, \lambda_n(t))$, for given initial condition $\boldsymbol{\lambda}(t') = \boldsymbol{\lambda}'$, $t_0 \leq t' \leq t_1$, is unique and continuous on $[t_0, t_1]$.

As a consequence of (7.74) and (7.79), we have

$$\boldsymbol{\lambda}(t) \cdot \boldsymbol{\eta}(t) = \text{const}, \qquad \forall t \in [t_0, t_1] \tag{7.80}†$$

Let us now choose the following initial conditions for (7.74) and (7.79), respectively:

(i) $\boldsymbol{\eta}' \neq 0$ and $\mathbf{x}^*(t') + \boldsymbol{\eta}' \in \Pi(\mathbf{x}^*(t'))$;
(ii) $\boldsymbol{\lambda}' \neq 0$ and normal to $\Pi(\mathbf{x}^*(t'))$.

Then it follows from (7.80) that

$$\boldsymbol{\lambda}(t) \cdot \boldsymbol{\eta}(t) = 0, \qquad \forall t \in [t_0, t_1] \tag{7.81}$$

Since (7.81) is valid for all $\boldsymbol{\eta}'$ satisfying (i) above, it follows that

$$\boldsymbol{\lambda}(t) \qquad \text{is normal to} \quad \Pi(\mathbf{x}^*(t)) \tag{7.82}$$

for all $t \in [t_0, t_1]$.

7.15 Properties of Separable Local Cones

7.151 Lemma 20

Let us now prove

Lemma 20. *Let* $\mathbf{x}^*(t')$ *and* $\mathbf{x}^*(t'')$, $t_0 \leq t' \leq t'' \leq t_1$, *be two points of optimal trajectory* Γ^*, *corresponding to control* $\mathbf{u}^*(t)$ *and solution* $\mathbf{x}^*(t)$, $t_0 \leq t \leq t_1$. *Let* $\boldsymbol{\eta}'$ *be a vector at* $\mathbf{x}^*(t')$, *and* $\boldsymbol{\eta}''$ *its transform at* $\mathbf{x}^*(t'')$, *due to linear transformation* $A(t', t'')$; *namely,*

$$\boldsymbol{\eta}'' = A(t', t'')\boldsymbol{\eta}'$$

If

$$\mathbf{x}^*(t') + \boldsymbol{\eta}' \in \overline{\mathscr{C}}_A(\mathbf{x}^*(t'))$$

then

$$\mathbf{x}^*(t'') + \boldsymbol{\eta}'' \in \overline{\mathscr{C}}_A(\mathbf{x}^*(t''))$$

† Dot denotes inner product; e.g., $\mathbf{a} \cdot \mathbf{b} \triangleq \sum_{j=0}^{n} a_j b_j$.

First of all, let us suppose that

$$\mathbf{x}^*(t') + \boldsymbol{\eta}' \in \mathscr{C}_A(\mathbf{x}^*(t'))$$

According to definition (7.13) of $\mathscr{C}_A(\mathbf{x})$, there exists a positive number α such that for all ε, $0 < \varepsilon < \alpha$,

$$\mathbf{x}^*(t') + \varepsilon\boldsymbol{\eta}' \in \widetilde{A/\Sigma} \tag{7.83}$$

Next consider a trajectory which starts at point $\mathbf{x}^*(t') + \varepsilon\boldsymbol{\eta}'$, and which is generated by the same control as Γ^*, namely $\mathbf{u}^*(t)$, $t_0 \leq t \leq t_1$, on $[t', t'']$. The solution of trajectory equation (7.44), corresponding to this trajectory, is

$$\mathbf{x}(t) = \mathbf{x}^*(t) + \varepsilon\boldsymbol{\eta}(t) + \mathbf{o}(t, \varepsilon) \tag{7.84}$$

where $\mathbf{o}(t, \varepsilon)/\varepsilon$ tends to zero uniformly as $\varepsilon \to 0$, $t' \leq t \leq t''$, and $\boldsymbol{\eta}(t)$ is the solution of variational equations (7.74) with initial condition $\boldsymbol{\eta}(t') = \boldsymbol{\eta}'$. Thus, $\boldsymbol{\eta}(t)$ is given by linear transformation $A(t', t)$.

According to (7.83), together with Theorem 1 and Corollary 1, we have

$$\mathbf{x}(t'') = \mathbf{x}^*(t'') + \varepsilon\boldsymbol{\eta}(t'') + \mathbf{o}(t'', \varepsilon) \in \widetilde{A/\Sigma}$$

for sufficiently small ε. Furthermore,

$$\boldsymbol{\eta}(t'') + \frac{\mathbf{o}(t'', \varepsilon)}{\varepsilon} \to \boldsymbol{\eta}(t'') \triangleq \boldsymbol{\eta}'' \qquad \text{as} \quad \varepsilon \to 0$$

Consequently, it follows from Lemma 6 that

$$\mathbf{x}^*(t'') + \boldsymbol{\eta}'' \in \bar{\mathscr{C}}_A(\mathbf{x}^*(t'')) \tag{7.85}$$

Thus, if $\mathscr{C}_A(\mathbf{x}^*(t'))$ is closed,

$$\mathscr{C}_A(\mathbf{x}^*(t')) = \bar{\mathscr{C}}_A(\mathbf{x}^*(t'))$$

and the lemma is established.

If $\mathscr{C}_A(\mathbf{x}^*(t'))$ is not closed, we must take into account the limit points of $\mathscr{C}_A(\mathbf{x}^*(t'))$ which do not belong to $\mathscr{C}_A(\mathbf{x}^*(t'))$; that is, we must consider

$$\mathbf{x}^*(t') + \boldsymbol{\eta}' \in \mathscr{S}(\mathbf{x}^*(t'))$$

Now our arguments are similar to those utilized in the proof of Lemma 17. In particular, we note that for every conic neighborhood

$$N(\mathbf{x}^*(t')) \triangleq \{x^*(t') + k\boldsymbol{\xi} : k > 0, \quad \mathbf{x}^*(t') + \boldsymbol{\xi} \in B(\mathbf{x}^*(t') + \boldsymbol{\eta}')\}$$

where $B(\mathbf{x}^*(t') + \boldsymbol{\eta}')$ is an open ball in E^{n+1} with center at point $\mathbf{x}^*(t') + \boldsymbol{\eta}'$, it follows from Lemma 8 that

$$N(\mathbf{x}^*(t')) \cap \mathscr{C}_A(\mathbf{x}^*(t')) \neq \phi$$

Hence, we may consider a sequence of vectors $\boldsymbol{\eta}_1', \boldsymbol{\eta}_2', \ldots, \boldsymbol{\eta}_\nu'$, such that

$$\mathbf{x}^*(t') + \boldsymbol{\eta}_i' \in \mathscr{C}_A(\mathbf{x}^*(t')), \qquad i = 1, 2, \ldots, \nu$$

$$\boldsymbol{\eta}_\nu' \to \boldsymbol{\eta}' \qquad \text{as} \quad \nu \to \infty$$

It follows from the first part of the proof that

$$\mathbf{x}^*(t'') + \boldsymbol{\eta}_\nu'' \in \overline{\mathscr{C}}_A(\mathbf{x}^*(t'')) \tag{7.86}$$

where

$$\boldsymbol{\eta}_\nu'' \triangleq \boldsymbol{\eta}_\nu(t'') = A(t', t'')\boldsymbol{\eta}_\nu'$$

Furthermore, since the transformation is linear,

$$\boldsymbol{\eta}_\nu'' \to \boldsymbol{\eta}'' \qquad \text{as} \quad \boldsymbol{\eta}_\nu' \to \boldsymbol{\eta}'$$

Suppose now that

$$\mathbf{x}^*(t'') + \boldsymbol{\eta}'' \notin \overline{\mathscr{C}}_A(\mathbf{x}^*(t''))$$

namely,

$$\mathbf{x}^*(t'') + \boldsymbol{\eta}'' \in \mathring{\mathscr{C}}_B(\mathbf{x}^*(t''))$$

Then there exists a positive number μ such that for $\nu > \mu$

$$\mathbf{x}^*(t'') + \boldsymbol{\eta}_\nu'' \in \mathring{\mathscr{C}}_B(\mathbf{x}^*(t''))$$

However, this contradicts (7.86); thus, Lemma 20 is established.

7.152 Lemma 21

Next we shall prove

Lemma 21. *Let* $\mathbf{x}^*(t')$ *and* $\mathbf{x}^*(t'')$, $t_0 \leq t' \leq t'' \leq t_1$, *be two points of optimal trajectory* Γ^*, *corresponding to control* $\mathbf{u}^*(t)$ *and solution* $\mathbf{x}^*(t)$, $t_0 \leq t \leq t_1$. *Let* $\boldsymbol{\eta}''$ *be a vector at* $\mathbf{x}^*(t'')$ *such that*

$$\mathbf{x}^*(t'') + \boldsymbol{\eta}'' \in \overline{\mathscr{C}}_B(\mathbf{x}^*(t''))$$

Then $\boldsymbol{\eta}''$ *is the transform, due to linear transformation* $A(t', t'')$, *of a vector* $\boldsymbol{\eta}'$ *at* $\mathbf{x}^*(t')$ *such that*

$$\mathbf{x}^*(t') + \boldsymbol{\eta}' \subset \overline{\mathscr{C}}_B(\mathbf{x}^*(t'))$$

Since the proof of this lemma is similar to that of Lemma 20, we shall only present its salient features. We shall suppose first that

$$\mathbf{x}^*(t'') + \boldsymbol{\eta}'' \in \mathscr{C}_B(\mathbf{x}^*(t''))$$

Then, according to definition (7.14) of $\mathscr{C}_B(\mathbf{x})$, there exists a positive number β such that for all ε, $0 < \varepsilon < \beta$,

$$\mathbf{x}^*(t'') + \varepsilon\boldsymbol{\eta}'' \in B/\Sigma \tag{7.87}$$

We shall consider a trajectory which passes through point $\mathbf{x}^*(t'') + \varepsilon\boldsymbol{\eta}''$, and which is generated by $\mathbf{u}^*(t)$, $t_0 \le t \le t_1$, on $[t', t'']$. As before, the corresponding solution of trajectory equation (7.44) is given by (7.84), but now with $\boldsymbol{\eta}(t'') = \boldsymbol{\eta}''$.

As a consequence of (7.87), together with Theorem 1 and Corollary 1, we have

$$\mathbf{x}(t') \notin \widetilde{A/\Sigma}$$

since

$$\mathbf{x}(t') \in \widetilde{A/\Sigma}$$

implies

$$\mathbf{x}(t'') = \mathbf{x}^*(t'') + \varepsilon\boldsymbol{\eta}'' \in \widetilde{A/\Sigma}$$

which contradicts (7.87). Thus,

$$\mathbf{x}(t') = \mathbf{x}^*(t') + \varepsilon\boldsymbol{\eta}(t') + \mathbf{o}(t', \varepsilon) \in B/\Sigma$$

for sufficiently small ε.

Furthermore,

$$\boldsymbol{\eta}(t') + \frac{\mathbf{o}(t', \varepsilon)}{\varepsilon} \to \boldsymbol{\eta}(t') \triangleq \boldsymbol{\eta}' \qquad \text{as} \quad \varepsilon \to 0$$

so that Lemma 7 leads to

$$\mathbf{x}^*(t') + \boldsymbol{\eta}' \in \overline{\mathscr{C}}_B(\mathbf{x}^*(t'))$$

In the second part of the proof, we consider

$$\mathbf{x}^*(t'') + \boldsymbol{\eta}'' \in \mathscr{S}(\mathbf{x}^*(t''))$$

Again, we shall employ a sequence of vectors $\boldsymbol{\eta}_1'', \boldsymbol{\eta}_2'', \ldots, \boldsymbol{\eta}_\nu''$ at $\mathbf{x}^*(t'')$, such that

$$\mathbf{x}^*(t'') + \boldsymbol{\eta}_i'' \in \mathscr{C}_B(\mathbf{x}^*(t'')), \qquad i = 1, 2, \ldots, \nu$$

$$\boldsymbol{\eta}_\nu'' \to \boldsymbol{\eta}'' \qquad \text{as} \quad \nu \to \infty$$

The existence of such a sequence is again ensured by Lemma 8 according to which

$$N(\mathbf{x}^*(t'')) \cap \mathscr{C}_B(\mathbf{x}^*(t'')) \neq \phi$$

for every conic neighborhood

$$N(\mathbf{x}^*(t'')) \triangleq \{\mathbf{x}^*(t'') + k\boldsymbol{\xi} : k > 0, \quad \mathbf{x}^*(t'') + \boldsymbol{\xi} \in B(\mathbf{x}^*(t'') + \boldsymbol{\eta}'')\}$$

From the first part of the proof, we have

$$\mathbf{x}^*(t') + \boldsymbol{\eta}_\nu' \in \overline{\mathscr{C}}_B(\mathbf{x}^*(t'))$$

where

$$\boldsymbol{\eta}_\nu' = A(t'', t')\boldsymbol{\eta}_\nu''$$

But

$$\boldsymbol{\eta}_\nu' \to \boldsymbol{\eta}' \qquad \text{as} \quad \boldsymbol{\eta}_\nu'' \to \boldsymbol{\eta}''$$

and we can show that

$$\mathbf{x}^*(t') + \boldsymbol{\eta}' \in \overline{\mathscr{C}}_B(\mathbf{x}^*(t'))$$

employing an argument analogous to the one used in Sec. 7.151. Hence, Lemma 21 is established.

7.153 Corollaries 6 and 7

The following corollaries are straightforward consequences of Lemmas 20 and 21.

Corollary 6. *If a vector* $\boldsymbol{\eta}'$ *at point* $\mathbf{x}^*(t')$ *of optimal trajectory* Γ^* *satisfies*

$$\mathbf{x}^*(t') + \boldsymbol{\eta}' \in \mathring{\mathscr{C}}_A(\mathbf{x}^*(t'))$$

then its transform $\boldsymbol{\eta}''$, *due to linear transformation* $A(t', t'')$, *at* $\mathbf{x}^*(t'')$, $t'' \geq t'$, *satisfies*

$$\mathbf{x}^*(t'') + \boldsymbol{\eta}'' \in \mathring{\mathscr{C}}_A(\mathbf{x}^*(t''))$$

and

Corollary 7. *If a vector* $\boldsymbol{\eta}''$ *at point* $\mathbf{x}^*(t'')$ *of optimal trajectory* Γ^* *satisfies*

$$\mathbf{x}^*(t'') + \boldsymbol{\eta}'' \in \mathring{\mathscr{C}}_B(\mathbf{x}^*(t''))$$

then it is the transform, due to linear transformation $A(t', t'')$, *of a vector* $\boldsymbol{\eta}'$ *at* $\mathbf{x}^*(t')$, $t' \leq t''$, *which satisfies*

$$\mathbf{x}^*(t') + \boldsymbol{\eta}' \in \mathring{\mathscr{C}}_B(\mathbf{x}^*(t'))$$

For instance, Corollary 6 follows at once from Lemma 21. For suppose our assertion is false, that is,

$$\mathbf{x}^*(t'') + \boldsymbol{\eta}'' \in \overline{\mathscr{C}}_B(\mathbf{x}^*(t''))$$

Then, according to Lemma 21, we have

$$\mathbf{x}^*(t') + \boldsymbol{\eta}' \in \mathscr{C}_B(\mathbf{x}^*(t'))$$

which contradicts the hypothesis of the corollary.

Corollary 7 can be proved in similar fashion, invoking Lemma 20.

7.154 Theorems 2 and 3

Let $\mathbf{x}^*(t')$ and $\mathbf{x}^*(t'')$, $t_0 \leq t' \leq t'' \leq t_1$, be two points of optimal trajectory Γ^*, corresponding to control $\mathbf{u}^*(t)$ and solution $\mathbf{x}^*(t)$, $t_0 \leq t \leq t_1$. We shall prove

Theorem 2. *If $\bar{\mathscr{C}}_B(\mathbf{x}^*(t'))$ is separable, then $\bar{\mathscr{C}}_B(\mathbf{x}^*(t''))$ is separable.*

Theorem 3. *If $\bar{\mathscr{C}}_A(\mathbf{x}^*(t''))$ is separable, then $\bar{\mathscr{C}}_A(\mathbf{x}^*(t'))$ is separable.*

To prove Theorem 2, let us consider an n-dimensional separating hyperplane $\mathscr{T}(\mathbf{x}^*(t'))$ of $\bar{\mathscr{C}}_B(\mathbf{x}^*(t'))$. This plane passes through point $\mathbf{x}^*(t')$, and determines closed half space $\bar{R}_B{}'$, $\mathscr{C}_B(\mathbf{x}^*(t')) \subseteq \bar{R}_B{}'$, and open half space comp $\bar{R}_B{}'$. Thus,

$$\mathbf{x}^*(t') + \boldsymbol{\eta}' \in \bar{\mathscr{C}}_B(\mathbf{x}^*(t')) \Rightarrow \mathbf{x}^*(t') + \boldsymbol{\eta}' \in \bar{R}_B{}' \tag{7.88}$$

Now let $\Pi(\mathbf{x}^*(t''))$ and P_B'' denote the transforms, by linear transformation $A(t', t'')$, of $\mathscr{T}(\mathbf{x}^*(t'))$ and $R_B{}'$, respectively.† Since transformation $A(t', t'')$ is linear and nonsingular, one can show readily that

(i) $\Pi(\mathbf{x}^*(t''))$ is the common boundary of P_B'' and comp $\bar{P}_B''$, namely, $\Pi(\mathbf{x}^*(t'')) = \bar{P}_B'' \cap \overline{\text{comp}\, \bar{P}_B''}$

(ii) the transform of comp $\bar{R}_B{}'$ is comp $\bar{P}_B''$.

Now consider any vector $\boldsymbol{\eta}''$ at $\mathbf{x}^*(t'')$, such that

$$\mathbf{x}^*(t'') + \boldsymbol{\eta}'' \in \bar{\mathscr{C}}_B(\mathbf{x}^*(t'')) \tag{7.89}$$

and suppose that

$$\mathbf{x}^*(t'') + \boldsymbol{\eta}'' \in \text{comp}\, \bar{P}_B''$$

Then, according to (ii) above, it is the transform of a vector $\boldsymbol{\eta}'$ at $\mathbf{x}^*(t')$, such that

$$\mathbf{x}^*(t') + \boldsymbol{\eta}' \in \text{comp}\, \bar{R}_B{}' \tag{7.90}$$

Moreover, in view of (7.89) and Lemma 21, we have

$$\mathbf{x}^*(t') + \boldsymbol{\eta}' \in \mathscr{C}_B(\mathbf{x}^*(t')) \tag{7.91}$$

† Note that $R_B{}'$ is open, by definition.

However, (7.91) together with (7.90) is incompatible with (7.88). Hence, we conclude that

$$\mathbf{x}^*(t'') + \boldsymbol{\eta}'' \in \bar{P}''_B$$

for every $\boldsymbol{\eta}''$ which satisfies (7.89). Consequently, we conclude that

(i) $\mathscr{C}_B(\mathbf{x}^*(t''))$ is separable;
(ii) $\Pi(\mathbf{x}^*(t''))$ is a separating hyperplane $\mathscr{T}(\mathbf{x}^*(t''))$ of $\bar{\mathscr{C}}_B(\mathbf{x}^*(t''))$; and
(iii) $\bar{\mathscr{C}}_B(\mathbf{x}^*(t''))$ belongs to $\bar{P}''_B$ which is the transform of $\bar{R}_B'$. Hence, we shall denote P''_B by R''_B. Thus, Theorem 2 is established.

Theorem 3 can be proved in a similar fashion, employing Lemma 20. In particular, if $\mathscr{T}(\mathbf{x}^*(t''))$ is a separating hyperplane of $\mathscr{C}_A(\mathbf{x}^*(t''))$, it determines a closed half space $\bar{R}''_A$, $\bar{\mathscr{C}}_A(\mathbf{x}^*(t'')) \subseteq \bar{R}''_A$, such that

(iv) $\mathscr{T}(\mathbf{x}^*(t''))$ is the transform, due to linear transformation $A(t', t'')$, of a separating hyperplane $\mathscr{T}(\mathbf{x}^*(t'))$ of $\bar{\mathscr{C}}_A(\mathbf{x}^*(t'))$;
(v) $\bar{\mathscr{C}}_A(\mathbf{x}^*(t'))$ belongs to $\bar{P}_A'$ whose transform is $\bar{R}''_A$. Thus, we shall denote P_A' by R_A'.

7.155 Corollaries 8 and 9

From Theorems 2 and 3 there follow at once

Corollary 8. *An optimal trajectory* Γ^* *cannot join points* $\mathbf{x}' \triangleq \mathbf{x}^*(t')$ *and* $\mathbf{x}'' \triangleq \mathbf{x}^*(t'')$, $t'' > t'$, *if* $\bar{\mathscr{C}}_B(\mathbf{x}')$ *is separable and* $\bar{\mathscr{C}}_B(\mathbf{x}'')$ *is not separable.*

and

Corollary 9. *An optimal trajectory* Γ^* *cannot join points* $\mathbf{x}' \triangleq \mathbf{x}^*(t')$ *and* $\mathbf{x}'' \triangleq \mathbf{x}^*(t'')$, $t'' > t'$, *if* $\bar{\mathscr{C}}_A(\mathbf{x}')$ *is not separable and* $\bar{\mathscr{C}}_A(\mathbf{x}'')$ *is separable.*

7.16 Attractive and Repulsive Subsets of a Limiting Surface

We shall now introduce two subsets of a limiting surface Σ:

An *attractive subset* M_{att} of Σ is a set of nonregular interior points of Σ, at each of which $\bar{\mathscr{C}}_B(\mathbf{x})$ is separable but $\bar{\mathscr{C}}_A(\mathbf{x})$ is not separable.

A *repulsive subset* M_{rep} of Σ is a set of nonregular interior points of Σ, at each of which $\bar{\mathscr{C}}_A(\mathbf{x})$ is separable but $\bar{\mathscr{C}}_B(\mathbf{x})$ is not separable.

7.161 Corollaries 10 and 11

The adjectives *attractive* and *repulsive* have been adopted in view of the following corollaries which are a direct consequence of Corollaries 8 and 9.

Corollary 10. *If* $\mathbf{x}^*(t')$ *and* $\mathbf{x}^*(t'')$, $t'' > t'$, *are points of optimal trajectory* Γ^* *on limiting surface* Σ, *and if* $\mathbf{x}^*(t')$ *belongs to* M_{att}, *then* $\mathbf{x}^*(t'')$ *cannot be a regular interior point of* Σ *nor can* $\mathbf{x}^*(t'')$ *belong to* M_{rep}.

However, apparently an optimal trajectory which emanates from a regular interior point of Σ, or from a point on a repulsive subset M_{rep}, can reach a point on an attractive subset M_{att}.

Corollary 11. *If* $\mathbf{x}^*(t')$ *and* $\mathbf{x}^*(t'')$, $t'' > t'$, *are points of optimal trajectory* Γ^* *on limiting surface* Σ, *and if* $\mathbf{x}^*(t')$ *is a regular interior point of* Σ, *or* $\mathbf{x}^*(t')$ *belongs to* M_{att}, *then* $\mathbf{x}^*(t'')$ *cannot belong to* M_{rep}.

However, apparently an optimal trajectory can leave a repulsive subset M_{rep}.

7.17 Regular Subset of a Limiting Surface

Yet another subset of a limiting surface Σ is a *regular subset* M_{reg} which is a set of regular interior points of Σ, that is, a set of points at each of which *both* $\bar{\mathscr{C}}_A(\mathbf{x})$ and $\mathscr{C}_B(\mathbf{x})$ are separable.

7.171 A Local Property of a Regular Subset; Corollary 12

One can readily prove

Corollary 12. *If* $\mathbf{x}^*(t')$ *and* $\mathbf{x}^*(t'')$, $t'' > t'$, *are points of an optimal trajectory* Γ^* *for which every point* $\mathbf{x}^*(t)$, $t \in [t', t'']$, *is an interior point of limiting surface* Σ, *and if* $\mathbf{x}^*(t')$ *and* $\mathbf{x}^*(t'')$ *belong to* M_{reg}, *then* $\mathbf{x}^*(t)$ *belongs to* M_{reg} *for all* $t \in [t', t'']$.

Indeed, since $\bar{\mathscr{C}}_A(\mathbf{x}^*(t''))$ is separable, it follows from Theorem 3 that $\bar{\mathscr{C}}_A(\mathbf{x}^*(t))$, $t \in [t', t'']$, is separable; and since $\mathscr{C}_B(\mathbf{x}^*(t'))$ is separable, it follows from Theorem 2 that $\mathscr{C}_B(\mathbf{x}^*(t))$, $t \in [t', t'']$, is separable. Thus, $\mathbf{x}^*(t)$ belongs to M_{reg} for all $t \in [t', t'']$.

7.172 A Maximum Principle; Theorem 4

Now we shall restrict our attention to a *regular optimal trajectory* Γ^*, namely, one for which $\mathbf{x}^*(t)$ belongs to M_{reg} for all $t \in [t_0, t_1]$. We shall derive Pontryagin's maximum principle for this case.

Let $\mathbf{x} = \mathbf{x}^*(t)$, $t \in [t_0, t_1]$, be a point of regular optimal trajectory Γ^*, and consider cones $\bar{\mathscr{C}}_A(\mathbf{x})$ and $\bar{\mathscr{C}}_B(\mathbf{x})$ at that point. From the analysis of Sec. 7.13, we know that

(i) $\bar{\mathscr{C}}_A(\mathbf{x})$ and $\bar{\mathscr{C}}_B(\mathbf{x})$ possess a common separating hyperplane $\mathscr{T}(\mathbf{x})$, and that this separating hyperplane is unique;
(ii) $\mathscr{T}(\mathbf{x}) = \mathscr{S}(\mathbf{x})$;
(iii) $\bar{\mathscr{C}}_A(\mathbf{x}) = \bar{R}_A(\mathbf{x})$ and $\bar{\mathscr{C}}_B(\mathbf{x}) = \bar{R}_B(\mathbf{x})$, where $R_A(\mathbf{x})$ and $R_B(\mathbf{x})$ are the two open half spaces determined by $\mathscr{T}(\mathbf{x})$.

For instance, consider the separating hyperplane $\mathscr{T}(\mathbf{x}^0)$ at the initial point $\mathbf{x}^0 = \mathbf{x}^*(t_0)$. Since $\mathscr{T}(\mathbf{x}^0)$ is the separating hyperplane of $\bar{\mathscr{C}}_B(\mathbf{x}^0)$, it follows from the proof of Theorem 2—see Sec. 7.154—that its transform at any time t, $t_0 \leq t \leq t_1$, due to linear transformation $A(t_0, t)$, is the separating hyperplane $\mathscr{T}(\mathbf{x})$ of $\bar{\mathscr{C}}_B(\mathbf{x}) = \bar{R}_B(\mathbf{x})$, $\mathbf{x} = \mathbf{x}^*(t)$.

In view of the uniqueness of the separating hyperplane, the cone $\mathscr{C}_n(\mathbf{x})$ of normals at point $\mathbf{x}$, defined in Sec. 7.122, contains a single vector $\mathbf{n}(\mathbf{x})$, $|\mathbf{n}(\mathbf{x})| = 1$, which is normal to $\mathscr{T}(\mathbf{x})$, and such that

$$\mathbf{x} + \mathbf{n}(\mathbf{x}) \in R_B(\mathbf{x}) \tag{7.92}$$

On the other hand, it follows from Lemma 15 that

$$\mathbf{x} + \mathbf{f}(\mathbf{x}, \mathbf{u}) \in \bar{\mathscr{C}}_A(\mathbf{x}) = \bar{R}_A(\mathbf{x}), \qquad \forall \mathbf{u} \in \Omega \tag{7.93}$$

and from Lemma 16 that

$$\left.\begin{array}{l} \mathbf{x} + \mathbf{f}_+{}^* \in \mathscr{S}(\mathbf{x}) \\ \mathbf{x} - \mathbf{f}_-{}^* \in \mathscr{S}(\mathbf{x}) \end{array}\right\} \qquad \mathscr{S}(\mathbf{x}) = \mathscr{T}(\mathbf{x}) \tag{7.94}$$

where

$$\mathbf{f}_+{}^* \triangleq \mathbf{f}(\mathbf{x}, \mathbf{u}_+{}^*), \qquad \mathbf{u}_+{}^* \triangleq \mathbf{u}^*(t+0)$$
$$\mathbf{f}_-{}^* \triangleq \mathbf{f}(\mathbf{x}, \mathbf{u}_-{}^*), \qquad \mathbf{u}_-{}^* \triangleq \mathbf{u}^*(t-0)$$

Now let us consider the solution $\boldsymbol{\lambda}(t)$, $t_0 \leq t \leq t_1$, of adjoint Eqs. (7.79) with initial condition $\boldsymbol{\lambda}(t_0) = \boldsymbol{\lambda}^0$ such that $\boldsymbol{\lambda}^0 \neq 0$, $\boldsymbol{\lambda}^0$ normal to $\mathscr{T}(\mathbf{x}^0)$ and directed into $R_B(\mathbf{x}^0)$; that is,

$$\boldsymbol{\lambda}^0 = \lambda^0 \mathbf{n}(\mathbf{x}^0), \qquad \lambda^0 > 0 \tag{7.95}$$

Then $\boldsymbol{\lambda}(t)$ is a nonzero vector which is normal to $\mathscr{T}(\mathbf{x})$, according to (7.82); namely,

$$\boldsymbol{\lambda}(t) = \lambda(t)\mathbf{n}(\mathbf{x}^*(t)), \qquad \forall t \in [t_0, t_1] \tag{7.96}$$

Since $\boldsymbol{\lambda}(t)$ and $\mathbf{n}(\mathbf{x}^*(t))$, $t_0 \leq t \leq t_1$, are nonzero continuous vector functions of t, it follows that $\lambda(t)$ is a nonzero continuous scalar function of t. Since

$\lambda(t_0) = \lambda^0 > 0$, we conclude that $\lambda(t) > 0$ for all $t \in [t_0, t_1]$. Consequently, (7.92) and (7.96) lead to

$$\begin{aligned} \mathbf{x} + \boldsymbol{\lambda}(t) &= \mathbf{x} + \lambda(t)\mathbf{n}(\mathbf{x}) \in R_B(\mathbf{x}) \\ \mathbf{x} = \mathbf{x}^*(t), &\qquad \lambda(t) = |\boldsymbol{\lambda}(t)| \end{aligned} \tag{7.97}$$

Conditions (7.93), (7.94), and (7.97) embody Pontryagin's maximum principle for the case of *regular* optimal trajectories. Thus, letting

$$\mathscr{H}(\boldsymbol{\lambda}, \mathbf{x}, \mathbf{u}) \triangleq \boldsymbol{\lambda} \cdot \mathbf{f}(\mathbf{x}, \mathbf{u}) \tag{7.98}$$

we may state

Theorem 4. *If* $\mathbf{u}^*(t)$, $t_0 \leq t \leq t_1$, *is an optimal control, and* $\mathbf{x}^*(t)$ *is the corresponding solution of trajectory equation* (7.44), *then there exists a nonzero continuous vector function* $\boldsymbol{\lambda}(t)$ *which is a solution of adjoint equations* (7.79), *such that*

(i) $\sup\limits_{\mathbf{u}\in\Omega} \mathscr{H}(\boldsymbol{\lambda}(t), \mathbf{x}^*(t), \mathbf{u}) = \mathscr{H}(\boldsymbol{\lambda}(t), \mathbf{x}^*(t), \mathbf{u}^*(t))$;
(ii) $\mathscr{H}(\boldsymbol{\lambda}(t), \mathbf{x}^*(t), \mathbf{u}^*(t)) = 0$;
(iii) $\lambda_0(t) = \text{const} \leq 0$;

for all $t \in [t_0, t_1]$.

Indeed, it follows from (7.93) and (7.97) that

$$\boldsymbol{\lambda}(t) \cdot \mathbf{f}(\mathbf{x}^*(t), \mathbf{u}) \leq 0, \qquad \forall \mathbf{u} \in \Omega$$

whence we have condition (i) of the theorem.

For condition (ii) we invoke (7.94) with (7.96). Here we distinguish between the two cases discussed in Sec. 7.112. Thus, if $\mathbf{u}^*(t)$ is discontinuous at $t = t_c$, and t_c belongs to a nonzero time interval on which $\mathbf{x}^*(t) \neq \text{const}$, we have

$$\boldsymbol{\lambda}(t_c - 0) \cdot \mathbf{f}_-^* = \boldsymbol{\lambda}(t_c + 0) \cdot \mathbf{f}_+^* = 0$$

On the other hand, if $\mathbf{x}^*(t) = \text{const}$ on a nonzero time interval $[t', t'']$, then

$$\boldsymbol{\lambda}(t' - 0) \cdot \mathbf{f}_-^* = \boldsymbol{\lambda}(t'' + 0) \cdot \mathbf{f}_+^* = 0$$

Furthermore,

$$\boldsymbol{\lambda}(t) \cdot \mathbf{f}(\mathbf{x}^*(t), \mathbf{u}^*(t)) = 0, \qquad t' \leq t \leq t''$$

since the orientation of $\boldsymbol{\lambda}(t)$ remains fixed during that time interval. Of course, this latter relation is also valid because

$$\mathbf{f}(\mathbf{x}^*(t), \mathbf{u}^*(t)) = 0, \qquad t' \leq t \leq t''$$

Finally, condition (ii) of the theorem is clearly satisfied at all other points of $[t_0, t_1]$.

Since functions $f_j(\mathbf{x}, \mathbf{u})$, $j = 0, 1, \ldots, n$, do not depend explicitly on x_0, we have

$$\dot{\lambda}_0 = \sum_{j=0}^{n} \frac{\partial f_j(\mathbf{x}, \mathbf{u}^*(t))}{\partial x_0}\bigg|_{\mathbf{x}=\mathbf{x}^*(t)} \lambda_j = 0$$

so that

$$\lambda_0(t) = \text{const}, \qquad \forall t \in [t_0, t_1]$$

Furthermore, it follows from (7.96) that

$$\lambda_0(t) = |\boldsymbol{\lambda}(t)| n_0(\mathbf{x}^*(t)) \tag{7.99}$$

where $n_0(\mathbf{x})$ is the zeroth component of $\mathbf{n}(\mathbf{x})$. We note also—see Sec. 7.71—that

$$L_- \subset \mathscr{C}_B(\mathbf{x}^0) = \bar{R}_B(\mathbf{x}^0)$$

so that, in view of (7.92),

$$n_0(\mathbf{x}^0) \le 0$$

Thus, condition (iii) of the theorem is established.

7.173 Relation between Gradient and Adjoint Vectors

If Σ is a *nice* limiting surface, then separating hyperplane $\mathscr{T}(\mathbf{x})$ is the tangent plane of Σ at point $\mathbf{x}$; namely, as shown in Sec. 7.13, we have

$$\mathscr{T}(\mathbf{x}) = \mathscr{S}(\mathbf{x}) = \mathscr{C}_\Sigma(\mathbf{x}) = T_\Sigma(\mathbf{x})$$

Let us recall the defining Eq. (7.6) of Σ, that is,

$$\Phi(\mathbf{x}) \triangleq x_0 + V^*(\mathbf{x}; \mathbf{x}^1) = C$$

If grad $\Phi(\mathbf{x})$ is defined at point $\mathbf{x}$, the following conditions apply:

(i) It is normal to tangent plane $T_\Sigma(\mathbf{x})$.

(ii) It is directed into region A/Σ; that is, there exists a $\sigma > 0$ such that for all ε, $0 < \varepsilon < \sigma$,

$$\mathbf{x} + \varepsilon \operatorname{grad} \Phi(\mathbf{x}) \in A/\Sigma$$

Indeed, this means that grad $\Phi(\mathbf{x})$ is directed into $\bar{R}_A(\mathbf{x})$.

(iii) The zeroth component of grad $\Phi(\mathbf{x})$ is

$$(\operatorname{grad} \Phi(\mathbf{x}))_0 \triangleq \frac{\partial \Phi(\mathbf{x})}{\partial x_0} = 1$$

From the definition of normal $\mathbf{n}(\mathbf{x})$, together with (i) and (ii) above, it follows that

$$\text{grad } \Phi(\mathbf{x}) = -|\text{grad } \Phi(\mathbf{x})| \, \mathbf{n}(\mathbf{x}) \tag{7.100}$$

and $|\text{grad } \Phi(\mathbf{x})|$ is defined, since grad $\Phi(\mathbf{x})$ is defined.

In view of (iii) above, grad $\Phi(\mathbf{x})$ is not normal to the x_0-axis, and hence neither is $\mathbf{n}(\mathbf{x})$. Thus, $n_0(\mathbf{x}) \neq 0$ and so, according to (7.99), $\lambda_0(t) \neq 0$ for $\mathbf{x} = \mathbf{x}^*(t)$.

From (iii) above, together with (7.100), we have

$$(\text{grad } \Phi(\mathbf{x}))_0 = 1 = -|\text{grad } \Phi(\mathbf{x})| \, n_0(\mathbf{x}) \tag{7.101}$$

Hence, for $\mathbf{x} = \mathbf{x}^*(t)$, it follows from (7.99) and (7.101) that

$$\frac{\lambda_0(t)}{(\text{grad } \Phi(\mathbf{x}^*(t)))_0} = -\frac{|\boldsymbol{\lambda}(t)|}{|\text{grad } \Phi(\mathbf{x}^*(t))|}$$

so that

$$\begin{aligned} \boldsymbol{\lambda}(t) &= \lambda_0(t) \text{ grad } \Phi(\mathbf{x}^*(t)) \\ \lambda_0(t) &= \text{const} < 0 \end{aligned}$$

Since $|\boldsymbol{\lambda}^0|$ can be chosen arbitrarily, we may write

$$\boldsymbol{\lambda}(t) = -\text{grad } \Phi(\mathbf{x}^*(t)) \tag{7.102}$$

Recall that (7.102) is valid provided Σ is nice and grad $\Phi(\mathbf{x})$ is defined at $\mathbf{x} = \mathbf{x}^*(t)$.

7.174 Relation to Dynamic Programming

Upon use of (7.102) in conditions (i) and (ii) of Theorem 4, we obtain

$$\sup_{\mathbf{u} \in \Omega} [\boldsymbol{\lambda}(t) \cdot \mathbf{f}(\mathbf{x}^*(t), \mathbf{u})] = \sup_{\mathbf{u} \in \Omega} [-\text{grad } \Phi(\mathbf{x}^*(t)) \cdot \mathbf{f}(\mathbf{x}^*(t), \mathbf{u})] = 0$$

Alternately, we have

$$\inf_{\mathbf{u} \in \Omega} \left[f_0(\mathfrak{x}, \mathbf{u}) + \sum_{j=1}^{n} f_j(\mathfrak{x}, \mathbf{u}) \frac{\partial V^*(\mathfrak{x}; \mathfrak{x}^1)}{\partial x_j} \right]_{\mathbf{x} = \mathbf{x}^*(t)} = 0 \tag{7.103}$$

which is the functional equation of dynamic programming.

Equation (7.103) may be obtained in a more direct way, invoking the global property of limiting surfaces. Consider a trajectory Γ, corresponding to solution $\mathbf{x}(t)$, $t_0 \leq t \leq t_1$, of trajectory equation (7.44).

Function $\Phi(\mathbf{x})$ is defined for all $\mathbf{x}$ in $\mathscr{E}^*$. Moreover, for $\mathbf{x} \in \Gamma$, $\Phi(\mathbf{x})$ becomes a function of t; namely,

$$\Phi(\mathbf{x}(t)) = x_0(t) + V^*(\mathfrak{x}(t); \mathfrak{x}^1) = C(t)$$

In other words, to each value of time t there corresponds a point $\mathbf{x} = \mathbf{x}(t)$ on Γ, and hence a Σ surface through that point.

From Theorem 1, together with the fact that the members of $\{\Sigma\}$ are ordered along the x_0-axis in the same way as the value of parameter C, it follows that $C(t)$ is a nondecreasing function along Γ. Thus, provided the derivative† exists, we have

$$\frac{d\Phi\,(\mathbf{x}(t))}{dt} \geq 0 \tag{7.104}$$

along Γ.

Furthermore, according to Lemma 2, an optimal trajectory Γ^* belongs entirely to one Σ surface; that is, $C(t) = \text{const}$, $t_0 \leq t \leq t_1$. Hence, we have

$$\frac{d\Phi\,(\mathbf{x}^*(t))}{dt} = 0 \tag{7.105}$$

along Γ^*.

Now if grad $\Phi(\mathbf{x})$ is defined at a point $\mathbf{x} \in \Gamma$ and Γ^*, we may write

$$\frac{d\Phi}{dt} = \sum_{j=0}^{n} \frac{\partial\Phi}{\partial x_j}\dot{x}_j$$

where $d\Phi/dt$ is evaluated along Γ and Γ^*, respectively. Thus, (7.104) leads to

$$\left[f_0(\mathfrak{x}, \mathbf{u}) + \sum_{j=1}^{n} f_j(\mathfrak{x}, \mathbf{u})\frac{\partial V^*(\mathfrak{x};\mathfrak{x}^1)}{\partial x_j}\right] \geq 0 \tag{7.106}$$

for $\mathbf{x} - \mathbf{x}^*(t)$, $\mathbf{u} = \mathbf{u}(t)$, whereas (7.105) results in

$$\left[f_0(\mathfrak{x}, \mathbf{u}) + \sum_{j=1}^{n} f_j(\mathfrak{x}, \mathbf{u})\frac{\partial V^*(\mathfrak{x};\mathfrak{x}^1)}{\partial x_j}\right] = 0 \tag{7.107}$$

for $\mathbf{x} = \mathbf{x}^*(t)$, $\mathbf{u} = \mathbf{u}^*(t)$. Functional equation (7.103) follows at once from (7.106) and (7.107).

It should be noted that (7.104) and (7.105) may be less restricted than (7.106) and (7.107), since the former may be valid even though $\mathbf{x}$ is not a regular interior point of Σ where grad $\Phi(\mathbf{x})$ is defined.

7.18 Antiregular Subset of a Limiting Surface

A set of interior points of a limiting surface Σ will be called an *antiregular subset* of Σ, if neither $\bar{\mathscr{C}}_A(\mathbf{x})$ nor $\bar{\mathscr{C}}_B(\mathbf{x})$ is separable at a point $\mathbf{x}$ of the set. We shall not discuss such subsets in detail at this time. However, one salient feature of an antiregular subset is embodied in the following corollary.

† We mean here the one-sided derivative $\lim\limits_{\Delta t \to 0} \dfrac{\Delta\Phi}{\Delta t}$.

7.181 Corollary 13

Theorems 2 and 3 lead at once to

Corollary 13. *Let* $\mathbf{x}^*(t')$ *and* $\mathbf{x}^*(t'')$, $t'' > t'$, *be points of optimal trajectory* Γ^* *on limiting surface* Σ.

(i) *If* $\mathbf{x}^*(t')$ *belongs to an antiregular subset, then* $\mathbf{x}^*(t'')$ *cannot belong to a regular or to a repulsive subset.*
(ii) *If* $\mathbf{x}^*(t')$ *belongs to a regular or to an attractive subset, then* $\mathbf{x}^*(t'')$ *cannot belong to an antiregular subset.*

7.19 Symmetrical Subset of Local Cone $\mathscr{S}(\mathbf{x})$

We shall call $I(\mathbf{x})$ a symmetrical subset of local cone $\mathscr{S}(\mathbf{x})$, if $I(\mathbf{x})$ is the set of all points, $\mathbf{x} + \boldsymbol{\eta}$, such that

$$\mathbf{x} + \boldsymbol{\eta} \in \mathscr{S}(\mathbf{x}) \qquad \text{and} \qquad \mathbf{x} - \boldsymbol{\eta} \in \mathscr{S}(\mathbf{x})$$

7.191 Lemmas 22 and 23

Let us now prove

Lemma 22. *Let* $\mathbf{x}' \triangleq \mathbf{x}^*(t')$ *and* $\mathbf{x}'' \triangleq \mathbf{x}^*(t'')$, $t'' \geq t'$, *be points of optimal trajectory* Γ^*. *If* $\overline{\mathscr{C}}_A(\mathbf{x}'')$ *is separable, then*

$$\mathbf{x}' + \boldsymbol{\eta}' \in I(\mathbf{x}') \Rightarrow \mathbf{x}'' + \boldsymbol{\eta}'' \in I(\mathbf{x}'')$$

where

$$\boldsymbol{\eta}'' = A(t', t'')\boldsymbol{\eta}'$$

Since $\overline{\mathscr{C}}_A(\mathbf{x}'')$ is supposed separable, it follows from Theorem 3 that $\overline{\mathscr{C}}_A(\mathbf{x}')$ is separable. Let $\mathscr{T}(\mathbf{x}'')$ be a separating hyperplane of $\overline{\mathscr{C}}_A(\mathbf{x}'')$. According to the results of Sec. 7.154, $\mathscr{T}(\mathbf{x}'')$ is the transform, due to linear transformation $A(t', t'')$, of a separating hyperplane $\mathscr{T}(\mathbf{x}')$ of $\overline{\mathscr{C}}_A(\mathbf{x}')$.

Let $\overline{R}''_A$ and $\overline{R}_A{}'$ denote the closed half spaces determined by $\mathscr{T}(\mathbf{x}'')$ and $\mathscr{T}(\mathbf{x}')$, respectively, where

$$\overline{\mathscr{C}}_A(\mathbf{x}') \subseteq \overline{R}_A{}' \qquad \text{and} \qquad \overline{\mathscr{C}}_A(\mathbf{x}'') \subseteq \overline{R}''_A$$

Recall here that $\overline{R}''_A$ is the transform of $\overline{R}_A{}'$, due to $A(t', t'')$—see Sec. 7.154, remark (v).

Consider a vector $\boldsymbol{\eta}'$ at $\mathbf{x}'$, such that

$$\mathbf{x}' + \boldsymbol{\eta} \in I(\mathbf{x}')$$

From the definition of symmetrical subset $I(\mathbf{x}')$, we have

$$\mathbf{x}' + \boldsymbol{\eta}' \in \mathscr{S}(\mathbf{x}') \qquad \text{and} \quad \mathbf{x}' - \boldsymbol{\eta}' \in \mathscr{S}(\mathbf{x}')$$

Thus,

$$\mathbf{x}' + \boldsymbol{\eta}' \in \overline{\mathscr{C}}_A(\mathbf{x}')$$

so that, according to Lemma 20,

$$\mathbf{x}'' + \boldsymbol{\eta}'' \in \overline{\mathscr{C}}_A(\mathbf{x}'')$$

Now, if

$$\mathbf{x}'' + \boldsymbol{\eta}'' \in \mathring{\mathscr{C}}_A(\mathbf{x}'')$$

then

$$\mathbf{x}'' + \boldsymbol{\eta}'' \in R_A''$$

which implies that

$$\mathbf{x}'' - \boldsymbol{\eta}'' \in \text{comp } \overline{R}_A''$$

But this is not possible, since

$$\mathbf{x}' - \boldsymbol{\eta}' \in \mathscr{S}(\mathbf{x}') \Rightarrow \begin{cases} \mathbf{x}' - \boldsymbol{\eta}' \in \overline{\mathscr{C}}_A(\mathbf{x}') \\ \mathbf{x}' - \boldsymbol{\eta}' \in \overline{R}_A' \\ \mathbf{x}'' - \boldsymbol{\eta}'' \in \overline{R}_A'' \end{cases}$$

Consequently,

$$\mathbf{x}'' + \boldsymbol{\eta}'' \in \mathscr{S}(\mathbf{x}'')$$

Moreover, since

$$\mathbf{x}' - \boldsymbol{\eta}' \in I(\mathbf{x}')$$

the same arguments apply to $-\boldsymbol{\eta}'$; hence,

$$\mathbf{x}'' - \boldsymbol{\eta}'' \in \mathscr{S}(\mathbf{x}'')$$

This establishes the lemma.

In an analogous fashion, employing Theorem 2 and Lemma 21, one can prove

Lemma 23. *Let* $\mathbf{x}' \triangleq \mathbf{x}^*(t')$ *and* $\mathbf{x}'' \triangleq \mathbf{x}^*(t'')$, $t'' \geq t'$, *be points of optimal trajectory* Γ^*. *If* $\overline{\mathscr{C}}_B(\mathbf{x}')$ *is separable, then*

$$\mathbf{x}'' + \boldsymbol{\eta}'' \in I(\mathbf{x}'') \rightarrow \mathbf{x}' + \boldsymbol{\eta}' \subset I(\mathbf{x}')$$

where

$$\boldsymbol{\eta}'' = A(t', t'')\boldsymbol{\eta}'$$

Of course, these lemmas are trivially valid for the case of null vectors.

7.192 Dimension of a Symmetrical Subset; Theorems 5 and 6

We shall say that points $\mathbf{x} + \boldsymbol{\eta}_\nu$, $\nu = 1, 2, \ldots, r$, are *linearly independent*, if

$$\sum_{\nu=1}^{r} \alpha_\nu \boldsymbol{\eta}_\nu = 0 \Rightarrow \alpha_1 = \alpha_2 = \cdots = \alpha_\nu = 0$$

In the absence of such an implication, we shall say that these points are *linearly dependent*.

Furthermore, we shall say that the *dimension of symmetrical subset* $I(\mathbf{x})$ is γ, if

(i) there exist γ points $\mathbf{x} + \boldsymbol{\eta}_\nu$, $\nu = 1, 2, \ldots, \gamma$, in $I(\mathbf{x})$, which are linearly independent; and
(ii) more than γ distinct points in $I(\mathbf{x})$ are necessarily linearly dependent.

Lemmas 22 and 23 lead readily to

Theorem 5. *Let* $\mathbf{x}' \triangleq \mathbf{x}^*(t')$ *and* $\mathbf{x}'' \triangleq \mathbf{x}^*(t'')$, $t'' \geq t'$, *be points of optimal trajectory* Γ^*, *and let* γ' *and* γ'' *be the dimensions of* $I(\mathbf{x}')$ *and* $I(\mathbf{x}'')$, *respectively. If* $\overline{\mathscr{C}}_A(\mathbf{x}'')$ *is separable, then* $\gamma'' \geq \gamma'$;

and

Theorem 6. *Let* $\mathbf{x}' \triangleq \mathbf{x}^*(t')$ *and* $\mathbf{x}'' \triangleq \mathbf{x}^*(t'')$, $t'' \geq t'$, *be points of optimal trajectory* Γ^*, *and let* γ' *and* γ'' *be the dimensions of* $I(\mathbf{x}')$ *and* $I(\mathbf{x}'')$, *respectively. If* $\overline{\mathscr{C}}_B(\mathbf{x}')$ *is separable, then* $\gamma'' \leq \gamma'$.

For instance, consider the case for which $\overline{\mathscr{C}}_A(\mathbf{x}'')$ is separable, and suppose the theorem is false; namely, $\gamma'' < \gamma'$. Then consider a set of $\gamma'' + 1$ linearly independent points $\mathbf{x}' + \boldsymbol{\eta}_\nu'$, $\nu = 1, 2, \ldots, \gamma'' + 1$, in $I(\mathbf{x}')$; obviously we can always do this in view of our hypothesis that $\gamma' > \gamma''$.

Since $A(t', t'')$ is linear and nonsingular, the points $\mathbf{x}'' + \boldsymbol{\eta}_\nu''$, $\nu = 1, 2, \ldots, \gamma'' + 1$, where

$$\boldsymbol{\eta}_\nu'' = A(t', t'')\boldsymbol{\eta}_\nu'$$

are also linearly independent. Indeed,

$$\sum_{\nu=1}^{\gamma''+1} \alpha_\nu \boldsymbol{\eta}_\nu' = A(t'', t') \sum_{\nu=1}^{\gamma''+1} \alpha_\nu \boldsymbol{\eta}_\nu''$$

Hence

$$\sum_{\nu=1}^{\gamma''+1} \alpha_\nu \boldsymbol{\eta}_\nu'' = 0 \Rightarrow \sum_{\nu=1}^{\gamma''+1} \alpha_\nu \boldsymbol{\eta}_\nu' = 0$$

which, in turn, implies $\alpha_\nu = 0$, $\nu = 1, 2, \ldots, \gamma'' + 1$, since points $\mathbf{x}' + \boldsymbol{\eta}_\nu'$, $\nu = 1, 2, \ldots, \gamma'' + 1$, are linearly independent.

Furthermore, according to Lemma 22, points $\mathbf{x}'' + \boldsymbol{\eta}_\nu''$, $\nu = 1, 2, \ldots, \gamma'' + 1$, belong to $I(\mathbf{x}'')$. Thus, we have arrived at a contradiction, since $I(\mathbf{x}'')$ has dimension γ''. This establishes Theorem 5. Theorem 6 follows from an analogous argument, invoking Lemma 23.

7.193 Symmetrical Subset as Hyperplane; Theorem 7

From Lemmas 22 and 23 one can readily deduce

Theorem 7. *If*

(i) *$I(\mathbf{x}')$ and $I(\mathbf{x}'')$ are hyperplanes at points $\mathbf{x}' \triangleq \mathbf{x}^*(t')$ and $\mathbf{x}'' \triangleq \mathbf{x}^*(t'')$, $t'' \geq t'$, of optimal trajectory Γ^*, where $\mathscr{C}_A(\mathbf{x}'')$ or $\mathscr{C}_B(\mathbf{x}')$ is separable; and*

(ii) *the dimensions of $I(\mathbf{x}')$ and $I(\mathbf{x}'')$ are equal; then $I(\mathbf{x}'')$ is the transform of $I(\mathbf{x}')$, due to linear transformation $A(t', t'')$.*

Suppose, for instance, that $\mathscr{C}_A(\mathbf{x}'')$ is separable. By hypothesis, the dimensions of $I(\mathbf{x}')$ and $I(\mathbf{x}'')$ are equal; that is, $\gamma' = \gamma'' \triangleq \gamma$.

Consider a set of γ linearly independent points $\mathbf{x}' + \boldsymbol{\eta}_\nu'$, $\nu = 1, 2, \ldots, \gamma$, in $I(\mathbf{x}')$. This set of points forms a basis for hyperplane $I(\mathbf{x}')$; namely to each point $\mathbf{x}' + \boldsymbol{\eta}'$ of plane $I(\mathbf{x}')$ one can associate one and only one set of γ real numbers $\alpha_\nu \lesseqgtr 0$, $\nu = 1, 2, \ldots, \gamma$, such that

$$\boldsymbol{\eta}' = \sum_{\nu=1}^{\gamma} \alpha_\nu \boldsymbol{\eta}_\nu' \tag{7.108}$$

Conversely, to each set of γ real numbers $\alpha_\nu \lesseqgtr 0$, $\nu = 1, 2, \ldots, \gamma$, one can associate one and only one point $\mathbf{x}' + \boldsymbol{\eta}'$ in $I(\mathbf{x}')$ by means of relation (7.108). This statement can be expressed by

$$\mathbf{x}' + \boldsymbol{\eta}' \in I(\mathbf{x}') \Leftrightarrow \boldsymbol{\eta}' = \sum_{\nu=1}^{\gamma} \alpha_\nu \boldsymbol{\eta}_\nu', \qquad \alpha_\nu \in \mathscr{R} \tag{7.109}$$

where $\mathscr{R}$ is the set of real numbers.

Since transformation $A(t', t'')$ is linear and nonsingular, the set of points

$$\mathbf{x}'' + \boldsymbol{\eta}_\nu'', \qquad \boldsymbol{\eta}_\nu'' = A(t', t'')\boldsymbol{\eta}_\nu', \quad \nu = 1, 2, \ldots, \gamma \tag{7.110}$$

is linearly independent, as discussed in Sec. 7.192. Moreover, it follows from Lemma 22 that this set of points belongs to $I(\mathbf{x}'')$. Thus since $I(\mathbf{x}'')$ is γ-dimensional, this set of points forms a basis for hyperplane $I(\mathbf{x}'')$.

Let us denote by $\mathbf{x}'' + \boldsymbol{\xi}''$ a point in $I(\mathbf{x}'')$.† We shall show that $\boldsymbol{\xi}'' = A(t', t'')\boldsymbol{\eta}'$ where $\mathbf{x}' + \boldsymbol{\eta}' \in I(\mathbf{x}')$, so that we will be able to set $\boldsymbol{\xi}'' = \boldsymbol{\eta}''$.

Since the set of points (7.110) forms a basis for hyperplane $I(\mathbf{x}'')$, it follows that

$$\mathbf{x}'' + \boldsymbol{\xi}'' \in I(\mathbf{x}'') \Leftrightarrow \boldsymbol{\xi}'' = \sum_{\nu=1}^{\gamma} \alpha_\nu \boldsymbol{\eta}_\nu'', \qquad \alpha_\nu \in \mathscr{R}$$

and hence

$$\mathbf{x}'' + \boldsymbol{\xi}'' \in I(\mathbf{x}'') \Leftrightarrow \boldsymbol{\xi}'' = A(t', t'') \sum_{\nu=1}^{\gamma} \alpha_\nu \boldsymbol{\eta}_\nu', \qquad \alpha_\nu \in \mathscr{R} \tag{7.111}$$

Upon comparing (7.109) and (7.111), we see that

$$\boldsymbol{\xi}'' = A(t', t'')\boldsymbol{\eta}', \qquad \boldsymbol{\eta}' \in I(\mathbf{x}')$$

and so we put

$$\boldsymbol{\xi}'' = \boldsymbol{\eta}''$$

and conclude that

$$\mathbf{x}' + \boldsymbol{\eta}' \in I(\mathbf{x}') \Leftrightarrow \mathbf{x}'' + \boldsymbol{\eta}'' \in I(\mathbf{x}'')$$

Employing Lemma 23, this result is obtained in similar fashion for the case of $\overline{\mathscr{C}}_B(\mathbf{x}')$ separable; and so Theorem 7 is established.

7.194 Symmetrical Subset and Separating Hyperplane; Lemmas 24 and 25

Finally, we shall prove

Lemma 24. *At an interior point* $\mathbf{x}$ *of limiting surface* Σ, *where* $\overline{\mathscr{C}}_A(\mathbf{x})$ *is separable, any separating hyperplane* $\mathscr{T}(\mathbf{x})$ *of* $\overline{\mathscr{C}}_A(\mathbf{x})$ *contains symmetrical subset* $I(\mathbf{x})$.

Let $\overline{R}_A$ be the closed half space which is determined by $\mathscr{T}(\mathbf{x})$ and contains $\overline{\mathscr{C}}_A(\mathbf{x})$; that is,

$$\overline{\mathscr{C}}_A(\mathbf{x}) \subseteq \overline{R}_A$$

Consider a vector $\boldsymbol{\eta}$ at point $\mathbf{x}$, such that

$$\mathbf{x} + \boldsymbol{\eta} \in I(\mathbf{x})$$

so that

$$\mathbf{x} + \boldsymbol{\eta} \in \mathscr{S}(\mathbf{x}) \qquad \text{and} \qquad \mathbf{x} - \boldsymbol{\eta} \in \mathscr{S}(\mathbf{x})$$

† Since we have not as yet shown that $\boldsymbol{\xi}''$ is the transform of vector $\boldsymbol{\eta}'$ we shall avoid the notation $\boldsymbol{\eta}''$.

Since

$$\mathbf{x} + \boldsymbol{\eta} \in \mathscr{S}(\mathbf{x}) \Rightarrow \mathbf{x} + \boldsymbol{\eta} \in \overline{\mathscr{C}}_A(\mathbf{x}) \Rightarrow \mathbf{x} + \boldsymbol{\eta} \in \overline{R}_A$$

it follows that

$$\mathbf{x} - \boldsymbol{\eta} \in \text{comp } R_A \tag{7.112}$$

where, indeed,

$$\text{comp } R_A = \overline{\text{comp } R_A} \tag{7.113}$$

On the other hand

$$\mathbf{x} - \boldsymbol{\eta} \in \mathscr{S}(\mathbf{x}) \Rightarrow \mathbf{x} - \boldsymbol{\eta} \in \overline{\mathscr{C}}_A(\mathbf{x}) \Rightarrow \mathbf{x} - \boldsymbol{\eta} \in \overline{R}_A \tag{7.114}$$

In view of (7.112)–(7.114), we have

$$\mathbf{x} - \boldsymbol{\eta} \in \overline{R}_A \cap \overline{\text{comp } R_A} = \mathscr{T}(\mathbf{x})$$

and consequently

$$\mathbf{x} + \boldsymbol{\eta} \in \mathscr{T}(\mathbf{x})$$

Hence, Lemma 24 is established.

Analogous arguments lead to

Lemma 25. *At an interior point* $\mathbf{x}$ *of limiting surface* Σ, *where* $\overline{\mathscr{C}}_B(\mathbf{x})$ *is separable, any separating hyperplane* $\mathscr{T}(\mathbf{x})$ *of* $\overline{\mathscr{C}}_B(\mathbf{x})$ *contains symmetrical subset* $I(\mathbf{x})$.

7.20 A Maximum Principle

7.201 Assumptions; Lemma 26

Let us now consider an optimal trajectory Γ^* represented parametrically by $\mathbf{x} = \mathbf{x}^*(t)$, $t_0 \leq t \leq t_1$. We shall make the following assumptions:

(i) The limiting surface Σ, which contains Γ^*, is *nice*.
(ii) All points of Γ^* are interior points of $\mathscr{E}^*$.
(iii) At every point $\mathbf{x} = \mathbf{x}^*(t)$, $t \in (t_0, t_1)$, $\overline{\mathscr{C}}_A(\mathbf{x}) = \overline{\mathring{\mathscr{C}}}_A(\mathbf{x})$, and $\overline{\mathscr{C}}_B(\mathbf{x}) = \overline{\mathring{\mathscr{C}}}_B(\mathbf{x})$.

A point $\mathbf{x}$ will be called a *degenerated point* if either $\mathring{\mathscr{C}}_A(\mathbf{x})$ or $\mathring{\mathscr{C}}_B(\mathbf{x})$ is empty. Thus, assumption (iii) above implies that no point of Γ^* is degenerated, except possibly its initial point $\mathbf{x}^0 = \mathbf{x}^*(t_0)$ and its terminal point $\mathbf{x}^1 = \mathbf{x}^*(t_1)$. However, we shall make the additional assumption that

(iv) not both $\mathbf{x}^0$ and $\mathbf{x}^1$ are degenerated points.

Let us recall the discussion of Sec. 7.112, according to which there exists a *forward tangent* and a *backward tangent* of Γ^* at every point $\mathbf{x} = \mathbf{x}^*(t)$, $t \in (t_0, t_1)$; namely, these tangents are the supporting rays of

$$\mathbf{f}_+{}^* \triangleq \mathbf{f}(\mathbf{x}, \mathbf{u}_+{}^*)$$

and of

$$-\mathbf{f}_-{}^* = -\mathbf{f}(\mathbf{x}, \mathbf{u}_-{}^*)$$

respectively.

Moreover, $\mathbf{f}_+{}^*$ may differ from $\mathbf{f}_-{}^*$ on the two sets of points described in cases (i) and (ii) of Sec. 7.112. Both of these sets of points are *sets of measure zero with respect to position variable* $\mathbf{x}$. At all other points of Γ^*, we have $\mathbf{u}_+{}^* = \mathbf{u}_-{}^*$ so that

$$\mathbf{f}_+{}^* = \mathbf{f}_-{}^* \triangleq \mathbf{f}^*$$

At such points, the tangent of Γ^* is defined, namely, the forward tangent and the backward tangent possess the same supporting line, *provided* $\mathbf{f}^* \neq 0$. It is readily seen that $\mathbf{f}^* = 0$ on a set of points which has measure zero with respect to $\mathbf{x}$. For other points, we shall find it convenient to consider unit vector

$$\mathbf{t}^* \triangleq \frac{\mathbf{f}^*}{|\mathbf{f}^*|}$$

According to property (i) of a *nice* limiting surface, there exists a partition $\{\Sigma_1, \Sigma_2, \ldots, \Sigma_\mu\}$ of Σ such that at every point $\mathbf{x}$ in $\bar{\Sigma}_i$, $i = 1, 2, \ldots, \mu$, the tangent cone $\mathscr{C}_{\Sigma_i}(\mathbf{x})$ is defined and belongs to a k-dimensional plane $T_{\Sigma_i}(\mathbf{x})$, $k \leq n$, through point $\mathbf{x}$.

Of course, every point $\mathbf{x} = \mathbf{x}^*(t)$, $t \in [t_0, t_1]$, belongs to a subset $\bigcap_{i=1}^{\gamma} \bar{\Sigma}_i$, $\gamma \leq \mu$, where the Σ_i, $i = 1, 2, \ldots, \gamma$, belong to the partition and are *all* the members of the partition whose closures contain $\mathbf{x}$. The subset $\bigcap_{i=1}^{\gamma} \bar{\Sigma}_i$ may not be the same for all points of Γ^*; not only γ, but also the members of the partition which make up the subset, may vary.† Henceforth, in order to emphasize the dependence of the subset on $\mathbf{x} = \mathbf{x}^*(t)$, $t_0 \leq t \leq t_1$, we shall write

$$M(\mathbf{x}) \triangleq \bigcap_{i=1}^{\gamma} \bar{\Sigma}_i$$

Note now that the number of such subsets is finite if μ is finite; if μ is not finite, the set of subsets is denumerable.‡

† This may require renumbering the members of the partition.
‡ See Appendix.

We shall now consider only those points of Γ^* where its tangent is defined and $\mathbf{f}^* \neq 0$, and we shall prove

Lemma 26. *At every point* $\mathbf{x} = \mathbf{x}^*(t)$, $t \in [t_0, t_1]$, *of optimal trajectory* Γ^*, *except on a set of measure zero with respect to* $\mathbf{x}$, *there exists a vector which is tangent both to* Γ^* *and to the subset* $M(\mathbf{x})$.

Let $B(\mathbf{x})$ be an open ball in E^{n+1} with center at $\mathbf{x} = \mathbf{x}^*(t)$, $t \in [t_0, t_1]$, and radius ε. We shall distinguish between two cases:

(i) There exists a $\sigma > 0$ such that, for all $\varepsilon < \sigma$, no point of Γ^*, other than $\mathbf{x}$, belongs to both $B(\mathbf{x})$ and $M(\mathbf{x})$.

(ii) No matter how small ε, there exists a point $\mathbf{x}_\varepsilon \neq \mathbf{x}$ which belongs to both Γ^* and $M(\mathbf{x})$.

Since the set of all distinct subsets $\bigcap_{i=1}^{\gamma} \bar{\Sigma}_i$ is either finite or at worst denumerable, we shall designate this set by

$$\{M_1, M_2, \ldots, M_\nu \ldots\}$$

Then $M(\mathbf{x})$ may be any member of this set. Of course,

$$M_1 \cup M_2 \cup \cdots \cup M_\nu \cdots = \bar{\Sigma}$$

Next consider the subsets of Γ^*

$$\Gamma^* \cap M_1, \Gamma^* \cap M_2, \ldots, \Gamma^* \cap M_\nu, \ldots$$

In each subset $\Gamma^* \cap M_i$, $i = 1, 2, \ldots, \nu, \ldots$, consider the set of points D_i for which the condition of case (i) above is met. Set D_i is clearly discrete, and hence has measure zero.

Now, since there is either a finite number or a denumerable infinity of subsets D_i, say

$$D_1, D_2, \ldots, D_\nu, \ldots$$

and since the union of a finite number or of a denumerable infinity of sets, each of which has measure zero, is a set of measure zero, it follows that the points of Γ^*, for which the condition of case (i) above applies, constitute a set of measure zero.

Next let us turn to case (ii). Since

$$\mathbf{x}_\varepsilon \neq \mathbf{x} = \mathbf{x}^*(t), \qquad t \in [t_0, t_1], \quad \mathbf{x}_\varepsilon \in \Gamma^*$$

we have

$$\mathbf{x}_\varepsilon = \mathbf{x}^*(t_\varepsilon), \qquad t_\varepsilon \in [t_0, t_1], \quad t_\varepsilon \neq t$$

We now distinguish between two subcases:

(a) t_ε belongs to an infinite sequence of times such that

$$t < t_\varepsilon \qquad \text{for all} \quad \varepsilon$$

and

$$|\mathbf{x}_\varepsilon - \mathbf{x}| \to 0 \qquad \text{as} \quad \varepsilon \to 0$$

(b) The condition of (a) is not met. Since ε may be arbitrarily small, t_ε belongs to an infinite sequence of times such that

$$t_\varepsilon < t \qquad \text{for all} \quad \varepsilon$$

and

$$|\mathbf{x}_\varepsilon - \mathbf{x}| \to 0 \qquad \text{as} \quad \varepsilon \to 0$$

Thus, for subcase (a),

$$\boldsymbol{\eta}(\varepsilon) \triangleq \frac{\mathbf{x}_\varepsilon - \mathbf{x}}{|\mathbf{x}_\varepsilon - \mathbf{x}|} \to \mathbf{t}^* \qquad \text{as} \quad \varepsilon \to 0$$

and for subcase (b),

$$\boldsymbol{\eta}(\varepsilon) \triangleq \frac{\mathbf{x}_\varepsilon - \mathbf{x}}{|\mathbf{x}_\varepsilon - \mathbf{x}|} \to -\mathbf{t}^* \qquad \text{as} \quad \varepsilon \to 0$$

Furthermore,

$$\mathbf{x}_\varepsilon = \mathbf{x} + m(\varepsilon)\boldsymbol{\eta}(\varepsilon) \in M(\mathbf{x})$$

where

$$m(\varepsilon) \triangleq |\mathbf{x}_\varepsilon - \mathbf{x}| \to 0 \qquad \text{as} \quad \varepsilon \to 0$$

Hence, according to Sec. 7.81, we conclude that

$$\mathbf{t}^* \text{ is tangent to } M(\mathbf{x}) \text{ in subcase (a)}$$
$$-\mathbf{t}^* \text{ is tangent to } M(\mathbf{x}) \text{ in subcase (b)}$$

Since both $\mathbf{t}^*$ and $-\mathbf{t}^*$ are tangent to Γ^*, Lemma 26 is established. By the way, of course, it may happen that both $\mathbf{t}^*$ and $-\mathbf{t}^*$ are tangent to $M(\mathbf{x})$.

Henceforth, we shall let $\mathbf{t}(\mathbf{x})$ denote a vector which is tangent to both Γ^* and $M(\mathbf{x})$ at point $\mathbf{x}$. Thus it follows from the discussion above that

$$\mathbf{t}^* = \mathbf{t}(\mathbf{x}) \qquad \text{or} \qquad -\mathbf{t}^* = \mathbf{t}(\mathbf{x}) \tag{7.115}$$

7.202 The Cone $\mathscr{C}''$

From now on we shall consider points of Γ^* for which the following conditions apply:

(i) The tangent of Γ^* is defined, and $\mathbf{f}^* \neq 0$.

(ii) There is a one-to-one correspondence between point $\mathbf{x} \in \Gamma^*$ and time $t \in [t_0, t_1]$; that is, $\mathbf{x} \neq \mathbf{x}^*(t)$, $t \in (t', t'')$, if $\mathbf{f}(\mathbf{x}^*(t), \mathbf{u}^*(t)) \equiv 0$ on $[t', t'']$.
(iii) Lemma 26 applies.
(iv) Point $\mathbf{x} \in \Gamma^*$ is a nondegenerated point. According to assumption (iii) of Sec. 7.201, no point of Γ^* is degenerated, except possibly the end points. Thus, we exclude from consideration $\mathbf{x}^*(t_0)$ or $\mathbf{x}^*(t_1)$, if it is degenerated.

Thus, we are disregarding a set of points which is of measure zero in E^{n+1}. On the other hand, we shall be concerned with those points of Γ^* for which (i)–(iv) above are met. The corresponding set of times, $t \in [t_0, t_1]$, will be denoted by Θ; that is,

$$\Theta \triangleq \{t : \mathbf{x}^*(t) \text{ satisfies (i)–(iv) above}\}$$

Now consider the set $\Delta_v(\mathbf{x})$ which is the union of all vectors $\mathbf{v}$, where $\mathbf{v}$ is

(i) $a\mathbf{f}(\mathbf{x}, \mathbf{u})$, $a \geq 0$, $\mathbf{u} \in \Omega$;
(ii) $b\mathbf{t}(\mathbf{x})$, $b \lesseqgtr 0$, $\mathbf{t}(\mathbf{x})$ tangent to both Γ^* and $M(\mathbf{x})$, $|\mathbf{t}(\mathbf{x})| = 1$;
(iii)† $c\mathbf{i}(\mathbf{x})$, $c > 0$, $\mathbf{i}(\mathbf{x}) \in L_+(\mathbf{x})$, $|\mathbf{i}(\mathbf{x})| = 1$;
at $\mathbf{x} = \mathbf{x}^*(t)$, $t \in \Theta$.

Let us note a fundamental property of any vector $\mathbf{v}$: namely, for all $\boldsymbol{\eta}$ such that

$$\mathbf{x} + \boldsymbol{\eta} \in \overline{\mathscr{C}}_A(\mathbf{x})$$

and $\alpha \geq 0$, $\mathbf{v} \in \Delta_v(\mathbf{x})$,

$$\mathbf{x} + \boldsymbol{\eta} + \alpha\mathbf{v} \in \overline{\mathscr{C}}_A(\mathbf{x}) \tag{7.116}$$

For vectors defined in (i) and (ii) above, this property follows from Lemmas 17 and 13, respectively.‡ For vectors defined in (iii) above, it is a consequence of the definitions of $\overline{\mathscr{C}}_A(\mathbf{x})$ and $\widetilde{A/\Sigma}$. We wish to prove that

$$\mathbf{x} + \boldsymbol{\eta} \in \overline{\mathscr{C}}_A(\mathbf{x})$$

implies

$$\mathbf{x} + \boldsymbol{\eta} + \alpha\mathbf{i}(\mathbf{x}) \in \overline{\mathscr{C}}_A(\mathbf{x}), \qquad \alpha \geq 0$$

First of all suppose that

$$\mathbf{x} + \boldsymbol{\eta} \in \mathscr{C}_A(\mathbf{x})$$

† Recall that, $L_+(\mathbf{x})$ and $L_-(\mathbf{x})$ are x_0-cylindrical half rays from $\mathbf{x}$, pointing into the positive and negative x_0-directions, respectively.
‡ Note that $\mathring{\mathscr{C}}_A(\mathbf{x}) \neq \phi$, according to assumption (iv) of this section.

namely, there exists a $\beta > 0$ such that for all ε, $0 < \varepsilon < \beta$,

$$\mathbf{x} + \varepsilon\boldsymbol{\eta} \in \widetilde{A/\Sigma}$$

Consequently, it follows from the definition of $\widetilde{A/\Sigma}$ that

$$\mathbf{x} + \varepsilon\boldsymbol{\eta} + \varepsilon\alpha\mathbf{i}(\mathbf{x}) \in \widetilde{A/\Sigma}, \qquad \alpha \geq 0, \quad 0 < \varepsilon < \beta$$

Hence, we conclude that

$$\mathbf{x} + \boldsymbol{\eta} + \alpha\mathbf{i}(\mathbf{x}) \in \mathscr{C}_A(\mathbf{x})$$

Secondly, suppose that

$$\mathbf{x} + \boldsymbol{\eta} \in \mathscr{S}(\mathbf{x})$$

and consider a sequence of vectors

$$\boldsymbol{\eta}_1, \boldsymbol{\eta}_2, \ldots, \boldsymbol{\eta}_\nu$$

such that

$$\boldsymbol{\eta}_\nu \to \boldsymbol{\eta} \qquad \text{as} \quad \nu \to \infty$$
$$\mathbf{x} + \boldsymbol{\eta}_i \in \mathscr{C}_A(\mathbf{x}), \qquad i = 1, 2, \ldots, \nu$$

Thus, as we just showed,

$$\mathbf{x} + \boldsymbol{\eta}_i + \alpha\mathbf{i}(\mathbf{x}) \in \mathscr{C}_A(\mathbf{x}), \qquad i = 1, 2, \ldots, \nu$$

But, if

$$\mathbf{x} + \boldsymbol{\eta} + \alpha\mathbf{i}(\mathbf{x}) \in \mathring{\mathscr{C}}_B(\mathbf{x})$$

then there exists a $\gamma > 0$ such that for all $\nu > \gamma$,

$$\mathbf{x} + \boldsymbol{\eta}_\nu + \alpha\mathbf{i}(\mathbf{x}) \in \mathring{\mathscr{C}}_B(\mathbf{x})$$

which leads to a contradiction. Since

$$\bar{\mathscr{C}}_A(\mathbf{x}) = \mathring{\mathscr{C}}_A(\mathbf{x}) \cup \mathscr{S}(\mathbf{x})$$

our result is established.

We shall be concerned with the vectors of the set

$$V \triangleq \{\mathbf{v} : \mathbf{v} \in \Delta_v(\mathbf{x}), \quad \mathbf{x} = \mathbf{x}^*(t), \quad \forall t \in \Theta\}$$

and with the cone

$$\mathscr{C}'' \triangleq \{\mathbf{x}'' + k\boldsymbol{\xi} : k \geq 0, \quad \boldsymbol{\xi} = A(t, t'')\mathbf{v}, \quad \forall \mathbf{v} \in V, \quad t \leq t''\} \qquad (7.117)$$

where $\mathbf{x}'' \triangleq \mathbf{x}^*(t'')$, $t'' \in [t_0, t_1]$, is a nondegenerated point. However, t'' need not belong to Θ.†

† Provided $t < t''$, of course.

As a direct consequence of (7.116), we have

$$\mathbf{x} + \mathbf{v} \in \bar{\mathscr{C}}_A(\mathbf{x})$$

so that Lemma 20 leads to

$$\mathbf{x}'' + \boldsymbol{\xi} \in \bar{\mathscr{C}}_A(\mathbf{x}'')$$

and consequently

$$\mathscr{C}'' \subseteq \bar{\mathscr{C}}_A(\mathbf{x}'') \tag{7.118}$$

We shall find it convenient to identify a particular member of set V by subscript; that is,

$$V = \{\mathbf{v}_1, \mathbf{v}_2, \ldots, \mathbf{v}_r, \ldots\}$$

Thus, an index r determines a time t^r, and hence a point $\mathbf{x}_r \triangleq \mathbf{x}^*(t^r)$ where set $\Delta_v(\mathbf{x}_r)$ is defined, as well as the member $\mathbf{v}_r \in \Delta_v(\mathbf{x}_r)$. We shall also let

$$\boldsymbol{\xi}_r \triangleq A(t^r, t'')\mathbf{v}_r, \qquad t^r \leq t'', \quad \mathbf{v}_r \in V \tag{7.119}$$

Clearly, in view of definition (7.117),

$$\mathbf{x}'' + \boldsymbol{\xi}_r \in \mathscr{C}'' \tag{7.120}$$

7.203 A Property of Cone $\mathscr{C}''$; Lemma 27

Consider now a vector $\boldsymbol{\varphi}$ which is a linear combination, having nonnegative coefficients, of a finite number of vectors $\boldsymbol{\xi}_r$ defined by (7.119); namely,

$$\boldsymbol{\varphi} \triangleq \sum_{r=1}^{s} \alpha_r \boldsymbol{\xi}_r, \qquad \alpha_r \geq 0 \tag{7.121}†$$

Cone $\mathscr{C}''$ has a noteworthy property embodied in

Lemma 27. *If* $\mathbf{x}'' \triangleq \mathbf{x}^*(t'')$ *is a nondegenerated point of optimal trajectory* Γ^*, *and* $\boldsymbol{\varphi}$ *is a vector at* $\mathbf{x}''$ *defined by* (7.121), *then*

$$\mathbf{x}'' + \boldsymbol{\varphi} \in \bar{\mathscr{C}}_A(\mathbf{x}'')$$

We shall suppose that

$$t^1 \leq t^2 \leq \cdots \leq t^s \leq t''$$

Then, in view of (7.119) and (7.121), we have

$$\begin{aligned}\boldsymbol{\psi} &= \sum_{r=1}^{s} \alpha_r A(t^r, t'')\mathbf{v}_r \\ &= \sum_{r=1}^{s} A(t^r, t'')\alpha_r \mathbf{v}_r\end{aligned} \tag{7.122}$$

† By appropriate renumbering of the set V, any such linear combination can be formed.

As pointed out in Sec. 7.141 since $[t^1, t'']$ is divided into subintervals

$$[t^1, t^2], [t^2, t^3], \ldots, [t^s, t'']$$

we have

$$\begin{aligned}
A(t^1, t'') &= A(t^s, t'') \cdots A(t^2, t^3)A(t^1, t^2) \\
A(t^2, t'') &= A(t^s, t'') \cdots A(t^3, t^4)A(t^2, t^3) \\
&\vdots \\
A(t^s, t'') &= A(t^s, t'')
\end{aligned}$$

This permits us to replace (7.122) by

$$\begin{aligned}
\boldsymbol{\eta}_1 &= \alpha_1 \mathbf{v}_1 \\
\boldsymbol{\eta}_2 &= A(t^1, t^2)\boldsymbol{\eta}_1 \\
\boldsymbol{\eta}_3 &= A(t^2, t^3)[\boldsymbol{\eta}_2 + \alpha_2 \mathbf{v}_2] \\
&\vdots \\
\boldsymbol{\eta}_s &= A(t^{s-1}, t^s)[\boldsymbol{\eta}_{s-1} + \alpha_{s-1}\mathbf{v}_{s-1}] \\
\varphi &= A(t^s, t'')[\boldsymbol{\eta}_s + \alpha_s \mathbf{v}_s]
\end{aligned} \tag{7.123}$$

The lemma will now be established by a recursive argument. As a consequence of (7.116), we have

$$\mathbf{x}_1 + \alpha_1 \mathbf{v}_1 \in \overline{\mathscr{C}}_A(\mathbf{x}_1)$$

so that (7.123) with Lemma 20 results in

$$\mathbf{x}_2 + \boldsymbol{\eta}_2 \in \overline{\mathscr{C}}_A(\mathbf{x}_2)$$

In general, if

$$\mathbf{x}_r + \boldsymbol{\eta}_r \in \overline{\mathscr{C}}_A(\mathbf{x}_r)$$

then (7.116) leads to

$$\mathbf{x}_r + \boldsymbol{\eta}_r + \alpha_r \mathbf{v}_r \in \overline{\mathscr{C}}_A(\mathbf{x}_r)$$

and (7.123) with Lemma 20 leads to

$$\mathbf{x}_{r+1} + \boldsymbol{\eta}_{r+1} \in \overline{\mathscr{C}}_A(\mathbf{x}_{r+1})$$

Thus, we conclude that

$$\mathbf{x}_s + \boldsymbol{\eta}_s + \alpha_s \mathbf{v}_s \in \overline{\mathscr{C}}_A(\mathbf{x}_s)$$

whence (7.123) with Lemma 20 establishes Lemma 27.

7.204 Convex Closure of Cone $\mathscr{C}''$

Since cone $\mathscr{C}''$ may be nonconvex, we shall find it useful to consider its convex closure

$$K_A \triangleq \{\mathbf{x}'' + \boldsymbol{\varphi} : \boldsymbol{\varphi} \text{ defined by (7.121)}\}$$

Note that the convexity of K_A follows from its definition together with that of $\boldsymbol{\varphi}$, whence

$$\left.\begin{array}{l}\mathbf{x}'' + \boldsymbol{\varphi}_1 \in K_A \\ \mathbf{x}'' + \boldsymbol{\varphi}_2 \in K_A\end{array}\right\} \Rightarrow \mathbf{x}'' + \alpha_1\boldsymbol{\varphi}_1 + \alpha_2\boldsymbol{\varphi}_2 \in K_A, \qquad \begin{array}{l}\alpha_1 \geq 0 \\ \alpha_2 \geq 0\end{array}$$

First of all, as a consequence of Lemma 27,

$$K_A \subseteq \overline{\mathscr{C}}_A(\mathbf{x}'') \tag{7.124}$$

Secondly, it is clear from their definitions that

$$\mathscr{C}'' \subseteq K_A \tag{7.125}$$

And finally, since linear transformation $A(t, t'')$ transforms a vector which is parallel to the x_0-axis into one which is parallel to the x_0-axis, and since

$$\mathbf{x} + c\mathbf{i}(\mathbf{x}) \in \Delta_v(\mathbf{x}), \qquad \mathbf{x} = \mathbf{x}^*(t), \quad t \in \Theta, \quad c > 0$$

it follows that

$$L_+(\mathbf{x}'') \subset \mathscr{C}''$$

and hence

$$L_+(\mathbf{x}'') \subset K_A \tag{7.126}$$

7.205 The Cone $\mathscr{C}'$; Lemma 28

Since the discussion of this section parallels that of the preceding sections, we shall avoid repeating the details of all arguments. We shall now consider the set $\Delta_w(\mathbf{x})$ which is the union of all vectors $\mathbf{w}$, where $\mathbf{w}$ is

(i) $-a\mathbf{f}(\mathbf{x}, \mathbf{u})$, $a \geq 0$, $\mathbf{u} \in \Omega$;
(ii) $b\mathbf{t}(\mathbf{x})$, $b \gtreqless 0$, $\mathbf{t}(\mathbf{x})$ tangent to both Γ^* and $M(\mathbf{x})$, $|\mathbf{t}(\mathbf{x})| = 1$;
(iii) $c\mathbf{j}(\mathbf{x})$, $c > 0$, $\mathbf{j}(\mathbf{x}) \in L_-(\mathbf{x})$, $|\mathbf{j}(\mathbf{x})| = 1$;
at $\mathbf{x} = \mathbf{x}^*(t)$, $t \in \Theta$.

Lemmas 18 and 14, respectively, on the one hand, and the definitions of $\mathscr{C}_B(\mathbf{x})$ and of B/Σ on the other hand, lead to the following property of $\mathbf{w}$: For all $\boldsymbol{\eta}$ such that

$$\mathbf{x} + \boldsymbol{\eta} \in \overline{\mathscr{C}}_B(\mathbf{x})$$

and $\alpha \geq 0$, $\mathbf{w} \in \Delta_w(\mathbf{x})$,

$$\mathbf{x} + \boldsymbol{\eta} + \alpha\mathbf{w} \in \overline{\mathscr{C}}_B(\mathbf{x}) \tag{7.127}$$

Here we shall be concerned with vectors of the set

$$W \triangleq \{\mathbf{w} : \mathbf{w} \in \Delta_w(\mathbf{x}), \quad \mathbf{x} = \mathbf{x}^*(t), \quad \forall t \in \Theta\}$$

and with the cone

$$\mathscr{C}' \triangleq \{\mathbf{x}' + k\boldsymbol{\zeta} : k \geq 0, \quad \boldsymbol{\zeta} = A(t, t')\mathbf{w}, \quad \forall \mathbf{w} \in W, \quad t \geq t'\} \tag{7.128}$$

where $\mathbf{x}' \triangleq \mathbf{x}^*(t')$, $t' \in [t_0, t_1]$, is a nondegenerated point. However, t' need not belong to Θ.†

In view of (7.127), we have

$$\mathbf{x} + \mathbf{w} \in \bar{\mathscr{C}}_B(\mathbf{x})$$

so that Lemma 21 leads to

$$\mathbf{x}' + \boldsymbol{\zeta} \in \bar{\mathscr{C}}_B(\mathbf{x}')$$

and consequently

$$\mathscr{C}' \subseteq \bar{\mathscr{C}}_B(\mathbf{x}') \tag{7.129}$$

We shall again use index r to identify a member of set

$$W = \{\mathbf{w}_1, \mathbf{w}_2, \ldots, \mathbf{w}_r, \ldots\}$$

and consider vectors

$$\boldsymbol{\zeta}_r \triangleq A(t^r, t')\mathbf{w}_r, \qquad t^r \geq t', \quad \mathbf{w}_r \in W$$

and

$$\boldsymbol{\psi} \triangleq \sum_{r=1}^{s} \alpha_r \boldsymbol{\zeta}_r, \qquad \alpha_r \geq 0 \tag{7.130}$$

where, in view of definition (7.128), it is clear that

$$\mathbf{x}' + \boldsymbol{\zeta}_r \in \mathscr{C}'$$

By arguments analogous to those employed in Sec. 7.203, one can prove

Lemma 28. *If* $\mathbf{x}' \triangleq \mathbf{x}^*(t')$ *is a nondegenerated point of optimal trajectory* Γ^*, *and* $\boldsymbol{\psi}$ *is a vector at* $\mathbf{x}'$ *defined by* (7.130), *then*

$$\mathbf{x}' + \boldsymbol{\psi} \in \bar{\mathscr{C}}_B(\mathbf{x}')$$

7.206 Convex Closure of Cone $\mathscr{C}'$

Now we consider the convex closure of $\mathscr{C}'$, namely,

$$K_B \triangleq \{\mathbf{x}' + \boldsymbol{\psi} : \boldsymbol{\psi} \text{ defined by } (7.130)\}$$

† Provided $t' < t$, of course.

From Lemma 28, we have

$$K_B \subseteq \overline{\mathscr{C}}_B(\mathbf{x}') \tag{7.131}$$

and from their definitions it follows that

$$\mathscr{C}' \subseteq K_B \tag{7.132}$$

Furthermore, by arguments similar to those used in Sec. 7.204, we conclude that

$$L_-(\mathbf{x}') \subset \mathscr{C}'$$

and hence

$$L_-(\mathbf{x}') \subset K_B \tag{7.133}$$

7.207 Theorem 8

Let us first suppose that

$$\mathring{\mathscr{C}}_A(\mathbf{x}^0) \neq \phi, \qquad \mathbf{x}^0 = \mathbf{x}^*(t_0) \tag{7.134}$$

and let $\mathbf{x}' = \mathbf{x}^0$, so that K_B is a cone with vertex at $\mathbf{x}^0$.

Since K_B is convex and, in view of (7.131), does not fill the entire space, there exists a separating hyperplane $\mathscr{T}(\mathbf{x}^0)$ of K_B at $\mathbf{x}^0$. In other words, K_B belongs to one of the closed half spaces determined by $\mathscr{T}(\mathbf{x}^0)$, say $\overline{R}_B(\mathbf{x}^0)$; that is,

$$K_B \subseteq \overline{R}_B(\mathbf{x}^0) \tag{7.135}$$

Let $\Pi(\mathbf{x}^*(t))$ and $\overline{P}_B(\mathbf{x}^*(t))$ denote the transforms, due to $A(t_0, t)$, $t \in \Theta$, of $\mathscr{T}(\mathbf{x}^0)$ and $\overline{R}_B(\mathbf{x}^0)$, respectively; that is

$$\mathbf{x}^0 + \boldsymbol{\eta} \in \mathscr{T}(\mathbf{x}^0) \Rightarrow \mathbf{x}^*(t) + A(t_0, t)\boldsymbol{\eta} \in \Pi(\mathbf{x}^*(t))$$
$$\mathbf{x}^0 + \boldsymbol{\eta} \in \overline{R}_B(\mathbf{x}^0) \Rightarrow \mathbf{x}^*(t) + A(t_0, t)\boldsymbol{\eta} \in \overline{P}_B(\mathbf{x}^*(t))$$

In fact, since the transformation is linear and nonsingular, $\Pi(\mathbf{x}^*(t))$ is the boundary of $\overline{P}_B(\mathbf{x}^*(t))$.

As a consequence of the definitions of $\Delta_w(\mathbf{x})$ and $\mathscr{C}'$, we have

$$\mathbf{x}^0 - A(t, t_0)\mathbf{f}(\mathbf{x}^*(t), \mathbf{u}) \in \mathscr{C}', \qquad \forall \mathbf{u} \in \Omega$$

where $\mathscr{C}'$ is now a cone at $\mathbf{x}^0$. Thus, it follows from (7.132) that

$$\mathbf{x}^0 - A(t, t_0)\mathbf{f}(\mathbf{x}^*(t), \mathbf{u}) \in K_B, \qquad \forall \mathbf{u} \in \Omega$$

which, in view of (7.135), implies

$$\mathbf{x}^0 - A(t, t_0)\mathbf{f}(\mathbf{x}^*(t), \mathbf{u}) \in \overline{R}_B(\mathbf{x}^0)$$

And so

$$\mathbf{x}^*(t) - \mathbf{f}(\mathbf{x}^*(t), \mathbf{u}) \in \bar{P}_B(\mathbf{x}^*(t)), \qquad \forall \mathbf{u} \in \Omega$$

whence we conclude that

$$\mathbf{x}^*(t) + \mathbf{f}(\mathbf{x}^*(t), \mathbf{u}) \in \overline{\text{comp } \bar{P}_B(\mathbf{x}^*(t))}, \qquad \forall \mathbf{u} \in \Omega \tag{7.136}$$

Furthermore, it follows from the definitions of $\Delta_w(\mathbf{x})$ and $\mathscr{C}'$ that

$$b\mathbf{t}(\mathbf{x}^*(t)) \in \Delta_w(\mathbf{x}^*(t)),\ b \gtrless 0 \Rightarrow \mathbf{x}^0 + bA(t, t_0)\mathbf{t}(\mathbf{x}^*(t)) \in \mathscr{C}'$$

Hence, we have

$$\mathbf{x}^0 + bA(t, t_0)\mathbf{t}(\mathbf{x}^*(t)) \in K_B, \qquad b \gtrless 0$$

and then

$$\mathbf{x}^0 + bA(t, t_0)\mathbf{t}(\mathbf{x}^*(t)) \in \bar{R}_B(\mathbf{x}^0), \qquad b \gtrless 0$$

This implies

$$\mathbf{x}^*(t) + b\mathbf{t}(\mathbf{x}^*(t)) \in \bar{P}_B(\mathbf{x}^*(t)), \qquad b \gtrless 0$$

which, in turn, implies

$$\mathbf{x}^*(t) \pm \mathbf{t}(\mathbf{x}^*(t)) \in \Pi(\mathbf{x}^*(t))$$

since $b \gtrless 0$.

Furthermore, it follows from (7.115) that

$$\mathbf{t}(\mathbf{x}^*(t)) = \pm\mathbf{t}^* \triangleq \pm \frac{\mathbf{f}(\mathbf{x}^*(t), \mathbf{u}^*(t))}{|\mathbf{f}(\mathbf{x}^*(t), \mathbf{u}^*(t))|}$$

so that

$$\mathbf{x}^*(t) + \mathbf{f}(\mathbf{x}^*(t), \mathbf{u}^*(t)) \in \Pi(\mathbf{x}^*(t)), \qquad \forall t \in \Theta \tag{7.137}$$†

Let us now consider the solution $\boldsymbol{\lambda}(t)$, $t_0 \leq t \leq t_1$, of adjoint equations (7.79) with initial condition $\boldsymbol{\lambda}(t_0) = \boldsymbol{\lambda}^0 \neq 0$ and such that

$$\begin{gathered} \boldsymbol{\lambda}^0 \text{ is normal to } \mathscr{T}(\mathbf{x}^0) \\ \mathbf{x}^0 + \boldsymbol{\lambda}^0 \in \bar{R}_B(\mathbf{x}^0) \end{gathered}$$

As a consequence of (7.82), and since $\boldsymbol{\lambda}(t)$ is a nonzero continuous vector function, we have

$$\begin{gathered} \boldsymbol{\lambda}(t) \text{ is normal to } \Pi(\mathbf{x}^*(t)) \\ \mathbf{x}^*(t) + \boldsymbol{\lambda}(t) \in \bar{P}_B(\mathbf{x}^*(t)) \end{gathered}$$

† Of course, this is trivially so if $\mathbf{f}(\mathbf{x}^*(t), \mathbf{u}^*(t)) = 0$.

And so, we conclude from (7.136) and (7.137) that

$$\boldsymbol{\lambda}(t) \cdot \mathbf{f}(\mathbf{x}^*(t), \mathbf{u}) \leq 0, \qquad \forall \mathbf{u} \in \Omega, \quad \forall t \in \Theta \tag{7.138}$$

and

$$\boldsymbol{\lambda}(t) \cdot \mathbf{f}(\mathbf{x}^*(t), \mathbf{u}^*(t)) = 0, \qquad \forall t \in \Theta \tag{7.139}$$

If $\mathring{\mathscr{C}}_A(\mathbf{x}^0) = \phi$, then we shall suppose that

$$\mathring{\mathscr{C}}_B(\mathbf{x}^1) \neq \phi, \qquad \mathbf{x}^1 = \mathbf{x}^*(t_1) \tag{7.140}$$

We arrive again at conditions (7.138) and (7.139) by letting $\mathbf{x}'' = \mathbf{x}^1$ and considering cone K_A at terminal point $\mathbf{x}^1$.

Cone K_A is convex, and since (7.124) applies, K_A does not fill the entire space. Hence, there exists a separating hyperplane $\mathscr{T}(\mathbf{x}^1)$ of K_A, so that

$$K_A \subseteq \bar{R}_A(\mathbf{x}^1) \tag{7.141}$$

where $\bar{R}_A(\mathbf{x}^1)$ is one of the closed half spaces determined by $\mathscr{T}(\mathbf{x}^1)$.

Let $\Pi(\mathbf{x}^*(t))$ and $\bar{P}_A(\mathbf{x}^*(t))$ denote the transforms, due to $A(t, t_1)$, $t \in \Theta$, of $\mathscr{T}(\mathbf{x}^1)$ and $\bar{R}_A(\mathbf{x}^1)$, respectively. In view of the definitions of $\Delta_v(\mathbf{x})$ and $\mathscr{C}''$, we have

$$\mathbf{x}^1 + A(t, t_1)\mathbf{f}(\mathbf{x}^*(t), \mathbf{u}) \in \mathscr{C}'', \qquad \forall \mathbf{u} \in \Omega$$

where $\mathscr{C}''$ is now a cone at $\mathbf{x}^1$. Thus, it follows from (7.125) that

$$\mathbf{x}^1 + A(t, t_1)\mathbf{f}(\mathbf{x}^*(t), \mathbf{u}) \in K_A, \qquad \forall \mathbf{u} \in \Omega$$

which implies, as a consequence of (7.141),

$$\mathbf{x}^1 + A(t, t_1)\mathbf{f}(\mathbf{x}^*(t), \mathbf{u}) \in \bar{R}_A(\mathbf{x}^1), \qquad \forall \mathbf{u} \in \Omega$$

whence

$$\mathbf{x}^*(t) + \mathbf{f}(\mathbf{x}^*(t), \mathbf{u}) \in \bar{P}_A(\mathbf{x}^*(t)), \qquad \forall \mathbf{u} \in \Omega \tag{7.142}$$

By arguments analogous to those utilized in the proof of (7.137), we can show again that

$$\mathbf{x}^*(t) + \mathbf{f}(\mathbf{x}^*(t), \mathbf{u}^*(t)) \in \Pi(\mathbf{x}^*(t)) \tag{7.143}$$

Here we consider the solution $\boldsymbol{\lambda}(t)$, $t_0 \leq t \leq t_1$, with "initial" condition $\boldsymbol{\lambda}(t_1) = \boldsymbol{\lambda}^1 \neq 0$ and such that

$$\boldsymbol{\lambda}^1 \text{ is normal to } \mathscr{T}(\mathbf{x}^1)$$
$$\mathbf{x}^1 + \boldsymbol{\lambda}^1 \in \text{comp } \bar{R}_A(\mathbf{x}^1)$$

As before, we conclude that

$$\boldsymbol{\lambda}(t) \text{ is normal to } \Pi(\mathbf{x}^*(t))$$
$$\mathbf{x}^*(t) + \boldsymbol{\lambda}(t) \in \text{comp } \bar{P}_A(\mathbf{x}^*(t))$$

and so conditions (7.138) and (7.139) are valid.

Finally, since $\mathbf{x}_0$ does not appear explicitly in the trajectory equation, we have

$$\lambda_0(t) = \text{const}, \qquad \forall t \in [t_0, t_1]$$

Furthermore, either

$$\mathbf{x}^0 + \boldsymbol{\lambda}(t_0) \in \bar{R}_B(\mathbf{x}^0)$$

and, by (7.133) and (7.135),

$$L_-(\mathbf{x}^0) \subset \bar{R}_B(\mathbf{x}^0)$$

or

$$\mathbf{x}^1 + \boldsymbol{\lambda}(t_1) \in \text{comp } \bar{R}_A(\mathbf{x}^1)$$

and, by (7.126) and (7.141),

$$L_+(\mathbf{x}^1) \subset \bar{R}_A(\mathbf{x}^1)$$

Thus, it follows that

$$\lambda_0(t) = \text{const} \leq 0, \qquad \forall t \in \Theta \tag{7.144}$$

In conclusion we can state

Theorem 8. *If the following assumptions are met:*

(i) *limiting surface Σ is nice;*
(ii) *every point of optimal trajectory Γ^* is an interior point of $\mathscr{E}^*$;*
(iii) *no point of Γ^* is degenerated, except possibly its initial or its terminal point but not both; and if $\mathbf{u}^*(t)$, $t_0 \leq t \leq t_1$, is an optimal control, and $\mathbf{x}^*(t)$ is the corresponding optimal solution of trajectory equation* (7.44),

then there exists a nonzero continuous vector function $\boldsymbol{\lambda}(t)$ which is a solution of adjoint equations (7.79), *such that*

(i) $\sup_{\mathbf{u}\in\Omega} \mathscr{H}(\boldsymbol{\lambda}(t), \mathbf{x}^*(t), \mathbf{u}) = \mathscr{H}(\boldsymbol{\lambda}(t), \mathbf{x}^*(t), \mathbf{u}^*(t))$;
(ii) $\mathscr{H}(\boldsymbol{\lambda}(t), \mathbf{x}^*(t), \mathbf{u}^*(t)) = 0$;
(iii) $\lambda_0(t) = \text{const} \leq 0$;

for all $t \in \Theta$.

7.21 Boundary Points of $\mathscr{E}^*$

Let us recall now the definitions of sets E and E^*, respectively. Set E is the set of all states in E^n, from which a given terminal state, $\mathfrak{x}^1$, can be reached along a path generated by means of an admissible rule. Set E^* is the set of all states in E^n, from which $\mathfrak{x}^1$ can be reached along an optimal path.

Limiting surfaces $\{\Sigma\}$ are defined in a domain $\mathscr{E}^*$ of E^{n+1}, whose projection on E^n is E^*. If E^* has a boundary, then $\mathscr{E}^*$ possesses an x_0-cylindrical boundary whose intersection with E^n is the boundary of E^*.

It is clear that $E^* \subseteq E$. Henceforth we shall assume that $E^* = E$; that is, terminal state $\mathbf{x}^1$ cannot be reached from a state from which it cannot be reached along an optimal path. Thus, we have

$$\mathscr{E}^* \triangleq E^* \times x_0 = E \times x_0 \triangleq \mathscr{E}$$

A point $\mathbf{x} \in E$ is an *interior* point of E if there exists an open ball in E^n, whose center is $\mathbf{x}$ and all of whose points belong to E. Then $\mathring{E}$ denotes the set of all interior points of E, and $\bar{E}$ denotes the closure of E in E^n, that is, the union of the set of all points of E and the set of all limit points of E in E^n.

Likewise, a point $\mathbf{x} \in \mathscr{E}$ is an interior point of $\mathscr{E}$ if there exists an open ball in E^{n+1}, whose center is $\mathbf{x}$ and all of whose points belong to $\mathscr{E}$. Then $\mathring{\mathscr{E}}$ denotes the set of all interior points of $\mathscr{E}$, and $\bar{\mathscr{E}}$ denotes the closure of $\mathscr{E}$ in E^{n+1}. Analogous definitions hold for $\overset{\circ}{\widehat{\text{comp}\,\mathscr{E}}}$ and $\overline{\text{comp}\,\mathscr{E}}$, the set of interior points of comp $\mathscr{E}$ and the closure of comp $\mathscr{E}$ in E^{n+1}.

Indeed, we have

$$\mathring{E} \subseteq E \subseteq \bar{E}$$

and

$$\mathring{\mathscr{E}} \subseteq \mathscr{E} \subseteq \bar{\mathscr{E}}$$

Furthermore, the boundaries of E and $\mathscr{E}$, respectively, are

$$\partial E \triangleq \bar{E} \cap \overline{\text{comp}\,E}, \qquad \text{comp}\,E \subseteq E^n$$

and

$$\partial\mathscr{E} \triangleq \bar{\mathscr{E}} \cap \overline{\text{comp}\,\mathscr{E}}, \qquad \text{comp}\,\mathscr{E} \subseteq E^{n+1}$$

so that, for instance, the boundary of comp $\mathscr{E}$

$$\partial(\text{comp}\,\mathscr{E}) = \partial\mathscr{E}$$

Note that E and $\mathscr{E}$ may be open, closed, or neither.

7.211 Lemma 29

We shall now prove

Lemma 29. *Let* $\mathbf{x}' \triangleq \mathbf{x}(t')$ *and* $\mathbf{x}'' \triangleq \mathbf{x}(t'')$ *be points of a trajectory* Γ *(optimal or nonoptimal) in* E^{n+1}. *If*

$$\mathbf{x}' \in \text{comp}\,\mathscr{E}$$

then

$$\mathbf{x}'' \notin \mathscr{E}, \qquad \forall t'' \geq t'$$

To prove this lemma let us suppose it is false; namely,

$$\mathbf{x}'' \in \mathscr{E}$$

Then there exists a trajectory which emanates from $\mathbf{x}''$ and intersects the line X^1 at some point $\mathbf{x}^1$, that is, a trajectory whose projection on E^n is a path which reaches the given terminal state $\mathbf{x}^1$. Consequently, there exists a trajectory which starts at $\mathbf{x}'$ and intersects the line X^1—namely, the union of the portion of Γ from $\mathbf{x}'$ to $\mathbf{x}''$ with the trajectory from $\mathbf{x}''$ to $\mathbf{x}^1$. But this conclusion is incompatible with the hypothesis that $\mathbf{x}' \in \operatorname{comp} \mathscr{E}$, and hence Lemma 29 is established.

7.212 Lemmas 30 and 31

Next we shall prove

Lemma 30. *Let* $\mathbf{x}' \triangleq \mathbf{x}(t')$ *and* $\mathbf{x}'' \triangleq \mathbf{x}(t'')$ *be points of a trajectory* Γ (*optimal or non-optimal*) *in* E^{n+1}. *If*

$$\mathbf{x}' \in \partial\mathscr{E}$$

then

$$\mathbf{x}'' \notin \mathring{\mathscr{E}}, \qquad \forall t'' \geq t'$$

First of all we note that

$$\operatorname{comp} \mathscr{E} \neq \phi$$

since

$$\operatorname{comp} \mathscr{E} = \phi \Rightarrow \mathscr{E} = E^{n+1} \Rightarrow \partial\mathscr{E} = \phi$$

But this is contrary to the hypothesis of the lemma.

Let $B(\mathbf{x}')$ be an open ball in E^{n+1}, whose center is at $\mathbf{x}'$. Now

$$B(\mathbf{x}') \cap \operatorname{comp} \mathscr{E} = \phi \Rightarrow B(\mathbf{x}') \subset \mathscr{E} \Rightarrow \mathbf{x}' \in \mathring{\mathscr{E}}$$

which contradicts the hypothesis of the lemma. Hence

$$B(\mathbf{x}') \cap \operatorname{comp} \mathscr{E} \neq \phi$$

no matter how small the radius of $B(\mathbf{x}')$.

Now consider a point

$$\mathbf{x}' + \varepsilon\boldsymbol{\eta}' \in \operatorname{comp} \mathscr{E}, \qquad \varepsilon > 0 \tag{7.145}$$

and let Γ' denote a trajectory which starts at point $\mathbf{x}' + \varepsilon\boldsymbol{\eta}'$ and which is generated by the *same control* that generates trajectory Γ for $t \geq t'$. At time

$t'' \geq t'$, the point of trajectory Γ' is given by the solution of trajectory equation (7.44) with initial condition $\mathbf{x} = \mathbf{x}' + \varepsilon\boldsymbol{\eta}'$ at $t = t'$; namely, it is

$$\mathbf{x}'' + \varepsilon\boldsymbol{\eta}'' + \mathbf{o}(t'', \varepsilon)$$

where $\mathbf{o}(t'', \varepsilon)/\varepsilon$ tends to zero uniformly as $\varepsilon \to 0$, and

$$\boldsymbol{\eta}'' = A(t', t'')\boldsymbol{\eta}'$$

Suppose now that the assertion of the lemma is false and

$$\mathbf{x}'' \in \mathring{\mathscr{E}}$$

Then there exists a positive number α such that

$$\mathbf{x}'' + \varepsilon\boldsymbol{\eta}'' + \mathbf{o}(t'', \varepsilon) \in \mathring{\mathscr{E}}, \qquad \forall\varepsilon < \alpha$$

However, this relation together with (7.145) violates Lemma 29; thus, Lemma 30 is valid.

Now we can establish

Lemma 31. *A trajectory whose initial point belongs to* $\overset{\circ}{\widehat{\text{comp}\,\mathscr{E}}}$ *has no point on boundary* $\partial\mathscr{E}$, *nor, indeed, a point in* $\mathscr{E}$.

First of all consider a point $\mathbf{x} \in \partial\mathscr{E}$, and let $B(\mathbf{x})$ be an open ball in E^{n+1} with center at $\mathbf{x}$. If

$$B(\mathbf{x}) \cap \mathscr{E} = \phi$$

then

$$B(\mathbf{x}) \subset \text{comp}\,\mathscr{E}$$

Hence $\mathbf{x}$ is an interior point of comp $\mathscr{E}$. But this is not possible since

$$\mathbf{x} \in \partial\mathscr{E} \Rightarrow \mathbf{x} \in \partial(\text{comp}\,\mathscr{E})$$

Consequently

$$\mathbf{x} \in \partial\mathscr{E} \Rightarrow B(\mathbf{x}) \cap \mathscr{E} \neq \phi \qquad (7.146)$$

Now let $\mathbf{x}' \triangleq \mathbf{x}(t')$ and $\mathbf{x}'' \triangleq \mathbf{x}(t'')$, $t'' > t'$, be points of a trajectory Γ, and suppose that

$$\mathbf{x}' \in \overset{\circ}{\widehat{\text{comp}\,\mathscr{E}}}$$

and

$$\mathbf{x}'' \in \partial\mathscr{E}$$

In other words, suppose that Lemma 31 is false.

Now let $B(\mathbf{x}'')$ be an open ball in E^{n+1} with center at $\mathbf{x}''$ and radius ρ, and consider a point

$$\mathbf{x}'' + \varepsilon\boldsymbol{\eta}'' \in B(\mathbf{x}'') \cap \mathscr{E}$$

According to (7.146), this is possible.

Consider also a trajectory Γ', generated by the same control that generates Γ on $[t', t'']$, which passes through point $\mathbf{x}'' + \varepsilon\boldsymbol{\eta}''$ at time t''. At time t', the point of Γ' is

$$\mathbf{x}' + \varepsilon\boldsymbol{\eta}' + \mathbf{o}(t', \varepsilon) \tag{7.147}$$

where $\mathbf{o}(t', \varepsilon)/\varepsilon$ tends to zero uniformly as $\varepsilon \to 0$, and

$$\boldsymbol{\eta}' = A(t'', t')\boldsymbol{\eta}'' \tag{7.148}$$

Since $\mathbf{x}' \in \overset{\circ}{\widehat{\text{comp}\,\mathscr{E}}}$ and $\mathbf{x}'' + \varepsilon\boldsymbol{\eta}'' \in B(\mathbf{x}'')$, it follows from (7.147) and (7.148) that

$$\mathbf{x}' + \varepsilon\boldsymbol{\eta}' + \mathbf{o}(t', \varepsilon) \in \overset{\circ}{\widehat{\text{comp}\,\mathscr{E}}}$$

for sufficiently small radius ρ. But this is not possible in view of Lemma 29 together with

$$\mathbf{x}'' + \varepsilon\boldsymbol{\eta}'' \in \mathscr{E}$$

Hence

$$\mathbf{x}' \in \overset{\circ}{\widehat{\text{comp}\,\mathscr{E}}} \Rightarrow \mathbf{x}'' \notin \partial\mathscr{E}$$

Of course, Lemma 29 leads at once to the result that

$$\mathbf{x}' \in \overset{\circ}{\widehat{\text{comp}\,\mathscr{E}}} \Rightarrow \mathbf{x}'' \notin \mathscr{E}$$

Thus, Lemma 31 is established.

7.213 Lemma 32

Another salient feature of boundary $\partial\mathscr{E}$ is embodied in

Lemma 32. *If point $\mathbf{x}^*(t')$ of optimal trajectory Γ^*, given by $\mathbf{x}^*(t)$, $t_0 \le t \le t_1$, belongs to boundary $\partial\mathscr{E}$, then $\mathbf{x}^*(t'')$ belongs to $\partial\mathscr{E}$, $t' \le t'' \le t_1$.*

As a consequence of Lemma 30, no point of Γ^* on $[t', t_1]$ belongs to $\mathring{\mathscr{E}}$. Also, since Γ^* reaches $\mathbf{x}^1$, no point of Γ^* belongs to comp $\mathscr{E}$. Hence

$$\left.\begin{aligned} \mathbf{x}^*(t) &\notin \overset{\circ}{\widehat{\text{comp}\,\mathscr{E}}} \\ \mathbf{x}^*(t) &\notin \mathring{\mathscr{E}} \end{aligned}\right\} \qquad \forall t \in [t', t_1]$$

But

$$\mathring{\mathscr{E}} \cup \overset{\circ}{\overbrace{\text{comp}\,\mathscr{E}}} \cup \partial\mathscr{E} = E^{n+1}$$

and so it follows that

$$\mathbf{x}^*(t) \in \partial\mathscr{E}, \qquad \forall t \in [t', t_1]$$

7.214 A Fundamental Analogy

It is readily seen that Lemmas 30, 31, and 32 exhibit strong similarities to Theorem 1, Corollary 1, and Lemma 2, respectively, provided we invoke the correspondence between:

$$\partial\mathscr{E} \text{ and } \Sigma$$

$$\mathring{\mathscr{E}} \text{ and } B/\Sigma$$

$$\overset{\circ}{\overbrace{\text{comp}\,\mathscr{E}}} \text{ and } A/\Sigma$$

However, there is one difference between these corresponding regions† namely, $\mathring{\mathscr{E}}$ or $\overset{\circ}{\overbrace{\text{comp}\,\mathscr{E}}}$ may be empty, whereas B/Σ and A/Σ are never empty. This difference plays a role in some of the derivations which follow.

Many of the results which have been established for interior points of $\mathscr{E}^*$ will be seen to apply for points of boundary $\partial\mathscr{E}$, provided we replace Σ by $\partial\mathscr{E}$, A/Σ by $\overset{\circ}{\overbrace{\text{comp}\,\mathscr{E}}}$, and B/Σ by $\mathring{\mathscr{E}}$. We shall not repeat the details of all derivations, but rather we shall list the pertinent properties of boundary points and point out their similarities to those of interior points.

7.215 Third Basic Assumption

Henceforth we shall make the following assumption:

Let $\boldsymbol{\eta}$ be a bound vector at point $\mathbf{x} \in \partial\mathscr{E}$. We shall *assume* that for every vector $\boldsymbol{\eta}$ there exists a scalar $\delta > 0$ such that for every ε, $0 < \varepsilon < \delta$, the point $\mathbf{x} + \varepsilon\boldsymbol{\eta}$ belongs either to region $\mathring{\mathscr{E}}$ or to region $\overline{\text{comp}\,\mathscr{E}}$.

This assumption is similar to the first basic assumption (see Sec. 7.61).

† It should also be noted that $\partial\mathscr{E}$, $\mathring{\mathscr{E}}$, and $\overset{\circ}{\overbrace{\text{comp}\,\mathscr{E}}}$ are unique, but there is a one-parameter family of Σ, B/Σ, and A/Σ. Thus, the correspondence is between $\partial\mathscr{E}$ and a *given* Σ, etc.

7.216 Definition of Local Cones $\mathscr{C}_I(\mathbf{x})$ and $\mathscr{C}_0(\mathbf{x})$

Next let us define two cones associated with every point $\mathbf{x}$ of $\partial\mathscr{E}$. Again let $\boldsymbol{\eta}$ be a bound vector at point $\mathbf{x} \in \partial\mathscr{E}$, and let

$$\mathscr{C}_T(\mathbf{x}) \triangleq \{\mathbf{x}+\boldsymbol{\eta} : \exists\alpha > 0 \quad \text{such that} \quad \forall\varepsilon, 0<\varepsilon<\alpha, \mathbf{x}+\varepsilon\boldsymbol{\eta} \in \mathring{\mathscr{E}}\} \tag{7.149}$$

and

$$\mathscr{C}_0(\mathbf{x}) \triangleq \{\mathbf{x}+\boldsymbol{\eta} : \exists\beta > 0 \quad \text{such that} \quad \forall\varepsilon, 0<\varepsilon<\beta, \mathbf{x}+\varepsilon\boldsymbol{\eta} \in \overline{\text{comp}\,\mathscr{E}}\} \tag{7.150}$$

Cones $\mathscr{C}_0(\mathbf{x})$ and $\mathscr{C}_I(\mathbf{x})$ are local cones with vertices at point $\mathbf{x}$. They correspond to cones $\mathscr{C}_A(\mathbf{x})$ and $\mathscr{C}_B(\mathbf{x})$, respectively. However, unlike $\mathscr{C}_A(\mathbf{x})$, cone $\mathscr{C}_I(\mathbf{x})$ may be empty; this happens if

$$B(\mathbf{x}) \cap \mathring{\mathscr{E}} = \phi$$

where $B(\mathbf{x})$ is an open ball with center at $\mathbf{x} \in \partial\mathscr{E}$ and sufficiently small radius. On the other hand, cone $\mathscr{C}_0(\mathbf{x})$ cannot be empty. For, if X denotes the x_0-cylindrical line through point $\mathbf{x} \in \partial\mathscr{E}$, then

$$X \subset \partial\mathscr{E} \subset \overline{\text{comp}\,\mathscr{E}}$$

and hence

$$\mathbf{x}+\boldsymbol{\eta} \in X \Rightarrow \mathbf{x}+\boldsymbol{\eta} \in \mathscr{C}_0(\mathbf{x})$$

7.217 Interior Points of $\mathscr{C}_I(\mathbf{x})$ and $\mathscr{C}_0(\mathbf{x})$; A Fourth Basic Assumption; Lemma 33

Here we shall invoke arguments similar to those of Sec. 7.63; namely, we shall say that $\mathbf{x}+\boldsymbol{\eta}$ is an interior point of $\mathscr{C}_I(\mathbf{x})$ (or $\mathscr{C}_0(\mathbf{x})$) if

(i) $\mathbf{x}+\boldsymbol{\eta} \in \mathscr{C}_I(\mathbf{x})$ (or $\mathscr{C}_0(\mathbf{x})$); and
(ii) there exists an open ball $B(\mathbf{x}+\boldsymbol{\eta})$ in E^{n+1} with center at $\mathbf{x}+\boldsymbol{\eta}$ such that all points of $B(\mathbf{x}+\boldsymbol{\eta})$ belong to $\mathscr{C}_I(\mathbf{x})$ (or $\mathscr{C}_0(\mathbf{x})$).

Then we have

$$\mathring{\mathscr{C}}_I(\mathbf{x}) \triangleq \{\mathbf{x}+\boldsymbol{\eta} : \mathbf{x}+\boldsymbol{\eta} \quad \text{is interior point of} \quad \mathscr{C}_I(\mathbf{x})\}$$
$$\mathring{\mathscr{C}}_0(\mathbf{x}) \triangleq \{\mathbf{x}+\boldsymbol{\eta} : \mathbf{x}+\boldsymbol{\eta} \quad \text{is interior point of} \quad \mathscr{C}_0(\mathbf{x})\}$$

Our *fourth basic assumption* is the following: Let $\mathbf{x}+\boldsymbol{\eta}'$ be an interior point of $\mathscr{C}_I(\mathbf{x})$ (or $\mathscr{C}_0(\mathbf{x})$); namely, there exists an open ball $B(\mathbf{x}+\boldsymbol{\eta}')$ in E^{n+1} which belongs to $\mathscr{C}_I(\mathbf{x})$ (or $\mathscr{C}_0(\mathbf{x})$). Then there exists an open ball $B'(\mathbf{x}+\boldsymbol{\eta}')$ in

E^{n+1} which belongs to $\mathscr{C}_I(\mathbf{x})$ (or $\mathscr{C}_0(\mathbf{x})$) and which has the property that for every point $\mathbf{x}+\boldsymbol{\eta}$ in $B'(\mathbf{x}+\boldsymbol{\eta}')$ there exists a positive number α (*independent of* $\boldsymbol{\eta}$) such that for all ε, $0<\varepsilon\le\alpha$, point $\mathbf{x}+\varepsilon\boldsymbol{\eta}$ belongs to $\mathring{\mathscr{E}}$ (or $\overline{\text{comp}\,\mathscr{E}}$).

The proof of the following lemma is similar to the proof of Lemma 4, provided we invoke the correspondence between the appropriate regions as discussed in Sec. 7.214.

Lemma 33. *Consider a point* $\mathbf{x}\in\partial\mathscr{E}$, *and a point* $\mathbf{x}+\boldsymbol{\eta}'\in\mathring{\mathscr{C}}_0(\mathbf{x})$. *Then there exists an open ball* $B'(\mathbf{x}+\boldsymbol{\eta}')\subset\mathscr{C}_0(\mathbf{x})$ *and a positive number* β *such that for all* $\mathbf{x}+\boldsymbol{\eta}\in B'(\mathbf{x}+\boldsymbol{\eta}')$ *and all* ε, $0<\varepsilon<\beta$, $\mathbf{x}+\varepsilon\boldsymbol{\eta}\in\overset{\circ}{\widehat{\text{comp}\,\mathscr{E}}}$.

7.218 Local Cone $\mathscr{B}(\mathbf{x})$

Let us now recall that $\mathscr{C}_0(\mathbf{x})\neq\phi$, and let us *define* another local cone at $\mathbf{x}\in\partial\mathscr{E}$. Let $\mathscr{B}(\mathbf{x})$ denote the boundary of $\mathscr{C}_0(\mathbf{x})$; that is,

$$\mathscr{B}(\mathbf{x})\triangleq\bar{\mathscr{C}}_0(\mathbf{x})\cap\overline{\text{comp}\,\mathscr{C}_0(\mathbf{x})} \tag{7.151}$$

If $\mathscr{C}_I(\mathbf{x})\neq\phi$, then it follows from definitions (7.149) and (7.150) that

$$\mathscr{C}_0(\mathbf{x})\cup\mathscr{C}_I(\mathbf{x})=E^{n+1} \tag{7.152}$$

Furthermore, we can readily see that

$$\mathscr{C}_0(\mathbf{x})\cap\mathscr{C}_I(\mathbf{x})=\phi \tag{7.153}$$

For suppose that

$$\mathscr{C}_0(\mathbf{x})\cap\mathscr{C}_I(\mathbf{x})\neq\phi$$

and consider a point

$$\mathbf{x}+\boldsymbol{\eta}\in\mathscr{C}_0(\mathbf{x})\qquad\text{and}\qquad\mathbf{x}+\boldsymbol{\eta}\in\mathscr{C}_I(\mathbf{x})$$

Then

$$\exists\alpha>0\quad\text{such that}\quad\forall\varepsilon,\quad 0<\varepsilon<\alpha,\quad\mathbf{x}+\varepsilon\boldsymbol{\eta}\in\mathring{\mathscr{E}}$$
$$\exists\beta>0\quad\text{such that}\quad\forall\varepsilon,\quad 0<\varepsilon<\beta,\quad\mathbf{x}+\varepsilon\boldsymbol{\eta}\in\overline{\text{comp}\,\mathscr{E}}$$

Suppose, for instance, that $\alpha<\beta$; then

$$\forall\varepsilon,\quad 0<\varepsilon<\alpha,\qquad\mathbf{x}+\varepsilon\boldsymbol{\eta}\in\mathring{\mathscr{E}},\quad\text{and}\quad\mathbf{x}+\varepsilon\boldsymbol{\eta}\in\overline{\text{comp}\,\mathscr{E}}$$

which implies that

$$\mathring{\mathscr{E}}\cap\overline{\text{comp}\,\mathscr{E}}\neq\phi$$

But this is impossible, and hence (7.153) is correct.

Finally, if

$$\mathscr{C}_1(\mathbf{x}) \neq \phi$$

then

$$\mathscr{C}_1(\mathbf{x}) = \text{comp}\, \mathscr{C}_0(\mathbf{x})$$

and hence

$$\mathscr{B}(\mathbf{x}) = \overline{\mathscr{C}}_0(\mathbf{x}) \cap \overline{\mathscr{C}}_1(\mathbf{x}) \tag{7.154}$$

7.219 Lemmas 34 and 35; Corollary 14

The proofs of the following two lemmas are similar to those of Lemmas 6 and 7. We shall not repeat the proofs, but merely state the lemmas.

Lemma 34. *Let* $\boldsymbol{\eta}$ *be a bound vector at a point* $\mathbf{x} \in \partial\mathscr{E}$. *If* $\boldsymbol{\eta} = \boldsymbol{\eta}(\varepsilon)$ *is a function of a parameter* ε *with the following properties*:

(i) $\boldsymbol{\eta}(\varepsilon) \to \mathbf{l}$ *as* $\varepsilon \to 0$,
(ii) $\exists \gamma > 0$ *such that* $\forall \varepsilon$, $0 < \varepsilon < \gamma$, $\mathbf{x} + \varepsilon\boldsymbol{\eta}(\varepsilon) \in \overline{\text{comp}\, \mathscr{E}}$

then

$$\mathbf{x} + \mathbf{l} \in \overline{\mathscr{C}}_0(\mathbf{x})$$

Lemma 35. *Let* $\boldsymbol{\eta}$ *be a bound vector at a point* $\mathbf{x} \in \partial\mathscr{E}$. *If* $\boldsymbol{\eta} = \boldsymbol{\eta}(\varepsilon)$ *is a function of a parameter* ε *with the following properties*:

(i) $\boldsymbol{\eta}(\varepsilon) \to \mathbf{l}$ *as* $\varepsilon \to 0$
(ii) $\exists \gamma > 0$ *such that* $\forall \varepsilon$, $0 < \varepsilon < \gamma$, $\mathbf{x} + \varepsilon\boldsymbol{\eta}(\varepsilon) \in \overline{\mathscr{E}}$

and provided

$$\mathscr{C}_1(\mathbf{x}) \neq \phi$$

then

$$\mathbf{x} + \mathbf{l} \in \overline{\mathscr{C}}_1(\mathbf{x})$$

The following corollary, which is the analog of Corollary 4, follows directly from Lemmas 34 and 35.

Corollary 14. *Let* $\boldsymbol{\eta}$ *be a bound vector at a point* $\mathbf{x} \in \partial\mathscr{E}$. *If* $\boldsymbol{\eta} = \boldsymbol{\eta}(\varepsilon)$ *is a function of a parameter* ε *with the following properties*:

(i) $\boldsymbol{\eta}(\varepsilon) \to \mathbf{l}$ *as* $\varepsilon \to 0$
(ii) $\exists \gamma > 0$ *such that* $\forall \varepsilon$, $0 < \varepsilon < \gamma$, $\mathbf{x} + \varepsilon\boldsymbol{\eta}(\varepsilon) \in \partial\mathscr{E}$,

and provided

$$\mathscr{C}_1(\mathbf{x}) \neq \phi$$

then

$$\mathbf{x} + \mathbf{l} \in \mathscr{B}(\mathbf{x})$$

7.2110 Lemmas 36 and 37

To deduce the next two lemmas we employ arguments similar to those used in the proof of Lemma 15.

Consider a field line, say L, defined parametrically by

$$\mathbf{x} = \mathbf{x}(t), \qquad t \in (-\infty, \infty) \tag{7.155}$$

and let

$$\boldsymbol{\eta}_+(\Delta t) \triangleq \frac{\Delta \mathbf{x}_+}{\Delta t}$$

where

$$\Delta \mathbf{x}_+ \triangleq \mathbf{x}(t_i + \Delta t) - \mathbf{x}(t_i)$$
$$\mathbf{x}(t_i) = \mathbf{x}, \qquad \Delta t > 0$$

Clearly

$$\mathbf{x} + \Delta \mathbf{x}_+ \in L$$

so that $\boldsymbol{\eta}_+(\Delta t)$ is a continuous function of Δt, and

$$\boldsymbol{\eta}_+(\Delta t) \to \mathbf{f}(\mathbf{x}, \mathbf{u}^b), \qquad \mathbf{u}^b \in \Omega, \quad \text{as} \quad \Delta t \to 0 \tag{7.156}$$

Suppose now that

$$\mathbf{x} \in \partial\mathscr{E}$$

Then it follows from Lemma 30 that

$$\mathbf{x} + \Delta \mathbf{x}_+ = \mathbf{x} + \boldsymbol{\eta}_+(\Delta t)\Delta t \in \overline{\text{comp } \mathscr{E}} \tag{7.157}$$

Condition (7.157) together with Lemma 34 leads at once to

Lemma 36. *At a point* $\mathbf{x} \in \partial\mathscr{E}$

$$\mathbf{x} + \mathbf{f}(\mathbf{x}, \mathbf{u}) \in \overline{\mathscr{C}}_0(\mathbf{x})$$

for all $\mathbf{u} \in \Omega$.

If we now assume that

$$\mathscr{C}_T(\mathbf{x}) \neq \phi$$

then we can utilize arguments similar to those employed in Sec. 7.111, and as a consequence of Lemma 35 we can state

Lemma 37. *If* $\mathscr{C}_\text{I}(\mathbf{x}) \neq \phi$ *at a point* $\mathbf{x} \in \partial\mathscr{E}$, *then*

$$\mathbf{x} - \mathbf{f}(\mathbf{x}, \mathbf{u}) \in \overline{\mathscr{C}}_\text{I}(\mathbf{x})$$

for all $\mathbf{u} \in \Omega$.

7.2111 Lemma 38

If

$$\mathscr{C}_I(\mathbf{x}) \neq \phi$$

then arguments similar to those of Sec. 7.112 can be used in conjunction with Corollary 14 to prove

Lemma 38. *If* $\mathscr{C}_I(\mathbf{x}) \neq \phi$ *at a point* $\mathbf{x} \in \partial\mathscr{E}$, *then*

$$\mathbf{x} + \mathbf{f}_+{}^* \in \mathscr{B}(\mathbf{x})$$
$$\mathbf{x} - \mathbf{f}_-{}^* \in \mathscr{B}(\mathbf{x})$$

provided $\mathbf{f}_+{}^*$ *and* $\mathbf{f}_-{}^*$, *respectively, are defined.*

7.2112 Separability of Local Cone $\bar{\mathscr{C}}_0(\mathbf{x})$ and $\bar{\mathscr{C}}_I(\mathbf{x})$

Henceforth we shall *assume* that

$$\mathscr{C}_I(\mathbf{x}) \neq \phi$$

and we shall introduce some *definitions* which are similar to those introduced in Sec. 7.12.

We shall say that an n-dimensional hyperplane $\mathscr{T}(\mathbf{x})$, containing a point $\mathbf{x} \in \partial\mathscr{E}$, is an *n-dimensional separating hyperplane* of closed cone $\bar{\mathscr{C}}_0(\mathbf{x})$ (or $\bar{\mathscr{C}}_I(\mathbf{x})$), if every point $\mathbf{x} + \boldsymbol{\eta} \in \bar{\mathscr{C}}_0(\mathbf{x})$ (or $\bar{\mathscr{C}}_I(\mathbf{x})$) lies in one of the closed half spaces determined by $\mathscr{T}(\mathbf{x})$.

The corresponding *closed* half space will be denoted by $\bar{R}_0$ (or $\bar{R}_I$), and the corresponding *open* half space by R_0 (or R_I).

Then, if there exists an n-dimensional separating hyperplane of $\bar{\mathscr{C}}_0(\mathbf{x})$ (or $\bar{\mathscr{C}}_I(\mathbf{x})$), we shall say that cone $\bar{\mathscr{C}}_0(\mathbf{x})$ (or $\bar{\mathscr{C}}_I(\mathbf{x})$) is *separable*.

7.2113 Cone of Normals at Boundary Point

If $\bar{\mathscr{C}}_0(\mathbf{x})$ (or $\bar{\mathscr{C}}_I(\mathbf{x})$) is separable, we shall consider a separating hyperplane $\mathscr{T}(\mathbf{x})$ and, at point $\mathbf{x} \in \partial\mathscr{E}$, a bound vector $\mathbf{n}(\mathbf{x})$, $|\mathbf{n}(\mathbf{x})| = 1$, which is normal to $\mathscr{T}(\mathbf{x})$. Furthermore,

(i) if $\bar{\mathscr{C}}_0(\mathbf{x})$ is separable, we shall choose $\mathbf{n}(\mathbf{x})$ such that

$$\mathbf{x} + \mathbf{n}(\mathbf{x}) \in \text{comp } \bar{R}_0 \tag{7.158}$$

(ii) if $\bar{\mathscr{C}}_I(\mathbf{x})$ is separable, we shall choose $\mathbf{n}(\mathbf{x})$ such that

$$\mathbf{x} + \mathbf{n}(\mathbf{x}) \in R_I \tag{7.159}$$

As in Sec. 7.122, we shall consider the set $\{\mathbf{n}(\mathbf{x})\}$ of vectors $\mathbf{n}(\mathbf{x})$ for all separating hyperplanes of $\overline{\mathscr{C}}_0(\mathbf{x})$ (or $\overline{\mathscr{C}}_{\text{I}}(\mathbf{x})$), and define the *cone of normals*

$$\mathscr{C}_n(\mathbf{x}) \triangleq \{\mathbf{x} + k\mathbf{n}(\mathbf{x}) : k > 0, \quad \mathbf{n}(\mathbf{x}) \in \{\mathbf{n}(\mathbf{x})\}\} \tag{7.160}$$

Here we know that the x_0-cylindrical line X through point $\mathbf{x} \in \partial\mathscr{E}$ belongs to $\partial\mathscr{E}$. Thus, if $\mathscr{T}(\mathbf{x})$ exists,

$$X \subset \mathscr{T}(\mathbf{x})$$

In other words, a separating hyperplane $\mathscr{T}(\mathbf{x})$ (of $\overline{\mathscr{C}}_0(\mathbf{x})$ or $\overline{\mathscr{C}}_{\text{I}}(\mathbf{x})$) is "vertical." Hence, $\mathbf{n}(\mathbf{x})$ is normal to X, and *the cone of normals* $\mathscr{C}_n(\mathbf{x})$ *belongs to a hyperplane which is perpendicular to the* x_0*-axis.*

7.2114 Regular and Nonregular Points of the Boundary

We shall say that $\mathbf{x} \in \partial\mathscr{E}$ is a *regular* point of the boundary, if *both* $\overline{\mathscr{C}}_0(\mathbf{x})$ and $\overline{\mathscr{C}}_{\text{I}}(\mathbf{x})$ are separable. On the other hand, if *not both* $\overline{\mathscr{C}}_0(\mathbf{x})$ and $\overline{\mathscr{C}}_{\text{I}}(\mathbf{x})$ are separable, point $\mathbf{x}$ will be called a *nonregular* point of $\partial\mathscr{E}$.

The discussion of Sec. 7.13 is applicable, provided one invokes the correspondence between appropriate quantities as specified in Sec. 7.214. The notions of regular and nonregular points of the boundary, together with their properties, are valuable since they permit one to extend the validity of Lemmas 20 and 21 to optimal trajectories which contain boundary points.

7.2115 Properties of Local Cones at Boundary Points; Lemmas 39–41; Theorems 9 and 10

One can easily prove

Lemma 39. *Let* $\mathbf{l}$ *be a bound vector at point* $\mathbf{x} \in \partial\mathscr{E}$. *If* $\mathbf{x} + \mathbf{l} \in \mathscr{B}(\mathbf{x})$ *and* $N(\mathbf{x})$ *is a conic neighborhood, that is,*

$$N(\mathbf{x}) \triangleq \{\mathbf{x} + k\boldsymbol{\eta} : k > 0, \quad \mathbf{x} + \boldsymbol{\eta} \in B(\mathbf{x} + \mathbf{l})\}$$

where $B(\mathbf{x} + \mathbf{l})$ *is an open ball in* E^{n+1} *with center at* $\mathbf{x} + \mathbf{l}$, *then*

$$N(\mathbf{x}) \cap \mathscr{C}_0(\mathbf{x}) \neq \phi$$

and

$$N(\mathbf{x}) \cap \mathscr{C}_{\text{I}}(\mathbf{x}) \neq \phi$$

The proof is similar to that of Lemma 8. Suppose that the lemma is false and that

$$N(\mathbf{x}) \cap \mathscr{C}_0(\mathbf{x}) = \phi$$

But, according to the results of Sec. 7.218,

$$\mathscr{C}_{\mathrm{I}}(\mathbf{x}) \neq \phi \Rightarrow \mathscr{C}_I(\mathbf{x}) = \text{comp } \mathscr{C}_0(\mathbf{x})$$

so that

$$N(\mathbf{x}) \subset \mathscr{C}_{\mathrm{I}}(\mathbf{x}) \tag{7.161}$$

In view of the definitions of $N(\mathbf{x})$ and $\mathscr{C}_{\mathrm{I}}(\mathbf{x})$, relation (7.161) implies that

$$\mathbf{x} + \mathbf{l} \in \mathring{\mathscr{C}}_{\mathrm{I}}(\mathbf{x})$$

However, this contradicts the hypothesis of the lemma, which states that $\mathbf{x} + \mathbf{l} \in \mathscr{B}(\mathbf{x})$.

Similarly, by supposing that

$$N(\mathbf{x}) \cap \mathscr{C}_{\mathrm{I}}(\mathbf{x}) = \phi$$

we again arrive at a contradiction. Thus the lemma is established.

Next we deduce the analog to Lemma 20, that is,

Lemma 40. *Let $\mathbf{x}^*(t')$ and $\mathbf{x}^*(t'')$, $t_0 \leq t' \leq t'' \leq t_1$, be two points of optimal trajectory Γ^*, corresponding to control $\mathbf{u}^*(t)$ and solution $\mathbf{x}^*(t)$, $t_0 \leq t \leq t_1$, such that $\mathbf{x}^*(t') \in \partial\mathscr{E}$ (and consequently $\mathbf{x}^*(t'') \in \partial\mathscr{E}$). Let $\boldsymbol{\eta}'$ be a vector at $\mathbf{x}^*(t')$, and $\boldsymbol{\eta}''$ its transform due to linear transformation $A(t', t'')$; namely,*

$$\boldsymbol{\eta}'' = A(t', t'')\boldsymbol{\eta}'$$

If

$$\mathbf{x}^*(t') + \boldsymbol{\eta}' \in \bar{\mathscr{C}}_0(\mathbf{x}^*(t'))$$

then

$$\mathbf{x}^*(t'') + \boldsymbol{\eta}'' \in \bar{\mathscr{C}}_0(\mathbf{x}^*(t''))$$

Let us first consider

$$\mathbf{x}^*(t') + \boldsymbol{\eta}' \in \mathscr{C}_0(\mathbf{x}^*(t'))$$

According to definition (7.150) of $\mathscr{C}_0(\mathbf{x})$, there exists a positive number β such that for all ε, $0 < \varepsilon < \beta$,

$$\mathbf{x}^*(t') + \varepsilon\boldsymbol{\eta}' \in \overline{\text{comp } \mathscr{E}} \tag{7.162}$$

Now consider a trajectory which starts at point $\mathbf{x}^*(t') + \varepsilon\boldsymbol{\eta}'$, and which is generated by the same control as Γ^*—that is, $\mathbf{u}^*(t)$, $t_0 \leq t \leq t_1$—on $[t', t'']$. This trajectory is defined by the corresponding solution of trajectory equation (7.44), which is

$$\mathbf{x}(t) = \mathbf{x}^*(t) + \varepsilon\boldsymbol{\eta}(t) + \mathbf{o}(t, \varepsilon)$$

where $\mathbf{o}(t, \varepsilon)/\varepsilon$ tends to zero uniformly for all $t \in [t', t'']$ as $\varepsilon \to 0$, and $\boldsymbol{\eta}(t) = A(t', t)\boldsymbol{\eta}'$.

From (7.162), together with Lemmas 30 and 31, we have

$$\mathbf{x}(t'') = \mathbf{x}^*(t'') + \varepsilon\boldsymbol{\eta}(t'') + \mathbf{o}(t'', \varepsilon) \in \overline{\text{comp}\,\mathscr{E}}$$

for all ε, $0 < \varepsilon < \beta$. Furthermore,

$$\boldsymbol{\eta}(t'') + \frac{\mathbf{o}(t'', \varepsilon)}{\varepsilon} \to \boldsymbol{\eta}(t'') \triangleq \boldsymbol{\eta}'' \qquad \text{as} \quad \varepsilon \to 0$$

Consequently, it follows from Lemma 34 that

$$\mathbf{x}^*(t'') + \boldsymbol{\eta}'' \in \overline{\mathscr{C}}_0(\mathbf{x}^*(t''))$$

Thus, if

$$\mathscr{C}_0(\mathbf{x}^*(t')) - \overline{\mathscr{C}}_0(\mathbf{x}^*(t'))$$

the lemma is established.

Thus far, the proof is entirely analogous to the first part of the proof of Lemma 20. The remainder of the proof is equally similar to the remainder of the proof of Lemma 20; we shall not repeat the whole derivation. Let us only note that the rest of the proof begins with the supposition that

$$\mathbf{x}^*(t') + \boldsymbol{\eta}' \in \mathscr{B}(\mathbf{x}^*(t'))$$

Then, employing Lemma 39 which corresponds to Lemma 8, one arrives at

$$\mathbf{x}^*(t'') + \boldsymbol{\eta}'' \in \overline{\mathscr{C}}_0(\mathbf{x}^*(t''))$$

This concludes the demonstration of Lemma 40.

By arguments analogous to those used in the proof of Lemma 21, one can also establish

Lemma 41. *Let* $\mathbf{x}^*(t')$ *and* $\mathbf{x}^*(t'')$, $t_0 \le t' \le t'' \le t_1$, *be two points of optimal trajectory* Γ^*, *corresponding to control* $\mathbf{u}^*(t)$ *and solution* $\mathbf{x}^*(t)$, $t_0 \le t \le t_1$, *such that* $\mathbf{x}^*(t') \in \partial\mathscr{E}$ *(and consequently* $\mathbf{x}^*(t'') \in \partial\mathscr{E}$*). Let* $\boldsymbol{\eta}''$ *be a vector at* $\mathbf{x}^*(t'')$ *such that*

$$\mathbf{x}^*(t'') + \boldsymbol{\eta}'' \in \overline{\mathscr{C}}_1(\mathbf{x}^*(t''))$$

Then $\boldsymbol{\eta}''$ *is the transform, due to linear transformation* $A(t', t'')$, *of a vector* $\boldsymbol{\eta}'$ *at* $\mathbf{x}^*(t')$ *such that*

$$\mathbf{x}^*(t') + \boldsymbol{\eta}' \in \overline{\mathscr{C}}_1(\mathbf{x}^*(t'))$$

Now one arrives readily at the analogs to Theorems 2 and 3. Let $\mathbf{x}^*(t')$ and $\mathbf{x}^*(t'')$, $t_0 \le t' \le t'' \le t_1$, be two points of optimal trajectory Γ^*, corresponding to control $\mathbf{u}^*(t)$ and solution $\mathbf{x}^*(t)$, $t_0 \le t \le t_1$, such that $\mathbf{x}^*(t') \in \partial\mathscr{E}$ (and consequently $\mathbf{x}^*(t'') \in \partial\mathscr{E}$). Then we have

Theorem 9. *If* $\bar{\mathscr{C}}_{\mathrm{I}}(\mathbf{x}^*(t'))$ *is separable, then* $\bar{\mathscr{C}}_{\mathrm{I}}(\mathbf{x}^*(t''))$ *is separable.*

and

Theorem 10. *If* $\bar{\mathscr{C}}_0(\mathbf{x}^*(t''))$ *is separable, then* $\bar{\mathscr{C}}_0(\mathbf{x}^*(t'))$ *is separable.*

The proofs of these theorems are similar to those of Theorems 2 and 3.

By analogy to the properties of optimal trajectories at interior points of $\mathscr{E}^*$, one can obtain many interesting properties of optimal trajectories at boundary points. Thus far we have stated some of the salient properties. However, we have not as yet defined the notion of a *nice boundary*; hence, we have not stated associated results. Some properties of an optimal trajectory at boundary points exhibit special features. We shall now turn to some of them.

7.2116 A Maximum Principle (Abnormal† Case); Theorem 11

We are now ready to state

Theorem 11. *If* $\mathbf{u}^*(t)$, $t_0 \le t \le t_1$, *is an optimal control, and* $\mathbf{x}^*(t)$ *is the corresponding solution of trajectory equation* (7.44), *and if* $\mathbf{x}^*(t)$ *is a regular point of boundary* $\partial\mathscr{E}$ *for all* $t \in [t_0, t_1]$, *then there exists a nonzero continuous vector function* $\boldsymbol{\lambda}(t)$ *which is a solution of adjoint equations* (7.79), *such that*

(i) $\sup\limits_{\mathbf{u}\in\Omega} \mathscr{H}(\boldsymbol{\lambda}(t), \mathbf{x}^*(t), \mathbf{u}) = \mathscr{H}(\boldsymbol{\lambda}(t), \mathbf{x}^*(t), \mathbf{u}^*(t))$;

(ii) $\mathscr{H}(\boldsymbol{\lambda}(t), \mathbf{x}^*(t), \mathbf{u}^*(t)) = 0$;

(iii) $\lambda_0(t) = \text{const} = 0$;

for all $t \in [t_0, t_1]$.

Conditions (i) and (ii) of the theorem can be proved by arguments similar to those used to establish conditions (i) and (ii) of Theorem 4. In particular, consider the separating plane $\mathscr{T}(\mathbf{x}^0)$ of both $\bar{\mathscr{C}}_{\mathrm{I}}(\mathbf{x}^0)$ and $\bar{\mathscr{C}}_0(\mathbf{x}^0)$ at initial point $\mathbf{x}^0 = \mathbf{x}^*(t_0)$. In view of the proof of Theorem 9, the transform of $\mathscr{T}(\mathbf{x}^0)$ due to linear transformation $A(t_0, t)$, $t_0 \le t \le t_1$, is the separating hyperplane $\mathscr{T}(\mathbf{x})$ of $\bar{\mathscr{C}}_{\mathrm{I}}(\mathbf{x}) = \bar{R}_{\mathrm{I}}(\mathbf{x})$, $\mathbf{x} = \mathbf{x}^*(t)$. Next consider the solution $\boldsymbol{\lambda}(t)$, $t_0 \le t \le t_1$, of adjoint equations (7.79) with initial condition $\boldsymbol{\lambda}(t_0) = \boldsymbol{\lambda}^0$ such that $\boldsymbol{\lambda}^0 \ne 0$, $\boldsymbol{\lambda}^0$ normal to $\mathscr{T}(\mathbf{x}^0)$ and directed into $R_{\mathrm{I}}(\mathbf{x}^0)$. Then $\boldsymbol{\lambda}(t)$ is normal to $\mathscr{T}(\mathbf{x}^*(t))$, $t_0 \le t \le t_1$. The remainder of the proof is similar to that of Theorem 4.

Condition (iii) is a consequence of the concluding remark of Sec. 7.2113; namely, $X \subset \mathscr{T}(\mathbf{x}^*(t))$ and $\mathbf{n}(\mathbf{x}^*(t))$ is normal to X. Consequently, $\boldsymbol{\lambda}(t)$ is normal to X and so $\lambda_0(t) = 0$.

† This nomenclature is adopted from the classical calculus of variations where the problem with $\lambda_0 = 0$ is dubbed "abnormal." See case (iii) of Sec. 7.243.

7.22 Boundary and Interior Points of $\mathscr{E}^*$

In general, some points of an optimal trajectory may be interior points while others may be boundary points of region $\mathscr{E}^*$. Thus, we require a theory which applies for both interior and boundary points.

We begin by defining two regions for each limiting surface Σ; namely,

$$\mathscr{E}_B \triangleq \mathscr{E} \cap (B/\Sigma) \tag{7.163}$$

and

$$\mathscr{E}_A \triangleq \text{comp } \mathscr{E}_B \tag{7.164}$$

Next we consider the boundary of $\mathscr{E}_B$ and $\mathscr{E}_A$, that is,

$$\Xi \triangleq \bar{\mathscr{E}}_B \cap \overline{\text{comp } \mathscr{E}_B} = \bar{\mathscr{E}}_B \cap \bar{\mathscr{E}}_A \tag{7.165†}$$

Since

$$\mathscr{E}_B = B/\Sigma$$

we have

$$\mathscr{E}_B \neq \phi \tag{7.166}$$

Moreover, $\mathscr{E}_B$ is not all of space E^{n+1}; hence

$$\mathscr{E}_A \neq \phi \tag{7.167}$$

A point $\mathbf{x} \in \mathscr{E}_B$ is an interior point of $\mathscr{E}_B$ if there exists an open ball $B(\mathbf{x})$ in E^{n+1}, whose center is at $\mathbf{x}$ and all of whose points belong to $\mathscr{E}_B$. The set of all interior points $\mathscr{E}_B$ is $\mathring{\mathscr{E}}_B$. The union of the set of all points of $\mathscr{E}_B$ and of all limit points of $\mathscr{E}_B$ is the closure $\bar{\mathscr{E}}_B$ of $\mathscr{E}_B$ in E^{n+1}. Entirely analogous remarks apply to $\mathscr{E}_A$. Similarly, we designate the closures in E^{n+1} of Σ, A/Σ and B/Σ by $\bar{\Sigma}$, $\overline{A/\Sigma}$, and $\overline{B/\Sigma} = \bar{\mathscr{E}}_B$, respectively.

Let us note that

$$\mathscr{E}_A \triangleq \text{comp } \mathscr{E}_B = \begin{cases} \text{comp}[\mathscr{E} \cap (B/\Sigma)] \\ (\text{comp } \mathscr{E}) \cup \text{comp}(B/\Sigma) \end{cases} \tag{7.168}$$

Since‡

$$(B/\Sigma) \cup \Sigma \cup (A/\Sigma) = \mathscr{E}$$

and

$$\mathscr{E} \cup \text{comp } \mathscr{E} = E^{n+1}$$

we have

$$\text{comp}(B/\Sigma) = \Sigma \cup (A/\Sigma) \cup \text{comp } \mathscr{E} \tag{7.169}$$

† Note there exists a one-parameter family of boundaries $\{\Xi\}$ corresponding to the one-parameter family of limiting surfaces $\{\Sigma\}$.

‡ More precisely, $\{B/\Sigma, \Sigma, A/\Sigma\}$ is a partition of $\mathscr{E}$, and $\{\mathscr{E}, \text{comp } \mathscr{E}\}$ is a partition of E^{n+1}.

Thus it follows from (7.168) that

$$\mathscr{E}_A = \Sigma \cup (A/\Sigma) \cup \text{comp}\, \mathscr{E} \tag{7.170}$$

7.221 Lemma 42

One can now prove

Lemma 42. *Let* $\mathbf{x}(t')$ *and* $\mathbf{x}(t'')$, $t'' > t'$, *be points of a trajectory in* E^{n+1}. *If* $\mathbf{x}(t')$ *belongs to* $\mathscr{E}_A$, *then* $\mathbf{x}(t'')$ *cannot belong to* $\mathscr{E}_B$.

In view of (7.170)

$$\mathbf{x}(t') \in \mathscr{E}_A \Rightarrow \begin{cases} \mathbf{x}(t') \in \text{comp}\, \mathscr{E}, & \text{or} \\ \mathbf{x}(t') \in \Sigma \cup (A/\Sigma) \end{cases}$$

If

$$\mathbf{x}(t') \in \text{comp}\, \mathscr{E}$$

then it follows from Lemma 29 that

$$\mathbf{x}(t'') \notin \mathscr{E}, \qquad t'' > t'$$

If

$$\mathbf{x}(t') \in \Sigma \cup (A/\Sigma)$$

then it follows from Theorem 1 and Corollary 1 that

$$\mathbf{x}(t'') \notin B/\Sigma, \qquad t'' > t'$$

In view of (7.163), Lemma 42 is then established.

7.222 Lemmas 43 and 44

Next we shall deduce

Lemma 43. *Let* $\mathbf{x}' \triangleq \mathbf{x}(t')$ *and* $\mathbf{x}'' \triangleq \mathbf{x}(t'')$, $t'' > t'$, *be points of a trajectory* Γ (*optimal or nonoptimal*) *in* E^{n+1}. *If* $\mathbf{x}' \in \Xi$ *then* $\mathbf{x}'' \notin \mathring{\mathscr{E}}_B$.

The proof of this lemma is similar to that of Lemma 30. First of all, note that

$$\mathscr{E}_A \triangleq \text{comp}\, \mathscr{E}_B \neq \phi$$

and, if $B(\mathbf{x}')$ is an open ball in E^{n+1} with center at $\mathbf{x}'$, then

$$B(\mathbf{x}') \cap \mathscr{E}_A \neq \phi$$

no matter how small the radius of $B(\mathbf{x}')$. For, if

$$B(\mathbf{x}') \cap \mathscr{E}_A = \phi$$

then

$$B(\mathbf{x}') \subset \mathscr{E}_B$$

and hence $\mathbf{x}'$ is an interior point of $\mathscr{E}_B$. But this contradicts the hypothesis of the lemma.

Let $\varepsilon\boldsymbol{\eta}'$, $\varepsilon > 0$, be a vector at point $\mathbf{x}'$, such that

$$\mathbf{x}' + \varepsilon\boldsymbol{\eta}' \in \mathscr{E}_A \tag{7.171}$$

and consider a trajectory Γ' which starts at point $\mathbf{x}' + \varepsilon\boldsymbol{\eta}'$ and which is generated by the same control which generates Γ on $[t', t'']$. At time $t'' > t'$, the point of Γ' is $\mathbf{x}'' + \varepsilon\boldsymbol{\eta}'' + \mathbf{o}(t'', \varepsilon)$ where $\boldsymbol{\eta}'' = A(t', t'')\boldsymbol{\eta}'$.

Suppose now that

$$\mathbf{x}'' \in \mathring{\mathscr{E}}_B$$

Then there exists an $\alpha > 0$ such that for all ε, $0 < \varepsilon < \alpha$,

$$\mathbf{x}'' + \varepsilon\boldsymbol{\eta}'' + \mathbf{o}(t'', \varepsilon) \in \mathring{\mathscr{E}}_B$$

However, according to Lemma 42 with (7.171), this is not possible; and so Lemma 43 is established.

Next we prove

Lemma 44. *A trajectory whose initial point belongs to $\mathring{\mathscr{E}}_A$ has no point on boundary Ξ, nor, indeed, a point in $\mathscr{E}_B$.*

The demonstration of this lemma is similar to that of Lemma 31. Let $B(\mathbf{x})$ be an open ball in E^{n+1} with center at point $\mathbf{x}$. Then it is readily shown that

$$\mathbf{x} \in \Xi \Rightarrow B(\mathbf{x}) \cap \mathscr{E}_B \neq \phi \tag{7.172}$$

Now consider points $\mathbf{x}' \triangleq \mathbf{x}(t')$ and $\mathbf{x}'' \triangleq \mathbf{x}(t'')$, $t'' > t'$, of trajectory Γ. Suppose that

$$\mathbf{x}' \in \mathring{\mathscr{E}}_A$$

and that

$$\mathbf{x}'' \in \Xi$$

Consider also an open ball $B(\mathbf{x}'')$ in E^{n+1} with center at $\mathbf{x}''$ and radius ρ. According to (7.172) we may choose a point

$$\mathbf{x}'' + \varepsilon\boldsymbol{\eta}'' \in B(\mathbf{x}'') \cap \mathscr{E}$$

Let Γ' be a trajectory which is generated by the same control that generates Γ on $[t', t'']$, and which passes through $\mathbf{x}'' + \varepsilon\boldsymbol{\eta}''$ at time t''. At time t' the point of Γ' is

$$\mathbf{x}' + \varepsilon\boldsymbol{\eta}' + \mathbf{o}(t', \varepsilon) \tag{7.173}$$

where $\mathbf{o}(t', \varepsilon)/\varepsilon$ tends to zero uniformly as $\varepsilon \to 0$, and

$$\boldsymbol{\eta}' = A(t'', t')\boldsymbol{\eta}'' \tag{7.174}$$

Now, since $\mathbf{x}' \in \mathring{\mathscr{E}}_A$ and $\mathbf{x}'' + \varepsilon\boldsymbol{\eta}'' \in B(\mathbf{x}'')$, it follows from (7.173) and (7.174) that

$$\mathbf{x}' + \varepsilon\boldsymbol{\eta}' + \mathbf{o}(t', \varepsilon) \in \mathring{\mathscr{E}}_A$$

for sufficiently small radius ρ. But this is impossible because of Lemma 42 with

$$\mathbf{x}'' + \varepsilon\boldsymbol{\eta}'' \in \mathscr{E}_B$$

Hence

$$\mathbf{x}' \in \mathring{\mathscr{E}}_A \Rightarrow \mathbf{x}'' \notin \Xi$$

Also, Lemma 42 leads at once to the result that

$$\mathbf{x}' \in \mathring{\mathscr{E}}_A \Rightarrow \mathbf{x}'' \notin \mathscr{E}_B$$

Thus, Lemma 44 is established.

7.223 An Assumption Concerning Boundary Ξ; Lemma 45

Henceforth we shall *assume* that

$$(A/\Sigma) \cap \Xi = \phi \tag{7.175}$$

However

$$\bar{\mathscr{E}}_B = \mathscr{E}_B \cup \Xi$$

and hence

$$\begin{aligned}\bar{\mathscr{E}}_B \cap (A/\Sigma) &= (\mathscr{E}_B \cup \Xi) \cap (A/\Sigma)\\ &= [\mathscr{E}_B \cap (A/\Sigma)] \cup [\Xi \cap (A/\Sigma)]\end{aligned}$$

Furthermore

$$\mathscr{E}_B = B/\Sigma$$

and

$$(A/\Sigma) \cap (B/\Sigma) = \phi$$

so that, in view of assumption (7.175), we have

$$\bar{\mathscr{E}}_B \cap (A/\Sigma) = \phi \tag{7.176}$$

An important property of boundary Ξ is embodied in

Lemma 45. *Let* Γ^* *be an optimal trajectory given by* $\mathbf{x}^*(t)$, $t_0 \le t \le t_1$. *If* $\mathbf{x}^*(t')$, $t' \in [t_0, t_1]$, *belongs to a boundary* Ξ, *and if* $(A/\Sigma) \cap \Xi = \phi$, *then* $\mathbf{x}^*(t)$ *belongs to* Ξ *for all* t, $t' \le t \le t_1$.

According to definition (7.165) of Ξ,

$$\mathbf{x}^*(t') \in \Xi \Rightarrow \begin{cases} \mathbf{x}^*(t') \in \bar{\mathscr{E}}_A \text{ and} \\ \mathbf{x}^*(t') \in \bar{\mathscr{E}}_B \end{cases}$$

Then it follows from Lemma 43 that

$$\mathbf{x}^*(t'') \notin \mathring{\mathscr{E}}_B, \qquad t'' > t' \tag{7.177}$$

Since $\bar{\mathscr{E}}_A = \text{comp } \mathring{\mathscr{E}}_B$, condition (7.177) implies that

$$\mathbf{x}^*(t'') \in \bar{\mathscr{E}}_A, \qquad t'' > t' \tag{7.178}$$

On the other hand, $\mathbf{x}^*(t')$ necessarily belongs to region $\mathscr{E}$, so that $\mathbf{x}^*(t') \in \Xi$ implies that

$$\mathbf{x}^*(t') \in \mathscr{E} \cap \bar{\mathscr{E}}_B$$

But

$$\mathscr{E} = (B/\Sigma) \cup \Sigma \cup (A/\Sigma)$$

and hence

$$\mathbf{x}^*(t') \in [((B/\Sigma) \cup \Sigma) \cap \bar{\mathscr{E}}_B] \cup [(A/\Sigma) \cap \bar{\mathscr{E}}_B]$$

Thus, in view of (7.176),

$$\mathbf{x}^*(t') \in [(B/\Sigma) \cup \Sigma] \cap \bar{\mathscr{E}}_B$$

Moreover, it follows from the definition of B/Σ that all points of Σ are limit points of B/Σ. But $\mathscr{E}_B = B/\Sigma$, so that

$$\begin{aligned} B/\Sigma &\subset \bar{\mathscr{E}}_B \\ \Sigma &\subset \bar{\mathscr{E}}_B \\ [(B/\Sigma) \cup \Sigma] &\subset \bar{\mathscr{E}}_B \end{aligned} \tag{7.179}$$

Consequently,

$$[(B/\Sigma) \cup \Sigma] \cap \bar{\mathscr{E}}_B = (B/\Sigma) \cup \Sigma$$

so that

$$\mathbf{x}^*(t') \in (B/\Sigma) \cup \Sigma \tag{7.180}$$

Then it follows from the global properties of a limiting surface, embodied in Lemma 2, that

$$\mathbf{x}^*(t'') \in (B/\Sigma) \cup \Sigma, \qquad t'' > t'$$

and hence, by (7.179), that

$$\mathbf{x}^*(t'') \in \bar{\mathscr{E}}_B, \qquad t'' > t' \tag{7.181}$$

Finally, (7.178) and (7.180) lead to

$$\mathbf{x}^*(t'') \in \bar{\mathscr{E}}_A \cap \bar{\mathscr{E}}_B = \Xi, \qquad t'' > t'$$

which establishes Lemma 45.

7.224 Another Fundamental Analogy

It is readily seen now that Lemmas 43, 44, and 45 are analogous to Lemmas 30, 31, and 32, and to Theorem 1, Corollary 1, and Lemma 2, respectively, provided one invokes the correspondence between:

$$\begin{array}{llll} \Xi & \text{and} & \partial\mathscr{E} & \text{or } \Sigma \\ \mathring{\mathscr{E}}_B & \text{and} & \mathring{\mathscr{E}} & \text{or } B/\Sigma \\ \mathring{\mathscr{E}}_A & \text{and} & \widehat{\text{comp}\,\mathring{\mathscr{E}}} & \text{or } A/\Sigma \end{array}$$

and provided one introduces assumptions which correspond to those introduced earlier in the discussion of interior points. Under these provisos, the properties deduced previously for interior points—and particularly those of optimal trajectories at interior points—of $\mathscr{E}^*$ are equally valid for boundary points of $\mathscr{E}^*$. The sole exception to this statement pertains to those properties which depend on the concept of a nice Σ surface, since we have not as yet introduced the notion of a *nice boundary* Ξ. Before taking up this latter concept, let us retrace some other steps of our earlier discussion.

7.225 Some Basic Assumptions; Local Cones $\mathscr{C}_a(\mathbf{x})$ and $\mathscr{C}_b(\mathbf{x})$

We shall now introduce a basic assumption which is similar to the first and third basic assumptions of Sec. 7.61 and 7.215, respectively. Let $\boldsymbol{\eta}$ be a bound vector at point $\mathbf{x} \in \Xi$. We shall *assume* that for every vector $\boldsymbol{\eta}$ there exists a scalar $\delta > 0$ such that for every ε, $0 < \varepsilon < \delta$, the point $\mathbf{x} + \varepsilon\boldsymbol{\eta}$ belongs either to region $\bar{\mathscr{E}}_A$ or to region $\mathring{\mathscr{E}}_B$.

Now we define two local cones, namely,

$$\mathscr{C}_a(\mathbf{x}) \triangleq \{\mathbf{x} + \boldsymbol{\eta} : \exists \alpha > 0 \quad \text{such that} \quad \forall \varepsilon, \quad 0 < \varepsilon < \alpha, \qquad \mathbf{x} + \varepsilon\boldsymbol{\eta} \in \bar{\mathscr{E}}_A\} \tag{7.182}$$

and

$$\mathscr{C}_b(\mathbf{x}) \triangleq \{\mathbf{x} + \boldsymbol{\eta} : \exists \beta > 0 \quad \text{such that} \quad \forall \varepsilon, \quad 0 < \varepsilon < \beta, \qquad \mathbf{x} + \varepsilon\boldsymbol{\eta} \in \mathring{\mathscr{E}}_B\} \tag{7.183}$$

In view of (7.170), we have

$$\bar{\mathscr{E}}_A = \bar{\Sigma} \cup \overline{(A/\Sigma)} \cup \overline{\text{comp}\,\mathscr{E}}$$

Furthermore, if L_+ denotes the half-ray which emanates from $\mathbf{x} \in \Xi$, and which is parallel to the x_0-axis and points into the positive x_0-direction, then

$$L_+ \subset \overline{\text{comp}\,\mathscr{E}} \cup \overline{(A/\Sigma)}$$

whence

$$L_+ \subset \bar{\mathscr{E}}_A$$

Consequently,

$$\mathscr{C}_a(\mathbf{x}) \neq \phi, \qquad \forall \mathbf{x} \in \Xi \tag{7.184}$$

Moreover, we shall *assume* that

$$\mathscr{C}_b(\mathbf{x}) \neq \phi, \qquad \forall \mathbf{x} \in \Xi \tag{7.185}$$

By arguments similar to those of Sec. 7.217, one can define *interior points* of $\mathscr{C}_a(\mathbf{x})$ and $\mathscr{C}_b(\mathbf{x})$, and then open cones $\mathring{\mathscr{C}}_a(\mathbf{x})$ and $\mathring{\mathscr{C}}_b(\mathbf{x})$. Finally, we now introduce another basic assumption which is analogous to the fourth basic assumption stated in Sec. 7.217; we need only replace $\mathscr{C}_0(\mathbf{x})$ by $\mathscr{C}_a(\mathbf{x})$, and $\mathscr{C}_1(\mathbf{x})$ by $\mathscr{C}_b(\mathbf{x})$.

7.226 Local Cone $\tilde{\mathscr{B}}(\mathbf{x})$

By analogy to cone $\mathscr{B}(\mathbf{x})$ defined in Sec. 7.218, we now have

$$\tilde{\mathscr{B}}(\mathbf{x}) \triangleq \bar{\mathscr{C}}_a(\mathbf{x}) \cap \bar{\mathscr{C}}_b(\mathbf{x}) \tag{7.186}$$

The properties of cones $\mathscr{C}_a(\mathbf{x})$, $\mathscr{C}_b(\mathbf{x})$, and $\tilde{\mathscr{B}}(\mathbf{x})$ can be deduced by arguments similar to those employed for cones $\mathscr{C}_0(\mathbf{x})$, $\mathscr{C}_1(\mathbf{x})$, and $\mathscr{B}(\mathbf{x})$, respectively. One arrives at analogous lemmas. We shall not repeat these derivations; rather, we shall discuss some of the salient features of boundary Ξ.

7.227 Tangent Cone $\mathscr{C}_\Xi(\mathbf{x})$ at a point of Ξ

We shall say that a *unit vector* $\mathbf{t}_\Xi$ *is tangent to boundary* Ξ at a point $\mathbf{x}$ in $\bar{\Xi}$, if the following conditions are fulfilled:

(i) There exists a vector function $(\boldsymbol{\eta}\varepsilon)$ and a positive scalar function $m(\varepsilon)$, both of the same parameter ε, such that

$$|\boldsymbol{\eta}(\varepsilon)| = 1 \qquad \text{and} \qquad \begin{matrix} \boldsymbol{\eta}(\varepsilon) \to \mathbf{t}_\Xi \\ m(\varepsilon) \to 0 \end{matrix} \quad \text{as} \quad \varepsilon \to 0$$

(ii) There exists an infinite sequence

$$S_\Xi \triangleq \{\varepsilon : \varepsilon = \varepsilon_i, \quad i = 1, 2, \ldots, k, \quad \text{and} \quad \varepsilon_k \to 0 \quad \text{as} \quad k \to \infty\}$$

and a positive number α such that, for all $\varepsilon \in S_\Xi$ and $0 < \varepsilon < \alpha$, the point

$$\mathbf{x} + m(\varepsilon)\boldsymbol{\eta}(\varepsilon) \in \Xi$$

Next we define the tangent cone $\mathscr{C}_\Xi(\mathbf{x})$ of Ξ at $\mathbf{x}$; namely,

$$\mathscr{C}_\Xi(\mathbf{x}) \triangleq \{\mathbf{x} + k\mathbf{t}_\Xi : k > 0, \quad \forall \mathbf{t}_\Xi\}$$

Properties of this cone can be derived readily by arguments similar to those of Sec. 7.8.†

7.228 A Nice Boundary Ξ; Lemma 46

Let us now turn to the concept of a *nice boundary* Ξ. In preparation, we shall deduce a lemma. Consider a point $\mathbf{x} \in \Xi$ and an open ball $B(\mathbf{x})$ in E^{n+1} with center at $\mathbf{x}$. As a consequence of definition (7.182) of $\mathscr{C}_b(\mathbf{x})$ together with the assumption that $\mathscr{C}_b(\mathbf{x})$ is not empty, we have

$$B(\mathbf{x}) \cap \mathring{\mathscr{E}}_B \neq \phi, \qquad \forall \mathbf{x} \in \Xi$$

no matter how small the radius of $B(\mathbf{x})$. If we *assume*, furthermore, that

$$B(\mathbf{x}) \cap \mathring{\mathscr{E}}_A \neq \phi, \qquad \forall \mathbf{x} \in \Xi$$

no matter how small the radius of $B(\mathbf{x})$, we can prove

Lemma 46. *If*

$$\mathbf{x}_A \in B(\mathbf{x}) \cap \mathring{\mathscr{E}}_A$$
$$\mathbf{x}_B \in B(\mathbf{x}) \cap \mathring{\mathscr{E}}_B$$

then there exists a positive number α *such that, for every pair of points* $\mathbf{x}_A$ *and* $\mathbf{x}_B$, *the point* $\alpha\mathbf{x}_A + (1 - \alpha)\mathbf{x}_B \in \Xi$.

† If Ξ_i is a subset of Ξ and $\mathbf{x} \in \bar{\Xi}_i$, one can also define tangent vector t_{Ξ_i} and tangent cone $\mathscr{C}_{\Xi_i}(\mathbf{x})$ at point $\mathbf{x}$.

Let us note, first of all, that

$$\Xi = \text{comp}(\mathring{\mathscr{E}}_A \cup \mathring{\mathscr{E}}_B) \tag{7.187}$$

Indeed, consider a point $\mathbf{x} \notin \mathring{\mathscr{E}}_A \cup \mathring{\mathscr{E}}_B$; namely,

$$\mathbf{x} \notin \mathring{\mathscr{E}}_A \tag{7.188}$$

$$\mathbf{x} \notin \mathring{\mathscr{E}}_B \tag{7.189}$$

Since $\mathscr{E}_A \triangleq \text{comp}\, \mathscr{E}_B$, whence $\mathring{\mathscr{E}}_A = \text{comp}\, \bar{\mathscr{E}}_B$ and $\mathring{\mathscr{E}}_B = \text{comp}\, \bar{\mathscr{E}}_A$, it follows from (7.188) and (7.189), respectively, that $\mathbf{x} \in \bar{\mathscr{E}}_B$ and $\mathbf{x} \in \bar{\mathscr{E}}_A$, and hence that $\mathbf{x} \in \bar{\mathscr{E}}_A \cap \bar{\mathscr{E}}_B \triangleq \Xi$. This establishes (7.187).

Our subsequent arguments are similar to those utilized in the proof of Lemma 9. Let L be the line segment (connected portion of a straight line) which joins points $\mathbf{x}_A$ and $\mathbf{x}_B$. If Lemma 46 is false, then it follows from (7.187) that a point of L belongs to one of the two sets

$$\Delta_A \triangleq L \cap \mathring{\mathscr{E}}_A, \qquad \Delta_B \triangleq L \cap \mathring{\mathscr{E}}_B$$

so that

$$\Delta_A \cup \Delta_B = L$$

Let $d(\mathbf{x}_i, \mathbf{x}_j)$ denote the distance between $\mathbf{x}_i \in L$ and $\mathbf{x}_j \in L$, and consider the two sets

$$\{\mathbf{x} : \mathbf{x} = \mathbf{x}_i^A \in \Delta_A, \quad i = 1, 2, \ldots, k\}$$

and

$$\{\mathbf{x} : \mathbf{x} = \mathbf{x}_i^B \in \Delta_B, \quad i = 1, 2, \ldots, k\}$$

constructed as follows: Consider the midpoint of L; it belongs either to Δ_A or to Δ_B. If it belongs to Δ_A, we shall denote it by $\mathbf{x}_1^A$ and let $\mathbf{x}_1^B = \mathbf{x}_B$. If it belongs to Δ_B, we shall denote it by $\mathbf{x}_1^B$ and let $\mathbf{x}_1^A = \mathbf{x}_A$. Then we consider the midpoint of the segment of L between $\mathbf{x}_1^A$ and $\mathbf{x}_1^B$, and proceed as before.

As in Sec. 7.74, we obtain two sets of points, $\mathbf{x}_i^A$ and $\mathbf{x}_i^B$, $i = 1, 2, \ldots, k$, such that $\mathbf{x}_k^A$ and $\mathbf{x}_k^B$ tend to the same limit, $\mathbf{x}_L$, as k increases; that is,

$$\begin{aligned} \mathbf{x}_k^A &\to \mathbf{x}_L \\ \mathbf{x}_k^B &\to \mathbf{x}_L \end{aligned} \qquad \text{as} \quad k \to \infty$$

According to our supposition, $\mathbf{x}_L$ belongs either to Δ_A or to Δ_B. Suppose, for instance, that $\mathbf{x}_L \in \Delta_A$ and hence $\mathbf{x}_L \in \mathring{\mathscr{E}}_A$. Then there exists a $\delta > 0$ such that an open ball $B(\mathbf{x}_L)$ in E^{n+1}, having its center at $\mathbf{x}_L$ and radius ρ, $0 < \rho < \delta$, belongs to $\mathring{\mathscr{E}}_A$. But this contradicts the fact that†

$$\mathbf{x}_k{}^B \to \mathbf{x}_L \quad \text{as} \quad k \to \infty$$

Thus, our supposition is incorrect, namely,

$$L \cap \Xi \neq \phi$$

whence follows Lemma 46.

Note now that Ξ possesses a property which is analogous to property (ii) of a nice Σ defined in Sec. 7.9. However, property (ii) of a nice Σ is introduced by way of the definition, whereas the analogous property of Ξ is assured by Lemma 46.

Now we can define a *nice boundary* Ξ as follows: Boundary Ξ is *nice* if there exists a partition $\{\Xi_1, \Xi_2, \ldots, \Xi_\mu\}$ of Ξ such that at every point $\mathbf{x}$ in Ξ_i, $i = 1, 2, \ldots, \mu$, the tangent cone $\mathscr{C}_{\Xi_i}(\mathbf{x})$ is defined and belongs to a k-dimensional plane $T_{\Xi_i}(\mathbf{x})$, $k \leq n$, through $\mathbf{x}$.

7.229 Concluding Remarks

One can readily verify that *all* the properties which we obtained for interior points of a nice Σ surface are also valid for points of a nice boundary Ξ, provided one invokes the correspondence specified in Sec. 7.224 together with the assumptions introduced throughout Sec. 7.22.

7.23 Degenerated Case

We should not close this chapter without saying a few words about the degenerated case; namely, the case in which either

(i) $\mathring{\mathscr{C}}_B(\mathbf{x}) = \phi$, or
(ii) $\mathring{\mathscr{C}}_A(\mathbf{x}) = \phi$
at an interior point of $\mathscr{E}^*$.

In case (i) point $\mathbf{x}$ will be called *B-degenerated*, and in case (ii) it will be called *A-degenerated*.

† Note here that $\mathring{\mathscr{E}}_A \cap \mathring{\mathscr{E}}_B = \phi$, since

$$\mathring{\mathscr{E}}_A \cap \mathring{\mathscr{E}}_B = (\text{comp } \overline{\mathscr{E}}_B) \cap \mathring{\mathscr{E}}_B, \qquad \mathring{\mathscr{E}}_B \subset \overline{\mathscr{E}}_B$$

and

$$(\text{comp } \overline{\mathscr{E}}_B) \cap \overline{\mathscr{E}}_B = \phi$$

7.231 *B*-Degenerated Point; Lemmas 47–49

Let us consider case (i) and prove

Lemma 47. *Let* $\mathbf{x}' \triangleq \mathbf{x}^*(t')$ *and* $\mathbf{x}'' \triangleq \mathbf{x}^*(t'')$, $t'' \geq t'$, *be points of optimal trajectory* Γ^*. *If* $\mathbf{x}'$ *is a B-degenerated point and* $\mathbf{x}''$ *is an interior point of* $\mathscr{E}^*$, *then* $\mathbf{x}''$ *is also B-degenerated.*

According to hypothesis of the lemma,

$$\mathring{\mathscr{C}}_B(\mathbf{x}') = \phi \tag{7.190}$$

Suppose the lemma is false, that is,

$$\mathring{\mathscr{C}}_B(\mathbf{x}'') \neq \phi$$

and consider a vector $\boldsymbol{\eta}''$ at point $\mathbf{x}''$ such that

$$\mathbf{x}'' + \boldsymbol{\eta}'' \in \mathring{\mathscr{C}}_B(\mathbf{x}'')$$

According to Corollary 7, $\boldsymbol{\eta}''$ is the transform, due to linear transformation $A(t', t'')$, of a vector $\boldsymbol{\eta}'$ at $\mathbf{x}'$ such that

$$\mathbf{x}' + \boldsymbol{\eta}' \in \mathring{\mathscr{C}}_B(\mathbf{x}')$$

This contradicts (7.190) and so establishes Lemma 47.

Another interesting lemma is

Lemma 48. *Let* $\mathbf{x}' \triangleq \mathbf{x}^*(t')$ *and* $\mathbf{x}'' \triangleq \mathbf{x}^*(t'')$, $t'' \geq t'$, *be points of optimal trajectory* Γ^*. *If* $\mathbf{x}'$ *is a B-degenerated point, and if* $\boldsymbol{\eta}''$ *is a vector at point* $\mathbf{x}''$ *such that*

$$\mathbf{x}'' + \boldsymbol{\eta}'' \in (\mathscr{S}\mathbf{x}'')$$

then $\boldsymbol{\eta}''$ *is the transform, due to linear transformation* $A(t', t'')$, *of a vector* $\boldsymbol{\eta}'$ *at* $\mathbf{x}'$ *such that*

$$\mathbf{x}' + \boldsymbol{\eta}' \in \mathscr{S}(\mathbf{x}')$$

In view of Lemma 21 together with the second hypothesis of the lemma, we have

$$\mathbf{x}' + \boldsymbol{\eta}' \in \overline{\mathscr{C}}_B(\mathbf{x}')$$

But as a consequence of the lemma's first hypothesis, $\mathring{\mathscr{C}}_B(\mathbf{x}') = \phi$. Thus it follows that

$$\overline{\mathscr{C}}_B(\mathbf{x}') = \mathscr{S}(\mathbf{x}')$$

and so the lemma is proved.

One can easily demonstrate the validity of

Lemma 49. *At a B-degenerated point* $\mathbf{x}$ *of a limiting surface* Σ,

$$\mathbf{x} - \mathbf{f}(\mathbf{x}, \mathbf{u}) \in \mathscr{S}(\mathbf{x}) \qquad \textit{for all} \quad \mathbf{u} \in \Omega$$

Since $\overline{\mathscr{C}}_B(\mathbf{x}) = \mathscr{S}(\mathbf{x})$, Lemma 49 is a direct consequence of Lemma 15.

7.232 *A*-Degenerated Point; Lemmas 50–52

In a manner entirely analogous to that used in proving the lemmas of Sec. 7.231, but employing Corollary 6, Lemma 20, and Lemma 15, respectively, one can deduce

Lemma 50. *Let* $\mathbf{x}' \triangleq \mathbf{x}^*(t')$ *and* $\mathbf{x}'' \triangleq \mathbf{x}^*(t'')$, $t'' \geq t'$, *be points of optimal trajectory* Γ^*. *If* $\mathbf{x}''$ *is an A-degenerated point and* $\mathbf{x}'$ *is an interior point of* $\mathscr{E}^*$, *then* $\mathbf{x}'$ *is an A-degenerated point.*

Lemma 51. *Let* $\mathbf{x}' \triangleq \mathbf{x}^*(t')$ *and* $\mathbf{x}'' \triangleq \mathbf{x}^*(t'')$, $t'' \geq t'$, *be points of optimal trajectory* Γ^*. *If* $\mathbf{x}''$ *is an A-degenerated point, and if* $\boldsymbol{\eta}'$ *is a vector at point* $\mathbf{x}'$ *such that*

$$\mathbf{x}' + \boldsymbol{\eta}' \in \mathscr{S}(\mathbf{x}')$$

then the transform of $\boldsymbol{\eta}'$, *due to linear transformation* $A(t', t'')$, *is a vector* $\boldsymbol{\eta}''$ *at* $\mathbf{x}''$, *such that*

$$\mathbf{x}'' + \boldsymbol{\eta}'' \in \mathscr{S}(\mathbf{x}'')$$

Lemma 52. *At an A-degenerated point* $\mathbf{x}$ *of a limiting surface* Σ,

$$\mathbf{x} + \mathbf{f}(\mathbf{x}, \mathbf{u}) \in \mathscr{S}(\mathbf{x}) \qquad \textit{for all} \quad \mathbf{u} \in \Omega$$

7.233 Corollary 15

Consider a nonzero vector $\boldsymbol{\eta}$ at point $\mathbf{x}$. In view of the discussion of Sec. 7.71, if

$$\mathbf{x} + \varepsilon\boldsymbol{\eta} \in L_+, \qquad \varepsilon > 0, \quad \text{then} \quad \mathbf{x} + \boldsymbol{\eta} \in \mathscr{C}_A(\mathbf{x})$$

and if

$$\mathbf{x} + \varepsilon\boldsymbol{\eta} \in L_-, \qquad \varepsilon > 0, \quad \text{then} \quad \mathbf{x} + \boldsymbol{\eta} \in \mathscr{C}_B(\mathbf{x})$$

However, if

$$\mathring{\mathscr{C}}_A(\mathbf{x}) = \phi \qquad \text{then} \quad \mathscr{C}_A(\mathbf{x}) \subset \mathscr{S}(\mathbf{x})$$

and if

$$\mathring{\mathscr{C}}_B(\mathbf{x}) = \phi \qquad \text{then} \quad \mathscr{C}_B(\mathbf{x}) \subset \mathscr{S}(\mathbf{x})$$

Thus we arrive at

Corollary 15. *At an A-degenerated point* $\mathbf{x}$ *of a limiting surface* Σ,

$$\mathbf{x} + \varepsilon\boldsymbol{\eta} \in L_+, \qquad \varepsilon > 0, \quad \Rightarrow \mathbf{x} + \boldsymbol{\eta} \in \mathscr{S}(\mathbf{x})$$

and at a B-degenerated point $\mathbf{x}$ *of a limiting surface* Σ,

$$\mathbf{x} + \varepsilon\boldsymbol{\eta} \in L_-, \qquad \varepsilon > 0, \quad \Rightarrow \mathbf{x} + \boldsymbol{\eta} \in \mathscr{S}(\mathbf{x})$$

7.234 A Trivial Maximum Principle†

Let us suppose that

(i) the initial point $\mathbf{x}^*(t_0) = \mathbf{x}^0$ of optimal trajectory Γ^* is a B-degenerated point;
(ii) $\mathscr{S}(\mathbf{x}^0) \subseteq T(\mathbf{x}^0)$ where $T(\mathbf{x}^0)$ is a n-dimensional hyperplane through point $\mathbf{x}^0$;
(iii) all points of Γ^* are interior points of $\mathscr{E}^*$.

From Lemma 47 together with hypotheses (i) and (iii) above, it follows at once that all points of Γ^* are B-degenerated.

Let $\mathbf{x} = \mathbf{x}^*(t)$, $t_0 \leq t \leq t_1$, be any point of Γ^*, and at that point consider a vector $\boldsymbol{\eta}$ such that

$$\mathbf{x} + \boldsymbol{\eta} \in \mathscr{S}(\mathbf{x}) \tag{7.191}$$

Vector $\boldsymbol{\eta}$ may be considered to be the transform, due to linear transformation $A(t_0, t)$, of a vector $\boldsymbol{\eta}^0$ at $\mathbf{x}^0$. According to Lemma 48, it follows that

$$\mathbf{x}^0 + \boldsymbol{\eta}^0 \in \mathscr{S}(\mathbf{x}^0)$$

so that, as a consequence of hypothesis (ii) above, we have

$$\mathbf{x}^0 + \boldsymbol{\eta}^0 \in T(\mathbf{x}^0)$$

Thus,

$$\mathbf{x} + \boldsymbol{\eta} \in T(\mathbf{x})$$

where $T(\mathbf{x})$ is the transform of $T(\mathbf{x}^0)$, due to linear transformation $A(t_0, t)$; and so it follows from (7.191) that

$$\mathscr{S}(\mathbf{x}) \subseteq T(\mathbf{x}) \tag{7.192}$$

† See also Sec. 8.4.

Now Lemma 49 together with (7.192) leads to

$$\mathbf{x} - \mathbf{f}(\mathbf{x}, \mathbf{u}) \in T(\mathbf{x}), \qquad \forall \mathbf{u} \in \Omega \tag{7.193}$$

Furthermore, it follows from Corollary 15 with (7.192) that $T(\mathbf{x})$ is a "vertical" plane, since

$$\mathbf{x} + \varepsilon\boldsymbol{\xi} \in L_-, \qquad \varepsilon > 0, \qquad \Rightarrow \mathbf{x} + \boldsymbol{\xi} \in T(\mathbf{x})$$

We are now ready to state

Theorem 12. *If* $\mathbf{u}^*(t)$, $t_0 \leq t \leq t_1$, *is an optimal control, and* $\mathbf{x}^*(t)$ *is the corresponding solution of trajectory equation* (7.44), *and if conditions* (*i*), (*ii*), *and* (*iii*) *above are fulfilled, then there exists a nonzero continuous vector function* $\boldsymbol{\lambda}(t)$ *which is a solution of adjoint equations* (7.79), *such that*

(i) $\mathscr{H}(\boldsymbol{\lambda}(t), \mathbf{x}^*(t), \mathbf{u}) = 0, \qquad \forall \mathbf{u} \in \Omega$
(ii) $\lambda_0(t) = 0$

for all at $t \in [t_0, t_1]$.

To prove this theorem we need only choose the initial value of $\boldsymbol{\lambda}(t)$ such that $\boldsymbol{\lambda}(t_0) = \boldsymbol{\lambda}^0$ is normal to $T(\mathbf{x}^0)$. Then, as shown in Section 7.142, $\boldsymbol{\lambda}(t)$ is normal to $T(\mathbf{x}^*(t))$ for all $t \in [t_0, t_1]$. But $T(\mathbf{x}^*(t))$ is a "vertical" plane so that

$$\lambda_0(t) = 0, \qquad \forall t \in [t_0, t_1]$$

Furthermore it follows from (7.193) that

$$\mathscr{H}(\boldsymbol{\lambda}(t), \mathbf{x}^*(t), \mathbf{u}) \triangleq \boldsymbol{\lambda}(t) \cdot \mathbf{f}(\mathbf{x}^*(t), \mathbf{u}) = 0, \qquad \forall \mathbf{u} \in \Omega$$

Thus, Theorem 12 is established.

7.235 Concluding Remarks

The results of the preceding sections can be extended to cover optimal trajectories containing boundary points; this can be done by employing the conclusions of Secs. 7.21 and 7.22. By degeneracy of a boundary point $\mathbf{x}$ we mean that either $\mathring{\mathscr{C}}_b(\mathbf{x}) = \phi$ or $\mathring{\mathscr{C}}_a(\mathbf{x}) = \phi$.

7.24 Some Illustrative Examples

In order to illustrate some of the concepts introduced in this chapter, we shall now discuss briefly three simple time-optimal control problems. Rather than present an exhaustive discussion, we shall state the equations of the Σ-surfaces and point out a few salient features. We shall leave it to the reader to utilize these examples for a further check on the results obtained in this chapter.

7.241 One-Dimensional Regulator Problem

Consider the system whose state equations are

$$\dot{x}_1 = x_2$$
$$\dot{x}_2 = u$$

and control set Ω given by

$$|u| \leq 1$$

It is required to transfer the system in minimum time from (x_1^0, x_2^0) to $(0, 0)$.

As is well known, optimal control is bang-bang with at most one switch. The switching curve—that is, the locus of states at which optimal control switches—divides the state space E^2 into two open regions denoted by regions I and II on Fig. 1.

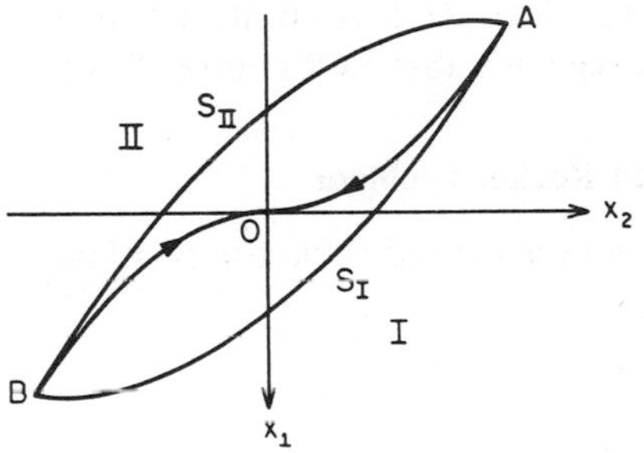

FIG. 1. S-surface.

The minimum cost $V^*(\mathbf{x}, \mathbf{x}^1)$—that is, the minimum transfer time from state $\mathbf{x} = (x_1, x_2)$ to $\mathbf{x}^1 = (0, 0)$—is given by

$$V^*(\mathbf{x}; \mathbf{x}^1) = \begin{cases} x_2 + \sqrt{2x_2^2 + 4x_1} & \text{if } \mathbf{x} \in \text{region I} \\ -x_2 + \sqrt{2x_2^2 - 4x_1} & \text{if } \mathbf{x} \in \text{region II} \\ \pm x_2 & \text{if } \mathbf{x} \in \text{switching curve} \end{cases}$$

The equations of S and Σ-surfaces are simply

$$S : V^*(\mathbf{x}; \mathbf{x}^1) = C$$
$$\Sigma : x_0 + V^*(\mathbf{x}; \mathbf{x}^1) = C$$

Figures 1 and 2 show an S and a Σ-surface, respectively.

An optimal isocost surface S consists of two parabolic arcs, S_I and S_{II}. The parabolic arc in region I is tangent to the switching curve at A, whereas the arc in region II is tangent to the switching curve at B.

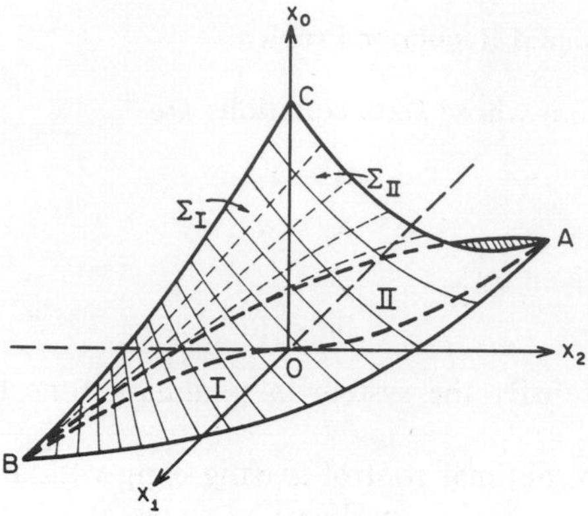

FIG. 2. Σ-surface.

A limiting surface Σ possesses an edge *ACB* whose projection on E^2 lies on the switching curve. Edge *ACB* is an attractive subset of Σ. The remaining portion of Σ is a regular subset. Of course, Σ is nice.

7.242 Power-Limited Rocket Problem

The behavior of a power-limited rocket in rectilinear flight is described by

$$\dot{x}_1 = u$$
$$\dot{x}_2 = u^2$$

with control set Ω given by

$$|u| \leq 1$$

Here we wish to transfer the system from $(x_1{}^0, x_2{}^0)$ to $(x_1{}^1, x_2{}^1)$ in minimum time.

The region E^* of initial states is the open half-plane given by $x_2 < x_2{}^1$. Region E^*, in turn, is divided by lines of slope 1 and -1 into regions I, II, and III as shown on Fig. 3. For $(x_1{}^0, x_2{}^0)$ in region I, any bang-bang control is

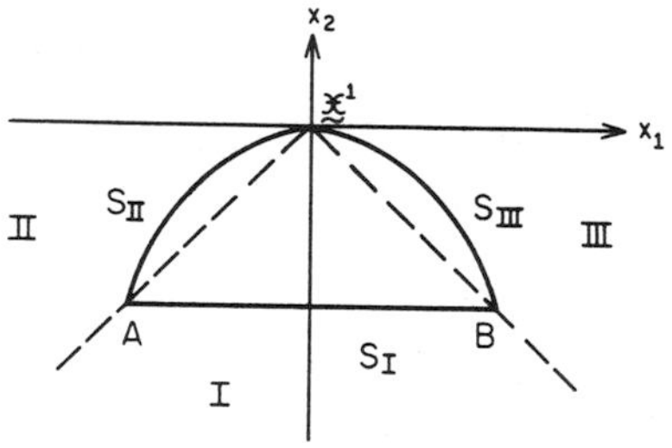

FIG. 3. S-surface. Note: Letters with a wavy underline in the figures are equivalent to boldface letters in the text.

optimal (provided it results in transfer to terminal state $\mathbf{x}^1$). For $(x_1{}^0, x_2{}^0)$ in region II or III, optimal control is constant and unique.

The minimum cost of transfer from $\mathbf{x}$ to $\mathbf{x}^1$ is given by

$$V^*(\mathbf{x}; \mathbf{x}^1) = \begin{cases} x_2{}^1 - x_2 & \text{if } \mathbf{x} \in \text{region I} \\ \dfrac{(x_1{}^1 - x_1)^2}{x_2{}^1 - x_2} & \text{if } \mathbf{x} \in \text{region II, III} \end{cases}$$

The lines separating regions I and II, and regions I and III, may be considered to belong to either region.

It is readily seen that an S-surface consists of a line segment, S_{I}, parallel to the x_1-axis and a parabolic arc, $S_{\mathrm{II}} - S_{\mathrm{III}}$, which is symmetric about the x_2-axis; see Fig. 3. A Σ-surface is made up of a triangular section of a plane, Σ_{I}, inclined at 45° to the state plane together with a portion of a parabolic cone, $\Sigma_{\mathrm{II}} - \Sigma_{\mathrm{III}}$, as shown in Fig. 4.

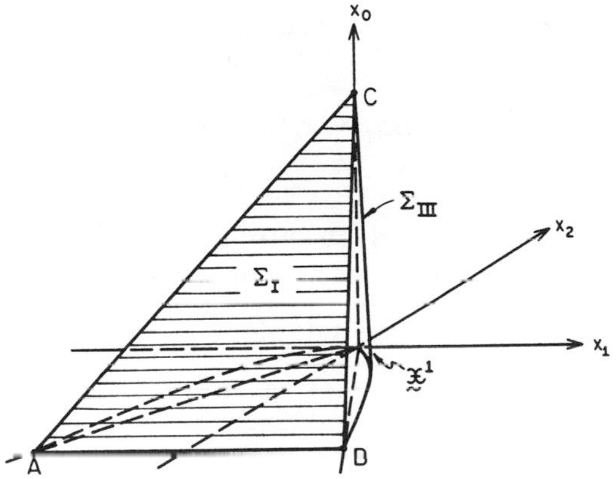

FIG. 4. Σ-surface.

A Σ-surface possesses two edges, AC and BC, each of which is an attractive subset. The remaining portion of Σ is a regular subset. Σ is nice.

7.243 A Navigation Problem

The state equations of a vehicle, which moves with constant speed relative to a stream having constant velocity, are

$$\dot{x}_1 = s + u_1$$
$$\dot{x}_2 = u_2$$

where $s = \text{const}$, and Ω is given by

$$u_1{}^2 + u_2{}^2 = 1$$

We require the time-optimal transfer from $(x_1{}^0, x_2{}^0)$ to $(x_1{}^1, x_2{}^1)$.

Here we distinguish among three cases; namely, (i) $s < 1$; (ii) $s = 1$; and (iii) $s > 1$. In each case optimal control corresponds to constant steering angle, that is,

$$u_1{}^*(t) \equiv \text{const}$$
$$u_2{}^*(t) \equiv \text{const}$$

However, concerning initial state region E^* and minimum cost $V^*(\mathbf{x}; \mathbf{x}^1)$, we must take up each case separately.

(i) $s < 1$. Here $E^* = E^2$, and

$$V^*(\mathbf{x}; \mathbf{x}^1) = \frac{-s\Delta x_1 + [(\Delta x_1)^2 + (1 - s^2)(\Delta x_2)^2]^{1/2}}{1 - s^2}$$

where

$$\Delta x_1 \triangleq x_1{}^1 - x_1$$
$$\Delta x_2 \triangleq x_2{}^1 - x_2$$

An S-surface is a circle which surrounds terminal state $\mathbf{x}^1$; see Fig. 5. A Σ-surface is a circular cone as shown in Fig. 6. Σ is regular and nice.

(ii) $s = 1$. Here E^* is the open half-plane given by $x_1 < x_1{}^1$, and

$$V^*(\mathbf{x}; \mathbf{x}^1) = \frac{(\Delta x_1)^2 + (\Delta x_2)^2}{2\Delta x_1}$$

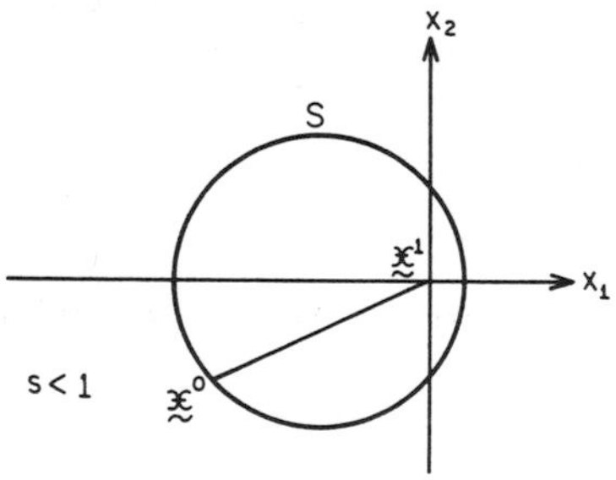

FIG. 5. S-surface.

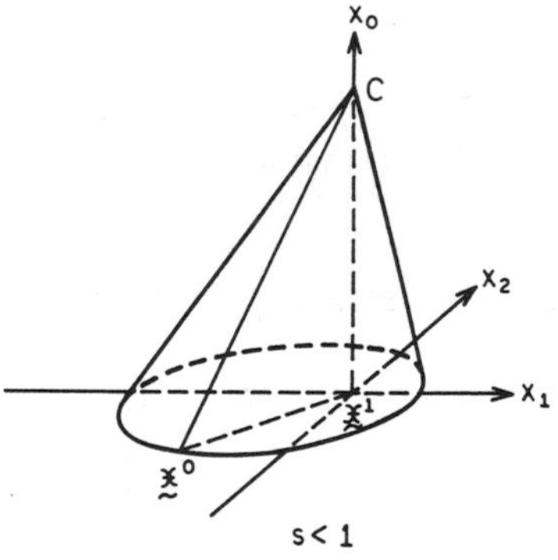

FIG. 6. Σ-surface.

An S-surface is a circle with terminal state $\mathfrak{x}^1$ deleted; that is, $\mathfrak{x}^1$ belongs to the boundary of E^*. This is shown in Fig. 7. A Σ-surface is a circular cone with the directrix on the x_0-axis deleted; see Fig. 8. Again, Σ is regular and nice.

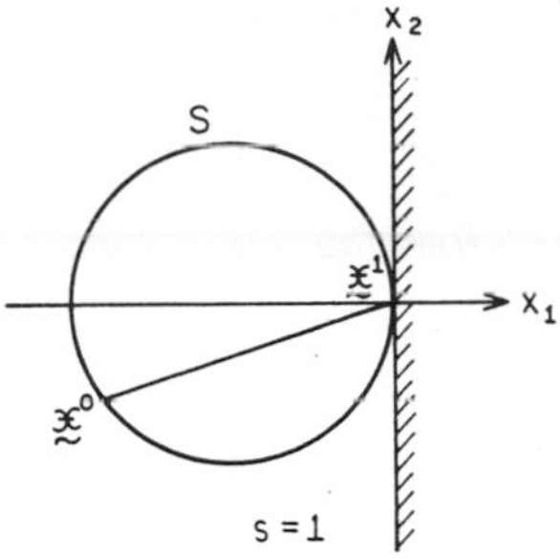

FIG. 7. S-surface.

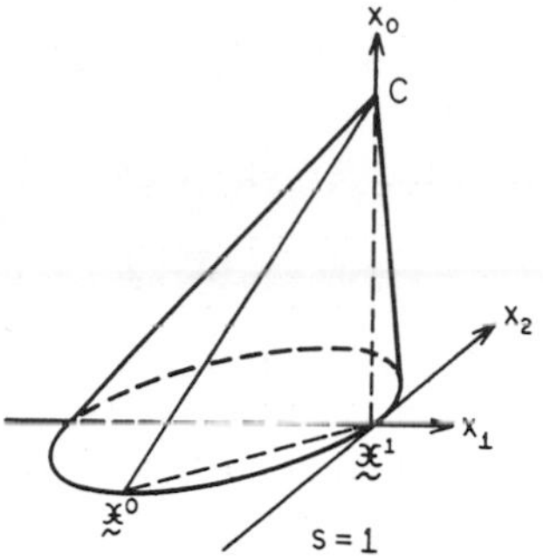

FIG. 8. Σ-surface.

(iii) $s > 1$. Here E^* is a closed triangular region in the left half-plane as shown in Fig. 9. Minimum cost is given by

$$V^*(\mathfrak{x}; \mathfrak{x}^1) = \frac{s\Delta x_1 + [(\Delta x_1)^2 - (s^2 - 1)(\Delta x_2)^2]^{1/2}}{s^2 - 1}$$

An S-surface is a circular arc which is tangent to the boundary of E^*; see Fig. 9. A Σ-surface is a portion of a circular cone as illustrated in Fig. 10. Σ possesses boundary points of $\mathscr{E}^*$ along AC and BC. At interior points, Σ is regular and nice. Boundary Ξ is made up of Σ and "vertical" planar sections $AC\mathfrak{x}^1$ and $BC\mathfrak{x}^1$. Boundary Ξ is nice.

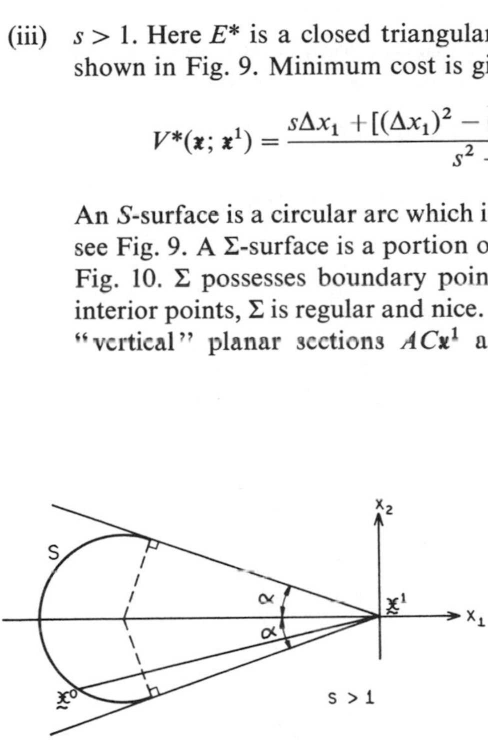

FIG. 9. S-surface.

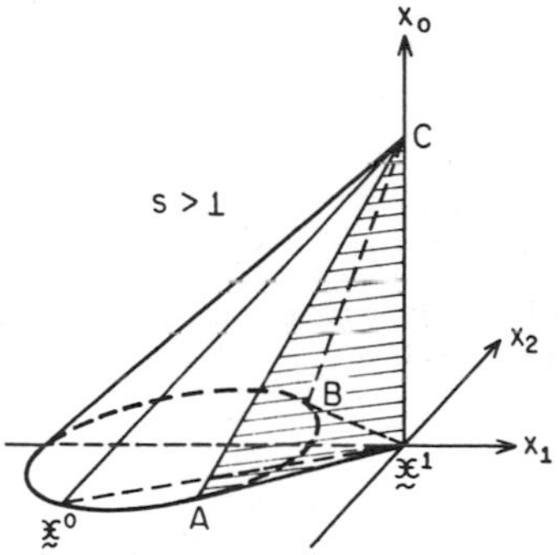

FIG. 10. Σ-surface.

APPENDIX

If

$$\{\Sigma_1, \Sigma_2, \ldots, \Sigma_\mu, \ldots\}$$

is a partition of Σ, we wish to show that the set of subsets $\bigcap_{i=1}^{\gamma}\overline{\Sigma}_i$ is denumerable.

Consider the set whose elements are

$$(\Sigma_i, \Sigma_j), \qquad i, j = 1, 2, \ldots, \mu, \ldots$$

that is, the Cartesian product $A \times A$, where

$$A \triangleq \{\Sigma_i : i = 1, 2, \ldots, \mu, \ldots\}$$

Similarly, the set whose elements are

$$(\Sigma_i, \Sigma_j, \Sigma_k), \qquad i, j, k = 1, 2, \ldots, \mu, \ldots$$

is $A \times A \times A$.

Since the Cartesian product of two denumerable sets is denumerable, the sets A, $A \times A$, $A \times A \times A, \ldots$ are denumerable, and the set

$$\{A, A \times A, A \times A \times A, \ldots\}$$

is also denumerable, since there is a one-to-one correspondence between its elements and the integers. Furthermore, since the union of a denumerable set of denumerable sets is itself denumerable, the set

$$A \cup (A \times A) \cup (A \times A \times A) \cdots$$

is denumerable. Now, the elements of this set are

$$\begin{array}{lr} \Sigma_i & i = 1, 2, \ldots, \mu, \ldots \\ (\Sigma_i, \Sigma_j) & i, j = 1, 2, \ldots, \mu, \ldots \\ (\Sigma_i, \Sigma_j, \overline{\Sigma}_k) & i, j, k = 1, 2, \ldots, \mu, \ldots \\ \vdots & \end{array}$$

With each such element of this set, we may associate an intersection

$$\begin{array}{lr} \overline{\Sigma}_i & i = 1, 2, \ldots, \mu, \ldots \\ \overline{\Sigma}_i \cap \overline{\Sigma}_j & i, j = 1, 2, \ldots, \mu, \ldots \\ \overline{\Sigma}_i \cap \overline{\Sigma}_j \cap \overline{\Sigma}_k & i, j, k = 1, 2, \ldots, \mu, \ldots \\ \vdots & \end{array}$$

Hence, the set of all such intersections is denumerable. In particular, the set of all distinct intersections is denumerable; we denote it by

$$\{M_1, M_2, \ldots, M_\nu, \ldots\}$$

and note that $\bigcap_{i=1}^{\gamma} \bar{\Sigma}_i$ may be any† member of this set whose union is clearly Σ.

Bibliography

1. A. Blaquière and G. Leitmann, On the Geometry of Optimal Processes, Parts I, II, III, Univ. of California, Berkeley, IER Repts. AM-64-10, AM-65-11, AM-66-1.
2. A. Blaquière, Sur la théorie de la commande optimale, course notes, Fac. Sci., Univ. of Paris (1963).
3. G. Leitmann, Some Geometrical Aspects of Optimal Processes, *J. SIAM, Ser. A: Control* **3**, No. 1, 53 ff (1965).
4. A. Blaquière, Further Investigation into the Geometry of Optimal Processes, *J. SIAM, Ser. A: Control*, **3**, No. 2, 19 ff (1965).
5. A. Blaquière and G. Leitmann, Some Geometric Aspects of Optimal Processes, Part I: Problems with Control Constraints, *Proc. Congr. Automatique Théorique, Paris* (1965).
6. K. V. Saunders and G. Leitmann, Some Geometric Aspects of Optimal Processes, Part II: Problems with State Constraints, *Proc. Congr. Automatique Théorique, Paris* (1965).
7. H. Halkin, The Principal of Optimal Evolution, *in* "Nonlinear Differential Equations and Nonlinear Mechanics" (J. P. LaSalle and S. Lefschetz, eds.) p. 284 ff. Academic Press, New York, 1963.
8. E. Roxin, A Geometric Interpretation of Pontryagin's Maximum Principle, *in* "Nonlinear Differential Equations and Nonlinear Mechanics" (J. P. LaSalle and S. Lefschetz, eds.) p. 303 ff. Academic Press, New York, 1963.
9. R. E. Bellman, "Dynamic Programming." Princeton Univ. Press, Princeton, New Jersey, 1957.
10. S. E. Dreyfus, "Dynamic Programming and the Calculus of Variations," RAND Rept. R-441-PR (1965)
11. R. E. Kalman, The Theory of Optimal Control and the Calculus of Variations, *in* "Mathematical Optimization Techniques." Univ. of California Press, Berkeley, California, 1964.
12. L. S. Pontryagin *et al.*, "The Mathematical Theory of Optimal Processes." Wiley (Interscience), New York, 1962.
13. J. L. Kelley, "General Topology." Van Nostrand, Princeton, New Jersey, 1955.
14. R. Isaacs, "Differential Games." Wiley, New York, 1965.

† Note again that this may require renumbering the elements of the partition.

8

The Pontryagin Maximum Principle†

STEPHEN P. DILIBERTO
DEPARTMENT OF MATHEMATICS, UNIVERSITY OF CALIFORNIA,
BERKELEY, CALIFORNIA

8.0 Introduction

The purpose of this paper is twofold: First, we present a reformulation of the proof of the Pontryagin maximum principle. Second, we apply these techniques to give a proof of the bang-bang principle. As a byproduct of these proof methods we shall readily establish the validity of the bang-bang principle for nonlinear systems.

Our object in reformulating the proof of the Pontryagin maximum principle is to emphasize one central fact. That fact is the existence of a simple family of controls—discontinuous in general—which produce effects on a solution which are differentiable. The types of controls so produced are rich enough (i.e., have enough different members) so as to provide a full range of comparison trajectories.

The measure of controllability introduced by Pontryagin *et al.*[1] is a cone attached to each point of the trajectory (and generated by the special perturbations of the control function). This cone is a measure of controllability in that it indicates what are possible changes in direction producible by a change in control at that instant or even for earlier control changes. Now cones in general are determined only by linear combinations of vectors with positive

† The work reported in this chapter was supported by ONR under Nonr-222(88).

coefficients. If, however, among the vectors one is using to span the cone, both some vector ζ and $-\zeta$ occur as generators then the cone will include a linear space containing ζ.

Our proof of the bang-bang principle stems from these facts: (1) If a one parameter family of vectors $\zeta(s)$ does not move in a "degenerate" way then in an arbitrarily small interval s_0 to s_n there will be $n+1$ linearly independent vectors $\zeta(s_0), \zeta(s_1), \ldots, \zeta(s_n)$ where $s_0 < s_1 < \cdots < s_n$. Thus if $\mathscr{K}$ is the cone spanned by them, $\mathscr{K}$ will include all of E^{n+1}. (2) If the control function has a regular point in the interior of the control set there must necessarily be such a vector ζ. Thus, to eliminate this optimality denying condition one must avoid interior points. (Since we are considering measurable controls the value of the control at individual points is, of course, immaterial. What is to be denied here is that the control variable will have any interior point sets with positive measure.)

If the boundaries of the control set are piecewise linear then our argument applies to any face of the boundary. Consequently, the final conclusion is that: "In general, the control variable must be at the vertex of the control set except for a set of measure zero." Note that the result derived is true for *any* set whose boundaries consist of flat space. In particular *our result does not require the control set to be convex.*

Notation. Vectors will be denoted by lowercase boldface Latin letters and components by subscripts, thus $\mathbf{x} = (x_1, \ldots, x_n)$, different vectors by superscripts, matrices by capital letters. We shall employ, except for these things, the notation of our only reference.[1]

8.1 The Extended Problem

The extended control problem begins with the differential equation

$$d\mathbf{x}/dt = f(\mathbf{x}, \mathbf{u}) \tag{8.1}$$

where it is assumed $\mathbf{x} = (x_0, x_1, \ldots, x_n)$, $\mathbf{f} = (f_0, f_1, \ldots, f_n)$, and $\mathbf{u} = (u_1, \ldots, u_m)$ are vectors, $\mathbf{f}$ is continuous in $(\mathbf{x}, \mathbf{u})$ but differentiable (continuously) in $\mathbf{x}$, and $\mathbf{f}$ is independent of x_0.

A successful control $\mathbf{u} = \mathbf{u}(t)$ is one such that it carries a solution with initial point $\mathbf{x}^0$ of the form $\mathbf{x}^0 = (0, \mathbf{y}^0)$ [i.e., its first component is zero] into a terminal point $\mathbf{x}^1 = (x_0{}^1, \mathbf{y}^1)$ where $\mathbf{y}^1$ is specified. An optimal control is one for which $x_0{}^1$ is a minimum.

Because the value of the control function is immaterial outside the time interval (t^0, t^1) during which the solution goes from $\mathbf{x}^0$ to $\mathbf{x}^1$ we may assume the control function defined for all t. To avoid certain trivial cases we shall assume that, if $\mathbf{x}(t^0) = \mathbf{x}^0$ and $\mathbf{x}(t^1) = \mathbf{x}^1$, there is no inbetween point τ such that $\mathbf{x}(\tau) = \mathbf{x}^0$ or $\mathbf{x}^1$.

To make certain that results are physically reasonable it has been customary to assume that $f_0(\mathbf{x}, \mathbf{u}) \geq 0$. For the results presented here it is only required that $x_0(t^1) > -\infty$. Any hypothesis that guarantees this is sufficient for our purposes, e.g., $f_0 \geq -M > -\infty$ (M being a positive constant).

If $E^{n+1} \times \Omega$ is the set in which $\mathbf{f}$ is defined (i.e., for $\mathbf{x}$ in E^{n+1} and $\mathbf{u}$ in Ω), then an *allowable control* function is one such that (i) $\mathbf{u}(t) \in \Omega$ for all t and (ii) $\mathbf{u}(t)$ is piecewise continuous.

The variations to be considered are only within the class of *admissible control sets.* These are determined by the three conditions: (i) The modification which changes any $\mathbf{u}(t)$ to an allowable constant in an interval is admissible. (ii) If a finite set of controls is admissible then any control which is equal to one of these on one finite set of intervals (whose union is the whole line) is admissible. (iii) The translation of an admissible control is admissible.

Formally, these conditions are: (i) If I is an interval $(-\infty, t^0]$ or $[t^0, t^1]$ or $[t^1, +\infty)$, and $\mathbf{u}(t)$ is admissible and $\mathbf{u}^0 \in \Omega$, then $\bar{\mathbf{u}}(t)$ is admissible where

$$\begin{aligned} \bar{\mathbf{u}}(t) &= \mathbf{u}(t) \qquad (t \notin I) \\ &= \mathbf{u}^0 \qquad\;\; (t \in I) \end{aligned}$$

(ii) If $\mathbf{u}^i$ $(i = 1, \ldots, k)$ are admissible, if I^i $(i = 1, \ldots, k)$ are disjoint intervals as above and $\bigcup_i^k I^i = (-\infty, +\infty)$, then $\bar{\mathbf{u}}(t)$ defined by

$$\bar{\mathbf{u}}(t) = \mathbf{u}^i(t) \qquad \text{in} \quad I^i \qquad (i = 1, \ldots, k)$$

is admissible.

A *regular* point of a control function $\mathbf{u}$ is a point t where

$$\lim_{h\to 0} \left| \frac{1}{h} \int_{t-h}^{t} [f(\mathbf{x}(t), \mathbf{u}(\tau)) - f(\mathbf{x}(t), \mathbf{u}(t))]\, d\tau \right| = 0 \tag{8.2}$$

For the two main classes of control functions, measurable ones or piecewise continuous ones, regular points are almost all points (measurable case) and nonjump points (piecewise continuous case).

Let $V(\mathbf{f}) \triangleq [\partial f_i/\partial x_j]$ be the Jacobian matrix of the vector $\mathbf{f}$ with respect to the argument $\mathbf{x} = (x_0, \ldots, x_n)$. Let $\boldsymbol{\lambda}(t)$ be the solution of the adjoint variational equations

$$\frac{d\boldsymbol{\lambda}}{dt} = -V^T(\mathbf{f})\boldsymbol{\lambda} \tag{8.3}$$

Here V^T denotes the transpose of V. It is to be assumed that in the $\mathbf{x}$-arguments of this equation an appropriate solution function has been substituted. Define

$$\mathscr{H}(\boldsymbol{\lambda}, \mathbf{x}, \mathbf{u}) \triangleq \boldsymbol{\lambda} \cdot \mathbf{f} = \boldsymbol{\lambda} \cdot \mathbf{f}(\mathbf{x}, \mathbf{u}) = \sum_0^n \lambda_\alpha \mathbf{f}_\alpha \tag{8.4}$$

Define $\mathscr{M}(\boldsymbol{\lambda}, \mathbf{x})$ by

$$\mathscr{M}(\boldsymbol{\lambda}, \mathbf{x}) \triangleq \sup_{\mathbf{u}\in\Omega} \mathscr{H}(\boldsymbol{\lambda}, \mathbf{x}, \mathbf{u}) \tag{8.5}$$

Theorem 1. (Maximum Principle of Pontryagin). *If* $\mathbf{x}^*(t)$ *is an optimal solution and* $\mathbf{u}^*(t)$ *its control function* ($t^0 \le t \le t^1$), *there exists a solution* $\lambda(t)$ *of the adjoint variational equations such that*

(1) *If* $\mathscr{H}^*(t, \mathbf{u}) \triangleq \mathscr{H}(\lambda(t), \mathbf{x}^*(t), \mathbf{u})$, *then* $\mathscr{H}^*$ *attains its maximum for* $\mathbf{u} = \mathbf{u}^*(t)$ *at all regular points, i.e.,*

$$\mathscr{H}^*(t, \mathbf{u}^*(t)) = \mathscr{M}(\lambda(t), \mathbf{x}^*(t))$$

(2) $\mathscr{M}(\lambda(t), \mathbf{x}^*(t)) = \text{const} = 0.$

8.2 The Control Lemma

Control Lemma.† *Let* $\mathbf{x}(t)$ *be a solution with control* $\mathbf{u}(t)$ *on* $t^2 \le t \le t^5$. *For positive constants* d_1, d_2, and ε *define inbetween points* $t^3 = t^5 - \varepsilon(d_1 + d_2)$ *and* $t^4 = t^5 - \varepsilon(d_2)$. *Let* $\mathbf{u}(t, \varepsilon)$ *be the control defined by*

$$\begin{aligned} \mathbf{u}(t, \varepsilon) &= \mathbf{u}(t) \qquad && (t^2 \le t < t^3) \\ &= \mathbf{v} && (t^3 \le t < t^4) \\ &= \mathbf{u}(t) && (t^4 \le t \le t^5) \end{aligned}$$

Let $\mathbf{u}(t)$ *be regular at* t^5 *and* $\mathbf{x}(t, \varepsilon)$ *be the solution with control* $\mathbf{u}(t, \varepsilon)$ *determined by the initial condition* $\mathbf{x}(t^2, \varepsilon) = \mathbf{x}(t^2)$ *for all* ε. *Let* $\mathbf{x}^i(\varepsilon) = \mathbf{x}(t^i, \varepsilon)$ *and* $\mathbf{x}^i = \mathbf{x}(t^i)$. *Also let* $\mathbf{u}^5 = \mathbf{u}(t^5)$. *Then the following size estimates hold for* $\mathbf{x}(t)$ *and* $\mathbf{x}(t, \varepsilon)$:

(1)′ $t^3 \le t \le t^5$, $\mathbf{x}(t) = \mathbf{x}^3 + (t - t^3)\mathbf{f}(\mathbf{x}^5, \mathbf{u}^5) + \mathbf{o}(\varepsilon)$
(2)′ $t^3 \le t < t^4$, $\mathbf{x}(t, \varepsilon) = \mathbf{x}^3(\varepsilon) + (t - t^3)\mathbf{f}(\mathbf{x}^5(\varepsilon), \mathbf{v}) + \mathbf{o}(\varepsilon)$
(3)′ $t^4 \le t \le t^5$, $\mathbf{x}(t, \varepsilon) = \mathbf{x}^3(\varepsilon) + \varepsilon\, d'\mathbf{f}(\mathbf{x}^5(\varepsilon), \mathbf{v}) + (t - t^4)\mathbf{f}(\mathbf{x}^5, \mathbf{u}^5) + \mathbf{o}(\varepsilon)$

Differences between $\mathbf{x}(t, \varepsilon)$ and $\mathbf{x}(t)$ may be established thus (recall $|f| \le M$):

(1) $\mathbf{x}^3(\varepsilon) = \mathbf{x}^3$
(2) $|\mathbf{x}(t, \varepsilon) - \mathbf{x}(t)| \le 2(t - t^3)M$ for $(t^3 \le t \le t^5)$
(3) $\mathbf{x}^5(\varepsilon) - \mathbf{x}^5 = \varepsilon\, d_1[\mathbf{f}(\mathbf{x}^5, \mathbf{v}) - \mathbf{f}(\mathbf{x}^5, \mathbf{u}^5)] + \mathbf{o}(\varepsilon\, d_1)$

Remark. This lemma is surprising for several reasons. First, if one wishes to discuss the possible differentiability of $\mathbf{x}(t, \varepsilon)$ *with respect to* ε one would expect to pattern the "standard" differentiability arguments. In these one writes the integral form of the differential equation

$$\mathbf{x}(t, \varepsilon) = \mathbf{x}^3 + \int_{t^3}^{t} \mathbf{f}(\mathbf{x}(\tau, \varepsilon), \mathbf{u}(\tau, \varepsilon))\, d\tau$$

† Points t^i, $i = 2, 3, 4, 5$, belong to (t^0, t^1).

and then differentiates with respect to ε. If we let $\mathbf{v} = d\mathbf{x}/d\varepsilon$, this will allow us to write the differentiated equation as†

$$\frac{d\mathbf{x}}{d\varepsilon} = \mathbf{v}(t, \varepsilon) = \int_{t^3}^{t} \left[\left(\frac{\partial \mathbf{f}}{\partial \mathbf{x}}\right) \mathbf{v}(\tau, \varepsilon) + \left(\frac{\partial \mathbf{f}}{\partial \mathbf{u}}\right) \frac{d\mathbf{u}}{d\varepsilon} \right] d\tau$$

But this is impossible here because we have assumed only that $\mathbf{f}$ is continuous in $\mathbf{u}$ and not differentiable. Despite this, (3) above asserts that $\mathbf{v}(t^5, 0)$ exists and is given by

$$\mathbf{v}(t^5, 0) = d_1[\mathbf{f}(\mathbf{x}^5, \mathbf{v}) - \mathbf{f}(\mathbf{x}^5, \mathbf{u}^5)]$$

Equally noteworthy with the existence of $\mathbf{v}(t^5, 0)$ is the fact that it does not contain d_2.

PROOF. Since $|\mathbf{f}| \leq M$ one has for $t \geq t^3$ that for *any* solution $\mathbf{z}$, with *any* control (we omit the $d\tau$ in the integrand)

$$|\mathbf{z}(t) - \mathbf{z}(t^3)| \leq \left| \int_{t^3}^{t} \mathbf{f} \right| \leq \int_{t^3}^{t} |\mathbf{f}| \leq (t - t^3)M$$

Using this for $\mathbf{z} = \mathbf{x}(t, \varepsilon)$ and $\mathbf{z} = \mathbf{x}(t)$ one has

$$|\mathbf{x}(t) - \mathbf{x}^3| \leq (t - t^3)M \tag{8.6}$$

$$|\mathbf{x}(t, \varepsilon) - \mathbf{x}^3| \leq (t - t^3)M \tag{8.7}$$

Put

$$\mathbf{x}(t, \varepsilon) - \mathbf{x}(t) = (\mathbf{x}(t, \varepsilon) - \mathbf{x}^3) + (\mathbf{x}^3 - \mathbf{x}(t))$$

take norms, and use $\mathbf{x}^3(\varepsilon) = \mathbf{x}^3$; this yields

$$|\mathbf{x}(t, \varepsilon) - \mathbf{x}(t)| \leq |\mathbf{x}(t, \varepsilon) - \mathbf{x}^3| + |\mathbf{x}^3 - \mathbf{x}(t)|$$

Now using these estimates for the two terms on the right hand side (RHS) one has

$$|\mathbf{x}(t, \varepsilon) - \mathbf{x}(t)| \leq 2(t - t^3)M$$

and this establishes (2).

We establish (1)′ in this manner: In the integral equation for $\mathbf{x}(t)$, namely,

$$\mathbf{x}(t) = \mathbf{x}^3 + \int_{t^3}^{t} \mathbf{f}(\mathbf{x}(\tau), \mathbf{u}(\tau))\, d\tau$$

add and subtract the terms $\mathbf{f}(\mathbf{x}^5, \mathbf{u}^5)$ and $\mathbf{f}(\mathbf{x}^5, \mathbf{u}(\tau))$, rearranging the terms in the following manner (we omit the $d\tau$ in the integrand)

$$\mathbf{x}(t) = \mathbf{x}^3 + \int_{t^3}^{t} \mathbf{f}(\mathbf{x}^5, \mathbf{u}^5) + \int_{t^3}^{t} \mathbf{f}(\mathbf{x}(\tau), \mathbf{u}(\tau)) - \mathbf{f}(\mathbf{x}^5, \mathbf{u}(\tau))$$

$$+ \int_{t^3}^{t} \mathbf{f}(\mathbf{x}^5, \mathbf{u}(\tau)) - \mathbf{f}(\mathbf{x}^5, \mathbf{u}^5) \tag{8.8}$$

† Here $\partial f/\partial \mathbf{u} = [\partial f_i/\partial u_k]$ with $\mathbf{u} = \mathbf{u}(t)$, $\mathbf{x} = \mathbf{x}(t)$.

Since $\mathbf{f}$ is Lipschitzian the integrand of the second term of the RHS is majorized by $K|\mathbf{x}(\tau) - \mathbf{x}^5|$, $K = \text{const} > 0$. By using (8.6) this is majorized by $K\varepsilon M$. This, in turn, implies the second integral of the RHS is majorized by $(t - t^3)\varepsilon M$ or $\varepsilon^2(d_1 + d_2)KM$. Thus the second term of the RHS is certainly $\mathbf{o}(\varepsilon)$.

For the third term of the RHS one has the ready estimate

$$|t - t^3| \sup_{\tau \in I_\varepsilon} |\mathbf{f}(\mathbf{x}^5, \mathbf{u}(\tau)) - \mathbf{f}(\mathbf{x}^5, \mathbf{u}^5)|$$

This means that

$$\left| \frac{1}{t - t^3} \int_{t^3}^{t} \mathbf{f}(\mathbf{x}^5, \mathbf{u}(\tau)) - \mathbf{f}(\mathbf{x}^5, \mathbf{u}^5) \right| \leq \sup_{\tau \in I_\varepsilon} |\mathbf{f}(\mathbf{x}^5, \mathbf{u}(\tau)) - \mathbf{f}(\mathbf{x}^5, \mathbf{u}^5)| \tag{8.9}$$

where I_ε is the interval $t^3 = t^5 - \varepsilon(d_1 + d_2) \leq t \leq t^5$. That the left hand side (LHS) of this inequality goes to zero (i.e., that the integral itself is $\mathbf{o}(\varepsilon)$) is now a consequence of the fact that the RHS does. And this in turn depends on the fact that t^5 is a regular point (i.e., point of continuity) of $\mathbf{u}(t)$.

Aside. For "measurable" control functions the argument changes here—but the conclusion remains. Namely, inequality (8.9) does not hold. However, that the LHS $\to 0$ with ε is precisely the definition of a regular point—and, of course, almost all points are regular for a measurable function.

Combining these two estimates with Eq. (8.8) it follows then that

$$\mathbf{x}(t) = \mathbf{x}^3 + (t - t^3) f(\mathbf{x}^5, \mathbf{u}^5) + \mathbf{o}(\varepsilon) \tag{8.10}$$

To establish (2)′ and (3)′ add and subtract the terms $\mathbf{f}(\mathbf{x}^5(\varepsilon), \mathbf{v})$ and $\mathbf{f}(\mathbf{x}^5(\varepsilon), \mathbf{u}(\tau, \varepsilon))$ to the integral equation for $\mathbf{x}(\varepsilon)$. Thus (again leave off the $d\tau$)

$$\mathbf{x}(t, \varepsilon) = \mathbf{x}^3 + \int_{t^3}^{t} \mathbf{f}(\mathbf{x}(\tau, \varepsilon), \mathbf{u}(\tau, \varepsilon))$$

becomes

$$\begin{aligned} \mathbf{x}(t) = \mathbf{x}^3 + \int_{t^3}^{t} \mathbf{f}(\mathbf{x}^5(\varepsilon), \mathbf{v}) + \int_{t^3}^{t} [\mathbf{f}(\mathbf{x}(\tau, \varepsilon), \mathbf{u}(\tau, \varepsilon)) \\ - \mathbf{f}(\mathbf{x}^5(\varepsilon), \mathbf{u}(\tau, \varepsilon))] + \int_{t^3}^{t} [\mathbf{f}(\mathbf{x}^5(\varepsilon), \mathbf{u}(\tau, \varepsilon) - \mathbf{f}(\mathbf{x}^5(\varepsilon), \mathbf{v})] \end{aligned}$$

The last two integrals of the RHS are both $\mathbf{o}(\varepsilon)$ precisely as before and so for $t^3 \leq t \leq t^5$,

$$\mathbf{x}(t, \varepsilon) = \mathbf{x}^3 + (t - t^3)\mathbf{f}(\mathbf{x}^5(\varepsilon), \mathbf{v}) + \mathbf{o}(\varepsilon)$$

Note that by putting $t = t^4$ in this equation it has the consequence that

$$\mathbf{x}^4(\varepsilon) = \mathbf{x}(t^4; \varepsilon) = \mathbf{x}^3 + \varepsilon\, d^1 \mathbf{f}(\mathbf{x}^5, \mathbf{v}) + \mathbf{o}(\varepsilon)$$

Paralleling the derivation for (1)′ and (2)′ one finds easily that in $t^4 \leq t \leq t^5$

$$\mathbf{x}(t, \varepsilon) = \mathbf{x}^4(\varepsilon) + (t - t^4)\mathbf{f}(\mathbf{x}^5(\varepsilon), \mathbf{u}^5) + \mathbf{o}(\varepsilon)$$

and this combined with the last equation establishes (3)′.

(1) is the definition of $\mathbf{x}^3(\varepsilon)$. (2) follows in one step from (8.6) and (8.7) by subtraction; (3) follows from (1)′ and (3)′ and (2). If in (1)′ and (3)′ one puts $t = t^5$ they become, respectively [also use (1)]

$$\mathbf{x}^5 = \mathbf{x}^3 + \varepsilon(d_1 + d_2)\mathbf{f}(\mathbf{x}^5, \mathbf{u}^5) + \mathbf{o}(\varepsilon)$$
$$\mathbf{x}^5(\varepsilon) = \mathbf{x}^3 + \varepsilon(d_1)\mathbf{f}(\mathbf{x}^5(\varepsilon), \mathbf{u}) + \varepsilon\, d_2(\mathbf{x}^5(\varepsilon), \mathbf{u}^5) + \mathbf{o}(\varepsilon)$$

(2) being valid for any t in the interval, implies for $t = t^5$, that $\mathbf{x}^5 = \mathbf{x}^5(\varepsilon) + \mathbf{o}(\varepsilon)$. Thus the expression for $\mathbf{x}^5(\varepsilon)$ just given may be rewritten by replacing each $\mathbf{x}^5(\varepsilon)$ on the RHS by $\mathbf{x}^5$ so that

$$\mathbf{x}^5(\varepsilon) = \mathbf{x}^5 + \varepsilon\, d_1\mathbf{f}(\mathbf{x}^5, \mathbf{v}) + \varepsilon\, d_2\mathbf{f}(\mathbf{x}^5, \mathbf{u}^5) + \mathbf{o}(\varepsilon)$$

Subtracting this from the last expression for $\mathbf{x}^5$ gives (3).

8.3 The Controllability Theorem

We shall first establish a lemma which will allow us to determine at time t the effect of a control at an earlier time. Using this lemma we define the cones which measure controllability. The principal result will be to prove the extent to which these cones do allow one to modify a solution.

Lemma. *Let $\mathbf{x}(t)$ be the solution of*

$$d\mathbf{x}/dt = \mathbf{f}(\mathbf{x}, \mathbf{u}) \tag{8.11}$$

defined by $\mathbf{x}(t^0) = \mathbf{x}^0$ and for given control $\mathbf{u}(t)$. Let $W(t, t^0)$ be the matrix solution of $dW/dt = V(\mathbf{f})W$ where $V(\mathbf{f}) = [\partial \mathbf{f}_i/\partial \mathbf{x}_j](\mathbf{x}(t), \mathbf{u}(t))$ and $W(t^0, t^0) = I$. If $\mathbf{x}(t, \varepsilon)$ is the solution of (8.1) determined by the initial value $\mathbf{x}(t^0, \varepsilon) = \mathbf{x}^0 + \varepsilon\zeta + \mathbf{o}(\varepsilon)$, ζ a fixed vector, then

$$\mathbf{x}(t, \varepsilon) = \mathbf{x}(t) + \varepsilon W(t, t^0)\zeta + \mathbf{o}(\varepsilon)$$

PROOF. If $\mathbf{v}^j = d\mathbf{x}\,(t, t^0, \mathbf{x}^0)/dx_j$ then

$$\mathbf{v}^j = W(t, t^0)\mathbf{E}^j$$

where $\mathbf{E}^j$ is the jth unit vector (all zeros and one in the jth spot). Since $\mathbf{x}(t, \varepsilon) = \mathbf{x}(t, t^0, \mathbf{x}^0 + \varepsilon\zeta)$,

$$\left.\frac{d\mathbf{x}}{d\varepsilon}(t, \varepsilon)\right|_{\varepsilon=0} = \sum_0^n \frac{\partial \mathbf{x}}{\partial \mathbf{x}_j^0}\zeta_j = \sum_0^n W(t, t^0)\mathbf{E}^j\zeta_j$$
$$= W(t, t^0)\Big(\sum_0^n \mathbf{E}^j\zeta_j\Big) = W(t, t^0)\zeta$$

And since $\mathbf{x}(t, \varepsilon) = \mathbf{x}(t) + \varepsilon(d\mathbf{x}/d\varepsilon) + \mathbf{o}(\varepsilon)$, the result is established.

Definition. For any $\mathbf{x}^0$, $\mathbf{u}^0$.

$k(\mathbf{x}^0, \mathbf{u}^0)$ = set of vectors generated by finite sums with *positive* coefficients of $[\mathbf{f}(\mathbf{x}^0, \mathbf{v}) - \mathbf{f}(\mathbf{x}^0, \mathbf{u}^0)]$ for all $\mathbf{v} \in \Omega$.

$\ell(\mathbf{x}^0, \mathbf{u}^0)$ = space generated by all finite linear combinations of $[\mathbf{f}(\mathbf{x}^0, \mathbf{v}) - \mathbf{f}(\mathbf{x}^0, \mathbf{u}^0)]$ for all $\mathbf{v} \in \Omega$—i.e., the coefficients are no longer required to be positive.

Definition. For any solution $\mathbf{x}(t)$ with control $\mathbf{u}(t)$ defined on $I\ (t^0 \leq t \leq t^1)$ and any $\tau \in I\ (\tau \neq t^0)$.

$\mathscr{K}(\tau) \triangleq \mathscr{K}(\mathbf{x}_\tau, \mathbf{u}_\tau)$ = set of vectors generated by finite linear sums with positive coefficients of $W(\tau, \tau')\zeta$ for all $\tau' < \tau$ and regular, and $\zeta \in k(\mathbf{x}_{\tau'}, \mathbf{u}_{\tau'})$.

$\mathscr{L}(\tau) \triangleq \mathscr{L}(\mathbf{x}_\tau, u_\tau)$ = space generated by all finite linear combinations of $W(\tau, \tau')\zeta$ for τ' regular and $\zeta \in \ell(\mathbf{x}_{\tau'}, \mathbf{u}_{\tau'})$.

For cones A and B of vectors let $A \oplus B$ be the cone generated by A and B, i.e., the set of all combinations $\alpha\mathbf{x} + \beta\mathbf{y}$ where $\alpha, \beta \geq 0$, $\mathbf{x} \in A$ and $\mathbf{y} \in B$.

Definition. $\overline{\mathscr{K}}(\tau) \triangleq \mathscr{K}(\tau) \oplus \mathbf{f}(\mathbf{x}_\tau, \mathbf{u}_\tau)$, and $\overline{\mathscr{L}}(\tau) \triangleq \mathscr{L}(\tau) \oplus \mathbf{f}(\mathbf{x}_\tau, \mathbf{u}_\tau)$.

Theorem 2. *If τ is a regular point, if $t^0 < \tau \leq t^1$, if* dim $\overline{\mathscr{K}}(\tau) = n + 1$ *and if the vertical segment below $\mathbf{x}(\tau)$ [i.e., $(x) = (x_0(\tau) + \mu, x_1(\tau), \ldots, x_n(\tau))$] with $-\delta < \mu < 0$ lies in $\overline{\mathscr{K}}$ then $\mathbf{x}(t)$ is not optimal.*

PROOF. To prove the theorem it is sufficient to show from the hypothesis that one can construct a solution $\tilde{\mathbf{x}}(t)$ such that $\tilde{x}_0(t^1) < x_0(t^1)$. This will be accomplished by (A) showing that if $\hat{\mathbf{x}}(t)$ is a solution such that $\hat{x}_0(\tau) < x_0(\tau)$ then $\tilde{\mathbf{x}}$ is directly constructable from $\hat{\mathbf{x}}$; (B) showing how to construct $\tilde{\mathbf{x}}$.

Part A. We shall assume $\mathbf{x}(t)$ with control $\mathbf{u}(t)$ and $\hat{\mathbf{x}}(t)$ with control $\hat{\mathbf{u}}(t)$ are both given where:

(i) $\hat{\mathbf{x}}^0 = \hat{\mathbf{x}}(t^0) = \mathbf{x}^0 = \mathbf{x}(t^0)$;

(ii) $\hat{\mathbf{x}}(\tau')$ lies on L, the vertical line through $\mathbf{x}(\tau)$, and below it, i.e., $\hat{\mathbf{x}}_0(\tau') < \mathbf{x}_0(\tau)$. Construct

$$\begin{aligned} \tilde{\mathbf{u}} &= \hat{\mathbf{u}}(t) && (t^0 \leq t \leq \tau') \\ &= \mathbf{u}(t) && (\tau' < t \leq t^1 + (\tau' - \tau)) \end{aligned}$$

Let $\tilde{\mathbf{x}}$ be the solution determined by $\tilde{\mathbf{x}}(t^0) = \mathbf{x}^0$ with control function $\tilde{\mathbf{u}}(t)$. We assert:

(i) $\tilde{\mathbf{x}}(t) = \hat{\mathbf{x}}(t) \qquad (t^0 \leq t \leq \tau')$

(ii) $\tilde{\mathbf{x}}(t) = \mathbf{x}(t - [\tau' - \tau]) + \mathbf{P} \qquad (\tau' \leq t \leq t^1 + (\tau' - \tau))$

for $\mathbf{P} = (\hat{\mathbf{x}}_0(\tau') - x_0(\tau), 0, 0, \ldots, 0)$. (i) is trivial. To prove (ii) we need only show that both LHS and RHS are solutions and that they agree at some value of t (in this case at $t = \tau'$). The LHS is a solution. Since the differential equation is independent of t and x_0 it follows that if $\mathbf{x}(t)$ is a solution so is $\mathbf{x}(t+h) + (a, 0, 0, \ldots, 0) = \mathbf{x}(t+h) + \mathbf{A}$. It remains to choose $\mathbf{A} = \mathbf{P}$ and $h = -[\tau' - \tau]$. For $t = \tau'$,

$$\begin{aligned} \mathbf{x}(t - [\tau' - \tau]) + \mathbf{P} = \mathbf{x}(\tau' - [\tau' - \tau]) + \mathbf{P} &= \mathbf{x}(\tau) + \mathbf{P} \\ &= \mathbf{x}(\tau) + (x_0(\tau') - x(\tau), 0, 0, \ldots, 0) \\ &= (\hat{x}_0(\tau'), x_1(\tau), x_2(\tau), \ldots, x_n(\tau)) \\ &= \hat{\mathbf{x}}(\tau') = \tilde{\mathbf{x}}(\tau') \end{aligned}$$

and (ii) is established.

Part B. First, we observe that the set of points B determined by $(d_1, \ldots, d_{n+1})$ where $d_i \geq 0$ and $\sum d_i = 1$ is an n-simplex. In fact it is that part of the n-plane cut off by the first quadrant in $(n+1)$ space by cutting the ith axis at d_i along it in the positive direction. The cone C_1 determined by B and the origin is the set of all points $\varepsilon(d_1, \ldots, d_n)$ with $0 \leq \varepsilon \leq 1$ and $\sum d_i = 1$. Let a be the extension to $0 \leq \varepsilon < a$. This cone has $n+1$ sides, the jth side S^j being determined by the conditions

$$0 \leq \varepsilon \leq 1, \qquad \text{and} \qquad d_i > 0, \quad i \neq j, \quad d_j = 0, \quad \sum d_i = 1$$

The existence of an $\hat{\mathbf{x}}$ of the type desired will be phrased as a mapping problem on a set of variables $(\varepsilon, d_1, \ldots, d_{n+1})$ where $\varepsilon \geq 0$, $d_i \geq 0$, and $\sum d_i = 1$. In particular, the properties of the mappings will be in terms of the sets B and S^j defined above.

The vertical segment downward through $\mathbf{x}(\tau)$ is given by

$$\mathbf{x}(\tau) - \mu \mathbf{E}^0$$

where $0 \leq \mu < +\infty$, $\mathbf{E}^0 = (1, 0, \ldots, 0)$. The fact that this segment lies *inside* the cone $\bar{\mathscr{K}}$ says that there are $n+1$ vectors ζ^i $(i = 1, \ldots, n+1)$ such that

$$\mathbf{E}^0 = \sum d_i \zeta^i \qquad (\sum d_i = 1, \quad d_i > 0)$$

The mapping m defined on $(\varepsilon, d, \ldots, d_n) = (\varepsilon, d)$ given by

$$m(\varepsilon, d) = \mathbf{x}(\tau) - \varepsilon \sum d_i \zeta^i$$

maps C_1 onto $\hat{\mathscr{K}}$, the part of $\bar{\mathscr{K}}$ spanned by $\zeta^1, \ldots, \zeta^{n+1}$.

The mapping m restricted to B and $S^1, \ldots, S^{n+1}$ determines a base $\hat{B}$ and sides $\hat{S}^i$ of $\hat{\mathscr{K}}$ which include part of the segment $\mathbf{x}(\tau) - \mu \mathbf{E}^0$ for $0 < \mu < \mu^0$ (μ^0 positive and determined by $\zeta^1, \ldots, \zeta^{n+1}$) in its interior.

Any map $\hat{m}$ defined for $0 \leq \varepsilon \leq \varepsilon^0$ and $d_i \geq 0$ with $\sum d_i = 1$ by

$$\hat{m} = m + \mathbf{o}(\varepsilon)$$

has the obvious properties

(i) $\hat{m}$ is $1-1$ if ε^0 is small enough.

(ii) For any $\delta > 0$ there is an ε^1 so that if $\varepsilon^0 < \varepsilon^1$ then

$$(1-\delta)|m| \leq |\hat{m}| < (1+\delta)|m|$$

(iii) For any $\theta^0 > 0$ there is an ε^2 so that if $\varepsilon^0 < \varepsilon^2$ $\measuredangle(m, \hat{m}) < \theta^0$.

From this it follows that if ε^0 is suitably chosen (i.e., small enough) the map $\hat{m}$ on the set of points $B, S^1, \ldots, S^{n+1}$ determines an image which is topologically a sphere and includes in its interior $\mathbf{x}(\tau) - \mu\mathbf{E}^0$ for $0 \leq \mu < \mu^1$.

Standard topological results—i.e., Brower's fixed point theorem—imply that the map $\hat{m}$ extended to the interior of C_1 will cover, i.e., map onto this segment.

To apply this result observe that it will be sufficient to find a control function $\mathbf{u}(t, \varepsilon, d)$ (which is a modification of $\mathbf{u}(t)$) so that the solution $\mathbf{x}(t, \varepsilon, d)$ based on it has the form

$$\mathbf{x}(t, \varepsilon, d) = \mathbf{x}(t) - \varepsilon \sum d_i \zeta^i + \mathbf{o}(\varepsilon)$$

This is done as follows: Each $\zeta^i = W(t, t^i)\mathbf{z}^i$ where $\mathbf{z}^i = \mathbf{f}(\mathbf{x}^i, \mathbf{v}^i) - \mathbf{f}(\mathbf{x}^i, \mathbf{u}^i)$, $\mathbf{x}^i = \mathbf{x}(t^i)$, and $\mathbf{u}^i = \mathbf{u}(t^i)$. The control change that replaces $\mathbf{u}(t)$ by the constant $\mathbf{v}^i$ in the interval $t^i - \varepsilon(d_1 + \delta_1)$ to $t^i - \varepsilon(d_2)$ changes $\mathbf{x}$ at t^i by the amount $\mathbf{z}^i$ and at τ by $\zeta^i = W(t, t^i)\mathbf{z}^i$. Let the control function incorporating all of these changes be $\mathbf{u}(t, \varepsilon, d)$. This is the desired family of changes required.

8.4 The Maximum Principle (Part I)

The last result—the controllability theorem—establishes that if a trajectory is optimal then its cone $\bar{\mathscr{K}}(t)$ will never be all of $(n+1)$-space (thus the cones $\mathscr{L}(t)$ have dimensions $< n+1$ at all points). This implies that there will always exist a hyperplane (a linear space of dim n) through the vertex of the cone having one open half space (not including the plane itself) with *no* points of the cone. If, therefore, a vector $\mathbf{a}$ with base at the vertex of the cone lies in this half space not containing the cone then $\measuredangle(\mathbf{a}, \zeta)$ for $\zeta \in \mathscr{K}$ is certainly positive. If $\mathbf{a}$ were perpendicular to the plane then $\measuredangle(\mathbf{a}, \zeta) \geq 90°$ and if $\theta = \measuredangle(\mathbf{a}, \zeta)$ denotes this angle then $\cos(\theta) \leq 0$. These observations plus the relationship of the solutions of the adjoint equations are the heart of the maximum principle.

Note that if $\bar{\mathscr{K}}$ had no point in the separating plane then sup $\zeta \in \mathscr{K}$ $\cos(\mathbf{a}, \zeta)$ could be negative. If, however, the cone happens to include an entire line—and ours shall—then $\bar{\mathscr{K}}$ must have points in the plane. This will imply that the smallest (least) value sup $\zeta \in \bar{\mathscr{K}}$ $\cos(\mathbf{a}, \zeta)$ can take is zero.

We emphasize here that the vector $\mathbf{a}$, which will be the initial value of $\boldsymbol{\lambda}$ will be arbitrary except for the restriction that $\cos(\mathbf{a}, \zeta) \leq 0$ for $\zeta \in \bar{\mathscr{K}}$. Therefore, $\mathbf{a}$ will be unique in one and only one case; namely, the cone $\bar{\mathscr{K}}$

is a half space and the vector $\mathbf{a}$ is perpendicular to the plane determining it (i.e., the boundary of $\mathscr{K}$).

Lemma. *If* $\dot{\boldsymbol{\lambda}} = -V(f)^T\boldsymbol{\lambda}$, $\quad \dot{\mathbf{v}} = V(f)\mathbf{v}$, *then* $\boldsymbol{\lambda}\cdot\mathbf{v} = \boldsymbol{\lambda}\cdot W(t, t^0)\mathbf{v} =$ const.

PROOF.

$$\frac{d}{dt}\boldsymbol{\lambda}\cdot\mathbf{v} = \dot{\boldsymbol{\lambda}}\cdot\mathbf{v} + \boldsymbol{\lambda}\cdot\dot{\mathbf{v}} = -V^T\boldsymbol{\lambda}\cdot\mathbf{v} + \boldsymbol{\lambda}\cdot V\mathbf{v} = -\boldsymbol{\lambda}\cdot V\mathbf{v} + \boldsymbol{\lambda}\cdot V\mathbf{v} = 0$$

Definition. A vector $\mathbf{x}$ is separated from a set of vectors V, denoted by $\mathbf{x}[S]V$, if $\exists$ a hyperplane containing V in one (closed) half space and $\mathbf{x}$ in the other (open) half space.

Lemma. *Let* $\mathbf{a} = \boldsymbol{\lambda}(\tau)$. *Then, if* $\mathbf{a}[S]\mathscr{K}(\tau)$ *or* $\mathbf{a}[S]\mathscr{L}(\tau)$ *or* $\mathbf{a}\perp\mathscr{K}(\tau)$ *or* $\mathbf{a}\perp\mathscr{L}(\tau)$ *one also has for* $t_1 < \tau$, *with both t and* τ *regular, that* $\boldsymbol{\lambda}(t)[S]\mathscr{k}(t)$ *or* $\boldsymbol{\lambda}(t)[S]\ell(t)$ *or* $\boldsymbol{\lambda}(t)\perp\mathscr{k}(t)$ *or* $\boldsymbol{\lambda}(t)\perp\ell(t)$, respectively.

PROOF. Let ζ be elementary, i.e., let

$$\zeta = \mathbf{f}(\mathbf{x}(t), \mathbf{v}) - \mathbf{f}(\mathbf{x}(t), \mathbf{u}(t)) \in \ell(t) \qquad (t < \tau)$$

Then $\mathbf{z} = W(\tau, t)\zeta \in \mathscr{L}(\tau)$. Let $\mathbf{a} = \boldsymbol{\lambda}(\tau)$. Then $\mathbf{a}\perp$ or $[S]\mathscr{L}(\tau)$ implies $\mathbf{a}\cdot\mathbf{z} = 0$ or $\mathbf{a}\cdot\mathbf{z} \le 0$. But by the last lemma $\mathbf{a}\cdot W(\tau, t)\zeta = \boldsymbol{\lambda}(\tau)\cdot W(\tau, t)$ is constant in t. Hence for $\tau = t$ $\boldsymbol{\lambda}(t)\cdot W(t, t)\zeta - \boldsymbol{\lambda}(t)\cdot\zeta = 0$ or ≤ 0 according as $\mathbf{a}\cdot\mathbf{z} = 0$ or ≤ 0. A similar proof is true for $\sum \alpha_i\zeta^i$ independently of whether or not the α_i are positive.

Definition. Let $\mathscr{H}(\boldsymbol{\lambda}, \mathbf{x}, \mathbf{u}) \triangleq \boldsymbol{\lambda}\cdot\mathbf{f}$, $\quad \mathscr{M}(\boldsymbol{\lambda}, \mathbf{x}) \triangleq \sup \mathbf{u} \in \Omega\, \mathscr{H}(\boldsymbol{\lambda}, \mathbf{x}, \mathbf{u})$.

Theorem 3. *Given any solution* $\mathbf{x}(t)$ *and control* $\mathbf{u}(t)$, *if* $\exists$ $\mathbf{a}$ *such that* $\mathbf{a}[S]\mathscr{K}(t^1)$ *then* $\exists$ $\boldsymbol{\lambda}(t)$ *such that*

$$\mathscr{M}(\boldsymbol{\lambda}(t), \mathbf{x}(t)) = \mathscr{H}(\boldsymbol{\lambda}(t), \mathbf{x}(t), \mathbf{u}(t))$$

at all regular $t < t^1$.

PROOF. It will be sufficient to show that for each regular t

$$\mathscr{H}(\boldsymbol{\lambda}(t), \mathbf{x}(t), \mathbf{u}(t)) \ge \mathscr{H}(\boldsymbol{\lambda}(t), \mathbf{x}(t), \mathbf{v}) \qquad (\text{all } \mathbf{v})$$

or

$$0 \ge \boldsymbol{\lambda}\cdot\mathbf{f}(\mathbf{x}(t), \mathbf{v}) - \boldsymbol{\lambda}(t)\cdot\mathbf{f}(\mathbf{x}(t), \mathbf{u}(t))$$

$$0 \ge \boldsymbol{\lambda}(t)\cdot[\mathbf{f}(\mathbf{x}(t), \mathbf{v}) - \mathbf{f}(\mathbf{x}(t), \mathbf{u}(t))] \qquad (\text{all } \mathbf{v})$$

$$0 \ge \boldsymbol{\lambda}(t)\cdot\zeta, \qquad \zeta \in \mathscr{k}(t)$$

i.e., if $\mathbf{x}(t)[S]\mathscr{k}(t)$ all t. By the last lemma this is possible if $\lambda(t^1) = \mathbf{a}[S]\bar{\mathscr{K}}(t^1)$. Since $\mathscr{K}(t^1) \subseteq \bar{\mathscr{K}}(t^1)$ it is enough to have $\mathbf{a}[S]\bar{\mathscr{K}}(t^1)$.

Corollary 1. *This theorem implies the first conclusion of the maximum principle.*

PROOF. *If* $\mathbf{x}^*(t)$ *with control* $\mathbf{u}^*(t)$ *is optimal we know that the cone* $\bar{\mathscr{K}}(t^1)$ *can* not *contain the vertical (downward) segment through* $\mathbf{x}^*(t^1)$. *It is an elementary proposition that if a cone does not contain a given segment then the segment can be separated from the cone (by a hyperplane).*

Corollary 2.† *If* $\dim \bar{\mathscr{K}}(t^1) < n + 1$ *there exists* $\lambda = \lambda(t)$ *such that* $\mathscr{H}^*(t, \mathbf{u}) \triangleq \mathscr{H}(\lambda(t), \mathbf{x}^*(t), \mathbf{u}) \equiv 0$ *for all* $\mathbf{u} \in \Omega$. *In this case, since* $\mathscr{H}^*(t, \mathbf{u})$ *is constant*

$$\max_{\mathbf{u}\in\Omega} \mathscr{H}^* = \min_{\mathbf{u}\in\Omega} \mathscr{H}^* = \mathscr{M}(\lambda(t), \mathbf{x}^*(t))$$

PROOF. $\dim \bar{\mathscr{K}}(t^1) = \dim \bar{\mathscr{L}}(t^1)$. If the dimension of $\bar{\mathscr{L}} \le n$, then $\bar{\mathscr{L}}$ lies in a hyperplane *and* there will exist an $\mathbf{a} = \lambda(t^1)$ such that $\mathbf{a} \perp \bar{\mathscr{L}}$. Then, by the last lemma $\lambda(t) \perp \bar{\mathscr{L}}(t)$, and, consequently, $\mathscr{H}^*(t, \mathbf{u}) \equiv 0$ for all $\mathbf{u} \in \Omega$.

8.5 The Maximum Principle (Part II)

The result of the last section established the most quoted part of the maximum principle—which states that for an optimal solution and its control there will always exist at least one solution of the adjoint variational equations for which $\mathscr{H} = \mathscr{M}$. The most profound part of the maximum principle, however, is the fact that for this choice of λ ($\lambda = \lambda(t)$) the *maximum function is continuous.* In other words, for every optimal trajectory there is a continuously moving plane through each point of the trajectory (λ is the normal to it) such that every discontinuity in the tangent to the trajectory lies in that plane.

Here we shall follow Pontryagin by introducing a function m which lies between $\mathscr{M}$ and $\mathscr{H}$. First, we establish that m is well behaved, and then use it as the key to the properties of $\mathscr{M}$.

Definition.

$$F \triangleq \{\mathbf{u} | \mathbf{u} \in \Omega \quad \text{and} \quad \mathbf{u} = \mathbf{u}(t),\, t^0 \le t \le t^1\}$$

$$G \triangleq \bar{F} \text{ (the closure of } F)$$

$$m(\lambda, \mathbf{x}) \triangleq \max_{\mathbf{u}\in\Omega} \mathscr{H}(\lambda, \mathbf{x}, \mathbf{u})$$

Lemma. $\mathscr{M}(\lambda, \mathbf{x}) \ge m(\lambda, \mathbf{x}) \ge \mathscr{H}(\lambda, \mathbf{x}, \mathbf{u})$.

† See also Chapter 7.

Lemma. *For an optimal solution* $\mathbf{x}^*(t)$ *there exists a* $\boldsymbol{\lambda}(t)$ *such that*

$$\mathscr{M}(t) \triangleq \mathscr{M}(\boldsymbol{\lambda}(t), \mathbf{x}^*(t)) = m(\boldsymbol{\lambda}(t), \mathbf{x}^*(t) = \mathscr{H}(\boldsymbol{\lambda}(t), \mathbf{x}^*(t), \mathbf{u}^*(t)) \triangleq \mathscr{H}(t))$$

all regular t.

Lemma. *For an optimal solution* $\mathbf{x}^*(t)$ *there is a* $\boldsymbol{\lambda}(t)$ *such that* $\mathscr{M}(\boldsymbol{\lambda}(t), \mathbf{x}^*(t))$ *is lower semicontinuous.*

Lemma. *For an optimal solution* $\mathbf{x}^*(t)$ *there is a* $\boldsymbol{\lambda}(t)$ *such that* $m(\mathbf{x}^*(t), \boldsymbol{\lambda}(t))$ *is absolutely continuous and*

$$dm/dt = 0$$

Lemma. *If* $a(t)$ *is* l.s.c., $b(t)$ *continuous,* $a(t) \geq b(t)$, *and* $a(t) = b(t)$ *almost everywhere then* $a(t) \equiv b(t)$.

The proof of the first lemma is a direct consequence of the definition of m and of Theorem 3.

The proof of the second lemma follows from the first and Theorem 3.

To prove the third lemma we need merely show that given $\varepsilon > 0 \, \exists \, f(t)$ such that

$$\mathscr{M}(t) \geq f(t) \geq \mathscr{M}(t) - \varepsilon$$

Given any t' by definition $\exists$ $\mathbf{u}'$ so that

$$\mathscr{H}(\boldsymbol{\lambda}(t), \mathbf{x}^*(t'), \mathbf{u}') \geq \mathscr{M}(\boldsymbol{\lambda}(t'), \mathbf{x}^*(t')) - \varepsilon/2$$

Since $\mathscr{H}(\boldsymbol{\lambda}(t), \mathbf{x}^*(t), \mathbf{u})$ is continuous in t for $\mathbf{u}$ fixed $\exists$ $\delta(t', \varepsilon)$ such that $\mathscr{H}(\boldsymbol{\lambda}(t), \mathbf{x}^*(t), \mathbf{u}') - \mathscr{H}(\boldsymbol{\lambda}(t'), \mathbf{x}^*(t'), \mathbf{u}') < \varepsilon/2$. For $|t - t'| \leq \delta(t', \varepsilon)$

$$\mathscr{M}(\boldsymbol{\lambda}(t), \mathbf{x}^*(t)) = \sup_{\mathbf{u} \in \Omega} \mathscr{H}(\boldsymbol{\lambda}(t), \mathbf{x}^*(t), \mathbf{u}) \geq \mathscr{H}(\boldsymbol{\lambda}(t), \mathbf{x}^*(t), \mathbf{u})$$

and

$$\mathscr{H}(\boldsymbol{\lambda}(t), \mathbf{x}^*(t), \mathbf{u}) \geq \mathscr{M}(\boldsymbol{\lambda}(t'), \mathbf{x}^*(t')) - \varepsilon$$

The statement that $m(t)$ *is absolutely continuous* is equivalent to the following: Given $\varepsilon \, \exists \, \delta$ such that if $\sum_1^N \delta_i = \delta \ (\delta_i \geq 0)$ and if $|t_i - t_i'| < \delta_i$, then $\sum_1^N |m(t_i) - m(t_i')| < \varepsilon$. Since $\mathbf{x}(t)$ and $\boldsymbol{\lambda}(t)$ are absolutely continuous (i.e., are integrals of measurable functions) and

$$\mathscr{H}(\boldsymbol{\lambda}, \mathbf{x}, \mathbf{u}) = \boldsymbol{\lambda} \cdot \mathbf{f}(\mathbf{x}, \mathbf{u}), \qquad \mathscr{H} \text{ is Lipschitzian in } (\boldsymbol{\lambda}, \mathbf{x})$$

for regular points t', it follows that

$$\begin{aligned} m(t) - m(t') &\triangleq m(\boldsymbol{\lambda}(t), \mathbf{x}^*(t)) - m(\boldsymbol{\lambda}(t'), \mathbf{x}^*(t')) \\ &= \mathscr{H}(\boldsymbol{\lambda}(t), \mathbf{x}^*(t), \mathbf{u}^*(t)) - \mathscr{H}(\boldsymbol{\lambda}(t_i'), \mathbf{x}^*(t_i'), \mathbf{u}^*(t_i')) \\ &\geq \mathscr{H}(\boldsymbol{\lambda}(t), \mathbf{x}^*(t), \mathbf{u}^*(t')) - \mathscr{H}(\boldsymbol{\lambda}(t'), \mathbf{x}^*(t'), \mathbf{u}^*(t')) \\ &\geq -K\{|\boldsymbol{\lambda}(t) - \boldsymbol{\lambda}(t')| + |\mathbf{x}^*(t) - \mathbf{x}^*(t')|\} \end{aligned}$$

where K is a positive constant. Similarly,

$$m(t) - m(t') \leq \mathscr{H}(\boldsymbol{\lambda}(t), \mathbf{x}^*(t), \mathbf{u}^*(t)) - \mathscr{H}(\boldsymbol{\lambda}(t'), \mathbf{x}^*(t'), \mathbf{u}^*(t))$$
$$\leq K\{|\boldsymbol{\lambda}(t) - \boldsymbol{\lambda}(t')| + |\mathbf{x}^*(t) - \mathbf{x}^*(t')|\}$$

Thus

$$|m(t) - m(t')| \leq K\{|\boldsymbol{\lambda}(t) - \boldsymbol{\lambda}(t')| + |\mathbf{x}^*(t) - \mathbf{x}^*(t')|\}$$

and the result follows. That is, m is Lipschitzian in $\boldsymbol{\lambda}$ and $\mathbf{x}$—for the right solution $\boldsymbol{\lambda}$.

We shall now prove that $dm/dt = 0$ at regular t'. Since

$$m(\boldsymbol{\lambda}(t'), \mathbf{x}^*(t')) = \mathscr{H}(\boldsymbol{\lambda}(t'), \mathbf{x}^*(t'), \mathbf{u}^*(t'))$$

one has for *any* t

$$m(\boldsymbol{\lambda}(t), \mathbf{x}^*(t)) \geq \mathscr{H}(\boldsymbol{\lambda}(t), \mathbf{x}^*(t), \mathbf{u}^*(t'))$$

Thus, subtracting and dividing by $t - t'$ one has

$$\frac{m(t) - m(t')}{t - t'} \geq \frac{\mathscr{H}(t) - \mathscr{H}(t')}{t - t'} \qquad \text{if} \quad t > t' \qquad \text{(case i)}$$

or

$$\frac{m(t) - m(t')}{t - t'} \leq \frac{\mathscr{H}(t) - \mathscr{H}(t')}{t - t'} \qquad \text{if} \quad t < t' \qquad \text{(case ii)}$$

Let

$$(t - t')Z(t, t') \triangleq [\mathscr{H}(\boldsymbol{\lambda}(t), \mathbf{x}^*(t), \mathbf{u}^*(t)) - \mathscr{H}(\boldsymbol{\lambda}(t'), \mathbf{x}^*(t), \mathbf{u}^*(t))]$$
$$+ [\mathscr{H}(\boldsymbol{\lambda}(t'), \hat{\mathbf{x}}^*(t), \mathbf{u}^*(t)) - \mathscr{H}(\boldsymbol{\lambda}(t'), \mathbf{x}^*(t'), \mathbf{u}^*(t))]$$

Then

$$\frac{\mathscr{H}(t) - \mathscr{H}(t')}{t - t'} = Z(t, t') + \frac{\mathscr{H}(\boldsymbol{\lambda}(t'), \mathbf{x}^*(t')\, \mathbf{u}^*(t)) - \mathscr{H}(\boldsymbol{\lambda}(t'), \mathbf{x}^*(t'), \mathbf{u}^*(t'))}{t - t'}$$
$$\leq Z(t, t') \qquad \text{if} \quad t < t'$$
$$\geq Z(t, t') \qquad \text{if} \quad t > t'$$

Since $\mathscr{H}$ is differentiable in the components of $\boldsymbol{\lambda}$ and $\mathbf{f}$, and $\mathbf{f}$ is differentiable in the components of $\mathbf{x}$, and $\mathbf{x}$ is differentiable in t, we conclude that $\lim_{t \to t'} Z(t, t')$ exists. Moreover, this limit exists with $t > t'$ or $t < t'$. The resulting limit (essentially equivalent to taking the derivative of $\mathscr{H}$ assuming $\mathbf{u}$ constant) may be computed thus: Since $\mathscr{H} = \boldsymbol{\lambda} \cdot \mathbf{f}$, we have

$$\frac{d\mathscr{H}}{d\boldsymbol{\lambda}} \cdot \frac{d\boldsymbol{\lambda}}{dt} = \frac{d\boldsymbol{\lambda}}{dt} \cdot \mathbf{f}$$

$$\frac{d\mathscr{H}}{dx} \cdot \frac{dx}{dt} = \boldsymbol{\lambda} \cdot \frac{\partial \mathbf{f}}{\partial \mathbf{x}} \frac{d\mathbf{x}}{dt} \qquad \text{where} \quad \frac{\partial \mathbf{f}}{\partial \mathbf{x}} \triangleq \left[\frac{\partial \mathbf{f}_i}{\partial x_j}\right] \triangleq V$$

Then

$$\lim_{t\to t'} Z = \frac{d\mathscr{H}}{d\boldsymbol{\lambda}} \cdot \frac{d\boldsymbol{\lambda}}{dt} + \frac{d\mathscr{H}}{d\mathbf{x}} \cdot \frac{d\mathbf{x}}{dt} = \frac{d\boldsymbol{\lambda}}{dt} \cdot f + \boldsymbol{\lambda} \cdot \frac{\partial \mathbf{f}}{\partial \mathbf{x}} \frac{dx}{dt}$$

$$= -V^T\boldsymbol{\lambda} \cdot \mathbf{f} + \boldsymbol{\lambda} \cdot V\mathbf{f} = -V^T\boldsymbol{\lambda} \cdot \mathbf{f} + V^T\boldsymbol{\lambda} \cdot \mathbf{f} = 0$$

Therefore, $dm/dt \leq 0$ and $dm/dt \geq 0$. These imply $dm/dt = 0$.

Remark. $\mathbf{a}[S]\mathscr{K} \Rightarrow \mathbf{a} \cdot \mathbf{f} = 0$ since $\pm\alpha\mathbf{f} \in \mathscr{K}$ and $\mathbf{a}[S]\mathscr{K} \Rightarrow \mathbf{a} \cdot \mathbf{z} \leq 0$ for all $\mathbf{z}$. This means that $\mathbf{a} \cdot \alpha\mathbf{f} \leq 0$ and $\mathbf{a} \cdot -\alpha\mathbf{f} \leq 0$. Thus, $\mathbf{a} \cdot \mathbf{f} = 0$. Since $0 \geq \mathscr{M}(t) \geq \mathscr{H}(t)$ and $\mathscr{H}(\lambda(t'), (\mathbf{x}^*(t'), \mathbf{u}^*(t') = 0$ it follows that

$$\mathscr{M}(\boldsymbol{\lambda}(t'), \mathbf{x}^*(t')) = 0$$

8.6 The Bang-Bang Principle

The result to be derived is this:

Theorem 4. *If the control set Ω is compact and bounded by a finite number of planes, the control $\mathbf{u}^*(t)$ for an optimal solution will have all its regular points at vertices of Ω provided the nondegeneracy conditions are satisfied at every regular point of the trajectory.*

Remark. The theorem says that if at any one regular point τ, $t^0 < \tau \leq t^1$, the conditions of nondegeneracy hold, then $\mathbf{u}^*(t)$ *must* be at a vertex for *all* t which $\mathbf{x}^*(t)$ is regular.

Remark. This result removes the restriction that the system be linear, that the control set be convex, and that the cost be time.

Nondegeneracy conditions. Let $\mathbf{f}(\mathbf{x}, \mathbf{u})$ have at least $n + 3$ derivatives (possibly mixed). Let

$$A(t) \triangleq (\partial\mathbf{f}/\partial\mathbf{x}) \qquad B(t) \triangleq (\partial\mathbf{f}/\partial\mathbf{u})$$

with $\mathbf{x} = \mathbf{x}^*(t)$, $\mathbf{u} = \mathbf{u}^*(t)$. Let ζ be a vector lying in Ω or in any of its faces. Let $\zeta^0 = B\zeta$ and $\zeta^k = A\zeta^{k-1} - d/dt(\zeta^{k-1})$, $k = 1, 2, \ldots, n$. Nondegeneracy requires the linear independence of $\zeta^0, \ldots, \zeta^n$.

Lemma. If $\pm\zeta \in \mathscr{k}(t)$ *all* t *and*

$$\frac{d}{dt} W(t) = AW, \qquad \text{a constant}$$

then $\mathscr{K} = \mathscr{K}(0)$ *contains* $\pm\zeta, \pm A\zeta, \ldots, \pm A^n\zeta$.

PROOF. For any ε there is a t_ε such that if $|t| < t_\varepsilon$ the difference between $(I + tA)\zeta$ and $(\sum_0^\infty (t^n A^n/n!))\ \zeta$ is less than $\boldsymbol{\varepsilon}t$, where $|\boldsymbol{\varepsilon}| \leq \varepsilon$. Thus, the difference $\zeta - W(t)\zeta$ can be written as $\zeta - (I + tA)\zeta + \boldsymbol{\varepsilon}t = tA\zeta + \boldsymbol{\varepsilon}t = t(A\boldsymbol{\varepsilon} + \boldsymbol{\varepsilon})$. When normalized to a unit vector this becomes $A\zeta + \boldsymbol{\varepsilon}$.

Because $W(t, t^0) = W(t - t^0)$ it follows that if a vector ζ in the cone at t^0 is transported to $t_0 + t$, it is at that point just $W(t)\zeta$. Therefore, the value at $t = 0$ of the control vector $\pm\zeta$ applied at time $-t$ is $\pm W(t)\zeta$. When this effect is added to $\mathscr{k}(0)$ determined by $\pm\zeta$, one has $A\zeta + \boldsymbol{\varepsilon}(t)$ and as $\varepsilon \to 0$ this is $A\zeta$. Thus the cone at $t = 0$ certainly includes $\pm\boldsymbol{\varepsilon}$ and $\pm A\zeta$.

A repetition of this argument establishes the lemma: By the above argument the cone at every point must contain both $\pm\zeta$ and $\pm A\zeta$ since the conditions at $t = 0$ are invariant under translation. Now, apply this argument to $\pm A\zeta$ (instead of ζ) and this implies that $\pm A^2\zeta$ is also in the cone at each point, etc.

Lemma. *If* $\pm\zeta \in \mathscr{k}(t)$ *all* t *and*

$$dW/dt = A(t)W \qquad (A(t) \text{ continuous})$$

then $\mathscr{K}(t)$ *contains* $\pm\zeta,\ \pm A(t)\zeta,\ \ldots,\ \pm A^n(t)\zeta$.

PROOF. Continuity of $A(t)$ implies that $W(t)\zeta = (I + tA(0) + t\varepsilon)\zeta$ where $\varepsilon \to 0$ as $t \to 0$. The last argument implies then that $\mathscr{k}(t)$ must contain both ζ and $A(t)\zeta$.

Lemma. *If* $\pm\zeta(t) \in \mathscr{k}(t)$ *and*

$$dW/dt = A(t)W$$

then $\mathscr{K}(t)$ *contains* $\zeta(t)$ and $A(t)\zeta(t) - \zeta'(t)$, *where* $\zeta'(t) = d\zeta(t)/dt$.

PROOF. Since

$$\begin{aligned} W(0, -t)\zeta(-t) &= \left\{I + \int_{-t}^{0} A(\tau)\, d\tau + \varepsilon t\right\}\zeta(-t) \\ &= \{I + tA(0) + \varepsilon t\}\{\zeta(0) - t\zeta'(0) + \boldsymbol{\varepsilon}t\} \\ &= \zeta(0) + t(A(0)\zeta - \zeta'(0)) + \boldsymbol{\varepsilon}t \end{aligned}$$

it follows that

$$\zeta(0) = W(0, -t)\zeta(-t) = -t[A(0)\zeta - \zeta'(0)] + \boldsymbol{\varepsilon}t$$

Normalizing and taking limits one has that $\mathscr{K}(0)$ contains $\pm(A(0)\zeta(0) - \zeta'(0))$.

Lemma. *If* $\pm\zeta(t) \in k(t)$ *and*

$$dW/dt = A(t)W$$

then $k(t)$ *contains*

$$\begin{aligned} &\zeta^0(t), \zeta^1(t), \ldots, \zeta^m(t) && \text{where} \quad \zeta^0 = \zeta \\ &\zeta^s(t) = A(t)\zeta^{s-1}(t) - \zeta'^{s-1}(t) && \text{for} \quad s = 1,2, \ldots, m \end{aligned}$$

PROOF. This result is obtained by iterating the statement of the last lemma.

The proof of the general bang-bang result now follows from the observations that if τ is a regular point with $\mathbf{u}^*(\tau)$ in the interior of Ω at which the nondegeneracy conditions are satisfied, there will be a set of positive measures whose closure includes τ for which the above lemmas hold. This would therefore imply that the cone at τ had dimension $n + 1$. The impossibility of this for optimal solutions implies thus that any regular point must be on the boundary of Ω. This argument does *not* use the dimensionality of Ω in any way. Let Σ be a face Ω. If $\mathbf{u}^*(\tau)$ is an interior point of Σ the same argument gives some vector $\pm\zeta \in \Sigma$. The nondegeneracy conditions, again, lead to a contradiction. Hence, if $\mathbf{u}^*(\tau)$ is on Σ it must be on a face of Σ. This keeps up until one runs out of dimensions—i.e., is at a vertex. From the above arguments it follows that, if there is an interior point in the control set and if the nondegeneracy condition holds at that point, then $\mathscr{K} = \mathscr{L}$ and dim $\mathscr{L} = n + 1$; however, if dim $\mathscr{L} = n + 1$ the trajectory cannot be optimal. This contradiction proves the theorem for it establishes that if the nondegeneracy condition holds at one regular point then the control must be bang-bang there.

Professor Gamkrelidze has pointed out to us that requiring the nondegeneracy condition at only one point is insufficient; it may happen that $\mathbf{f}(\mathbf{x}, \mathbf{u})$ is independent of $\mathbf{u}$ on some interval of time. There are extensions of the above result which relate all conditions to one point. These follow by applying the last lemma not only to $\zeta(t) = B\zeta^0$ but also to $W(t, t')\zeta(t')$.

REFERENCE

1. L. S. Pontryagin, V. G. Boltyanskii, R. V. Gamkrelidze, and E. F. Mishchenko, "The Mathematical Theory of Optimal Processes" (K. N. Trirogoff, transl.; L. W. Neustadt, ed.), Wiley (Interscience), New York, 1962.

9

Synthesis of Optimal Controls

BERNARD PAIEWONSKY
INSTITUTE FOR DEFENSE ANALYSES,
ARLINGTON, VIRGINIA

9.0 Introduction

Optimization problems for linear systems with bounded controls are generally easy to formulate using the maximum principle but from a computational standpoint they are often difficult to solve. Many ideas have been put forward for synthesizing minimum time and minimum effort controllers for linear systems but only a few of these have proved successful when applied to actual computation. Algorithms for synthesizing minimum time and minimum effort controllers have been developed by Neustadt[1-3] and these algorithms do provide convergent iterative procedures for solving the two-point boundary value problems associated with the optimization. The best accounts of Neustadt's methods for the time-optimal control problem and the minimum-effort control problem are found in Neustadt's original papers. These papers are clearly written and combine a lucid presentation with a high standard of mathematical rigor and precision.

The purpose of this chapter is to present an introductory account of these optimal control synthesis ideas together with some examples of engineering applications and computational techniques.

There have been other investigations along the general mathematical lines followed by Neustadt. Krasovskii[4] and Gamkrelidze[5] independently derived synthesis procedures for time-optimal problems similar in some respects to Neustadt's. Results of Russian computational studies along these lines have not yet appeared in publication. Eaton[6] has also investigated a synthesis procedure based on similar geometrical ideas but again no computational results are available. Fadden and Gilbert[7] have applied Neustadt's method to the time-optimal regulation of the system $\ddot{x} = u$ ($|u| \leq 1$) and have made numerical studies of the convergence of the iterations.

9.1 Neustadt's Synthesis Method

The synthesis method described here was developed by Neustadt for the time-optimal problem with bounded controls and was later extended to include time-optimal systems with control effort constraints as well as minimum effort controllers. The time-optimal control problem will be discussed in detail first; the extension to systems with effort constraints will be taken up afterward.

9.11 Time-Optimal Control

Let us suppose that we want to control a system governed by linear differential equations with variable coefficients of the form:

$$\dot{\mathbf{x}}(t) = A(t)\mathbf{x}(t) + B(t)\mathbf{u}(t) \tag{9.1}$$

In this equation $\mathbf{x}$, and n-vector, is the state of the system at time t, $\mathbf{u}$ is an m-vector of control variables, A is an $(n \times n)$ matrix, and B is an $(n \times m)$ matrix. Suppose also that we are given the initial conditions $\mathbf{x}(0) = \mathbf{x}^0$. We want to determine $\mathbf{u}(t)$ on the interval $[0, t^*]$ such that t^* is the smallest value of t for which $\mathbf{x}(t^*) = 0$. Neustadt treats the case where the system is to be transferred fom $\mathbf{x}^0$ to $\mathbf{x}^1$ but in this section we will discuss only the case of $\mathbf{x}^1 = 0$.

The control vector function $\mathbf{u}(t)$ is assumed to be piecewise continuous and the values of $\mathbf{u}(t)$ are required to lie in a set Ω. This set is closed, bounded, and convex and contains the origin as an interior point. Any $\mathbf{u}(t)$ satisfying these conditions is called an admissible control function.

To find the optimal control we introduce the adjoint variables $\lambda_i(t)$ ($i = 0, \ldots, n$), form the Hamiltonian†

$$\mathscr{H} = \sum_{ijk} \lambda_i(A_{ij}x_j + B_{jk}u_k) + \lambda_0 \tag{9.2}$$

† The elements of matrices A and B are denoted by A_{ij} and B_{jk}, respectively; A_{ij}^T denotes an element of A^T, the transpose of A.

and maximize it over all admissible $\mathbf{u}$. The adjoint variables satisfy the differential equations

$$\dot{\lambda}_i = -\frac{\partial \mathscr{H}}{\partial x_i} = -A_{ij}^T \lambda_j \qquad (i = 1, \ldots, n)$$
$$\dot{\lambda}_0 = 0 \tag{9.3}$$

The solutions of the adjoint equations can be found in terms of the inverse of the fundamental solution matrix to the system (9.1). The matrix $\mathrm{X}^{-1}(t)$ satisfies the differential equation:

$$\frac{d}{dt}\mathrm{X}^{-1} = -\mathrm{X}^{-1}A \qquad (\mathrm{X}^{-1}(0) = I) \tag{9.4}$$

We may write

$$\boldsymbol{\lambda}(t) = -[\mathrm{X}^{-1}]^T \boldsymbol{\eta} \tag{9.5}$$

with $\lambda_i(0) = -\eta_i$. The relation between the optimal control and the adjoint comes from the maximization condition:

$$\max_{\mathbf{u}\in\Omega} \mathscr{H} = \max_{\mathbf{u}\in\Omega} \sum_{i=1}^{n} \sum_{k=1}^{m} \lambda_i B_{ik} u_k$$

It is assumed that for almost every t a unique maximum exists. In the time-optimal bang-bang problem this is LaSalle's normality condition.[8]

The optimal control law obtained from the maximum principle contains $(n - 1)$ parameters. These are the $(n - 1)$ independent initial conditions for the homogeneous system of adjoint differential equations.

The problem now is to find the initial conditions $\lambda_i(0) = -\eta_i$ for the adjoint variables so that the system (9.1) goes from the initial state to the final state when the control $\mathbf{u}^*(t, \boldsymbol{\eta})$ derived from the maximum principle is applied.

The solution of the system (9.1) can be written as

$$\mathbf{x}(t) = \mathrm{X}(t)\left[\mathbf{x}(0) + \int_0^t \mathrm{X}^{-1}(\tau)B(\tau)\mathbf{u}(\tau, \boldsymbol{\eta})\, d\tau\right] \tag{9.6}$$

where $\mathrm{X}(t)$ is the fundamental solution matrix of (9.1). Let the desired final state, $\mathbf{x}(T)$, be the origin. The set $C(t)$, $t \geq 0$, consisting of the set of points swept out by the vectors

$$\mathbf{z}(t) = -\int_0^t \mathrm{X}^{-1}(\tau)B(\tau)\mathbf{u}(\tau)\, d\tau \tag{9.7}$$

for a given positive t and for all admissible $\mathbf{u}$ is called the reachable set with respect to the origin. This set contains all points from which the origin can be reached within time t. The boundary of $C(t)$ for each t is an optimal isochrone. The conditions that Ω be compact and convex insure that $C(t)$ will be closed, bounded, and convex. Furthermore, if $t < t'$ then $C(t)$ is contained in $C(t')$. The normal to the support plane or tangent plane at a point of the boundary of $C(t)$ is the vector $\boldsymbol{\eta}$, i.e., the initial condition for the adjoint. The function

$$\mathbf{z}(t, \boldsymbol{\eta}) = -\int_0^t X^{-1}(\tau)B(\tau)\mathbf{u}(\tau, \boldsymbol{\eta})\, d\tau \tag{9.8}$$

for any $\boldsymbol{\eta} \neq 0$ and $t > 0$ is a mapping of vectors $\boldsymbol{\eta}$ into vectors $\mathbf{z}(t, \boldsymbol{\eta})$. This function generates the boundary of $C(t)$ for a given $t > 0$.

We begin an iterative search for the optimal $\boldsymbol{\eta}$ by guessing the slope of the support plane at $\mathbf{x}(0)$, i.e., guessing a starting value for $\boldsymbol{\eta}$ (call it $\boldsymbol{\eta}^1$). In computational studies it may be convenient to use a unit vector parallel to $\mathbf{x}(0)$ as a starting value for $\boldsymbol{\eta}$ ($\boldsymbol{\eta}^1 = -\mathbf{x}(0)/|\mathbf{x}(0)|$ if no better information is available).

The key to understanding the geometrical significance of the various steps involved in this method is found in the theory of convex sets. We generate the vector $\mathbf{z}(t, \boldsymbol{\eta}^i)$ as a function of t and we seek the point where this curve crosses the trial support plane with normal $\boldsymbol{\eta}^i$ through $\mathbf{x}(0)$.

This is shown in Fig. 1(a). More specifically, we seek the time when $\boldsymbol{\eta}^i\cdot[\mathbf{z}(t, \boldsymbol{\eta}^i) - \mathbf{x}(0)] = 0$. This time is called $F(\boldsymbol{\eta}^i)$, i.e., $\boldsymbol{\eta}^i\cdot[\mathbf{z}(F(\boldsymbol{\eta}^i), \boldsymbol{\eta}^i) - \mathbf{x}(0)] = 0$. Let $f(t, \boldsymbol{\eta})$ denote the function $\boldsymbol{\eta}\cdot[\mathbf{z}(t, \boldsymbol{\eta}) - \mathbf{x}(0)]$. This relationship can be rewritten as $f(F(\boldsymbol{\eta}), \boldsymbol{\eta}) = 0$.

The scalar product $\boldsymbol{\eta}^i\cdot[\mathbf{z}(t, \boldsymbol{\eta}^i) - \mathbf{x}(0)]$ is a monotonic increasing function of time. It starts from a negative value $\mathbf{n}^i\cdot(-\mathbf{x}(0))$ and vanishes when $\mathbf{z}(t, \boldsymbol{\eta}^i)$ crosses the hyperplane through $\mathbf{x}(0)$ with normal $\boldsymbol{\eta}^i$. The location of this point on the hyperplane is also shown in Fig. 1(a). This $\boldsymbol{\eta}^i$ is optimal for the point $\mathbf{z}[F(\boldsymbol{\eta}^i), \boldsymbol{\eta}^i]$, so $\boldsymbol{\eta}^i$ is the normal to the boundary of $C[F(\boldsymbol{\eta}^i)]$ at the point $\mathbf{z}[F(\boldsymbol{\eta}^i), \boldsymbol{\eta}^i]$. The time $F(\boldsymbol{\eta}^i)$ is less than the optimal time t^* because $C[F(\boldsymbol{\eta}^i)]$ is contained in $C(t^*)$.

The justification for these assertions depends on the convexity of $C(t)$. We see that $\mathbf{x}(0)$ lies on the boundary of the set $C(t^*)$. The convexity of $C[F(\boldsymbol{\eta}^i)]$ assures us that $\boldsymbol{\eta}^i\cdot\mathbf{z}[F(\boldsymbol{\eta}^i), \boldsymbol{\eta}^i] > \boldsymbol{\eta}^i\cdot\mathbf{y}$ for all vectors $\mathbf{y}$, $\mathbf{y} \neq \mathbf{z}[F(\boldsymbol{\eta}^i), \boldsymbol{\eta}^i]$, in $C[F(\boldsymbol{\eta}^i)]$. This is easy to see by looking at the projection of $\mathbf{z}[F(\boldsymbol{\eta}^i), \boldsymbol{\eta}^i]$ onto the normal to the hyperplane as shown in Fig. 1. But $\boldsymbol{\eta}^i\cdot\mathbf{x}(0) = \boldsymbol{\eta}^i\cdot\mathbf{z}[F(\boldsymbol{\eta}^i), \boldsymbol{\eta}^i]$ by definition of $F(\boldsymbol{\eta}^i)$. Therefore, $\mathbf{x}(0)$ is not in $C[F(\boldsymbol{\eta}^i)]$ but lies outside it and the optimal time t^* is greater than $F(\boldsymbol{\eta}^i)$ unless $\mathbf{z}[F(\boldsymbol{\eta}^i), \boldsymbol{\eta}^i] = \mathbf{x}(0)$; in that case $F(\boldsymbol{\eta}^i) = t^*$. This means that $F(\boldsymbol{\eta})$ is maximized when $\mathbf{z}[F(\boldsymbol{\eta}), \boldsymbol{\eta}] = \mathbf{x}(0)$.

The two-point boundary-value problem is now transformed into the problem of locating the maximum value of a function of several variables.

The goal of this iterative method is to find the $\boldsymbol{\eta}$ that maximizes $F(\boldsymbol{\eta})$. This vector, $\boldsymbol{\eta}^*$, causes the boundary conditions to be satisfied when $\mathbf{u}^*(t, \boldsymbol{\eta}^*)$ is applied to the system (9.1). It is important to note that it is the location of the maximum value of $F(\boldsymbol{\eta})$ which determines the optimal control. The

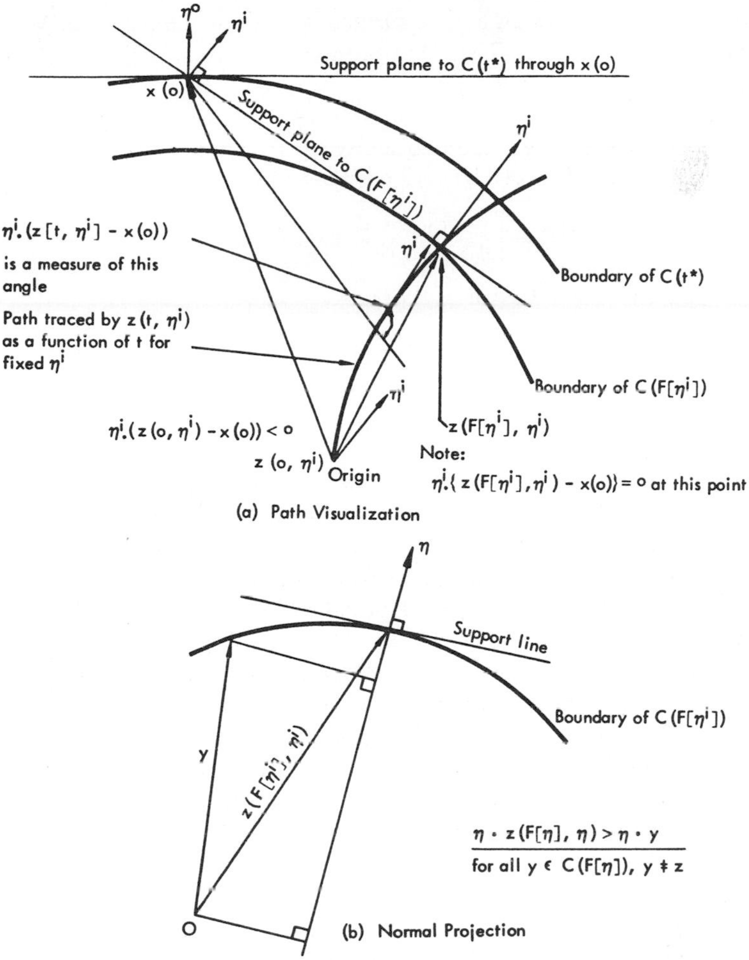

FIG. 1. Geometrical aspects of Neustadt's method.

maximum value itself is not used in the solution of the two-point boundary-value problem.

Neustadt has shown, in the references cited, that $\mathbf{z}(t, \boldsymbol{\eta})$ is a continuous function of $\boldsymbol{\eta}$, and the gradient of the function being maximized, $\nabla F(\boldsymbol{\eta}^i)$, lies along the error vector $\mathbf{z}[F(\boldsymbol{\eta}^i), \boldsymbol{\eta}^i] - \mathbf{x}(0)$. This result is the key to the practical application of steep ascent methods in maximizing $F(\boldsymbol{\eta})$.

Example 1. Here is a concrete example which will illustrate the method. Consider the second order system:

$$\dot{x}_1 = x_2 \qquad \dot{x}_2 = u \qquad (|u| \leq 1)$$

Suppose we want to design a time optimal regulator, i.e., $\mathbf{x}^1 = 0$. We apply the maximum principle. The Hamiltonian is: $\mathscr{H} = \lambda_1 x_2 + \lambda_2 u + 1$. The optimal control is: $u^* = \operatorname{sgn} \lambda_2$.

The adjoint equations $\dot{\lambda}_1 = 0$, $\dot{\lambda}_2 = -\lambda_1$ are easily integrated to give $\lambda_1 = -\eta_1$, $\lambda_2 = -\eta_2 + \eta_1 t$. Consequently $u^* = \operatorname{sgn}(\eta_1 t - \eta_2)$.

The matrices $\mathrm{X}(t)$ and $\mathrm{X}^{-1}(t)$ are easily found:

$$\mathrm{X}(t) = \begin{bmatrix} 1 & t \\ 0 & 1 \end{bmatrix}, \qquad \mathrm{X}^{-1}(t) = \begin{bmatrix} 1 & -t \\ 0 & 1 \end{bmatrix}$$

The components of $\mathbf{z}(t, \boldsymbol{\eta})$ are

$$\mathrm{Z}_1(t, \boldsymbol{\eta}) = \int_0^t -\tau \operatorname{sgn}(\eta_1 \tau - \eta_2)\, d\tau$$

$$\mathrm{Z}_2(t, \boldsymbol{\eta}) = \int_0^t \operatorname{sgn}(\eta_1 \tau - \eta_2)\, d\tau$$

The boundaries of $C(t)$ (optimal isochrones) corresponding to four values of t are shown in Fig. 2. The isochronal curves in this example have sharp corners at the switching curves and the $\boldsymbol{\eta}$ vectors are not unique at these points.† To examine what takes place when we apply Neustadt's method, let us focus our attention on a typical initial point, $\mathbf{x}(0)$, shown in the upper right hand portion of the figure. The first trial value $\boldsymbol{\eta}^1$ is taken opposite $\mathbf{x}(0)$ and a piece of the trial support plane normal to $\boldsymbol{\eta}^1$ is shown passing through $\mathbf{x}(0)$. The path traced by the function $\mathbf{z}(t, \boldsymbol{\eta}^1)$ is shown by the dashed line beginning at the origin, coinciding with the upper branch of the switching curve for a short time and then reversing direction and intersecting the plane normal to $\boldsymbol{\eta}^1$ when $f(t, \eta^1) = 0$. The gradient of $F(\boldsymbol{\eta}^1)$ lies along the line $\mathbf{z}(F(\boldsymbol{\eta}^1), \boldsymbol{\eta}^1) - \mathbf{x}(0)$, and a small change in $\boldsymbol{\eta}$ taken in this direction will rotate $\boldsymbol{\eta}^2$ to the left and reduce the inclination of the trial support plane for the next iteration.

The eighth and ninth trials using steepest ascent also appear in the figure and it can be seen that relatively small changes in the slope of supporting hyperplane produces relatively large changes in the error vector $\mathbf{z}(F(\boldsymbol{\eta}), \boldsymbol{\eta}) - \mathbf{x}(0)$. This is due in part to the small curvature of the isochrones in the vicinity of the initial point.

The numerical aspects of the iterations such as the number of trials to obtain satisfactory results will be discussed in more detail later on in connection with another example.

Remark. A digital computer study of a simplified rocket steering problem using the equations

$$\dot{x}_1 = \frac{\beta c_0}{m - \beta t} \cos \alpha, \qquad \dot{x}_2 = x_3, \qquad \dot{x}_3 = \frac{\beta c_0 \sin \alpha}{m - \beta t} - g \tag{9.9}$$

† See also Chapter 7.

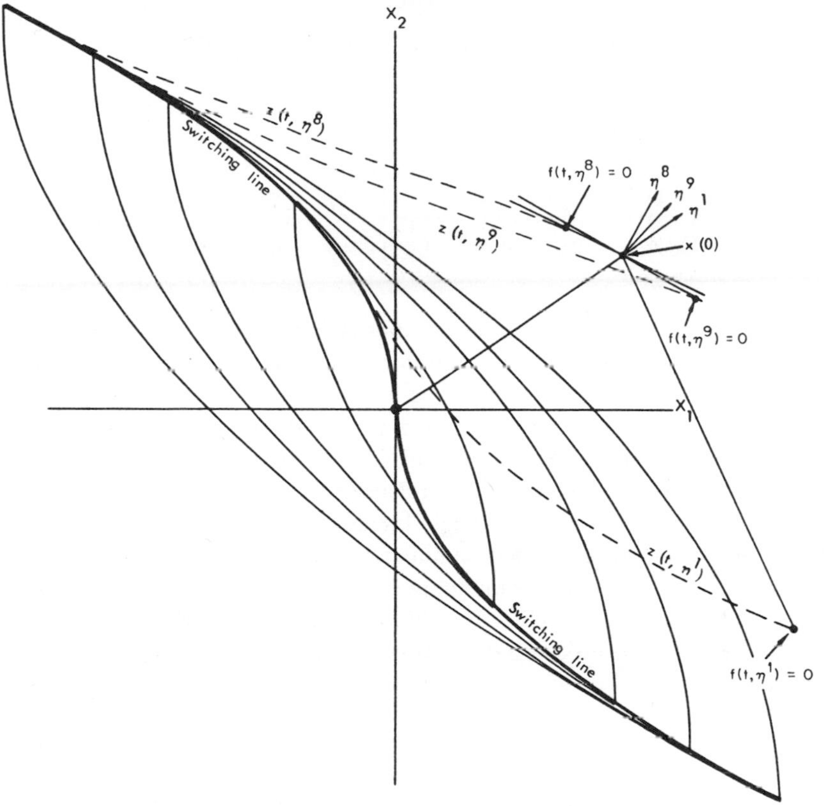

FIG. 2. Optimal isochrones, $\dot{x}_1 = \dot{x}_2$, $x_2 = u(t)$.

pointed out certain aspects of the problem which had not been fully appreciated at the start. The function $F(\boldsymbol{\eta})$ was a very flat function of $\boldsymbol{\eta}$. The optimum step size could not be found satisfactorily by comparing values of $F(\boldsymbol{\eta})$.

Table I (from Paiewonsky *et al.*[9a,b]) shows the insensitivity of $F(\boldsymbol{\eta})$ to small changes in $\boldsymbol{\eta}$. The error vector $\mathbf{z}(F(\boldsymbol{\eta}), \boldsymbol{\eta}) - \mathbf{x}^0$, however, is a very sensitive function of $\boldsymbol{\eta}$, and Table I also shows how this varied in a particular instance.

These digital computer studies[9a] showed that a significant reduction in computation time was possible by integrating the $\mathbf{z}(t, \boldsymbol{\eta})$ equations in advance and avoiding numerical integration. In general, however, it is not possible to evaluate the integrals explicitly and the problem of the growth of numerical integration errors must be faced.

Powell's method worked very well here but the details are omitted (see Paiewonsky[9a]) because Example 2 provides a more comprehensive comparison of several methods used for accelerating steep ascent.

TABLE I

TYPICAL VALUES OF $F(\eta)$ AND $|\mathbf{z}(F(\eta), \eta) - \mathbf{x}(0)|$

η_1	η_2	η_3	$F(\eta)$	$\lvert\mathbf{z} - \mathbf{x}(0)\rvert$
0.54580027	0.01316405	1.0729829	148.56863	22,700
0.54580027	0.01316405	1.0729839	148.56906	52,705
0.54580027	0.01316405	1.0734830	148.56824	7,410
0.54580027	0.01314405	1.0734830	148.56763	121,610

Hybrid analog-digital computer studies (Paiewonsky *et al.*[10]) showed that it is entirely feasible to carry out the iterations using simplified step selection procedures. The computation time can be made quite short by proper scaling but the accuracy of the computation is poorer than in the digital studies. In these examples time scales of 320 and 3200 times real time were used with typical run times of 500 and 50 ms, respectively. Convergence was obtained, in typical cases, in less than 20 trials including 7 steps; the time was 15 sec. Higher speed operation yielded similar results in 1.5 sec. The upper limit on time scale is due to the particular capacitors on the integrators. Special purpose analog computers could undoubtedly operate in swifter modes.

It makes sense to talk about iteration convergence time only when some measure of terminal error is prescribed and there is a preassigned threshold of acceptance for terminal errors. The digital computer iterations were terminated whenever the system terminal errors were within one part in 5000 of the specified end conditions. The hybrid analog-digital computer used a criterion which ranged between 1 part in 50 and 1 part in 200. This accuracy can be improved by rescaling and using digital techniques for selecting the step size.

9.12 Time-Optimal Control with Effort Constraints

We have so far discussed only the time-optimal control problem for linear systems with bounded controls. Many engineering problems, however, require consideration of a different type of constraint on the controls. These constraints are due to controls which depend on the storage or accumulation of required commodities. For example, systems depending upon controls which act by the expulsion of mass are clearly limited by the total amount of expellant carried along. The expelled mass may be accelerated by a mechanism which depends on a supply of stored energy. Separately powered rockets (e.g., ion rockets) require a source of electrical power and a supply of propellant, and there will be two constraints to examine. Chemical rockets, on the other hand, supply their own energy for the expulsion of the propellant and only a constraint on the total propellant mass may appear. The limitations on the systems as just described can be concisely expressed as follows:

$$E(\mathbf{u}(t)) = \int_0^t \varphi(\mathbf{u})\, dt \leq M \tag{9.10}$$

The functional $E(\mathbf{u}(t))$ is called the control effort and $\varphi(\mathbf{u})$ is called the effort function. There may be more than one effort function appearing in the problem.

We now ask for an admissible control which transfers the system from an initial state point to a terminal state point in the least time, and has the property that $E(\mathbf{u}(t)) \leq M$. The constant M represents an assigned storage limit of the general type just described. It is important to keep in mind that these effort constraints are quite different from restrictions or bounds on the state variables. Constraints on the state variables are more difficult to handle and they will not be treated here at all.

The synthesis of time optimal controllers for systems with effort constraints follows the general path described in Sec. 9.11. The notion of the reachable sets $C(t)$ in n-space is modified to include the control effort as coordinate $n + 1$. The additional component to the adjoint will be η_{n+1} ($\eta_{n+1} > 0$). The Hamiltonian for this problem contains terms dependent on the control effort:

$$\mathscr{H} = \boldsymbol{\lambda} \cdot (A\mathbf{x} + B\mathbf{u}) + \boldsymbol{\eta}_{n+1}\varphi(\mathbf{u}) + \lambda_0$$

Define $\tilde{C}(t)$ as the set swept out by vectors

$$\tilde{\mathbf{z}}(t, \boldsymbol{\eta}) = \left\{\int_0^t X^{-1}(\tau)B(\tau)\mathbf{u}(\tau)\, d\tau,\ \int_0^t \varphi(\mathbf{u}(t))\, d\tau\right\} \tag{9.11}$$

for all admissible controls ($\mathbf{u} \in \Omega$). The system can be brought to the origin from any point $\tilde{\mathbf{x}} = (x_1, \ldots, x_n, x_{n+1})$ in $\tilde{C}(t)$ by an admissible control with effort x_{n+1}. The reachable sets are nested as before:

$$\tilde{C}(t') \supset \tilde{C}(t) \qquad \text{if} \quad t' > t$$

We again assume that Ω is closed, convex, and contains the origin as an interior point. We do not need to assume that Ω is bounded. This allows us to remove the constraint on the control magnitude and to treat certain idealized physical problems with impulsive controls.

Neustadt's derivations[2,3] show that two further assumptions on A, B, φ, and Ω are needed. First, we assume that $\tilde{C}(t)$ is closed and convex for every $t \geq 0$ and furthermore, if $\tilde{\mathbf{x}} \in \tilde{C}(\tau)$ for all $\tau > t$, then $\tilde{\mathbf{x}} \in \tilde{C}(t)$. Second, we required a generalized unique maximum condition to be satisfied. It is assumed that $\boldsymbol{\lambda}(t, \boldsymbol{\eta})\cdot B\mathbf{u} + \eta_{n+1}\varphi(\mathbf{u}, (t, \boldsymbol{\eta}))$ has a unique maximum in Ω for almost every t, $0 \leq t < \infty$. The function $\varphi(\mathbf{u})$ vanishes at the origin and Ω contains the origin so the maximum is nonnegative.

Neustadt's results show that if the above conditions are satisfied and if there is an admissible control which satisfies the effort constraint and which also brings the system from $\mathbf{x}^0$ to the origin, then there is a unique time optimal control $\mathbf{u}^*(t, \boldsymbol{\eta})$ and $\boldsymbol{\eta}$ is any vector which maximizes $\hat{F}(\tilde{\boldsymbol{\eta}}, \mathbf{x}^0)$. This function is the smallest value of t for which $\hat{f}(t, \boldsymbol{\eta}, \mathbf{x}^0)$ vanishes, where

$$\hat{f}(t, \tilde{\boldsymbol{\eta}}, \mathbf{x}^0) = \boldsymbol{\eta} \cdot [(\mathbf{z}(t, \boldsymbol{\eta}) - \mathbf{x}^0] + \eta_{n+1}(z_{n+1} - M)$$

The computation of the optimal $\tilde{\boldsymbol{\eta}}$ may be a little more complicated in this case because of the nonlinear maximization which occurs in the application of maximum principle, and also because of possible discontinuities in $\hat{F}(\tilde{\boldsymbol{\eta}}, \mathbf{x}^0)$.

If there is an optimal control which satisfies the conditions of the problem and if the effort is less than the maximum allowed then the solution is clearly the same as the corresponding time optimal control without the constraint. As the boundary conditions are changed to make them more difficult to satisfy or as the allowed control effort is reduced in magnitude the problem will resemble a classical isoperimetric problem with an equality constraint of the form $\int \varphi(\mathbf{u})\, dt = M$.

9.13 Minimum Effort Control

There is a third optimization problem, closely related to the time-optimal problem with an effort constraint. They are, in effect, dual problems. We are given a time $T > 0$. We seek to find an admissible control $\mathbf{u}(t)$ which transfers the system (9.1) from $\mathbf{x}^0$ to the origin in time T, and minimizes the control effort $\int \varphi(\mathbf{u})\, dt$. Assume as before in Sec. 9.12 that Ω is closed and convex, $\tilde{C}(T)$ is closed and convex, $\varphi(\mathbf{u})$ is continuous and bounded from below on Ω, and the generalized unique maximum condition is satisfied. We also assume that there is an admissible control which will transfer $\mathbf{x}^0$ to the origin in time T and, furthermore, there is more than one possible value for the control effort so that the minimization is not trivial.

Neustadt has proved that if the foregoing conditions are met then there is a unique minimum effort control $\hat{\mathbf{u}}(t, \tilde{\boldsymbol{\eta}})$ where $\tilde{\boldsymbol{\eta}} = (\boldsymbol{\eta}, -1)$, and $\boldsymbol{\lambda}(t, \boldsymbol{\eta})$ is the solution of the adjoint equation with $\boldsymbol{\lambda}(0) = -\boldsymbol{\eta}$, and $\boldsymbol{\eta}$ is any vector which maximizes the function $\boldsymbol{\eta} \cdot \mathbf{x}(0) - \tilde{\boldsymbol{\eta}}\tilde{\mathbf{z}}(T, \tilde{\boldsymbol{\eta}})$. In the expression above $\tilde{\mathbf{z}} = \mathbf{z} + z_{n+1}$ where $z_{n+1}(T, \boldsymbol{\eta}) = \int_0^T \cdot \varphi[\mathbf{u}(t, \boldsymbol{\eta})]\, dt$. The maximum of $-\boldsymbol{\eta} \cdot \mathbf{z}(\tau, \eta)$ is the minimum effort $\left(\int_0^T \varphi(u(t, \tilde{\boldsymbol{\eta}})\, dt\right)$.

The computation of the optimal control in this case is actually the most direct of the three. As before, an iteration procedure based on steepest ascent can be used. Neustadt[3] shows that the gradient of $[-\tilde{\boldsymbol{\eta}}\cdot\tilde{\mathbf{z}}(T, \boldsymbol{\eta})] = -\tilde{\mathbf{z}}(T, \tilde{\boldsymbol{\eta}})$ (n components).

Furthermore,†

$$z_i(T, \boldsymbol{\eta}) = \sum_j X_{ij}^{-1}(T)x_j(T, \boldsymbol{\eta}) \qquad (i = 1, \dots, n)$$

where $\mathbf{x}(t, \boldsymbol{\eta})$ is the solution of the system (9.1) with $\mathbf{u}(t) = \mathbf{u}^*(t, \tilde{\boldsymbol{\eta}})$.

9.2 Computational Considerations

We have seen that Neustadt's synthesis procedures for the three optimal control problems require the solution of an ordinary maximization problem in each case. In fact the successful application of Neustadt's method depends almost entirely on being able to accurately locate the maximum point with a reasonable amount of computation.

In this section we discuss some methods which can be used and we shall also present examples and results of computational studies.

It was pointed out in Sect. 9.1 that the gradient of the function being maximized lies along the error-vector $\mathbf{z}(F(\boldsymbol{\eta}), \boldsymbol{\eta}) - \mathbf{x}(0)$. This function can easily be computed and it should come as no surprise that we attempt to use the gradient in a hill-climbing routine.

The terms "gradient method" and "steep ascent method" as used here apply to maximization techniques which take successive steps in directions obtained by linear transformations of the local gradient vector. The method of steepest ascent is the special case wherein steps are always taken in the direction of the local gradient vector. It is well known that the convergence of steep ascent iterations can be slow and, because of this, special techniques have been developed to speed up the rate of convergence and eliminate time consuming oscillations. These accelerated gradient methods determine the direction of successive steps from observations of the gradient vectors at several points instead of using only the local gradient.

Suppose we want to maximize a given function of n variables, $F(\mathbf{x})$. We make an initial guess at the solution and at the kth step the algorithm determines a vector $\mathbf{g}^k$ (the step direction) and a real number h^k (the step size). The $(k+1)$st point in the iteration is $\mathbf{x}^{k+1} = \mathbf{x}^k + h^k\mathbf{g}^k$.

The variations of the steep ascent idea differ according to the rules used to generate the step size h^k and the direction of the step $\mathbf{g}^k$. One rule for choosing the step size is simply to make it a constant. This rule is easy to apply but it may lead to difficulties in obtaining convergent iterations.

As successive steps are taken in a given direction, say in the direction of ∇F, the values of $F(\mathbf{x})$ (in that direction) will increase initially but may begin

† The elements of matrix X^{-1} are denoted by X_{ij}^{-1}.

to decrease again for a large enough step away from the initial point. The step $(h^k)^*$ corresponding to the point where the rate of change of $F(\mathbf{x})$ along the line of march vanishes is called the optimum step. That is, the optimum step occurs at the first local maximum along a line whose direction is specified by the rule of the gradient method being used. An obvious way to compute the optimum step is to search for it. Select a small quantity δh and successively compute F in the direction given by $\mathbf{g}^k$ at the points

$$\mathbf{x}^k + \delta h\, \mathbf{g}^k, \quad \mathbf{x}^k + 2\delta h\, \mathbf{g}^k, \cdots$$

Sooner or later F will decrease; if this happens at the point $\mathbf{x}^k + m\, \delta h\, \mathbf{g}^k$, go one step back and halve δh and try the point $\mathbf{x}^k + (m - \frac{1}{2})\, \delta h\, \mathbf{g}^k$, etc.

One of the best available methods[9a] to find $(h^k)^*$ makes use of the fact that the derivative of the function along the line of march,

$$\frac{d}{dh}[F(\mathbf{x}^k + h\, \nabla F(\mathbf{x}^k))] = \nabla F[\mathbf{x}^k + h\, \nabla F(\mathbf{x}^k)] \cdot \nabla F(\mathbf{x}^k)$$

vanishes at $h^k = (h^k)^*$. We have to solve the equation

$$\nabla F(\mathbf{x}^k + (h^k)^*\, \nabla F(\mathbf{x}^k)) \cdot \nabla F(\mathbf{x}^k) = 0 \tag{9.12}$$

for $(h^k)^*$, the optimal step size.

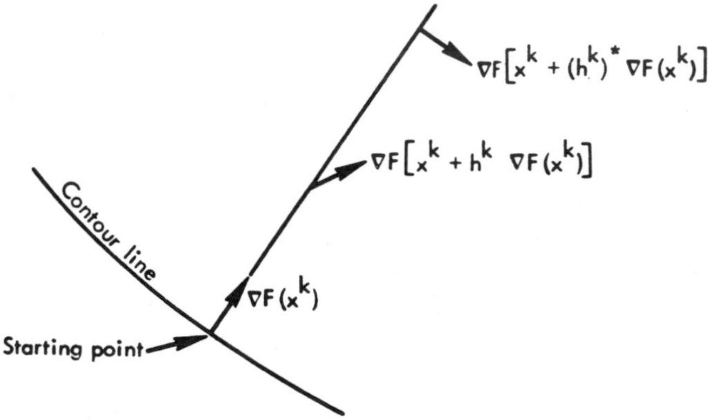

FIG. 3. The gradient direction method for finding the optimum step.

Suppose we start at the point $\mathbf{x}^k$ and march in the direction ∇F as shown in Fig. 3. As we move along the line the direction of the local gradient is calculated at successive points. The arrows show the angle between $\nabla F(\mathbf{x}^k + h^k\, \nabla F(\mathbf{x}^k))$ and $\nabla F(\mathbf{x}^k)$ at a typical point. The local gradient will be orthogonal to the original direction at the optimal step. In many cases it will be unnecessary to find the optimal step with great accuracy. It may suffice to ensure that the size of the step is less than the optimum. The sign and magnitude of the dot product $\nabla F(\mathbf{x}^k + h\,\nabla F(\mathbf{x}^k))\cdot\nabla F(\mathbf{x}^k)$ provide useful criteria for this.

9.21 Two Convergence Acceleration Methods

Davidon-Fletcher-Powell Method. This convergence acceleration scheme was originally due to Davidon[11] and later modified by Fletcher and Powell.[12] The papers discuss the problem of minimizing functions of n variables but the method can be applied to maximization by making obvious modifications. It is an iterative gradient technique which computes the gradient of $F(\mathbf{x})$ at successive values of the n-vector $\mathbf{x}$ and attempts to find the places where $\nabla F = 0$, and $[\partial^2 F/\partial x_i\,\partial x_j]$ is positive definite. If the function being minimized is quadratic, then $[\partial^2 F/\partial x_i\,\partial x_j]$ is a matrix of constants. If this matrix (the Hessian) is known then the minimum point can be found in one step

$$\mathbf{x}^0 - \mathbf{x} = -\left[\frac{\partial^2 F}{\partial x_i\,\partial x_j}\right]^{-1} \nabla F(\mathbf{x}) \tag{9.13}$$

For a general function the Hessian is not a constant but is a function of position. Furthermore the Hessian is often not known explicitly but must be obtained by numerical differentiation.

In Davidon's method the inverse of the Hessian is not computed directly but successive approximations are made. A positive definite symmetric matrix H is chosen initially and is modified at each step according to a prescribed rule. That is, instead of stepping in the direction opposite the gradient at all times (as in the steepest descent method) the direction of the step is modified so that the step at the ith stage is taken in the direction $-H^i\,\nabla F^i$. The unit matrix is a satisfactory first choice for H. The sequence of operations at the ith stage is listed below. The superscript indicates the stage of the iterations.

1. Find the optimum step in the direction $-H^i\,\nabla F(\mathbf{x}^i)$
2. Evaluate $F(\mathbf{x}^{i+1})$ and $\nabla F(\mathbf{x}^{i+1})$
3. Set $\mathbf{y}^i = \nabla F(\mathbf{x}^{i+1}) - \nabla F(\mathbf{x}^i)$
4. Modify H: $H^{i+1} = H^i + A^i + B$. The matrices A^i and B^i are obtained by direct calculation according to these definitions:

$$A^i = \frac{\alpha^i[-H^i\,\nabla F(\mathbf{x}^i)] \otimes \alpha^i[-H^i\,\nabla F(\mathbf{x}^i)]}{[-\alpha^i H^i\,\nabla F(\mathbf{x}^i)]\cdot y^i}$$

$$B^i = \frac{-H^i y^i \otimes y^i H^i}{y^i \cdot H^i y^i}$$

The symbol $\mathbf{a} \otimes \mathbf{b}$ means that a linear operator D_{ij} is formed from vectors $\mathbf{a}$ and $\mathbf{b}$; the matrix elements of this operator are $D_{ij} = a_i b_j$. α^i is a positive constant corresponding to the length of the optimal step at the ith stage.

Fletcher and Powell show that the process is stable and that the minimum of a quadratic form in n variables is obtained in n iterations.

Powell's Method. Powell[13] has described an effective method which is also guaranteed to converge to the maximum in the ideal case of a quadratic, negative definite polynomial in n variables. Powell's method is closely related to the parallel tangent or "Par-Tan" methods developed by Shah *et al.*[14] The method depends on the following fact: If $F(\mathbf{x})$ is a quadratic function with a maximum at $\mathbf{x}^*$ then pairs of points $\mathbf{x}^1$, $\mathbf{x}^2$ lying on a line through $\mathbf{x}^*$ have the property that $\nabla F(\mathbf{x}^1)$ is parallel to $\nabla F(\mathbf{x}^2)$. Conversely, if the gradients at two distinct points $\mathbf{x}^1$ and $\mathbf{x}^2$ are parallel, then $\mathbf{x}^*$ lies on the line connecting $\mathbf{x}^1$ and $\mathbf{x}^2$ or its extension.

In Powell's method, whenever steps are to be taken in the gradient direction, this means the optimum size, although this may not be stated explicitly each time. In practice, because of finite computing accuracy, a step size close to the optimum, but consistently smaller, will have to do. Powell shows that the maximization problem can be solved in n dimensions if it can be solved in $(n - 1)$ dimensions. This leads to a recursive procedure in which a series of problems of decreasing dimension are solved in a cyclic order. For example, to solve two-dimensional maximization problems it is necessary to solve a series of one-dimensional problems (the determination of the optimum step is a one-dimensional problem). Three-dimensional maximizations required the use of a computational routine to do maximizations in spaces of only two dimensions.

Suppose that we are given a point $\mathbf{x}^1$ in an n-dimensional space. We must find a second point $\mathbf{x}^2$, $\mathbf{x}^1 \neq \mathbf{x}^2$, such that $\nabla F(\mathbf{x}^2)$ is parallel to $\nabla F(\mathbf{x}^1)$. A two-dimensional case is shown in Fig. 4(a) with the initial point at $\mathbf{x}^1$. We travel in the direction of steepest ascent. At the point ζ, the vectors $\nabla F(\mathbf{x}^1)$ and $\nabla F(\zeta)$ are orthogonal and so ζ corresponds to the optimal step from $\mathbf{x}^1$. Now, using $\nabla F(\zeta)$ as the new direction, we find $\mathbf{x}^2$ such that $\nabla F(\mathbf{x}^2)$ is orthogonal to $\nabla F(\zeta)$. Consequently, $\nabla F(\mathbf{x}^1)$ is parallel to $\nabla F(\mathbf{x}^2)$. If $F(\mathbf{x})$ is a quadratic function, then the maximum point $\mathbf{x}^*$ will lie on the line through $\mathbf{x}^1$ and $\mathbf{x}^2$ (or on its extension beyond $\mathbf{x}^1$ or $\mathbf{x}^2$).

Suppose that $F(\mathbf{x})$ is not quadratic. In that case the maximum point along the line connecting $\mathbf{x}^1$ and $\mathbf{x}^2$ may not be the maximum of $F(\mathbf{x})$. The process is to be repeated until the absolute value of the gradient of $F(\mathbf{x})$ is below a preselected threshold and the maximum point is considered to be located within desired tolerances. Each set of $n(n - 1)$ iterations is called a cycle of Powell's method.

A three-dimensional example is shown in Fig. 4(b) for a single cycle. Starting at the initial point $\mathbf{x}^1$ we compute $\nabla F(\mathbf{x}^1)$ and determine the point $\mathbf{x}^2$ along that line where $\nabla F(\mathbf{x}^1)$ is orthogonal to $\nabla F(\mathbf{x}^2)$. We now restrict our

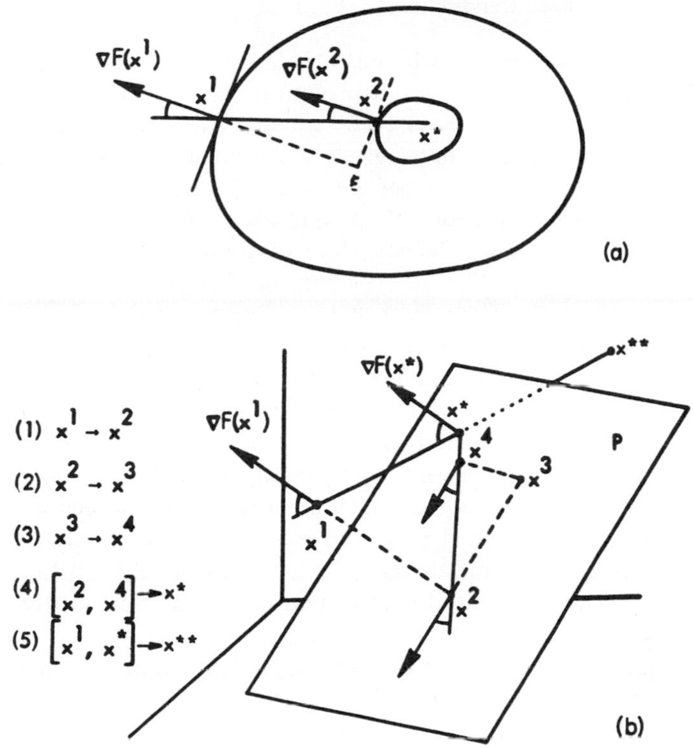

FIG. 4. (a) Powell's method in two dimensions. (b) Powell's method in three dimensions.

attention to the plane P through $\mathbf{x}^2$ and normal to $\nabla F(\mathbf{x}^1)$. Suppose that the maximum of $F(\mathbf{x})$ in the plane P occurs at $\mathbf{x}^*$. We know that the projection of $\nabla F(\mathbf{x}^*)$ onto P vanishes, and it follows that $\nabla F(\mathbf{x}^*)$ is parallel to $\nabla F(\mathbf{x}^1)$ and the maximum of $F(\mathbf{x})$ in the three-dimensional space lies on the line passing through $\mathbf{x}^1$ and $\mathbf{x}^*$. We have already described how to find the maximum in a plane and the steps involved are also depicted in Fig. 3. We go in the plane P in the direction of the projection of $\nabla F(\mathbf{x}^2)$ on P until a local maximum is reached. Call this point $\mathbf{x}^3$ and now follow $\nabla F(\mathbf{x}^3)$ until another local maximum is reached at a point we call $\mathbf{x}^4$. The final step in the planar maximization requires the maximum to be found along the line joining $\mathbf{x}^2$ and $\mathbf{x}^4$. Recall that this was named $\mathbf{x}^*$. The final step in the cycle is the determination of the maximum $\mathbf{x}^{**}$ along the line connecting $\mathbf{x}^1$ and $\mathbf{x}^*$.

Some of the more important technical details involved in the programming of Powell's method for a computer are described in reports by Woodrow[15] and Paiewonsky and Woodrow.[16]

9.22 Optimal Space Rendezvous

Example 2. This example is based on a linearized three-dimensional time-optimal terminal rendezvous problem with bounded thrust and limited fuel. The three-dimensional powered flight equations are linearized by assuming that the distance between the target and the maneuvering vehicle is always small compared to the distance between the target and the center of the earth. It is also assumed that the total propellant used is a small fraction (e.g., 5%) of the vehicle's total mass. The equations of motion do not include the effect of the time-varying total mass. The aim of this example is to outline the computational results. The results of the rendezvous study and the optimal trajectories can be found in Paiewonsky and Woodrow.[16]

A uniformly rotating coordinate system is employed as shown in Fig. 5. The rotating rectangular system with axes labeled x_1, x_3, and x_5 has its origin at the nominal target radius and moves with the target's mean motion. The x_1-axis is in the orbital plane in the tangential direction, opposite to the direction of the rotation, the x_3-axis is in the outward radial direction and the x_5 axis is orthogonal to both the x_1- and x_3-axis. Figure 5 shows the $x_1x_3x_5$ trihedron located at the radius R_0. The trihedron XYZ is an earth-centered nonrotating rectangular coordinate system used as a reference frame for the initial orbit.

A target in a circular orbit at the nominal radius will be stationary if placed at the origin of the rotating system. Target vehicles in orbits with eccentricity correspond to a rendezvous with an object moving with respect to the origin of the $x_1x_3x_5$ system; i.e., there will be relative motion between the target and the origin of the coordinate system.

The linearized equations of motion are:

$$\begin{aligned} \dot{x}_1 &= x_2 & \dot{x}_4 &= -2\omega x_2 + 3\omega^2 x_3 + u_2 \\ \dot{x}_2 &= 2\omega x_4 + u_1 & \dot{x}_5 &= x_6 \\ \dot{x}_3 &= x_4 & \dot{x}_6 &= -\omega^2 x_5 + u_3 \end{aligned} \tag{9.14}$$

where the dot indicates d/dt and

$$u_1 = A(t)\cos\theta\cos\varphi, \qquad u_2 = A(t)\cos\theta\sin\varphi \qquad \text{and} \qquad u_3 = A(t)\sin\theta$$

The thrust acceleration constraint is given by the equation

$$u_1^2 + u_2^2 + u_3^2 = A^2(t) \qquad (0 \le A(t) \le A_{\max})$$

and the propellant constraint is given by the requirement that $(m_0/c)\int_0^T A(t)\,dt \le m_p(0)$ where $m_p(0)$ is the initial propellant mass. The total vehicle mass, m_0, is assumed to be constant.

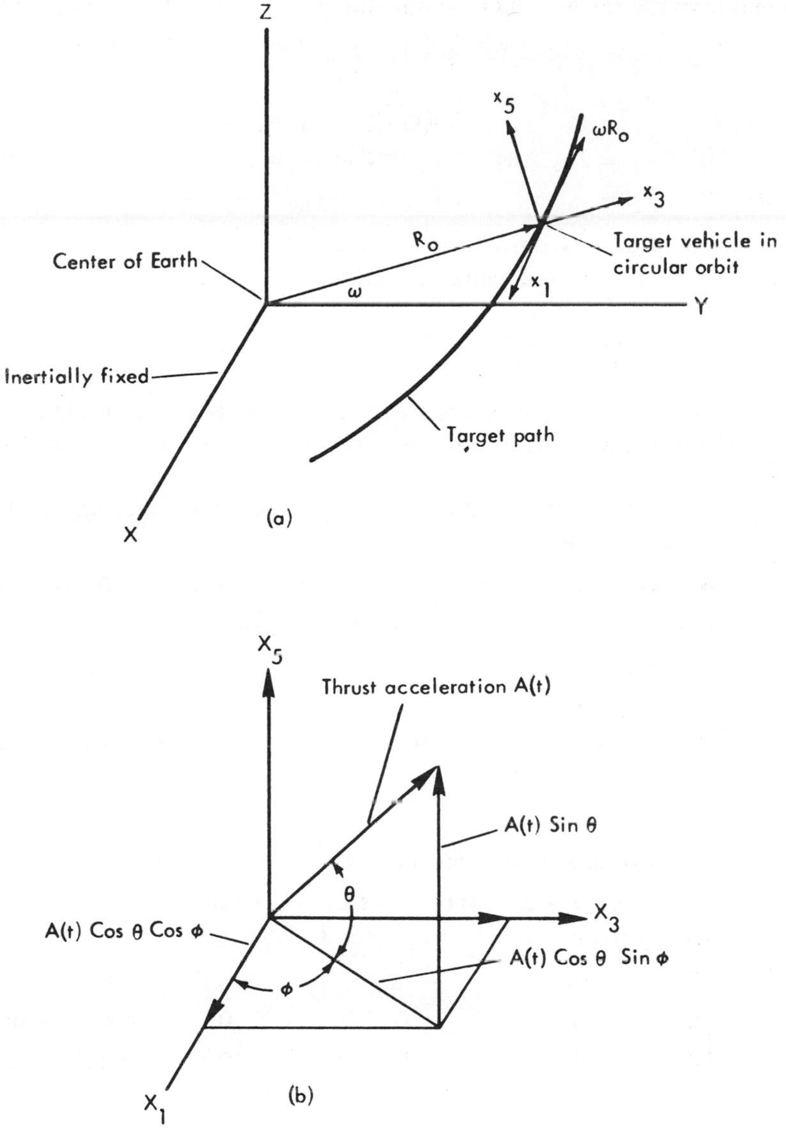

FIG. 5. Definition of coordinate system and steering angles. (a) Coordinate system. (b) Steering angles.

It is convenient to transform the variables and rescale the time in terms of the angular velocity ω. Let $t' = \omega t$, and define

$$y_1 = \omega^2 x_1, \quad y_2 = \omega x_2, \quad y_3 = \omega^2 x_3, \quad y_4 = \omega x_4, \quad y_5 = \omega^2 x_5, \quad y_6 = \omega x_6$$

The transformed equations of motion are written below. The prime denotes d/dt'.

$$\begin{aligned} &dy_1/dt' = y_1' = y_2 && dy_4/dt' = y_4' = -2y_2 + 3y_3 + u_2 \\ &dy_2/dt' = y_2' = 2y_4 + u_1 && dy_5/dt' = y_5' = y_6 \\ &dy_3/dt' = y_3' = y_4 && dy_6/dt' = y_6' = -y_5 + u_3 \end{aligned} \tag{9.15}$$

A new variable, y_7, is introduced to account for the fuel constraint. The variable y_7 satisfies the differential equation

$$\frac{dy_7}{dt'} = -\omega \frac{c}{m_0} \frac{dm_p}{dt'} = -A(t') \qquad y_7(0) = \omega x_7(0) = \omega \, \Delta V \tag{9.16}$$

where $x_7(0) = -c\ell n[(m_0 - m_p)/m_0] = \Delta V$, dm_p/dt' is the propellant mass flow, c is the rocket effective exhaust velocity, and m_0 is the total vehicle mass.

The fundamental matrix solution and its inverse for the first six equations are obtained by a straightforward calculation:

$$Y(t) = \begin{bmatrix} 1 & 4\sin t' - 3t' & 6(t' - \sin t') & 2(1 - \cos t') & 0 & 0 \\ 0 & 4\cos t' - 3 & 6(1 - \cos t') & 2\sin t' & 0 & 0 \\ 0 & 2(\cos t' - 1) & -3\cos t' + 4 & \sin t' & 0 & 0 \\ 0 & -2\sin t' & 3\sin t' & \cos t' & 0 & 0 \\ 0 & 0 & 0 & 0 & \cos t' & \sin t' \\ 0 & 0 & 0 & 0 & -\sin t' & \cos t' \end{bmatrix} \tag{9.17}$$

$$Y^{-1}(t) = \begin{bmatrix} 1 & -4\sin t' + 3t' & 6(\sin t' - t') & 2(1 - \cos t') & 0 & 0 \\ 0 & 4\cos t' - 3 & 6(1 - \cos t') & -2\sin t' & 0 & 0 \\ 0 & 2(\cos t' - 1) & -3\cos t' + 4 & -\sin t' & 0 & 0 \\ 0 & 2\sin t' & -3\sin t' & \cos t' & 0 & 0 \\ 0 & 0 & 0 & 0 & \cos t' & -\sin t' \\ 0 & 0 & 0 & 0 & \sin t' & \cos t' \end{bmatrix} \tag{9.18}$$

Recall that $\mathbf{z}(t'\boldsymbol{\eta}) = -\int_0^{t'} Y^{-1}(\tau)B(\tau)\mathbf{u}(\tau, \boldsymbol{\eta})\, d\tau$ where $\mathbf{u}(\tau, \boldsymbol{\eta})$ is obtained from the maximum principle. The matrix $B(\tau)$ is obtained by inspection of the equations of motion.

We can now write out the components of $\mathbf{z}(t', \boldsymbol{\eta})$:

$$\begin{aligned}
z_1(t', \eta) &= -\int_0^{t'} [(3\tau - 4 \sin \tau)u_1 + 2(1 - \cos \tau)u_2]\, d\tau \\
z_2(t,' \eta) &= -\int_0^{t'} [4(\cos \tau - 3)u_1 - (2 \sin \tau)u_2]\, d\tau \\
z_3(t', \eta) &= -\int_0^{t'} [2(\cos \tau - 1)u_1 - (\sin \tau)u_2]\, d\tau \\
z_4(t', \eta) &= -\int_0^{t'} [(2 \sin \tau)u_1 + (\cos \tau)u_2]\, d\tau \\
z_5(t', \eta) &= -\int_0^{t'} [(-\sin \tau)u_3]\, d\tau \\
z_6(t', \eta) &= -\int_0^{t'} [(\cos \tau)u_3]\, d\tau \\
z_7(t', \eta) &= -\int_0^{t'} A(\tau, \boldsymbol{\eta})\, d\tau
\end{aligned} \tag{9.19}$$

We now introduce adjoint variables λ_i, $i = 1, \ldots, 6$, satisfying the differential equations $\boldsymbol{\lambda}' = -A^T\boldsymbol{\lambda}$. The solution of these equations is:

$$\mathbf{x}(t') = -[Y^{-1}(t')]^T \boldsymbol{\eta} \tag{9.20}$$

where $\lambda_i(0) = -\eta_i$. The matrix A is obtained by inspection of the equations of motion. The adjoint variable λ_7 corresponding to y_7 satisfies the equation $dx_7/dt' = 0$. We may expand the vector equation and obtain relations between the components of $\boldsymbol{\lambda}$ and $\boldsymbol{\eta}$:

$$\begin{aligned}
\lambda_1(t') &= -\eta_1 \\
\lambda_2(t') &= (4\eta_1 - 2\eta_4) \sin t' - (6\eta_2 + 3\eta_3) \cos t' \\
&\qquad - 3\eta, t' + 3\eta_2 + 2\eta_3 \\
\lambda_3(t') &= 16(2\eta_1 - \eta_4) \sin t' + 3(2\eta_2 + \eta_3) \cos t' \\
&\qquad + 6\eta, t' - (6\eta_2 + 4\eta_3) \\
\lambda_4(t') &= (2\eta_2 + \eta_3) \sin t' + (4\eta_1 - 2\eta_4)\cos t' - 2\eta_1 \\
\lambda_5(t') &= \eta_6 \sin t' - \eta_5 \cos t' \\
\lambda_6(t') &= \eta_5 \sin t' - \eta_6 \cos t' \\
\lambda_7(t') &= -\eta_7
\end{aligned} \tag{9.21}$$

We find the time-optimal control by forming the Hamiltonian $\mathscr{H} = \sum_{i=1}^{7} \lambda_i y_i' + \lambda_0$ from the adjoint variables and the state velocity vector, and then maximizing it with respect to $\mathbf{u}$ subject to all constraints on $\mathbf{u}$.

Bounded thrust:

$$\sqrt{u_1^{\,2} + u_2^{\,2} + u_3^{\,2}} \le A_{\max} \tag{9.22}$$

Limited propellant:

$$\int_0^{t'} \sqrt{u_1^{\,2} + u_2^{\,2} + u_3^{\,2}}\, d\tau \le c \ln \frac{1}{1 - (m_p/m_0)} = \Delta V = x_7(0) \tag{9.23}$$

In this expression, m_p is the total propellant mass and m_0 is total mass at the initial time. The propellant constraint can be thought of as a limit on the total ideal fieldfree ΔV available for the maneuver.

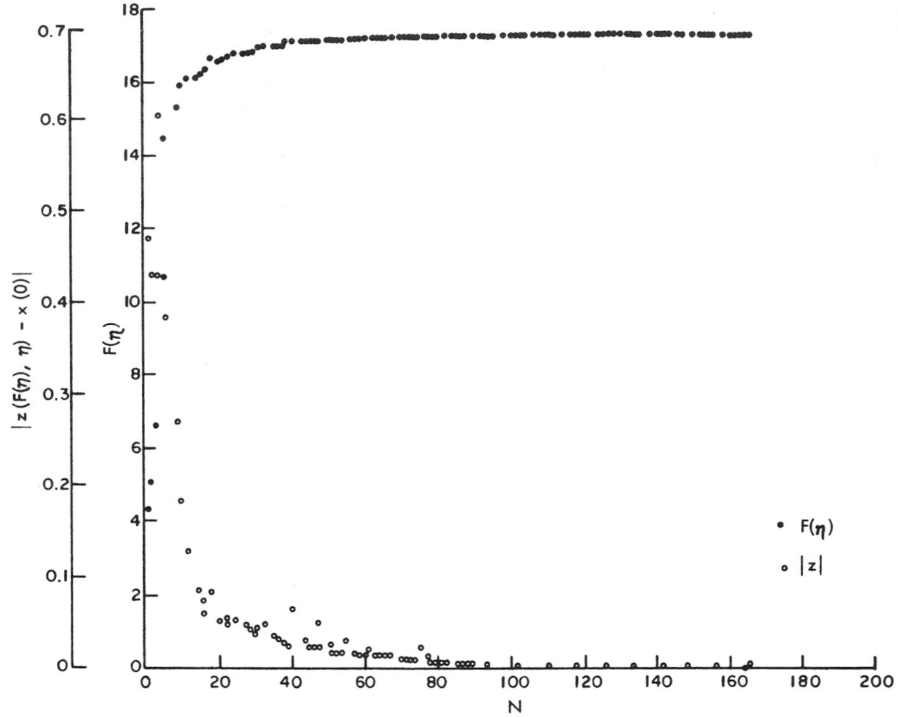

FIG. 6. Error vector length and stopping time vs total number of steps for a modified steepest ascent method. Each mark represents an acceptable step. A step is accepted when $\nabla F(\eta^k + h^k \nabla F(\eta^k)) \cdot \nabla F(\eta^k) > 0$.

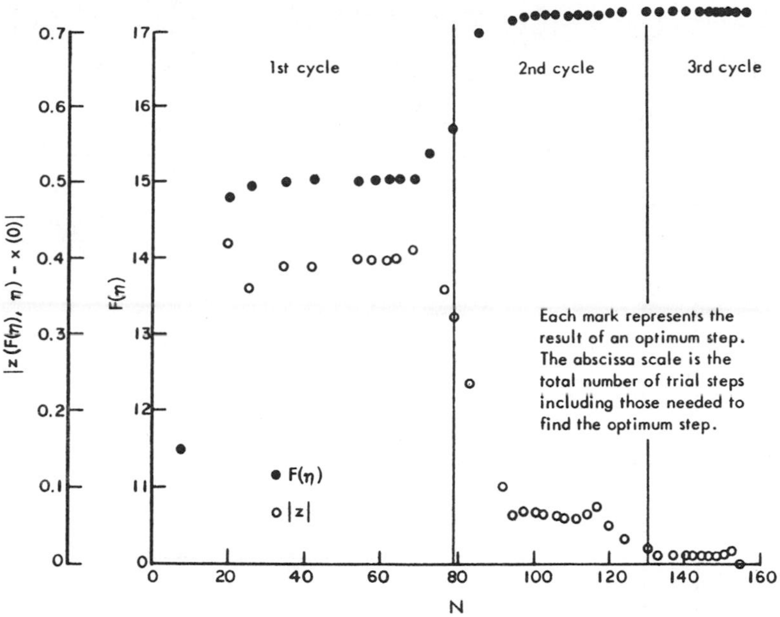

FIG. 7. Error vector length and stopping time vs total number of steps for Powell's method.

When the Hamiltonian is maximized with respect to θ, φ, and A, we find that:

$$\tan \varphi^* = \lambda_4/\lambda_2 \tag{9.24}$$

$$\tan \theta^* = \frac{\lambda_6}{\sqrt{\lambda_2^{\,2} + \lambda_4^{\,2}}} \tag{9.25}$$

and

$$\begin{aligned} A^*(t') &= A_{\max} \qquad \text{when} \quad (\lambda_2^{\,2} + \lambda_4^{\,2} + \lambda_6^{\,2} - \lambda_7) < 0 \\ &= 0 \qquad\quad\; \text{when} \quad (\lambda_2^{\,2} + \lambda_4^{\,2} + \lambda_6^{\,2} - \lambda_7) > 0 \end{aligned} \tag{9.26}$$

The optimal control components are

$$\begin{aligned} u_1^* &= A^*(t')\lambda_2/r \\ u_2^* &= A^*(t')\lambda_4/r \qquad (r = \sqrt{\lambda_2^{\,2} + \lambda_4^{\,2} + \lambda_6^{\,2}}) \\ u_3^* &= A^*(t')\lambda_6/r \end{aligned} \tag{9.27}$$

It is now possible to compute $\mathbf{z}(t', \boldsymbol{\eta})$ as all of the required functions are available.

The results of a computational study on this problem are reported in Paiewonsky and Woodrow,[16] and Figs. 5–10 are based on that work. Figures 6–9 show convergence of $|\mathbf{z}(F(\boldsymbol{\eta}), \boldsymbol{\eta}) - \mathbf{x}(0)|$ to zero and $F(\boldsymbol{\eta})$ to the optimal

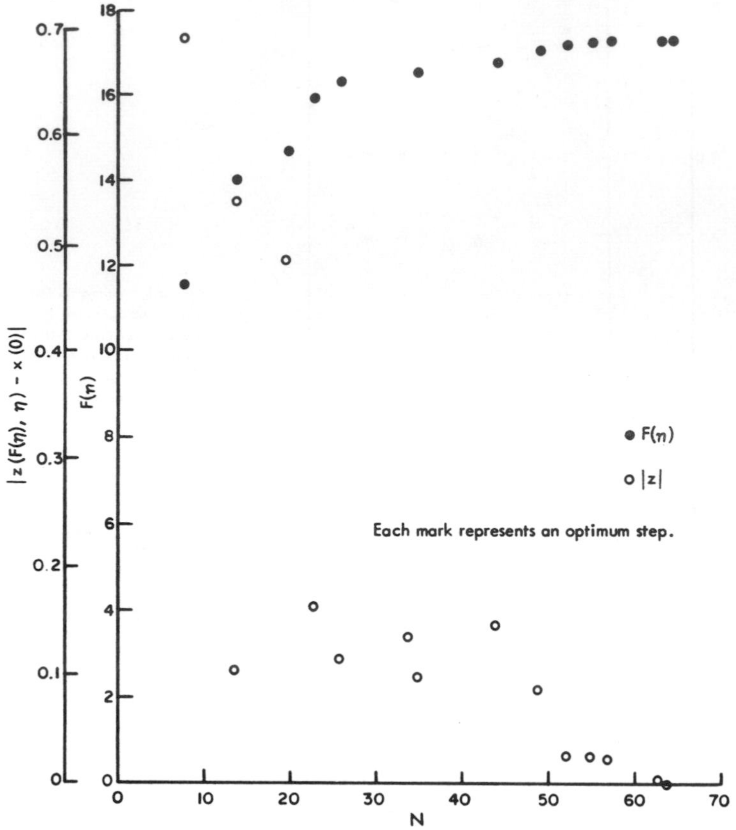

FIG. 8. Error vector length and stopping time vs total number of steps for Davidon-Fletcher-Powell method.

time for the initial point $x_1(0) = x_3(0) = x_5(0) = 100{,}000$ ft and $x_2(0) = x_4(0) = x_6(0) = -100$ ft/sec.

A modified method of steep ascent is shown in Fig. 6, Powell's method in Fig. 7, and Davidon, Fletcher, Powell's method in Fig. 8, and an unaccelerated steepest ascent is in Fig. 9. In each case the optimal time is established after relatively few iterations but the rate of reduction in the error varies widely between the different techniques.

It is important to keep in mind that the significant quantities are the errors in the boundary conditions in the physical coordinates. These are the errors which would be incurred at time $T = F(\boldsymbol{\eta}^i)$ if the control $\mathbf{u}^*(t, \boldsymbol{\eta}^i)$ were applied to the physical system.

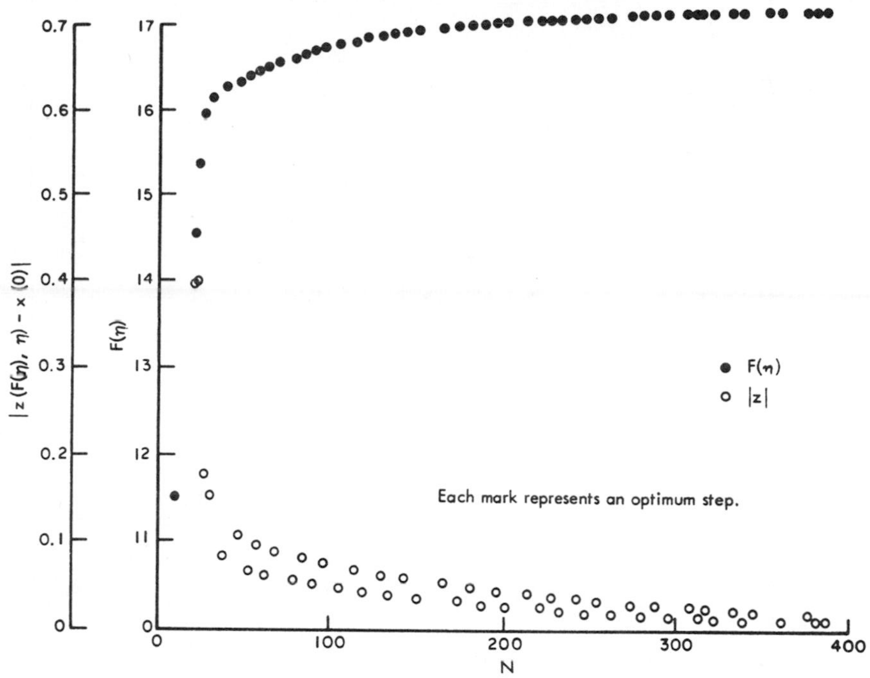

FIG. 9. Error vector length and stopping time vs total number of steps for an unaccelerated steepest ascent.

Figure 10 shows how the terminal errors in range $(x_1^2 + x_3^2 + x_5^2)^{1/2}$ are reduced as the number of iterations increase. The terminal errors in velocity $(x_2^2 + x_4^2 + x_6^2)^{1/2}$ follow a similar pattern.

In this problem the terminal velocity error threshold was 1 ft/sec and the terminal range error threshold was 300 ft. The initial range was on the order of 20 miles and the magnitude of the initial velocity was on the order of 200 ft/sec (vehicles separating).

9.3 Final Remarks

We have shown how Neustadt's method can be implemented to compute optimal controls and two convergence acceleration methods have been described. It should be understood that there are many other ways to carry out the maximization and in particular instances some of these may prove to be simpler or quicker, or just more appealing to the individual's taste. The examples presented are illustrations of steep ascent techniques which worked

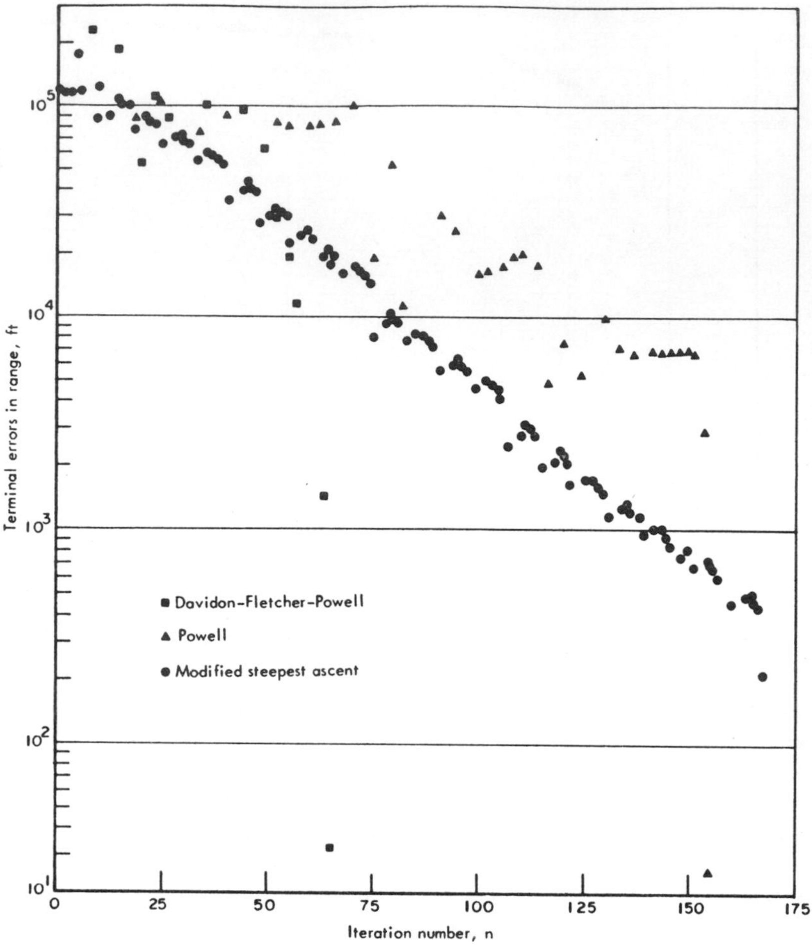

FIG. 10. Terminal errors in range vs total number of iterations.

for specific cases. A brief account of some methods which did not work is contained in Paiewonsky *et al.*[9a]

A fuller account of steep ascent methods and convergence acceleration schemes can be found in Shah *et al.*,[14] Edelbaum,[17] Wilde,[18] and Spang.[19] An analysis by Neustadt[20] of optimal space trajectories is available.

ACKNOWLEDGMENT

The numerical examples are drawn from studies carried out while the author was at Aeronautical Research Associates of Princeton Inc. (ARAP). This work was supported in part by the U.S. Air Force Flight Dynamics Laboratory under Contract AF33(657)7781. I wish to acknowledge the assistance of Peter Woodrow of ARAP in carrying out the numerical analyses and preparing the computer programs.

Portions of Example 2 and Figs. 5–10 will appear in the Journal of Spacecraft and Rockets and are used here with permission of the AIAA.

REFERENCES

1. L. W. Neustadt, Synthesizing time-optimal control systems, *J. Math. Anal. Appl.* **1**, 484–493 (1960).
2. L. W. Neustadt, Minimum effort control systems, *Soc. Ind. Appl. Math. I, Control* **1**, 16–31 (1960).
3. L. W. Neustadt and B. H. Paiewonsky, On synthesizing optimal controls, *Proc. 2nd IFAC Congr., London, 1963.* Butterworth, London, 1965.
4. N. N. Krasovskii, On the theory of optimal controls, *Automat. Remote Control* **18**, No. 11, 960–970 (1957); see also *Prikl. Mat. Meth.* **23**, 625–639 (1959).
5. R. V. Gamkrelidze, Theory of time-optimal processes in linear systems, *Izv. Akad. Nauk SSSR. Ser. Mat.* **22** 449–474 (1958) (English transl., Dept. of Eng., Univ. of California, Los Angeles, California, Rept. 61–7 (1961).)
6. J. N. Eaton, An iterative solution to time-optimal control, *J. Math. Anal. Appl.* **5**, 329–344 (1962); see also Errata and Addenda to above article, *J. Math. Anal. Appl.* **9**, 147–152 (1964).
7. E. J. Fadden and E. G. Gilbert, Computational aspects of the time-optimal problem, *in* "Computing Methods in Optimization Problems" (A. V. Balakrishnan and L. W. Neustadt, eds.) pp. 167–192. Academic Press, New York, 1964.
8. J. P. LaSalle, The time-optimal control problem, *in* "Contributions to the Theory of Nonlinear Oscillations" (S. Lefschetz, ed.), vol. V, pp. 1–24. Princeton Univ. Press, Princeton, New Jersey, 1960.

9a. B. H. Paiewonsky, P. J. Woodrow, F. Terkelsen, and J. McIntyre, A study of synthesis techniques for optimal control, Aeronautical Systems Div., Wright-Patterson AFB, Ohio, Rept. ASD–TDR–63–239 (June, 1964).

9b. B. H. Paiewonsky and P. J. Woodrow, The synthesis of optimal controls for a class of rocket steering problems, *AIAA Paper* 63-224, June, 1963.

10. B. H. Paiewonsky, P. J. Woodrow, W. Brunner, and P. Halbert, Synthesis of Optimal Controllers Using Hybrid Analog-Digital Computers *in:* "Computing Methods in Optimization Problems" (A. V. Balakrishnan and L. W. Neustadt, eds.). Academic Press, New York, 1964.
11. W. L. Davidon, Variable metric method for minimization, Argonne Natl. Lab., Argonne, Illinois, Rept. ANL-5990-Rev. (May, 1959).
12. R. Fletcher and M. J. D. Powell, A rapidly convergent descent method for minimization, *Comput. J.* pp. 163–168 (July, 1963).
13. M. J. D. Powell, An iterative method for finding stationary values of a function of several variables, *Comput. J.* pp. 147–151 (1962).
14. B. V. Shah, R. J. Buehler, and O. Kempthorne, Some algorithms for minimizing a function of several variables, *J. SIAM* **12**, 74 (1964).
15. P. J. Woodrow, Dept. of Electrical Eng., Princeton Univ., Princeton, New Jersey, Control Systems Lab. Tech. Rept. No. 4, November, 1963.
16. B. H. Paiewonsky and P. J. Woodrow, A study of time-optimal rendezvous in three dimensions, AFFDL-TR-65-20, vol. I (January, 1965).
17. T. N. Edelbaum, Theory of maxima and minima, *in* "Optimization Techniques" (George Leitmann, ed.), Chapter I. Academic Press, New York, 1962.

18. D. J. Wilde, "Optimum Seeking Methods." Prentice-Hall, Englewood Cliffs, New Jersey, 1964.
19. H. A. Spang, III, A review of minimization techniques for nonlinear functions, *SIAM Rev.* **4** (1962).
20. L. W. Neustadt, A general theory of minimum fuel space trajectories, *J. Soc. Ind. Appl. Math. Ser. A, Control* **3**, 317–356 (1965).

10

The Calculus of Variations, Functional Analysis, and Optimal Control Problems

E. K. BLUM

DEPARTMENT OF MATHEMATICS,
UNIVERSITY OF SOUTHERN CALIFORNIA, LOS ANGELES, CALIFORNIA

10.0 Introduction

The calculus of variations has a venerable place in the history of mathematics and physics. Its roots lie deep in the classical analysis of the eighteenth and nineteenth centuries and its development extends well into the current century. From it stems at least one branch of modern abstract mathematics, the branch now referred to as functional analysis, although this origin is usually lost sight of by modern functional analysts. In this article, we shall develop some of the relationships between the classical calculus of variations and that part of functional analysis which we shall call "abstract analysis" and show how the abstract approach simplifies the derivation of classical results.

We shall do this by introducing another subject of current research in mathematics and engineering: optimal control theory. It is generally recognized that many of the problems of optimal control theory are subsumed by the classical results of the calculus of variations. Conversely, many basic problems in the calculus of variations can be restated as optimal control problems. We shall review how this equivalence is established and then apply the methods of abstract analysis to certain general problems in optimal control theory and thereby arrive at theorems in the calculus of variations. Furthermore, we shall show how these abstract methods can be used to construct practical methods of solving optimal control problems. Finally, we shall consider some specific examples which arise in orbital mechanics concerned with low-thrust rocket trajectories. Thus, we shall run the gamut from classical mathematical analysis to modern abstract analysis and then from pure mathematics to very applied mathematics, hopefully illuminating some general unifying principles along the way and showing how these general ideas can be used to produce specific practical methods for solving very real problems.

10.1 The Problem of Mayer

We have said that the calculus of variations had its beginnings in the eighteenth century. Actually, one of the most famous problems in the calculus of variations was originally discussed by Galileo in the early seventeenth century.[1,2] This is the brachistochrone problem. Notwithstanding the fact that most readers are familiar with the brachistochrone problem and that it is discussed in every book on the calculus of variations (e.g., see Bliss[3]) we shall present it here for convenient reference, since we shall use it as an example to show how a problem of Mayer can be transformed into an optimal control problem and to illustrate a computational method of solving variational problems.

It will be recalled that the brachistochrone problem deals with a unit mass moving along an arc in a uniform gravitational field—for example, a bead sliding down a frictionless wire. The endpoints, P_0 and P_1, of the arc are fixed, as is the initial velocity at time $t = 0$. Hence, the time of descent of the bead from P_0 to P_1 depends only on the shape of the arc. It is required to find, in a certain class of arcs joining P_0 and P_1, that arc which minimizes the time of descent. The brachistochrone ("shortest time") problem was posed as a challenge to mathematicians of the time by James Bernoulli in 1696 and solved by James and his brother John[4] in 1697. The origin of the calculus of variations may be traced to that event.

It is a simple matter for us now to formulate the brachistochrone problem analytically. To simplify it even further, we shall assume that the arc lies in the (x, y)-plane so that the equation of motion is given by

$$\frac{d^2s}{dt^2} = g \cos \theta = g \frac{dy}{ds} \tag{10.1}$$

where g is the gravitational constant, θ is the angle between the vertical gravity vector (in the y-direction) and the tangent to the arc at a point $P{:}(x, y)$ and

s is arc length from P_0 to P. Integrating (10.1) with respect to t, we obtain $(ds/dt)^2 = 2gy + \text{const.}$ Without loss of generality, we may take P_0 as the point (0, 1) and P_1 as $(x_1, 2)$. Assume further, for illustrative purposes, that the initial velocity is zero. In this case, we have

$$\frac{dt}{dx} = \frac{dt}{ds}\frac{ds}{dx} = \left(\frac{1 + y'^2}{2gy}\right)^{1/2}$$

where $y' = dy/dx$. Integrating with respect to x, we obtain the formula for the time of descent, J:

$$J = J(y) = \int_0^{x_1} \left(\frac{1 + y'^2}{2gy}\right)^{1/2} dx \tag{10.2}$$

The brachistochrone problem then is to find in the class of arcs, $y = y(x)$ with $y(0) = 1$ and $y(x_1) = 2$, that arc which minimizes the integral in (10.2). This is typical of the kind of problem we are interested in here. We shall reformulate it below after considering the problem of Mayer.

The problem of Mayer includes a very general class of problems in the calculus of variations. As formulated by Bliss,[3] the problem of Mayer may be stated as follows.

Let† $\mathbf{y}^T = \mathbf{y}^T(t) = (y_1(t), \ldots, y_q(t))$ be a vector function of t in the real interval $t_0 \le t \le t_1$. $\mathbf{y}$ is assumed to be a member of some set of "admissible" functions, S. For example, Bliss takes S to consist of all functions which are piecewise continuously differentiable in $[t_0, t_1]$ and have values $\mathbf{y}(t)$ in some open region of R^q, q-dimensional Euclidean space. Further, let

$$\Phi_i(t, \mathbf{y}, \mathbf{y}') = 0, \qquad i = 1, \ldots, n < q \tag{10.3}$$

be a set of differential equations, where the functions Φ_i are assumed to have continuous third-order partial derivatives in some suitable $(2q + 1)$ – dimensional open region R_1 and the matrix $(\partial\Phi_i/\partial y_j')$ is to have rank n in R_1. Let

$$\psi_j(t_0, \mathbf{y}(t_0), t_1, \mathbf{y}(t_1)) = 0, \qquad j = 1, \ldots, p \le 2q + 2 \tag{10.4}$$

be endpoint constraints, where the functions ψ_j have continuous third-order partial derivatives in some $(2q + 2)$ – dimensional open region R_2 in which the matrix

$$\left(\frac{\partial\psi_j}{\partial t_0}, \frac{\partial\psi_j}{\partial y_k(t_0)}, \frac{\partial\psi_j}{\partial t_1}, \frac{\partial\psi_j}{\partial y_k(t_1)}\right)$$

has rank p. Finally, let the function of endvalues

$$J = J(t_0, \mathbf{y}(t_0), t_1, \mathbf{y}(t_1)) \tag{10.5}$$

† $(\ )^T$ denotes the transpose of ( ).

have continuous third-order partials in the region R_2. The problem of Mayer is to find $\mathbf{y} \in S$ which minimizes J while satisfying Eqs. (10.3) and (10.4). (If J is to be maximized, we simply minimize $-J$.)

As an example of a problem of Mayer let us again consider the brachistochrone problem. First, we change the independent variable from x to t. Thus, $y(x)$ becomes $y_1(t)$ and $y_1' = dy_1/dt$. We introduce

$$y_2(t) = \int_0^t \left(\frac{1 + (y_1')^2}{2gy_1}\right)^{1/2} dt$$

and let $\mathbf{y} = (y_1, y_2)$. Then

$$\Phi_1(t, \mathbf{y}, \mathbf{y}') = y_2' - \left(\frac{1 + (y_1')^2}{2gy_1}\right)^{1/2} = 0 \tag{10.6}$$

is a differential equation which must be satisfied by $(y_1(t), y_2(t))$. Also, y_1 and y_2 must satisfy the endpoint conditions

$$\begin{aligned} \psi_1 &= y_1(t_0) - 1 = 0, \\ \psi_2 &= y_2(t_0) = 0, \\ \psi_3 &= y_1(t_1) - 2 = 0 \end{aligned} \tag{10.7}$$

where $t_0 = 0$ and $t_1 = x_1$. Finally, the time of descent, J, is given by

$$J = y_2(t_1) \tag{10.8}$$

It is required to find $\mathbf{y}^T = (y_1(t), y_2(t))$ satisfying (10.6) and (10.7) and minimizing J in (10.8). Thus, (10.6), (10.7), (10.8) is a special instance of (10.3), (10.4), (10.5) which represents the brachistochrone problem formulated as a problem of Mayer.

10.2 Optimal Control Problems

A large class of problems in the theory of optimal control can be formulated as variational problems of the following type.

Let $\mathbf{x}^T = \mathbf{x}^T(t) = (x_1(t), \ldots, x_n(t))$ and $\mathbf{u}^T = \mathbf{u}^T(t) = (u_1(t), \ldots, u_m(t))$ be functions of t on the interval $t_0 \le t \le t_1$. $\mathbf{x}$ is the "state" function and $\mathbf{u}$ is the "control" function. The control is assumed to be in some specified set of admissible controls. For example, $\mathbf{u}$ is usually assumed to be piecewise continuous with values in some region, Ω, of R^m. We shall take Ω to be an open set, although other alternatives are possible. Let

$$\frac{d\mathbf{x}}{dt} = \mathbf{f}(\mathbf{x}, \mathbf{u}) \tag{10.9}$$

be a system of n differential equations, where $\mathbf{f}^T = (f_1, \ldots, f_n)$ and the f_i, $1 \le i \le n$, are assumed to have continuous partials $\partial f_i/\partial x_j$ and $\partial f_i/\partial u_k$ in some prescribed open set, $\Gamma \subset R^n \times R^m$. We assume further that the control region Ω is contained in the projection of Γ on R^m. Let

$$\psi_j(t_0, \mathbf{x}(t_0), t_1, \mathbf{x}(t_1)) = 0, \qquad 1 \leq j \leq p, \quad p \leq 2n + 2 \tag{10.10}$$

be a set of endpoint constraints on the state function, where the ψ_j have continuous first-order partial derivatives in some open set, R_2, and the matrix

$$\left(\frac{\partial \psi_j}{\partial t_0}, \frac{\partial \psi_j}{\partial x(t_0)}, \frac{\partial \psi_j}{\partial t_1}, \frac{\partial \psi_j}{\partial x(t_1)}\right)$$

has rank p. Finally, let

$$J = J(t_0, x(t_0), t_1, x(t_1)) \tag{10.11}$$

be a function of endvalues of the state and time. We assume that J has continuous first partials in R_2. For each admissible control, $\mathbf{u}$, a state function $\mathbf{x}$ which satisfies the "control equations" (10.9)† is called a "trajectory corresponding to $\mathbf{u}$." An "optimal" control is one which has a corresponding trajectory which satisfies the constraints (10.10) and minimizes J. The "optimal control problem" is to find such an optimal control $\mathbf{u}$ and its corresponding trajectory $\mathbf{x}$. The pair $(\mathbf{x}, \mathbf{u})$ is an "optimal solution" of the problem. One should, of course, remark that there are other kinds of problems in control theory which are referred to as optimal control problems. In particular, mention should be made of problems in which the constraints are in the form of inequalities (see Pontryagin *et al.*).[5]‡ We shall restrict ourselves to equality constraints in this paper, although the connections between these two kinds of problems is well known (see Refs. 5–7).

The optimal control problem becomes a problem of Mayer if we let $y_i = x_i$, $1 \leq i \leq n$ and $y_{n+j} = u_j$, $1 \leq J \leq q$. Conversely, the problem of Mayer is transformed into the optimal control problem as follows. First, we solve Eqs. (10.3) for n of the derivatives, say $y_1', \ldots, y_n'$ and set $x_i = y_i$, $1 \leq i \leq q$, and $u_j = y'_{n+j}$, $1 \leq j \leq q - n$. Then we adjoin to the n differential equations obtained by solving (10.3) for y_i, $1 \leq i \leq n$, the additional equations $x'_{j+n} = u_j$, $1 \leq j \leq q - n$. This produces a system of q differential equations for the q state variables as in (10.9). Similarly, (10.4) and (10.5) become (10.10) and (10.11) respectively, thereby establishing the well-known equivalence of the problem of Mayer and the optimal control problem.

As a simple illustration of these ideas, let us return to the brachistochrone problem. It was formulated as a problem of Mayer in (10.6), (10.7), (10.8). To restate it as an optimal control problem, we introduce the state function

† Also called "state equations."
‡ See also Chapters 1, 6, and 7.

$\mathbf{x}(t) = (x_1(t), x_2(t))$, where $x_1 = y_1$ and $x_2 = y_2$. Then we introduce the control function $u(t) = u_1(t) = y_1'$. Equation (10.6) and the latter equation yield the control equations,

$$\begin{aligned} \frac{dx_1}{dt} &= u_1 \\ \frac{dx_2}{dt} &= \left(\frac{1 + u_1^2}{2gx_1}\right)^{1/2} \end{aligned} \tag{10.6'}$$

Similarly, the endpoint conditions (10.7) become the endpoint constraints on the state function,

$$\begin{aligned} \psi_1 &= x_1(t_0) - 1 = 0, \\ \psi_2 &= x_2(t_0) = 0, \\ \psi_3 &= x_1(t_1) - 2 = 0 \end{aligned} \tag{10.7'}$$

Finally, the function of endvalues of the state and time which is to be minimized is just the final value of x_2, that is,

$$J = x_2(t_1) \tag{10.8'}$$

We shall show later how to solve the brachistochrone problem as an optimal control problem by an approximation procedure. The solution given by this procedure can then be compared with the known analytic solution.

A first necessary condition for a solution of the problem of Mayer and, therefore, for a solution of the optimal control problem as formulated above is given by the classical multiplier rule.[3] Most derivations of the multiplier rule are based on classical methods of the calculus of variations. In the following sections, we shall give an alternate derivation using methods of abstract analysis insofar as possible. The main ideas of this new derivation have been known for some time, but they do not seem to have been applied as they are here. Indeed, as we have already remarked in the Introduction, much of the research in abstract analysis was initially motivated by the problems of the calculus variations. We cite the early work of Volterra, at the turn of the century, on what he called "functions of lines" and the work of Hadamard at that time, which he termed "analyse fonctionnelle," giving the subject its name. The paper by Bolza[8] contains a result similar to one of our theorems. The works of Fréchet[9] and Gâteaux[10] set forth the main concepts which we shall use, in a somewhat modified form. Later work of Goldstine[11,12] and Liusternik[13] comes closest to the approach taken here. More recent research using functional analysis in variational theory is that of Hestenes,[14] Balakrishnan,[15] Neustadt,[29] Browder,[28] and the author.[17] Several books[18-21] give fuller accounts of the basic ideas in various forms.

We believe that the techniques of our proof, being geometrical in spirit, are easily grasped. They are based on very natural generalizations of the ideas used in establishing the Lagrange multiplier rule of ordinary calculus. The main theorem (Theorem 2) is formulated in an abstract setting so that it applies at once to minimization problems with equality constraints in both the ordinary calculus (finite dimensional spaces) and the calculus of variations (function spaces). It also provides the bases for a new method of solving such problems, the "convergent gradient method" to be explained later.

10.3 Abstract Analysis, Basic Concepts

In this section and the next are assembled some general results of abstract analysis based on ideas going back to Fréchet[9] and Gâteaux.[10] Essentially, the abstract analysis which concerns us is the generalization of the differential calculus to abstract spaces. The development of abstract analysis which we shall present here parallels that given in such references as Hille[18] and Liusternik and Sobolev,[19] and the reader is referred to these sources for general background information. However, our development differs in details which are important for the intended application to the optimum control problem. For example, Liusternik and Sobolev formulate the definition of abstract differential for functions defined on a normed linear space, whereas we restrict ourselves to functions defined on a pre-Hilbert space. In this respect, their treatment is more general. However, we require differentials of functionals to exist only in finitely open sets (Definition 1), whereas they deal with open sets. In this respect, our results are more general and more directly applicable to the optimal control problem. Furthermore, the weaker hypothesis of finitely open sets and the existence of an inner product permits us to give a simpler proof of the abstract multiplier rule. For example, our proofs are based on the classical implicit function theorem for real functions of several real variables rather than on the implicit function theorem in abstract spaces.[27] Our results are designed to have just the right amount of generality for application to the optimal control problem considered here, i.e., with equality constraints. There are indications that problems with inequality constraints may require the greater generality of the results in Liusternik and Sobolev.[19]

Throughout this and the following section, E and E_1 will denote normed linear spaces over the real numbers, and f will denote an arbitrary mapping from a subset of E to E_1. In particular, E_1 may be one-dimensional (i.e., the real line) in which case f is a functional. For $\mathbf{u} \in E$ we write $||\mathbf{u}||$ for the norm of $\mathbf{u}$. We begin with some definitions.

Definition 1. A subset $D \subset E$ is *finitely open at* $\mathbf{u}$, $\mathbf{u} \in D$, if for any $\mathbf{h}_1, \ldots, \mathbf{h}_n \in E$, $n \geq 1$, there is a neighborhood, $N = N(\mathbf{h}_1, \ldots, \mathbf{h}_n)$, of the origin in

R^n such that for any $(t_1, \ldots, t_n) \in N$ the point $\mathbf{u} + \sum_1^n t_i\mathbf{h}_i$ is in D. Let D_u denote the totality of such points; i.e.,†

$$D_u = \left\{\mathbf{u} + \sum_1^n t_i\mathbf{h}_i \,\middle|\, n \geq 1, \quad \mathbf{h}_i \in E, \quad (t_1, \ldots, t_n) \in N(\mathbf{h}_1, \ldots, \mathbf{h}_n)\right\}$$

D_u is called a *star-neighborhood* of $\mathbf{u}$ relative to D. If D is finitely open at every $\mathbf{u} \in D$, then we say that D is a *finitely open* set.

We observe that a star-neighborhood, D_u, of $\mathbf{u}$ need not be a neighborhood of $\mathbf{u}$ in the norm topology, that is, there may be no $\delta > 0$ such that the sphere $\|\mathbf{y} - \mathbf{u}\| < \delta$ is contained in D_u. On the other hand, it is clear that a star-neighborhood of $\mathbf{u}$ is finitely open at every point in the star-neighborhood. In the applications, the functionals which arise have certain desired properties in sets which are finitely open but not necessarily open in the usual norm topology. The continuity property given in the next definition is an example of such a property, as we shall see later.

Definition 2. Let f be defined on $D \subset E$, with D finitely open at $\mathbf{u}$. Let D_u be a star-neighborhood of u and let $\mathbf{y} \in D_u$. We say that f is *finitely continuous at* $\mathbf{y}$ if

$$f(\mathbf{y} + \sum_1^n t_i\mathbf{h}_i)$$

is a continuous function of $(t_1, \ldots, t_n)$ in R^n at the origin in R^n for all choices of $\mathbf{h}_i \in E$ and n. f is *finitely continuous in* D_u if it is finitely continuous at all $\mathbf{y}$ in D_u.

In the applications, D will be a set of controls in the space, E, of admissible controls. Using well-known continuity properties of solutions of ordinary differential equations, we shall show that various functions on D are finitely continuous.

We come now to the matter of generalizing the concept of a differential. There are several ways to do this, all being variations of the Gâteaux[10] or Fréchet[9] differentials (also see Refs. 18 and 19). We shall choose one which is close to the Gâteaux differential.

Definition 3. Let f be defined on a set $D \subset E$ which is finitely open at $\mathbf{u}$. If

$$\lim_{t \to 0} (f(\mathbf{u} + t\mathbf{h}) - f(\mathbf{u})/t = \delta f(\mathbf{u}; \mathbf{h})$$

exists for all $\mathbf{h} \in E$, it is called the *weak differential* of f at $\mathbf{u}$ with increment $\mathbf{h}$.

† $\{e|P\}$ denotes the set with member e having property P.

Remark 1. It is evident that

$$\frac{d}{dt} f(\mathbf{u} + t\mathbf{h}) \Big|_{t=0} = \delta f(\mathbf{u}; \mathbf{h}) \tag{10.12}$$

This follows at once from the usual definition of the derivative of a vector function of a scalar t. It is also obvious that $\delta f(\mathbf{u}, \mathbf{h})$ is homogeneous in $\mathbf{h}$; i.e.,

$$\begin{aligned} \delta f(\mathbf{u}; s\mathbf{h}) &= \lim_{t \to 0} (f(\mathbf{u} + ts\mathbf{h}) - f(\mathbf{u}))/t \\ &= s \lim_{t' \to 0} (f(\mathbf{u} + t'\mathbf{h}) - f(\mathbf{u}))/t' = s\, \delta f(\mathbf{u}; \mathbf{h}) \end{aligned}$$

where $t' = ts$. If f is a real functional, then for $\mathbf{u}$ fixed $\delta f(\mathbf{u}; \mathbf{h})$ is also a real functional, defined for all $\mathbf{h} \in E$. In the case where f is a real functional and $\delta f(\mathbf{y}; \mathbf{h})$ exists for $\mathbf{y}$ in a star-neighborhood of $\mathbf{u}$ and is finitely continuous at the point $\mathbf{u}$, it is easy to show that $\delta f(\mathbf{u}; \mathbf{h})$ is also an additive real functional of $\mathbf{h}$. For arbitrary $\mathbf{h}_1, \mathbf{h}_2 \in E$ and real variables t_1 and t_2, let us define

$$g(t_1, t_2) = f(\mathbf{u} + t_1\mathbf{h}_1 + t_2\mathbf{h}_2)$$

g is a real-valued function of t_1 and t_2. From (10.12) we see that

$$\frac{\partial g}{\partial t_1} = \delta f(\mathbf{u} + t_1\mathbf{h}_1 + t_2\mathbf{h}_2; \mathbf{h}_1)$$

and

$$\frac{\partial g}{\partial t_2} = \delta f(\mathbf{u} + t_1\mathbf{h}_1 + t_2\mathbf{h}_2; \mathbf{h}_2)$$

for $|t_1|$ and $|t_2|$ sufficiently small to ensure that $\mathbf{u} + t_1\mathbf{h}_1 + t_2\mathbf{h}_2$ is in D. It follows that $\partial g/\partial t_1$ and $\partial g/\partial t_2$ are continuous in t_1 and t_2 at (0, 0) and exist in a neighborhood of (0, 0). By ordinary calculus,

$$g(t_1, t_2) = g(0, 0) + t_1\, \partial g/\partial t_1 |_{(0,0)} + t_2\, \partial g/\partial t_2 |_{(0,0)} + \varepsilon$$

where $\varepsilon/(t_1{}^2 + t_2{}^2)^{1/2} \to 0$ as $(t_1, t_2) \to (0, 0)$ along a ray through the origin. This may be rewritten as

$$f(\mathbf{u} + t_1\mathbf{h}_1 + t_2\mathbf{h}_2) - f(\mathbf{u}) = t_1\, \delta f(\mathbf{u}; \mathbf{h}_1) + t_2\, \delta f(\mathbf{u}; \mathbf{h}_2) + \varepsilon$$

Taking $t_1 = t_2 = t$, we obtain

$$\lim_{t \to 0} (f(\mathbf{u} + t(\mathbf{h}_1 + \mathbf{h}_2)) - f(\mathbf{u}))/t = \delta f(\mathbf{u}; \mathbf{h}_1) + \delta f(\mathbf{u}; \mathbf{h}_2)$$

The left member of this equation is $\delta f(\mathbf{u}; \mathbf{h}_1 + \mathbf{h}_2)$, by definition. This establishes the additivity.

In the application to optimal control theory, we shall be concerned with a linear space of functions in which a naturally defined inner product exists, that is, with a pre-Hilbert space. A real pre-Hilbert space is a real linear space, E, in which a real inner product, $\langle \mathbf{u}, \mathbf{v} \rangle$, is defined for all $\mathbf{u}, \mathbf{v} \in E$. From this point on, E will denote a pre-Hilbert space unless there is an explicit statement to the contrary. A Hilbert space is a complete pre-Hilbert space. As is well known, if g is a bounded linear functional on a Hilbert space, H, then there exists a $\mathbf{y} \in H$ such that $g(h) = \langle \mathbf{y}, \mathbf{h} \rangle$ for all $\mathbf{h} \in H$. Although this result does not hold in general in a pre-Hilbert space, it holds in many cases important in our applications. In particular, it may hold for $\delta f(\mathbf{u}; \mathbf{h})$, which is a real functional of $\mathbf{h}$ when f is a real functional and is linear in $\mathbf{h}$ when the continuity conditions in Remark 1 are satisfied. These considerations lead us to the next definition.

Definition 4. Let f be a real functional defined on a subset of the pre-Hilbert space E. If there exists a vector $\nabla f(\mathbf{u}) \in E$ such that $\delta f(\mathbf{u}; \mathbf{h}) = \langle \nabla f(\mathbf{u}), \mathbf{h} \rangle$ for all $\mathbf{h} \in E$, then $\nabla f((\mathbf{u})$ is called the *weak gradient* of f at $\mathbf{u}$.

If $\nabla f(\mathbf{u})$ exists at a point $\mathbf{u}$, then $\delta f(\mathbf{u}; \mathbf{h})$ is obviously a bounded linear functional of $\mathbf{h}$. Note that in this case to obtain linearity in $\mathbf{h}$ it is not necessary to assume that $\delta f(\mathbf{u}; \mathbf{h})$ is finitely continuous at $\mathbf{u}$. In fact, not even the existence of $\delta f(\mathbf{y}; \mathbf{h})$ for $\mathbf{y} \neq \mathbf{u}$ need be assumed, We remark that for $\mathbf{h}$ a unit vector $\langle \nabla f(\mathbf{u}), \mathbf{h} \rangle$ may be regarded as a "directional derivative" of f in the direction of $\mathbf{h}$.

It is of some interest to consider now the "strong differential." Although we shall make no use of this notion until Sec. 10.8, it is nevertheless pertinent to discuss it here for purposes of comparison with the weak differential and for its possible application to other types of optimal control problems.

Definition 5. Let f be defined in a neighborhood of $\mathbf{u} \in E$ where E is any normed linear space, with values in a normed linear space E_1. If there exists a bounded (i.e., continuous) linear operator, $f'(\mathbf{u})$, mapping E into E_1 and such that

$$f(\mathbf{u} + \mathbf{h}) - f(\mathbf{u}) = f'(\mathbf{u})\mathbf{h} + \boldsymbol{\varepsilon}(\mathbf{u}, \mathbf{h})$$

where $\|\boldsymbol{\varepsilon}\| / \|\mathbf{h}\| \to 0$ as $\mathbf{h} \to 0$, then $f'(\mathbf{u})\mathbf{h}$ is the *strong differential of f at* $\mathbf{u}$ *with increment* $\mathbf{h}$ and $f'(\mathbf{u})$ is the *strong derivative of f at* $\mathbf{u}$.

Note that $f'(\mathbf{u})\mathbf{h}$ is an element of E_1, the result of the linear operator $f'(\mathbf{u})$ applied to $\mathbf{h}$. $f'(\mathbf{u})\mathbf{h}$ is defined for every $\mathbf{h} \in E$. The strong differential is essentially Fréchet's concept. If f is a real functional (i.e., E_1 is the real line) and E is a Hilbert space, then the operator $f'(\mathbf{u})$ is also a real functional on E. Since it is bounded and linear, there exists an element, $\nabla_s f(\mathbf{u})$, in E such that $f'(\mathbf{u})\mathbf{h} = \langle \nabla_s f(\mathbf{u}), \mathbf{h} \rangle$ for all $\mathbf{h} \in E$. We shall call $\nabla_s f(\mathbf{u})$ the *strong gradient* of f at $\mathbf{u}$.

It is a simple matter to show that if the strong differential exists at **u**, then the weak differential also exists and the two differentials are equal. In proof, we have

$$f(\mathbf{u} + t\mathbf{h}) - f(\mathbf{u}) = tf'(\mathbf{u})\mathbf{h} + \varepsilon(\mathbf{u}, t\mathbf{h})$$

for any $\mathbf{h} \in E$ and scalar t, where $\|\varepsilon\|/|t|\ \|\mathbf{h}\| \to 0$ as $t \to 0$. Thus,

$$\delta f(\mathbf{u}; \mathbf{h}) = \lim_{t \to 0} (f(\mathbf{u} + t\mathbf{h}) - f(\mathbf{u}))/t = f'(\mathbf{u})\mathbf{h}$$

If f is a functional and the strong gradient exists, then so does the weak gradient and the two are equal.

On the other hand, the weak gradient may exist when the strong gradient does not. For example, let f be the function given in polar coordinates in the plane by $f(r, \theta) = \cos(r/\theta)$ for $0 < \theta < 2\pi$ and $f(r, 0) = 1$ for all r. (Thus, f is a functional on a two-dimensional vector space.) The directional derivative of f at (0, 0) along any ray is zero; i.e., for $\theta \neq 0$, $\partial f/\partial r = -\sin(r/\theta)/\theta$, which is zero for $r = 0$. Hence, the weak gradient of f at (0, 0) is the zero vector. Now, if the strong gradient exists at (0, 0), it must also be the zero vector, since it must be equal to the weak gradient. However, this would imply that $\cos(r/\theta) - 1 = f(r, \theta) - f(0, 0) = \varepsilon(r, \theta)$, where $\varepsilon/r \to 0$ as $r \to 0$. But $|\cos(r/\theta) - 1|/r = 1/r$ for $\theta = 2r/\pi$, which contradicts $\varepsilon/r \to 0$ as $r \to 0$. Hence, the strong gradient does not exist.

It may also happen that the weak differential exists when the weak gradient does not. A simple example illustrates this. Let

$$f(x, y) = (x^2 + y^2)^{1/2}$$

and consider **u** to be the origin. Then for any vector $\mathbf{h} = (h_1, h_2)$,

$$\lim_{t \to 0} (f(\mathbf{u} + t\mathbf{h}) - f(\mathbf{u}))/t = \lim_{t \to 0} f(th_1, th_2)/t = (h_1{}^2 + h_2{}^2)^{1/2} = \|\mathbf{h}\|$$

Thus, $\delta f(0; h) = \|\mathbf{h}\|$, which is clearly not a linear functional of **h**. Therefore, the weak gradient of f cannot exist at the origin. It follows that the strong gradient also does not exist.

The relation between the weak and strong differential is further illuminated by the following theorem, a proof of which can be found in Liusternik and Sobolev.[19]

Theorem. *If the weak differential* $\delta f(\mathbf{u}; \mathbf{h})$ *exists for* $\|\mathbf{u}' - \mathbf{u}\| \leq r$ *and is uniformly continuous in* **u** *and continuous in* **h**, *then the strong differential also exists in this set (and the two differentials are equal).*

10.4 The Multiplier Rule in Abstract Analysis

Using the concepts of the preceding section, we shall now consider extremal problems in abstract spaces.

Definition 6. Let J and $g_1, \ldots, g_p$ $(p \geq 1)$ be real functionals defined on $D \subset E$. The set $C(g_i) = \{\mathbf{y} | g_i(\mathbf{y}) = 0\}$ is an *equality constraint*. The intersection $C = \bigcap_1^p C(g_i)$ is also an *equality constraint*. Let $\mathbf{u} \in C$. If there is a neighborhood, N_u, of $\mathbf{u}$ such that $J(\mathbf{y}) \geq J(\mathbf{u})$ for all $\mathbf{y}$ in $C \cap N_u \cap D$, then $\mathbf{u}$ is a *relative minimum* of J on the constraint C.

Definition 7. Let $C = \bigcap_1^p C(g_i)$ be an equality constraint defined by the functionals $g_1, \ldots, g_p$. Let $\mathbf{u} \in C$ and let the gradients $\nabla g_1(\mathbf{u}), \ldots, \nabla g_p(\mathbf{u})$ exist. The set of all $\mathbf{h} \in E$ such that $\langle \nabla g_i(\mathbf{u}), \mathbf{h} \rangle = 0$, $i = 1, \ldots, p$ is called the *tangent subspace* of C at the point $\mathbf{u}$ and is denoted by T_u.

A first necessary condition for $\mathbf{u}$ to be a relative minimum of J on the constraint C is given by the Lagrange multiplier rule. We shall now establish an abstract generalization of the multiplier rule in pre-Hilbert spaces. This generalization includes the multiplier rule of the ordinary calculus and the multiplier rule of the calculus of variations as special cases. As we have previously pointed out, our generalization differs from others in its assumptions about the domains of definition of the functionals and their differentials. In particular, we shall not require differentials to exist in neighborhoods but only in finitely open sets. Furthermore, we shall not require strong differentials but shall make weak gradients suffice. The basis for most proofs of the multiplier rule is a theorem of the type represented by Theorem 1, which follows.

Theorem 1. (i) *Let $J, g_1, \ldots, g_p$ $(p \geq 1)$ be real functionals defined on a set D in a real pre-Hilbert space, E, and let* $\mathbf{u}$ *be a relative minimum of J on the constraint $C = \bigcap_1^p C(g_i)$. Let D be finitely open at* $\mathbf{u}$.

(ii) *Let the weak gradients $\{\nabla g_1(\mathbf{u}), \ldots, \nabla g_p(\mathbf{u})\}$ exist and form a linearly independent set in E.*

(iii) *Let T_u be the tangent subspace of C at* $\mathbf{u}$. *For any $\mathbf{h} \in T_u$, let $\nabla J(\mathbf{y})$ and $\nabla g_i(\mathbf{y})$, $1 \leq i \leq p$, exist for all $\mathbf{y} = \mathbf{u} + t_0 \mathbf{h} + \sum_1^p t_i \nabla g_i(\mathbf{u})$, where $(t_0, t_1, \ldots, t_p)$ is any point in some neighborhood, N, of the origin in R^{p+1}. Further, suppose that the $\nabla g_i(\mathbf{y})$ are continuous in the t_i in the neighborhood N and that $\nabla J(\mathbf{y})$ is continuous in the t_i at the origin. If $\mathbf{h} \in T_u$, then $\langle \nabla J(\mathbf{u}), \mathbf{h} \rangle = 0$.*

PROOF. Let $\mathbf{t} = (t_1, \ldots, t_p)$ be a real p-dimensional vector and s a real scalar. Define

$$\mathbf{y}_{st} = \mathbf{u} + s\mathbf{h} + \sum_1^p t_i \nabla g_i(\mathbf{u}),$$

where $\mathbf{h}$ is an arbitrary point in T_u. (We assume $\mathbf{h} \neq 0$, since the result follows trivially for $\mathbf{h} = 0$.) Then we define the functions $F_i(t, s) = F_i(t_1, \ldots, t_p, s) = g_i(\mathbf{y}_{ts})$, $i = 1, \ldots, p$. The functions F_i have the properties:

1. $F_i(0, 0) = g_i(\mathbf{u}) = 0$;
2. the partial derivatives $F_{ij} = \partial F_i/\partial t_j$ and $F_{is} = \partial F_i/\partial s$ exist as continuous functions of (t, s) in some neighborhood of $(0, 0)$;
3. the Jacobian matrix $(F_{ij}(t, s))$ has rank p for (t, s) in some neighborhood of $(0, 0)$. Also $F_{is}(0, 0) = 0$ for all $i = 1, \ldots, p$.

To establish property 2, we observe that

$$F_{ij}(t, s) = \lim_{\Delta t_j \to 0} (g_i(\mathbf{y}_{ts} + \Delta t_j \nabla g_j(\mathbf{u})) - g_i(\mathbf{y}_{ts}))/\Delta t_j$$
$$= \delta g_i(\mathbf{y}_{ts}; \nabla g_j(\mathbf{u})) = \langle \nabla g_i(\mathbf{y}_{ts}), \nabla g_j(\mathbf{u}) \rangle$$

This is a consequence of hypothesis (iii) which asserts that the g_i and their gradients are defined for $|t_i|$ and $|s|$ sufficiently small. The continuity of F_{ij} in (t, s) follows from the assumed continuity of $\nabla g_i(\mathbf{y}_{ts})$.

To obtain property 3, we note that

$$F_{ij}(0, 0) = \langle \nabla g_i(\mathbf{u}), \nabla g_j(\mathbf{u}) \rangle$$

Since the $\{\nabla g_i(\mathbf{u})\}$ are assumed to be linearly independent, it follows by well-known results of finite-dimensional linear algebra that the $p \times p$ matrix $(F_{ij}(0, 0))$ has rank p. By continuity, the matrix $(F_{ij}(t, s))$ also has rank p for (t, s) in some neighborhood of $(0, 0)$. Finally,

$$F_{is}(t, s) = \lim_{\Delta s \to 0} (g_i(\mathbf{y}_{ts} + \Delta s\, \mathbf{h}) - g_i(\mathbf{y}_{ts}))/\Delta s$$
$$= \delta g_i(\mathbf{y}_{ts}; \mathbf{h}) = \langle \nabla g_i(\mathbf{y}_{ts}), \mathbf{h} \rangle$$

Hence, $F_{is}(t, s)$ is continuous in a neighborhood of $(0, 0)$ and $F_{is}(0, 0) = \langle \nabla g_i(\mathbf{u}), \mathbf{h} \rangle = 0$ for $i = 1, \ldots, p$, since $\mathbf{h} \in T_u$.

By virtue of these properties, we can invoke the classical implicit function theorem to obtain functions $G_i(s)$, $i = 1, \ldots, p$, such that $F_i(G_1(s), \ldots, G_p(s), s) = 0$ for all s in a neighborhood. Furthermore, $G_i(0) = 0$ and the G_i are continuously differentiable in a neighborhood of $s = 0$. In fact, since $F_{js}(0, 0) = 0$ for all $j = 1, \ldots, p$, it follows from classical results that $G_i'(0) = 0$ for all $i = 1, \ldots, p$. Since $G_i(s) = sG_i'(\theta_{is}s)$ for s sufficiently small $(0 < \theta_{is} < 1)$, we see that

$$\lim_{s \to 0} G_i(s)/s = G_i'(0) = 0$$

Now, consider the vectors $\mathbf{y}_s = \mathbf{u} + s\mathbf{h} + \sum_1^p G_j(s) \nabla g_j(\mathbf{u})$. For all s in some neighborhood of $s = 0$,

$$g_i(\mathbf{y}_s) = F_i(G_1(s), \ldots, G_p(s), s) = 0$$

Hence, for all such s, we have $\mathbf{y}_s \in C$. Furthermore, since $\lim_{s \to 0} G_j(s) = 0$, we have $\lim_{s \to 0} \mathbf{y}_s = \mathbf{u}$. Defining $H(t, s) = J(\mathbf{y}_{ts})$, we obtain for the partial derivatives of H, using the same methods as above, $H_{t_j}(0, 0) = \langle \nabla J(\mathbf{u}), \nabla g_j(\mathbf{u}) \rangle$ and $H_s(0, 0) = \langle \nabla J(\mathbf{u}), \mathbf{h} \rangle$. Since H_{t_j} and H_s exist in a neighborhood of (0, 0) and are continuous at (0,0) we have

$$J(\mathbf{y}_s) - J(\mathbf{u}) = s\left(\sum_1^p \langle \nabla J(\mathbf{u}), \nabla g_j(\mathbf{u}) \rangle\, G_j'(0) + \langle \nabla J(\mathbf{u}), \mathbf{h} \rangle + \varepsilon\right)$$
$$= s(\langle \nabla J(\mathbf{u}), \mathbf{h} \rangle + \varepsilon)$$

where $\varepsilon \to 0$ as $s \to 0$. If $\langle \nabla J(\mathbf{u}), \mathbf{h} \rangle = -a^2 \neq 0$, then for all sufficiently small positive s we would have $J(\mathbf{y}_s) < J(\mathbf{u})$, contradicting the hypothesis that $\mathbf{u}$ is a relative minimum of J on C. Likewise, if $\langle \nabla J(\mathbf{u}), \mathbf{h} \rangle = a^2 \neq 0$, then for $s < 0$ and $|s|$ sufficiently small we obtain the same contradiction. Therefore, $\langle \nabla J(\mathbf{u}), \mathbf{h} \rangle = 0$, as was to be proven.

Remark. It is of interest to note that if we assume that the strong gradient of J merely exists at $\mathbf{u}$, the theorem remains valid. In proof, let $\mathbf{h}_s = s\mathbf{h} + \sum_1^p G_j(s) \nabla g_j(\mathbf{u})$. Then $\mathbf{y}_s = \mathbf{u} + \mathbf{h}_s$ and $\|\mathbf{h}_s\| \leq |s|(\|\mathbf{h}\| + \sum_1^p |G_j(s)/s| \cdot \|\nabla g_j(u)\|)$ and $\mathbf{h}_s \to 0$ as $s \to 0$. By the definition of strong gradient, we have $J(\mathbf{y}_s) - J(\mathbf{u}) = \langle \nabla_s J(\mathbf{u}), \mathbf{h}_s \rangle + \varepsilon$, where $\varepsilon/\|\mathbf{h}_s\| \to 0$ as $\mathbf{h}_s \to 0$. But

$$\langle \nabla_s J(\mathbf{u}), \mathbf{h}_s \rangle = s\left(\langle \nabla_s J(\mathbf{u}), \mathbf{h} \rangle + \sum_1^p G_j(s)/s\, \langle \nabla_s J(\mathbf{u}), \nabla g_j(\mathbf{u}) \rangle\right)$$

Since $G_j(s)/s \to 0$ as $s \to 0$, we have

$$J(\mathbf{y}_s) - J(\mathbf{u}) = s(\langle \nabla_s J(\mathbf{u}), \mathbf{h} \rangle + \varepsilon_1 + \varepsilon/s)$$

where $\varepsilon_1 \to 0$ as $s \to 0$. Since $\|\mathbf{h}_s\| \leq |s|(\|\mathbf{h}\| + \varepsilon_2)$, we have $\varepsilon/|s| \leq \varepsilon(\|\mathbf{h}\| + \varepsilon_2)/\|\mathbf{h}_s\|$ so that $\varepsilon/s \to 0$ as $s \to 0$. We may then apply the argument of the theorem to obtain $\langle \nabla_s J(\mathbf{u}), \mathbf{h} \rangle = 0$.

The geometric interpretation of Theorem 1 is self-evident and leads directly to the multiplier rule as follows.

Theorem 2. *Let* $J, g_1, \ldots, g_p$ *be real functionals satisfying conditions* (i), (ii), *and* (iii) *of Theorem* 1. *If* $\nabla J(\mathbf{u}) \neq 0$, *then there exist unique real scalars* $\lambda_1, \ldots, \lambda_p$ *not all zero such that*

$$\nabla J(\mathbf{u}) = \sum_1^p \lambda_j \nabla g_j(\mathbf{u}) \tag{10.13}$$

PROOF. Let $(\lambda_1, \ldots, \lambda_p)$ be the unique solution of the linear system of equations

$$\sum_{j=1}^p \langle \nabla g_i(\mathbf{u}), \nabla g_j(\mathbf{u}) \rangle \lambda_j = \langle \nabla g_i(\mathbf{u}), \nabla J(\mathbf{u}) \rangle, \qquad i = 1, \ldots, p$$

Let T_u be the tangent subspace at $\mathbf{u}$. By Theorem 1, if $\mathbf{h} \in T_u$, then $\langle \nabla J(\mathbf{u}), \mathbf{h} \rangle = 0$. Hence, $\nabla J(\mathbf{u})$ cannot be in T_u, for that would imply $\nabla J(\mathbf{u}) = 0$. Consequently, for some $\nabla g_i(\mathbf{u})$ we must have $\langle \nabla g_i(\mathbf{u}), \nabla J(\mathbf{u}) \rangle \neq 0$; i.e., the above linear system is nonhomogeneous. (Its determinant is nonzero because the $\{\nabla g_i(\mathbf{u})\}$ are linearly independent.) Hence, not all the λ_j are zero.

Now, define $\mathbf{v} = \nabla J(\mathbf{u}) - \sum_1^p \lambda_j \nabla g_j(\mathbf{u})$. We have $\langle \nabla g_i(\mathbf{u}), \mathbf{v} \rangle = 0$ for $i = 1, \ldots, p$. Therefore, $\mathbf{v} \in T_u$. However, for any $\mathbf{h} \in T_u$,

$$\langle \mathbf{v}, \mathbf{h} \rangle = \langle \nabla J(\mathbf{u}), \mathbf{h} \rangle - \sum_1^p \lambda_j \langle \nabla g_j(\mathbf{u}), \mathbf{h} \rangle = 0$$

again by Theorem 1 and the definition of T_u. Hence, $\langle \mathbf{v}, \mathbf{v} \rangle = 0$, which implies

$$\nabla J(\mathbf{u}) - \sum_1^p \lambda_j \nabla g_j(\mathbf{u}) = 0$$

as was to be proven.

Corollary (*The Multiplier Rule*). *Let $J, g_1, \ldots, g_p$ $(p \geq 1)$ be real functionals defined on a set D in a real pre-Hilbert space E. Let $\mathbf{u}$ be a relative minimum of J on the constraint $C = \bigcap_1^p C(g_i)$ and let D be finitely open at $\mathbf{u}$. Let the weak gradients $\nabla g_1(\mathbf{y}), \ldots, \nabla g_p(\mathbf{y})$ exist and be finitely continuous in a star-neighborhood, D_u, of $\mathbf{u}$. Let the weak gradient $\nabla J(y)$ exist in D_u and be finitely continuous at $\mathbf{u}$. Finally, let $\{\nabla g_1(\mathbf{u}), \ldots, \nabla g_p(\mathbf{u})\}$ be a linearly independent set in E. If $\nabla J(\mathbf{u}) \neq 0$, then there exists a unique nonzero real vector $(\lambda_1, \ldots, \lambda_p)$ such that*

$$\nabla J(\mathbf{u}) = \sum_1^p \lambda_j \nabla g_j(\mathbf{u})$$

Remark. Following Liusternik and Sobolev, we could have proceeded by introducing the constraint $g(\mathbf{y}) = g_1(\mathbf{y}), \ldots, g_p(\mathbf{y}))$. Thus, g is not a functional but has its values in R^p. They require the strong derivative $g'(\mathbf{y})$ to exist in a neighborhood of $\mathbf{u}$. Since $g'(\mathbf{y}) = (g_1'(\mathbf{y}), \ldots, g_p'(\mathbf{y}))$, the same requirement applies to the g_i'. Also, they require $g'(\mathbf{u})$ to be a mapping from E onto all of R^p. This is equivalent to the linear independence of the functionals $\{g_1'(\mathbf{u}), \ldots, g_p'(\mathbf{u})\}$, since $g'(\mathbf{u})\mathbf{h} = (g_1'(\mathbf{u})\mathbf{h}, \ldots, g_p'(\mathbf{u})\mathbf{h})$ for $h \in E$.

10.5 Necessary Conditions for Optimal Controls

We shall now apply the abstract multiplier rule of the previous section to the optimal control problem described in Sec. 10.2 and shall obtain necessary conditions for an optimal solution. In view of the equivalence of the optimal control problem and the problem of Mayer, this will yield a new derivation of the multiplier rule for the problem of Mayer.

Let Ω be an open set in R^m, Euclidean m-space. A control,

$$\mathbf{u}^T = \mathbf{u}^T(t) = (u_1(t), \ldots, u_m(t))$$

is "admissible" on the closed interval $[t_0, t_1]$ if it is a piecewise continuous function of t for $t_0 \leq t \leq t_1$ and the values $\{\mathbf{u}(t)\}$ lie in Ω for all such t.

Now, the set, $\bar{C}_m$, of all piecewise continuous functions $\mathbf{u}(t)$ defined on an interval $[a, b]$ and having values in R^m constitutes a linear space in the usual way, i.e., $\mathbf{u} + \mathbf{v} = \mathbf{u}(t) + \mathbf{v}(t)$ and $\lambda\mathbf{u} = \lambda\mathbf{u}(t)$ define the operations of addition and scalar multiplication in the space. It becomes a pre-Hilbert space if we define the inner product, $\langle \mathbf{u}, \mathbf{v} \rangle$, of any two functions $\mathbf{u}, \mathbf{v} \in \bar{C}_m$, where $\mathbf{u}^T = \mathbf{u}^T(t) = (u_1(t), \ldots, u_m(t))$, $\mathbf{v}^T = \mathbf{v}^T(t) = (v_1(t), \ldots, v_m(t))$, as

$$\langle \mathbf{u}, \mathbf{v} \rangle = \int_a^b (u_1 v_1 + \cdots + u_m v_m)\, dt = \int_a^b \mathbf{u}^T \mathbf{v}\, dt$$

For t_0 and t_1 in $[a, b]$, the set of admissible controls on $[t_0, t_1]$ is a subset of $\bar{C}_m$, if we take $\mathbf{u}(t) = 0$ for t outside of $[t_0, t_1]$. In the ensuing discussion, we shall take $\bar{C}_m$ as the underlying pre-Hilbert space.

Suppose that the initial values $\mathbf{x}(t_0)$ and the initial time t_0 are fixed. Suppose further that there exists an admissible control $\mathbf{u} = \mathbf{u}(t)$ such that the control equations (10.9) have a solution $\mathbf{x}(t)$ in the interval $t_0 \leq t \leq t_1$, with initial values $\mathbf{x}(t_0)$, and the points $(\mathbf{x}(t), \mathbf{u}(t))$ lie in the open region Γ in which $\mathbf{f}(\mathbf{x}, \mathbf{u})$ has continuous partials. Consider the one-parameter system of differential equations

$$\frac{d\mathbf{x}}{dt} = \mathbf{f}(\mathbf{x}, \mathbf{u} + s\mathbf{h}) \qquad (10.9_s)$$

where $\mathbf{h} = \mathbf{h}(t)$ is an arbitrary admissible control on $[t_0, t_1]$ and s is a scalar parameter. From the theory of ordinary differential equations (see Coddington and Levinson,[23] p. 29, for example), it is known that (10.9_s) has a solution in $[t_0, t_1]$ for all sufficiently small $|s|$. In fact, for k arbitrary admissible controls $h_1, \ldots, h_k$, the k-parameter system

$$\frac{d\mathbf{x}}{dt} = \mathbf{f}(\mathbf{x}, \mathbf{u} + \sum_1^k s_i \mathbf{h}_i)$$

has a solution in $[t_0, t_1]$ for $\sum_1^k |s_i|$ sufficiently small. In all cases, the initial value is taken to be $\mathbf{x}(t_0)$.

We shall designate the solution of (10.9_s) by $\mathbf{x}(t, s)$ when $\mathbf{h}$ is being held fixed in the discussion. The final values $\mathbf{x}(t_1, s)$ are then functionals depending on the control $\mathbf{y} = \mathbf{u} + s\mathbf{h}$. In the general case, we have solutions $\mathbf{x}(t, s_1, \ldots, s_k)$ with final values depending on $\mathbf{y} = \mathbf{u} + \sum_1^k s_i \mathbf{h}_i$. Thus, the final values of the solutions of (10.9_s) with initial values $\mathbf{x}(t_0)$ are functionals defined on a domain, $D \subset \bar{C}_m$, which is finitely open at $\mathbf{u}$ (Definition 1) for any $\mathbf{u} \in D$. We express this by writing $\mathbf{x}(t_1) = \mathbf{x}_1(\mathbf{y})$ for $\mathbf{y} \in D$. It follows immediately that the functions ψ_j in (10.10) which define the endpoint constraints can also be regarded as functionals on D. With Definition 6 in mind, let us define

$$g_j(\mathbf{y}) = \psi_j(t_0, \mathbf{x}(t_0), t_1, \mathbf{x}_1(\mathbf{y})), \qquad j = 1, \ldots, p$$

Similarly, we define

$$J(\mathbf{y}) = J(t_0, \mathbf{x}(t_0), t_1, \mathbf{x}_1(\mathbf{y}))$$

If $\mathbf{u}$ minimizes J on the constraint $C = \bigcap_1^p C(g_i)$ (see Definition 6), then $J(\mathbf{y}) \geq J(\mathbf{u})$ for all $\mathbf{y} \in D \cap C \cap N_u$, where N_u is some neighborhood of $\mathbf{u}$. If $\nabla J(\mathbf{y})$ and $\nabla g_j(\mathbf{y})$ exist and satisfy the hypotheses of the abstract multiplier rule (Theorem 2, Corollary), then we may apply it immediately to the control problem to obtain the necessary conditions of the multiplier rule of the problem of Mayer. Thus, the derivation from this point on consists primarily of a calculation of the gradients of J and the g_i. We shall now carry out this calculation using the well-known technique of the adjoint equation.

In the following discussion, let $\mathbf{h} = \mathbf{h}(t)$ be an arbitrary but fixed function in $\bar{C}_m$. Let $\mathbf{u} = \mathbf{u}(t)$ be an optimal control on $[t_0, t_1]$. For all $|s|$ sufficiently small, $\mathbf{u} + s\mathbf{h}$ is an admissible control and, as explained above, has a corresponding trajectory $\mathbf{x}(t, s)$ in $[t_0, t_1]$. For $s = 0$, the corresponding trajectory is the optimal trajectory $\mathbf{x} = \mathbf{x}(t, 0)$. Using the notation explained above, we have $\mathbf{x}_1(u + sh) = \mathbf{x}(t_1, s)$. Now, let $(\partial J/\partial \mathbf{x}_1)_*$ denote the $n \times 1$ matrix of partial derivatives, $\partial J/\partial x_{1j}$, of $J(t_0, \mathbf{x}(t_0), t_1, \mathbf{x}(t_1))$ with respect to the variables $x_j(t_1)$, $j = 1, \ldots, n$, and evaluated for $\mathbf{x}(t_1) = \mathbf{x}(t_1, 0) = \mathbf{x}_1(u)$, i.e., at the final value of the optimal trajectory. It is assumed that the point $(t_0, \mathbf{x}(t_0), t_1, \mathbf{x}(t_1, 0))$ lies in the region R_2 in which J and ψ_j have continuous first-order partials (see Sec. 10.2). Since R_2 is an open set, and since $\mathbf{x}(t_1, s)$ is continuous in the parameter s (for a proof see Ref. 23 again), it follows that the points Q_s: $(t_0, \mathbf{x}(t_0), t_1, \mathbf{x}(t_1, s))$ are also in R_2 for sufficiently small $|s|$. Hence, $J(Q_s)$ and $\psi_j(Q_s)$ are defined for $|s|$ sufficiently small and J and ψ_j have continuous first-order partials at such Q_s. In this discussion, t_0, $\mathbf{x}(t_0)$ and t_1 are not being varied. Therefore, we assume that $p \leq n$ and that the $p \times n$ matrix $(\partial \psi_j/\partial \mathbf{x}(t_1))$ has rank p.

Now, by Definition 3, Remark 1, we have

$$\delta J(\mathbf{u}; \mathbf{h}) = \left.\frac{dJ(\mathbf{u} + s\mathbf{h})}{ds}\right|_{s=0} = \left(\frac{\partial J}{\delta \mathbf{x}_1}\right)_*^T \delta \mathbf{x}_1(\mathbf{u}; \mathbf{h}) \tag{10.14}$$

Let $\partial f/\partial u$ denote the $n \times m$ matrix of partial derivatives $(\partial f_i/\partial u_j)$ and $\partial f/\partial x$ the $n \times n$ matrix $(\partial f_i/\partial x_j)$, both evaluated at a point P_t : $(\mathbf{x}(t, s), \mathbf{u} + s\mathbf{h})$, where $\mathbf{x}(t, s)$ is the trajectory corresponding to $\mathbf{u} + s\mathbf{h}$. Observe that $P_t \in \Gamma$ for $t_0 \leq t \leq t_1$ so that f has continuous first-order partials at P_t. Writing $\mathbf{x}(t, s) = (x_1(t, s), \ldots, x_n(t, s))$, we let $\partial \mathbf{x}/\partial s$ be the $n \times 1$ matrix of partials $(\partial x_i/\partial s)$.

Once again, by appeal to known results in the theory of ordinary differential equations (e.g., see Struble,[24] p. 72), we can assert the existence of the $\partial x_i/\partial s$ for $|s|$ sufficiently small. For any such s, the partial derivatives satisfy the variational equations

$$\frac{d}{dt}\left(\frac{\partial \mathbf{x}}{\partial s}\right) = \frac{\partial f}{\partial u}\mathbf{h} + \frac{\partial f}{\partial x}\frac{\partial \mathbf{x}}{\partial s}$$

Since

$$\delta \mathbf{x}_1(\mathbf{u}; \mathbf{h}) = \left.\frac{d\mathbf{x}_1(\mathbf{u} + s\mathbf{h})}{ds}\right|_{s=0} = \left.\frac{\partial \mathbf{x}(t_1, s)}{\partial s}\right|_{s=0}$$

it follows that $\delta \mathbf{x}_1(\mathbf{u}; \mathbf{h})$ exists and is the final value of a solution of the nth order system,

$$\frac{d\mathbf{v}}{dt} = \left(\frac{\partial f}{\partial u}\right)_* \mathbf{h} + \left(\frac{\partial f}{\partial x}\right)_* \mathbf{v} \tag{10.15}$$

where the asterisk subscripts indicate that the partials are to be evaluated at the point $(\mathbf{x}(t, 0), \mathbf{u}(t))$ of the optimal solution. The initial values $\mathbf{v}(t_0)$ are to be taken as zero when $\mathbf{x}(t_0)$ is not to be varied. Otherwise, $\mathbf{v}(t_0)$ will be arbitrary.

The adjoint equations of (10.15) are given by

$$\frac{d\mathbf{y}}{dt} = -\left(\frac{\partial f}{\partial x}\right)_*^T \mathbf{y} \tag{10.16}$$

Hence, $d(\mathbf{y}^T\mathbf{v})/dt = \mathbf{y}^T(\partial f/\partial u)^*\mathbf{h}$ for any solutions $\mathbf{y}$ of (10.16) and $\mathbf{v}$ of (10.15). Integrating with respect to t, we get

$$\mathbf{y}^T(t_1)\mathbf{v}(t_1) = \int_{t_0}^{t_1} \mathbf{y}^T \left(\frac{\partial f}{\partial u}\right)_* \mathbf{h}\, dt + \mathbf{y}^T(t_0)\mathbf{v}(t_0) \tag{10.17}$$

If we take for $\mathbf{y}$ the solution, $\mathbf{J}_x(t)$, of (10.16) which has final values $\mathbf{J}_x(t_1) = (\partial J/\partial x_1)_*$, then since $\mathbf{v}(t_1) = \delta \mathbf{x}_1(\mathbf{u}, \mathbf{h})$, it follows from (10.14) and (10.17) that

$$\delta J(\mathbf{u}; \mathbf{h}) = \int_{t_0}^{t_1} \mathbf{J}_x{}^T \left(\frac{\partial f}{\partial u}\right)_* \mathbf{h}\, dt + \mathbf{J}_x{}^T(t_0)\mathbf{v}(t_0) \tag{10.18}$$

The function $\mathbf{J}_x{}^T(\partial f/\partial u)_*$ is piecewise continuous on $[t_0, t_1]$, since $\mathbf{J}_x{}^T$ is a solution of the system of differential equations (10.16). Hence, $\mathbf{J}_x{}^T(\partial f/\partial u)_* \in \bar{C}_m$. Since t_0, $\mathbf{x}(t_0)$ and t_1 are not being varied in this discussion, we must take $\mathbf{v}(t_0) = 0$. Using the inner product notation, (10.18) can be rewritten as $\delta J(\mathbf{u}; \mathbf{h}) = \langle \mathbf{J}_x{}^T(\partial f/\partial u)_*, \mathbf{h}\rangle$.

$$\nabla J(\mathbf{u}) = \mathbf{J}_x{}^T\left(\frac{\partial f}{\partial u}\right)_* \tag{10.19}$$

that is, the gradient of J exists at $\mathbf{u}$ and may actually be computed by solving the adjoint Eqs. (10.16) for $\mathbf{J}_x{}^T(t)$, integrating backward from t_1 to t_0 with the "starting" values $(\partial J/\partial x_1)_*$. (Since $\mathbf{u}$ is piecewise continuous in $[t_0, t_1]$, so is $(\partial f/\partial x)_*$ and a piecewise differentiable solution of (10.16) exists in $[t_0, t_1]$ for all starting values.)

By similar calculations it is easy to show that the gradients of the g_j are

$$\nabla g_j(\mathbf{u}) = \boldsymbol{\psi}_{jx}^T\left(\frac{\partial f}{\partial u}\right)_*, \qquad j = 1, \ldots, p \tag{10.20}$$

where $\boldsymbol{\psi}_{jx}(t)$ is the solution of the adjoint Eqs. (10.16) having as final values $\boldsymbol{\psi}_{jx}(t_1) = (\partial\psi_j/\partial x_1)_*$. Finally, as we have already remarked, for any admissible controls $\mathbf{h}_1, \ldots, \mathbf{h}_k$ and all $(s_1, \ldots, s_k)$ with $\sum_1^k |s_i| < \delta$, the control $\mathbf{u} + \sum_1^k s_i\mathbf{h}_i$ is also admissible and has a corresponding trajectory $\mathbf{x}(t, s_1, \ldots, s_k)$ which is continuous in $(s_1, \ldots, s_k)$. Hence, the matrices $(\partial f/\partial u)$ and $(\partial f/\partial x)$ evaluated at the points $(\mathbf{x}(t, s_1, \ldots, s_k), \mathbf{u} + \sum_1^k s_i\mathbf{h}_i)$ in $R^n \times R^m$ are continuous functions of the parameters $(s_1, \ldots, s_k)$ in some neighborhood of the origin in R^k. Consequently, any solution $\overline{\boldsymbol{\Psi}}_{jx}$ of $d\mathbf{y}/dt = -(\partial f/\partial x)^T\mathbf{y}$ is also continuous in the parameters $s_1, \ldots, s_k$ in the same neighborhood in R^k. It follows from this that the gradients

$$\nabla g_j(\mathbf{u} + \sum_1^k s_i\mathbf{h}_i) = \overline{\boldsymbol{\Psi}}_{jx}^T\left(\frac{\partial f}{\partial u}\right), \qquad j = 1, \ldots, p \tag{10.21}$$

exist and are continuous in the s_i. This means that ∇g_j, $j = 1, \ldots, p$, exists and is finitely continuous (Definition 2) in a star-neighborhood D_u, i.e., D_u is the set of all controls of the form $\mathbf{u} + \sum_1^k s_i\mathbf{h}_i$ for arbitrary $\mathbf{h}_1, \ldots, \mathbf{h}_k \in \bar{C}_m$ and $\sum_1^k |s_i| < d$, where $d > 0$ depends on the choice of $\mathbf{h}_i$. D_u is, as we pointed out in Sec. 10.3, a set which is finitely open at $\mathbf{u}$. In similar fashion, we establish that ∇J also exists and is finitely continuous in a set which is finitely open at $\mathbf{u}$. This is actually more than is required by the Corollary of Theorem 2 with respect to ∇J, where we require only that ∇J be finitely continuous at u. Thus, we have proven that ∇J and ∇g_j satisfy all the hypotheses of that corollary except for the linear independence of the set $\{\nabla g_1(\mathbf{u}), \ldots, \nabla g_p(\mathbf{u})\}$.

Let us now consider the gradients $\{\nabla g_j(\mathbf{u})\}$. If they are not linearly independent, then there are scalar multipliers $\lambda_1, \ldots, \lambda_p$ not all zero and such that $\sum_1^p \lambda_j \nabla g_j(\mathbf{u}) = 0$. On the other hand, if the $\{\nabla g_j(\mathbf{u})\}$ are linearly independent, then the multiplier rule (Theorem 2, Corollary) can be applied, that is, there are again scalar multipliers $\lambda_1, \ldots, \lambda_p$ not all zero and such that $\nabla J(\mathbf{u}) = \sum_1^p \lambda_j \nabla g_j(\mathbf{u})$, as in (10.13). Both of these cases can be subsumed under one general principle by asserting the existence of scalars $l_0, \lambda_1, \ldots, \lambda_p$ not all zero such that

$$l_0 \nabla J(\mathbf{u}) + \sum_1^p \lambda_j \nabla g_j(\mathbf{u}) = 0 \tag{10.22}$$

where $l_0 = 1$ if the $\{\nabla g_j(\mathbf{u})\}$ are linearly independent and $l_0 = 0$ if they are not linearly independent (note that if $\nabla J(\mathbf{u}) = 0$, we simply take $l_0 = 1$ and $\lambda_j = 0, j = 1, \ldots, p$).

Applying (10.22) to the optimal control problem, we obtain the following necessary conditions for an optimal solution:

$$-l_0\, \mathbf{J}_x{}^T \left(\frac{\partial f}{\partial u}\right)_* = \sum_1^p \lambda_j\, \psi_{jx}^T \left(\frac{\partial f}{\partial u}\right)_* \tag{10.23a}$$

$$\frac{d\mathbf{J}_x}{dt} = -\left(\frac{\partial f}{\partial x}\right)_*^T \mathbf{J}_x \tag{10.23b}$$

$$\mathbf{J}_x(t_1) = \left(\frac{\partial J}{\partial x_1}\right)_* \tag{10.23c}$$

$$\frac{d\psi_{jx}}{dt} = -\left(\frac{\partial f}{\partial x}\right)_*^T \psi_{jx}, \qquad j = 1, \ldots, p \tag{10.23d}$$

$$\psi_{jx}(t_1) = \left(\frac{\partial \psi_j}{\partial x_1}\right)_* \tag{10.23e}$$

Equations (10.23b) and (10.23d) can be combined into a single set of differential equations as follows. Let

$$\boldsymbol{l}(t) = -l_0\, \mathbf{J}_x(t) - \sum_1^p \lambda_j\, \psi_{jx}(t) \tag{10.24}$$

From (10.23b)–(10.23e) it follows at once that $\boldsymbol{l}_x$ is the solution of the system of differential equations

$$\frac{d\boldsymbol{l}_x}{dt} = -\left(\frac{\partial f}{\partial x}\right)_*^T \boldsymbol{l}_x \tag{10.25}$$

with final values

$$\boldsymbol{l}_x(t_1) = -\boldsymbol{l}_0 \left(\frac{\partial J}{\partial x_1}\right)_* - \sum_1^p \lambda_j \left(\frac{\partial \psi_j}{\partial x_1}\right)_* \tag{10.26}$$

Equation (10.23a) then becomes

$$\boldsymbol{l}_x{}^T \left(\frac{\partial f}{\partial u}\right)_* = 0 \tag{10.27}$$

We shall show that the components $\boldsymbol{l}_{xi}(t)$, $i = 1, \ldots, n$, of $\boldsymbol{l}_x$ are the "multipliers" of Bliss' formulation of the multiplier rule (see Bliss,[3] p. 202) and Eqs. (10.25) and (10.27) are the Euler–Lagrange equations. In order to prove this, we refer to Bliss[3] (p. 203) and to the statement of the problem of Mayer given in Sec. 10.1.

Following Bliss, we introduce the function

$$F(t, \mathbf{y}, \mathbf{y}') = \sum_1^n l_j(t)\Phi_j(t, \mathbf{y}, \mathbf{y}')$$

where the Φ_j are the functions in (10.3). Let F_y be the $n \times 1$ matrix of partials $(\partial F/\partial y_i)$, $i = 1, \dots, n$. Similarly, let $F_{y'}$ be the $n \times 1$ matrix of partials $(\partial F/\partial y_i')$. The Euler–Lagrange equations may be written in vector form as

$$\frac{dF_{y'}}{dt} = F_y \qquad (10.28)$$

Now, in the optimal control problem, the functions Φ_j are of the form

$$\Phi_j = x_j' - f_j(x_1, \dots, x_n, u_1, \dots, u_m), \qquad j = 1, \dots, n$$

As explained in Sec 10.2, the optimal control problem is transformed into a problem of Mayer by setting $y_i = x_i$, $i = 1, \dots, n$, and $y_{n+k} = u_k$, $k = 1, \dots, m$. Hence, for $i = 1, \dots, n$, we have

$$\frac{\partial F}{\partial y_i} = -\sum_{j=1}^n l_j \frac{\partial f_j}{\partial x}$$

and

$$\frac{\partial F}{\partial y_i'} - \frac{\partial F}{\partial x_i'} = l_i$$

Substituting in (10.28), we obtain the Euler–Lagrange equations in the form

$$\frac{dl_i}{dt} = -\sum_{j=1}^n l_j \frac{\partial f_j}{\partial x_i}, \qquad i = 1, \dots, n \qquad (10.29)$$

and for $i = n + k$, $k = 1, \dots, m$,

$$\frac{\partial F}{\partial y_{n+k}} = -\sum_{j=1}^n l_j \frac{\partial f_j}{\partial u_k}$$

$$\frac{\partial F}{\partial y_{n+k}'} = 0 \qquad (10.30)$$

$$\sum_{j=1}^n l_j \frac{\partial f_j}{\partial u_k} = 0$$

Comparing (10.29), (10.30) with (10.25), (10.27), we see that they are identical systems of equations. This proves that the Euler–Lagrange equations are necessary conditions for a solution of the problem of Mayer. Furthermore, Eqs. (10.26) for the final values are just the "transversality conditions" obtained by Bliss[3] (p. 202, Eqs. 74.9) by setting the coefficients of his $d_{y_{i2}}$ equal to zero, $i = 1, \ldots, n$. The constants e_μ of Bliss correspond to our λ_j and the multipliers $l_0, l_1, \ldots, l_n$ of Bliss are precisely our $l_0, l_{x1}, \ldots, l_{xn}$, respectively. As in Bliss, it is clear that l_0 and $l_{xi}(t)$, $i = 1, \ldots, n$, do not all vanish simultaneously at any point $\bar{t}$ in the interval $[t_0, t_1]$. If $l_0 = 1$, this is trivially the case. If $l_0 = 0$, then $l_{xi}(\bar{t}) = 0$ for all $i = 1, \ldots, n$ implies that $\mathbf{l}_x(t) = 0$ for all t in $[t_0, t_1]$, since $\boldsymbol{l}_x$ is the unique solution of the system of homogeneous linear equations (10.25). Consequently,

$$0 = \boldsymbol{l}_x(t_1) = -\sum_1^p \lambda_j \boldsymbol{\psi}_{jx}(t_1) = -\sum_1^p \lambda_j \left(\frac{\partial \psi_j}{\partial x_1}\right)_*$$

by (10.23) and (10.24). However, this contradicts the hypothesis that the matrix $(\partial\psi_j/\partial x_1)_*$ has rank p. Hence, $\boldsymbol{l}_x(t) \neq 0$ for all t in $[t_1, t_2]$, which completes the derivation of the multiplier rule as formulated in Bliss for the case in which the endpoints, t_0 and t_1, and the initial conditions $\mathbf{x}(t_0)$ are not varied. In the next section, we shall consider the case in which these quantities are varied also.

At this point, it is pertinent to make some observations regarding "normality." In Bliss[3] (pp. 210–219), an arc, $\mathbf{y}(t)$, which satisfies the multiplier rule for the problem of Mayer (or the equivalent problem of Bolza, as it is presented in Bliss), is said to have "abnormality of order q" if it has exactly q linearly independent sets of multipliers of the form $\{l_1^{(\sigma)} = 0, l_x^{(\sigma)}\}$, $\sigma = 1, \ldots, q$. If $q = 0$, then $\mathbf{y}(x)$ is said to be a "normal" arc. It is clear that a normal arc can have at most one (hence exactly one) set of multipliers with $l_0 = 1$.

The concept of normality is illuminated very clearly by looking at the corresponding optimal control problem. We see at once that normality is equivalent to the linear independence of the set of gradients $\{\nabla g_1(\mathbf{u}), \ldots, \nabla g_p(\mathbf{u})\}$, with all that this connotes geometrically. Abnormality of order q is equivalent to the existence of precisely $p - q$ linearly independent vectors among the $\{\nabla g_i(\mathbf{u})\}$, that is, the dimension of the subspace, G, spanned by the gradients $\{\nabla g_1(\mathbf{u}), \ldots, \nabla g_p(\mathbf{u})\}$ is precisely $p - q$. When viewed from this abstract standpoint, many of the results concerning normality are easily derived by the methods used in the proof of Theorem 1. For example, Theorem 77.1 in Bliss[3] (p. 214) asserts that near a normal arc which satisfies the differential equations (10.3) and the end-conditions (10.4) there is a one-parameter family of such arcs. The equivalent assertion in abstract spaces is that in a neighborhood of a point $\mathbf{u}$ on the constraint $C = \bigcap_1^p C(g_i)$ which is such that the gradients $\{\nabla g_1(\mathbf{u}), \ldots, \nabla g_p(\mathbf{u})\}$ are linearly independent, there is a one-parameter family of points which also lie on the constraint C. We established this result in the proof of Theorem 1 (Sec. 10.4).

Another remark of a rather different nature is appropriate at this juncture. Let us consider the Hamiltonian function

$$\mathscr{H}(\boldsymbol{l}_x, \mathbf{x}, \mathbf{u}) = \sum_{j=1}^{n} l_{xj} f_j(\mathbf{x}, \mathbf{u}) = \boldsymbol{l}_x^T \mathbf{f}$$

where $\mathbf{x}$, $\mathbf{u}$ and $\boldsymbol{l}_x$ are regarded as independent vector variables of dimension n, m, and n, respectively. We have

$$\frac{\partial \mathscr{H}}{\partial u_i} = \sum_{j=1}^{n} l_{xj} \frac{\partial f_j}{\partial u_i}, \qquad i = 1, \ldots, m$$

If $(\mathbf{x}(t), \mathbf{u}(t))$ is an optimal solution of the optimal control problem and $\boldsymbol{l}_x(t)$ is the corresponding solution of (10.25), given by (10.24), then (10.27) yields

$$\frac{\partial \mathscr{H}}{\partial u}(\boldsymbol{l}_x(t), \mathbf{x}(t), \mathbf{u}(t)) = 0$$

for all t in the interval $[t_1, t_2]$. But this is a necessary condition for $\mathscr{H}(\boldsymbol{l}_x(t), \mathbf{x}(t), \mathbf{u})$ to attain a relative maximum with respect to $\mathbf{u}$ at the point $\mathbf{u} = \mathbf{u}(t)$. Hence, we obtain in this case (i.e., when the control region Ω is an open set) conditions which are an immediate consequence of the maximum principle of Pontryagin, without appeal to that principle.

The Pontryagin principle also contains the result that $\mathscr{H} = \mathscr{H}(t) = \mathscr{H}(\boldsymbol{l}_x(t), \mathbf{x}(t), \mathbf{u}(t))$ is a constant along an optimal solution. This property of the Hamiltonian was, of course, long known in the case where $\mathbf{u}(t)$ is piecewise differentiable. Indeed, we then have

$$d\mathscr{H}/dt = d(\boldsymbol{l}_x^T \mathbf{f})/dt = (d\boldsymbol{l}_x^T/dt)\mathbf{f} + \boldsymbol{l}_x^T (\partial f/\partial x)\, d\mathbf{x}/dt + \boldsymbol{l}_x^T (\partial f/\partial u)(d\mathbf{u}/dt)$$

Since $d\boldsymbol{l}_x^T/dt = -\boldsymbol{l}_x^T (\partial f/\partial x)$ by (10.25), $d\mathbf{x}/dt = \mathbf{f}$ and $\boldsymbol{l}_x^T(\partial f/\partial u) = 0$ by (10.27), we obtain $d\mathscr{H}/dt = 0$ for all t. Thus, $\mathscr{H}$ is constant along an optimal solution.

10.6 Variation of Endpoints and Initial Conditions

We shall now extend the results of the previous section to the case where t_0, $\mathbf{x}(t_0)$, t_1, $\mathbf{x}(t_1)$ are all varied simultaneously. This can readily be done if we choose the underlying pre-Hilbert space to be $E = \overline{C}_m \times R^n \times R^2$ in which an arbitrary element is of the form $\mathbf{e} = (\mathbf{u}(t), \mathbf{v}_1, t_{01})$ with $\mathbf{u} = \mathbf{u}(t) \in \overline{C}_m$, $\mathbf{v}_1 \in R^n$ and $\mathbf{t}_{01} = (t_0, t_1) \in R^2$. Thus, E is the direct sum of $\overline{C}_m$ as the "control space," R^n as the "initial-value space," and R^2 as the "space of endpoints." If $\mathbf{e}^* = (\mathbf{u}^*(t), \mathbf{v}^*{}_1, \mathbf{t}_{01}^*)$ is any element of E, then we have the usual definition of the sum $\mathbf{e} + \mathbf{e}^* = (\mathbf{u}(t) + \mathbf{u}^*(t), \mathbf{v}_1 + \mathbf{v}_1^*, \mathbf{t}_{01} + \mathbf{t}_{01}^*)$. The inner product of $\mathbf{e}$ and $\mathbf{e}^*$ is defined as

$$\langle \mathbf{e}, \mathbf{e}^* \rangle = \int_a^b \mathbf{u}^T\mathbf{u}^* \, dt + \mathbf{v}_1{}^T\mathbf{v}_1{}^* + \mathbf{t}_{01}^T\mathbf{t}_{01}^*$$

Suppose for an arbitrary initial point t_0, an arbitrary final point t_1, an arbitrary set of initial values $\mathbf{x}(t_0) \in R^n$, and an arbitrary admissible control $\mathbf{u}$, that system (10.9) has a solution, $\mathbf{x}(t)$, $t_0 \leq t \leq t_1$. The final value $\mathbf{x}(t_1)$ can be regarded as a function on E to R^n. Writing $\mathbf{e} = (\mathbf{u}, \mathbf{x}(t_0), \mathbf{t}_{01})$, we can denote this function by $\mathbf{x}_2(\mathbf{e})$, following the usage of the previous section. It is clear that J and the ψ_j are functionals on E. The results of Sec. 10.5 can be extended in a very natural way to apply to this more general space.

We begin by noting that system (10.9) is autonomous and, therefore, we may shift the origin of the time axis without changing the problem. This allows us to set $t_0 = 0$, which we shall do for convenience in the derivation to follow. Thus, variation of the endpoints can be effected by varying t_1 only, and we are dealing with the initial-value problem

$$d\mathbf{x}/dt = \mathbf{f}(\mathbf{x}, \mathbf{u})$$
$$\mathbf{x}(0) = \mathbf{x}_0$$

where $\mathbf{x}_0$ denotes an arbitrary initial value which we may treat as a parameter of the problem. Now, let $\mathbf{y} = \mathbf{x} - \mathbf{x}_0$, so that $\mathbf{y}(0) = \mathbf{x}(0) - \mathbf{x}_0 = 0$. We obtain a corresponding initial-value problem for $\mathbf{y}$, that is,

$$\begin{aligned} d\mathbf{y}/dt &= \bar{\mathbf{f}}(\mathbf{y}, \mathbf{u}, \mathbf{x}_0) \\ \mathbf{y}(0) &= 0 \end{aligned} \tag{10.31}$$

where $\bar{\mathbf{f}}(\mathbf{y}, \mathbf{u}, \mathbf{x}_0) = \mathbf{f}(\mathbf{y} + \mathbf{x}_0, \mathbf{u})$. Thus, the parameter $\mathbf{x}_0$ is included in the differential equations themselves rather than in the initial conditions. At the same time, the endpoint constraints (10.10) are replaced by the constraints

$$\bar{\psi}_j(\mathbf{x}_0, t_1, \mathbf{y}(t_1)) = 0, \qquad j = 1, \dots, p \tag{10.32}$$

where $\bar{\psi}_j(\mathbf{x}_0, t_1, \mathbf{y}(t_1)) = \psi_j(0, \mathbf{x}_0, t_1, \mathbf{y}(t_1) + \mathbf{x}_0)$. Similarly, the functional to be minimized is now $\bar{J} = \bar{J}(\mathbf{x}_0, t_1, \mathbf{y}(t_1))$, where $\bar{J}(\mathbf{x}_0, t_1, \mathbf{y}(t_1)) = J(0, \mathbf{x}_0, t_1, \mathbf{y}(t_1) + \mathbf{x}_0)$. Then, instead of $\bar{C}_q \times R^n \times R^2$, we may take $E = \bar{C}_q \times R^n + R$, so that an arbitrary $\mathbf{e} \in E$ is of the form $\mathbf{e} = (\mathbf{u}(t), \mathbf{x}_0, t_1)$. If $\mathbf{e} \in E$ is such that system (10.31) has a solution in the interval $0 \leq t \leq t_1$, we may solve (10.31) and obtain the final values $\mathbf{y}(t_1)$. Hence, the final values may be regarded as a function of $\mathbf{e}$ and we can write $\mathbf{y}(t_1) = \mathbf{y}_1(\mathbf{e})$ as in Sec. 10.5. Similarly, we have $\bar{J}(\mathbf{x}_0, t_1, \mathbf{y}(t_1)) = \bar{J}(\mathbf{x}_0, t_1, \mathbf{y}_1(\mathbf{e})) = \bar{J}(\mathbf{e})$ and $\bar{\psi}_j(\mathbf{x}_0, t_1, \mathbf{y}(t_1)) = \bar{\psi}_j(\mathbf{e})$.

To calculate gradients, we consider $\bar{J}(\mathbf{e} + s\bar{\mathbf{h}})$, where $\bar{\mathbf{h}} = (\mathbf{h}(t), d\mathbf{x}_0, dt_1) \in E$ and $\mathbf{e}$ is a relative minimum of $\bar{J}$ satisfying $\bar{\Psi}_j(\mathbf{e}) = 0$. As before, $\mathbf{y}(t, s)$ is the trajectory corresponding to $\mathbf{e} + s\bar{\mathbf{h}}$ and $\mathbf{y}(t, 0)$ is the optimal solution. Following the procedure in Sec. 10.5, we have

$$\delta\bar{J}(\mathbf{e}, \bar{\mathbf{h}}) = \left.\frac{d\bar{J}(\mathbf{e} + s\bar{\mathbf{h}})}{ds}\right|_{s=0} = \left.\frac{dJ(\mathbf{e} + s\mathbf{h})}{ds}\right|_{s=0}$$

$$\begin{aligned} \bar{J}(\mathbf{e} + s\bar{\mathbf{h}}) &= \bar{J}(\mathbf{x}_0 + s\, d\mathbf{x}_0, t_1 + s\, dt_1, \mathbf{y}_1(\mathbf{e} + s\bar{\mathbf{h}})) \\ &= J(0, \mathbf{x}_0 + s\, d\mathbf{x}_0, t_1 + s\, dt_1, \mathbf{x}_1(\mathbf{e} + s\bar{\mathbf{h}}) + \mathbf{x}_0 + s\, d\mathbf{x}_0) \end{aligned} \tag{10.33}$$

$$\left.\frac{d\bar{J}(\mathbf{e} + s\bar{\mathbf{h}})}{ds}\right|_{s=0} = \left(\frac{\partial \bar{J}}{\partial x_0}\right)_*^T d\mathbf{x}_0 + \left(\frac{\partial \bar{J}}{\partial t_1}\right)_* dt_1 + \left(\frac{\partial \bar{J}}{\partial y(t_1)}\right)_*^T \left.\frac{d\mathbf{y}_1(\mathbf{e} + s\bar{\mathbf{h}})}{ds}\right|_{s=0}$$

We note that

$$\begin{aligned} \frac{\partial \bar{J}}{\partial x_0} &= \frac{\partial J}{\partial x(t_0)} + \frac{\partial J}{\partial x(t_1)}, \\ \frac{\partial \bar{J}}{\partial t_1} &= \frac{\partial J}{\partial t_1}, \\ \frac{\partial \bar{J}}{\partial y(t_1)} &= \frac{\partial J}{\partial x(t_1)} \end{aligned} \tag{10.34}$$

where all partials of J are evaluated at the point $(0, \mathbf{x}_0, t_1, \mathbf{y}(t_1) + \mathbf{x}_0)$. Also, $d\mathbf{x}/dt = d\mathbf{y}/dt$. Since $\mathbf{y}_1(\mathbf{e} + s\bar{\mathbf{h}}) = \mathbf{y}(t_1 + s\, dt_1, s)$,

$$\begin{aligned} \left.\frac{d\mathbf{y}_1(\mathbf{e} + s\mathbf{h})}{ds}\right|_{s=0} &= \left(\frac{\partial y}{\partial t}\right)_{t_1,0} dt_1 + \left(\frac{\partial y}{\partial s}\right)_{t_1,0}, \\ &= (\mathbf{y}'(t_1))_*\, dt_1 + (\mathbf{y}_s(t_1))_* \end{aligned} \tag{10.35}$$

where we have written $\mathbf{y}_s$ for $\partial y/\partial s$ and the asterisk denotes the optimal solution (i.e., $s = 0$). Now, $\mathbf{y}(t, s)$ is a solution of the differential equation $d\mathbf{y}/dt = \bar{f}(\mathbf{y}, \mathbf{u} + s\mathbf{h}, \mathbf{x}_0 + s\, d\mathbf{x}_0)$. Letting $\mathbf{v}(t) = \mathbf{y}_s(t, 0)$, we know that $\mathbf{v}$ is a solution of the variational equations

$$\frac{d\mathbf{v}}{dt} = \frac{\partial \bar{f}}{\partial y}(\mathbf{y}(t, 0), \mathbf{u}(t), \mathbf{x}_0)\mathbf{v} + \left(\frac{\partial \bar{f}}{\partial s}\right)_*$$

But

$$\partial \bar{f}/\partial s = (\partial \bar{f}/\partial u)\mathbf{h} + (\partial \bar{f}/\partial x_0)\, dx_0$$

$$\left(\frac{\partial \bar{f}}{\partial u}\right)_* = \frac{\partial \bar{f}}{\partial u}(\mathbf{y}(t, 0), \mathbf{u}(t), \mathbf{x}_0) = \frac{\partial f}{\partial u}(\mathbf{y}(t, 0) + \mathbf{x}_0, \mathbf{u})$$

$$\left(\frac{\partial \bar{f}}{\partial x_0}\right)_* = \frac{\partial \bar{f}}{\partial x_0}(\mathbf{y}(t, 0), \mathbf{u}(t), \mathbf{x}_0) = \frac{\partial f}{\partial y}(\mathbf{y}(t, 0) + \mathbf{x}_0, \mathbf{u})$$

Thus, $(\partial\bar{f}/\partial u)_* = (\partial f/\partial u)_*$ and $(\partial\bar{f}/\partial x_0)_* = (\partial f/\partial y)_*$. Furthermore, $\partial\bar{f}/\partial y = \partial f/\partial y$, which means that $\mathbf{y}_s(t, 0)$ is the solution of the system

$$\frac{d\mathbf{v}}{dt} = \left(\frac{\partial f}{\partial y}\right)_* \mathbf{v} + \left(\frac{\partial f}{\partial u}\right)_* \mathbf{h} + \left(\frac{\partial f}{\partial y}\right)_* d\mathbf{x}_0, \qquad \mathbf{v}(0) = 0$$

(Note that $\mathbf{v}(0) = \mathbf{y}_s(0, 0) = \lim_{s\to 0} (\mathbf{y}(0, s) - \mathbf{y}(0, 0))/s = 0$.) Letting $\bar{\mathbf{v}} = \mathbf{v} + d\mathbf{x}_0$, we have

$$\frac{d\bar{\mathbf{v}}}{dt} = \left(\frac{\partial f}{\partial y}\right)_* \bar{\mathbf{v}} + \left(\frac{\partial f}{\partial u}\right)_* \mathbf{h} = \left(\frac{\partial f}{\partial x}\right)_* \bar{\mathbf{v}} + \left(\frac{\partial f}{\partial u}\right)_* \mathbf{h}, \qquad \bar{\mathbf{v}}(0) = d\mathbf{x}_0$$

For any solution, $\mathbf{z}$, of the adjoint equation $d\mathbf{z}/dt = -(\partial f/\partial x)_*{}^T \mathbf{z}$,

$$\mathbf{z}^T(t_1)\bar{\mathbf{v}}(t_1) = \int_0^{t_1} \mathbf{z}^T (\partial f/\partial u)_* \mathbf{h}\, dt + \mathbf{z}^T(0)\bar{\mathbf{v}}(0) \tag{10.36}$$

If $\mathbf{z}$ is $\mathbf{J}_x(t)$, the solution having final values $\mathbf{J}_x(t_1) = (\partial\bar{J}/\partial y\,(t_1))_* = (\partial J/\partial x\,(t_1))_*$, then since $\bar{\mathbf{v}}(t_1) = \mathbf{v}(t_1) + d\mathbf{x}_0$, Eq. (10.36) becomes

$$\left(\frac{\partial\bar{J}}{\partial y(t_1)}\right)_*^T (\mathbf{y}_s(t_1))_* = \int_0^{t_1} \mathbf{J}_x{}^T \left(\frac{\partial f}{\partial u}\right)_* \mathbf{h}\, dt + \mathbf{J}_x{}^T(0)\, d\mathbf{x}_0 - \left(\frac{\partial\bar{J}}{\partial y(t_1)}\right)_*^T d\mathbf{x}_0 .$$

Combining this with (10.34), (10.35) in (10.33), we get

$$\begin{aligned}\left.\frac{dJ}{ds}\right|_{s=0} = \left.\frac{d\bar{J}(e + s\bar{h})}{ds}\right|_{s=0} &= \left[\left(\frac{\partial J}{\partial x(t_0)}\right)_*^T + \mathbf{J}_x{}^T(0)\right] d\mathbf{x}_0 \\ &+ \left[\left(\frac{\partial J}{\partial t_1}\right)_* + \left(\frac{\partial\bar{J}}{\partial y(t_1)}\right)_*^T (\mathbf{x}'(t_1))_*\right] dt_1 \\ &+ \int_0^{t_1} \mathbf{J}_x{}^T \left(\frac{\partial f}{\partial u}\right)_* \mathbf{h}\, dt\end{aligned}$$

Since $dJ/ds|_{s=0} = \langle \nabla J(\mathbf{e}), \bar{\mathbf{h}}\rangle$, we obtain

$$\nabla J(\mathbf{e}) = \left(\mathbf{J}_x{}^T \left(\frac{\partial f}{\partial u}\right)_*, \mathbf{J}_x{}^T(0) + \left(\frac{\partial J}{\partial x(t_0)}\right)_*^T, \left(\frac{\partial J}{\partial t_1}\right)_* + \left(\frac{\partial J}{\partial x(t_1)}\right)_*^T (\mathbf{x}'(t_1))_*\right) \tag{10.37}$$

where $\mathbf{J}_x{}^T(t)$ is the solution of the adjoint equation (10.16) having final values $\mathbf{J}_x{}^T(t_1) = (\partial J/\partial x(t_1))_*$ and the subscript $_*$ indicates that all quantities are evaluated on the optimal solution $(\mathbf{x}(t), \mathbf{u}(t), \mathbf{x}_0, t_1)$.

A formula analogous to (10.37) holds for $\nabla g_j(e)$ with ψ_j replacing J. The remainder of the derivation of Sec. 10.5 carries over *mutatis mutandis* to the present case. We obtain the following additional transversality conditions arising from the variation of $\mathbf{x}_0$ and t_1, respectively:

$$-\mathbf{l}_x(t_0) + l_0 \left(\frac{\partial J}{\partial x(t_0)}\right)_* + \sum_1^p \lambda_j \left(\frac{\partial \psi_j}{\partial x(t_0)}\right)_* = 0 \tag{10.38}$$

$$l_0 \left(\frac{\partial J}{\partial t_1}\right)_* + \sum_1^p \lambda_j \left(\frac{\partial \psi_j}{\partial t_1}\right)_* + \left[\left(\frac{\partial J}{\partial x(t_1)}\right)_*^T l_0 + \sum_1^p \lambda_j \left(\frac{\partial \psi_j}{\partial x(t_1)}\right)_*^T\right]\mathbf{x}'(t_1) = 0 \tag{10.39}$$

Together with the transversality conditions in (10.26) and the Euler–Lagrange equations in (10.25), (10.27), the transversality conditions (10.38), (10.39) constitute the multiplier rule for the problem of Mayer formulated as an optimal control problem. In the case where J and ψ_j do not involve t_1 explicitly, we have $\partial J/\partial t_1 = 0$ and $\partial \psi_j/\partial t_1 = 0$. The transversality condition (10.39) then becomes the relation $\mathbf{l}_x^T(t_1)\mathbf{x}'(t_1) = 0$. However, this means that $\mathscr{H}(t_1) = 0$. Since the Hamiltonian, $\mathscr{H}$, is constant along an optimal solution, we obtain the result that $\mathscr{H}(t) \equiv 0$ along an optimal solution when the endpoint t_1 is being varied.

Finally, we observe that in the case of a nonautonomous system of control equations, the same techniques can be applied to obtain an additional transversality condition, arising from the variation of t_0, and of the same form as (10.39) with t_1 replaced by t_0. (We proceed by introducing the new independent variable $\bar{t} = t - t_0$ and the system $d\mathbf{x}/dt = \mathbf{f}(\mathbf{x}, \mathbf{u}, t)$ becomes $d\mathbf{x}/d\bar{t} = \mathbf{f}(\mathbf{x}, \mathbf{u}, \bar{t} + t_0)$, containing t_0 as a parameter. We shall not carry out the detailed steps here.)

10.7 Examples of Optimal Control Problems

We have already presented one example of an optimal control problem in our reformulation of the brachistochrone problem. We shall now consider two examples which arise in the flight mechanics of low-thrust rockets and which have recently received attention in the study of certain space missions.

For purposes of illustration, we shall limit our attention to two-dimensional trajectories, although our remarks apply equally well to three-dimensional trajectories. Thus, we consider a rocket of unit mass moving in a central inverse-square-law gravitational field under the force of a continuous (i.e., nonimpulsive) thrust engine. Let (r, θ) be the polar coordinates of the rocket at time t and let u and v be the radial and circumferential components of velocity, respectively. Let a_r and a_θ be the radial and circumferential components of thrust acceleration, respectively. Then the equations of motion are, as is well known,

$$\begin{aligned} du/dt &= v^2/r - 1/r^2 + a_r, \\ dv/dt &= -uv/r + a_\theta, \\ dr/dt &= u, \\ d\theta/dt &= v/r \end{aligned} \tag{10.40}$$

For given initial conditions at time $t = 0$ and a particular choice of the functions $a_r(t)$, $a_\theta(t)$, Eqs. (10.40) determine the motion of the rocket for $0 \le t \le t_1$. It is required to choose a_r and a_θ from a class of admissible controls so as to produce a trajectory which satisfies certain end conditions at time t_1 and also minimizes the amount of rocket fuel consumed. It can be shown (e.g., see Irving and Blum[30]) that minimizing the fuel consumed is effected analytically by minimizing the integral

$$J = J(t_1) = \int_0^{t_1} (a_r^2 + a_\theta^2)\, dt$$

or, if we write $dJ/dt = a_r^2 + a_\theta^2$, by minimizing the final value of the function $J(t)$. The other requirements, as represented by the end conditions, are determined by the mission to be accomplished. We shall consider two missions, "escape" and "rendezvous." In both missions it will be assumed that the rocket is initially in a circular orbit so that at time $t = 0$,

$$\begin{gathered} u(0) = u_0, \qquad v(0) = v_0, \qquad r(0) = r_0 \\ \theta(0) = 0, \qquad J(0) = 0 \end{gathered} \tag{10.41}$$

where $u_0 = 0$. (We shall continue to write u_0 to show that most of the discussion applies also to arbitrary initial conditions.)

In the escape mission, it is required to escape from the gravitational pull in a fixed time t_1, that is, the total energy, E_1, at time t_1 must be zero. The total energy is given by

$$E = (u^2 + v^2)/2 - 1/r \tag{10.42}$$

Actually, we shall consider "escape" to mean $E_1 \ge 0$. To formulate the escape problem as an optimal control problem, we let $x_1 = u$, $x_2 = v$, $x_3 = r$, $x_4 = J$ be the state variables and $u_1 = a_r$, $u_2 = a_\theta$ be the control variables. Using (10.40) and the differential equation for J, we obtain for the control equations,

$$\begin{aligned} dx_1/dt &= x_2^2/x_3 - 1/x_3^2 + u_1, \\ dx_2/dt &= -x_1x_2/x_3 + u_2, \\ dx_3/dt &= x_1, \\ dx_4/dt &= u_1^2 + u_2^2 \end{aligned} \tag{10.43}$$

The endpoint constraints are obtained from (10.41), (10.42):

$$
\begin{aligned}
\psi_1 &= x_1(0) - u_0 = 0, \\
\psi_2 &= x_2(0) - v_0 = 0, \\
\psi_3 &= x_3(0) - r_0 = 0, \\
\psi_4 &= x_4(0) = 0, \\
\psi_5 &= [(x_1(t_1))^2 + (x_2(t_1))^2]/2 - 1/x_3(t_1) - E_1 = 0
\end{aligned}
\tag{10.44}
$$

where u_0, v_0, r_0, E_1 are constants determined by physical conditions. Finally, the function to be minimized is simply

$$J = x_4(t_1) \tag{10.45}$$

Comparing (10.43), (10.44), (10.45) with (10.9), (10.10), (10.11), respectively, we see that we have an optimal control problem of the type described in previous sections. Hence, an optimal solution must satisfy the multiplier rule conditions as given by (10.23a)–(10.23e). It is useful to calculate the gradients of J and the ψ_j in this case, both for illustrative purposes and for use in the convergent gradient procedure to be described below.

From (10.19) we see that we need the function $J_x(t)$ and the matrix $(\partial f/\partial u)$. The latter is easily calculated from (10.43) to be

$$
\left(\frac{\partial f}{\partial u}\right) = \begin{pmatrix} 1 & 0 \\ 0 & 1 \\ 0 & 0 \\ 2u_1 & 2u_2 \end{pmatrix}
\tag{10.46}
$$

$J_x(t)$ usually cannot be given analytically but must be obtained numerically as the solution of the adjoint equations (10.16). In this example, the adjoint equations are as follows:

$$
\begin{aligned}
dy_1/dt &= (x_2/x_3)_* \, y_2 y_3, \\
dy_2/dt &= -(2x_2/x_3)_* \, y_1 + (x_1/x_3)_* \, y_2, \\
dy_3/dt &= (-2/x_3^3 + x_2^2/x_3^2)_* \, y_1 - (x_1 x_2/x_3^2)_* \, y_2, \\
dy_4/dt &= 0
\end{aligned}
\tag{10.47}
$$

The end values which determine $\mathbf{J}_x(t)$ are the values of $(\partial J/\partial x(t_1))_*$. Hence, from (10.45) we obtain

$$\mathbf{J}_x^T(t_1) = (0, 0, 0, 1) \tag{10.48}$$

In this case it is a trivial matter to solve the adjoint equations (10.47). Clearly, we have $\mathbf{J}_x^T(t) = (0, 0, 0, 1)$ for all t. Hence, applying (10.19), we obtain

$$\nabla J(\mathbf{u}) = (2u_1(t), 2u_2(t)) \tag{10.49}$$

A similar procedure may be applied to the constraints (10.44). First, however, since the initial conditions are not being varied, we may discard the first four constraints. Thus, we have a problem with $p = 1$ constraint, $\psi_5 = 0$. The corresponding function, $\boldsymbol{\psi}_x = \boldsymbol{\psi}_{5x}(t)$, is the solution of (10.47) with final values $(\partial\psi_5/\partial x(t_1))_*$. From (10.45) we get

$$\boldsymbol{\psi}_{5x}(t_1) = (x_1(t_1), x_2(t_1), 1/(x_3(t_1))^2, 0)$$

Using these final values as starting values, we can integrate (10.48) backward in time to obtain the components of $\boldsymbol{\psi}_x = (\psi_{x1}(t), \psi_{x2}(t), \psi_{x3}(t), \psi_{x4}(t))$. We see at once that $\psi_{x4}(t) = 0$ for all t. Hence, by (10.47) and (10.20), we obtain

$$\nabla g_5(\mathbf{u}) = (\psi_{x1}(t), \psi_{x2}(t)) \tag{10.50}$$

Formulas (10.49) and (10.50) give the gradients for any control $\mathbf{u}$ as well as for the optimal control. The asterisk in (10.47) is thus to be interpreted as specifying that $x_1 = x_1(t)$, $x_2 = x_2(t)$ and $x_3 = x_3(t)$ which appear in the equations are the components of the state function, $\mathbf{x}(t)$, which is obtained by solving (10.43) with the given control $\mathbf{u}$ and the fixed initial conditions. We shall return to these points again when we consider methods of computation.

The second example which we shall consider is the mission of rendezvous by low-thrust rocket. The equations of motion are given by (10.40), as before, and the function to be minimized is the same J. However, in place of (10.42), the end conditions to be satisfied are given by

$$\begin{aligned} u(t_1) - u_1 &= 0, & r(t_1) - r_1 &= 0 \\ v(t)_1 - v_1 &= 0, & \theta(t_1) - \theta_1 &= 0 \end{aligned} \tag{10.51}$$

In physical terms, it is required to arrive at a preassigned point, (r_1, θ_1), in space with a preassigned velocity (u_1, v_1) in a fixed time t_1. Of all the thrust "programs," $\mathbf{u}(t)$, which will bring the rocket to this rendezvous, we wish to find the one which minimizes J.

Again, we shall assume the rocket starts from a circular orbit so that the initial values are fixed and given by (10.41). To formulate the rendezvous problem as an optimal control problem, we proceed as before, introducing state and control variables, except that now we have the additional state variable, θ. We set $x_1 = u$, $x_2 = v$, $x_3 = r$, $x_4 = \theta$, $x_5 = J$. The control equations are as in (10.43) with x_4 replaced by x_5 and the additional equation,

$$dx_4/dt = x_2/x_3$$

The adjoint equations are

$$\begin{aligned} dy_1/dt &= (x_2/x_3)y_2 - y_3, \\ dy_2/dt &= (-2x_2/x_3)y_1 + (x_1/x_3)y_2 - (1/x_3)y_4, \\ dy_3/dt &= (-2/x_3^3 + x_2^2/x_3^2)y_1 - (x_1x_2/x_3^2)y_2 + (x_2/x_3^2)y_4, \\ dy_4/dt &= 0, \\ dy_5/dt &= 0 \end{aligned} \tag{10.52}$$

We now have $\mathbf{J}_x{}^T(t_1) = (0, 0, 0, 0, 1)$ so that the gradient of J is again given by (10.49). The endpoint constraints are obtained from (10.52) as the $p = 4$ constraints,

$$\begin{aligned} \psi_1 &= x_1(t_1) - u_1 = 0, \qquad & \psi_3 &= x_3(t_1) - r_1 = 0 \\ \psi_2 &= x_2(t_1) - v_1 = 0, \qquad & \psi_4 &= x_4(t_1) - \theta_1 = 0 \end{aligned} \tag{10.53}$$

To obtain $\nabla g_1(\mathbf{u})$ we must compute the function $\boldsymbol{\psi}_{1x}(t)$, which is the solution of the adjoint equations (10.52) having $\boldsymbol{\psi}_{1x}^T(t_1) = (\partial\psi_1/\partial x(t_1))^T = (1, 0, 0, 0, 0)$. Similarly, $\boldsymbol{\psi}_{2x}^T(t_1) = (0, 1, 0, 0, 0)$, $\boldsymbol{\psi}_{3x}^T(t_1) = (0, 0, 1, 0, 0)$ and $\boldsymbol{\psi}_{4x}^T(t_1) = (0, 0, 0, 1, 0)$. It is clear that the last component of $\boldsymbol{\psi}_{jx}(t)$, $j = 1, \ldots, 4$, is the identically zero function. Therefore, by (10.20) and (10.46),

$$\nabla g_j(u) = (\psi_{jx_1}(t), \psi_{jx_2}(t)), \qquad j = 1, \ldots, 4 \tag{10.54}$$

where ψ_{jx_1} and ψ_{jx_2} are the first two components of $\boldsymbol{\psi}_{jx}$. We repeat that these results hold for any control, $\mathbf{u}$, and its corresponding trajectory $\mathbf{x}$.

It is easy to show that the $\nabla g_j(\mathbf{u})$ in (10.54) are linearly independent. Suppose $\sum_1^4 \lambda_j \nabla g_j(\mathbf{u}) = 0$. This implies $\sum_1^4 \lambda_j \psi_{jx_1}(t_1) = \sum_1^4 \lambda_j \psi_{jx_2}(t_1) = 0$. The first summation is just λ_1 and the second is λ_2. Thus, $\lambda_1 = \lambda_2 = 0$. This implies that $\lambda_3 \psi_{3x_2}(t) + \lambda_4 \psi_{4x_2}(t) = 0$ and $\lambda_3 \psi_{3x_1}(t) + \lambda_4 \psi_{4x_1}(t) = 0$. If $\lambda_4 \neq 0$, then $d\psi_{4x}/dt = \lambda\, d\psi_{3x}/dt$, where $\lambda = -\lambda_3/\lambda_4$. From the first equation in (10.52), we see that $d\psi_{3x_1}/dt = 1$ and $d\psi_{4x_1}/dt = 0$ at t_1. Hence, $\lambda = 0$, which means $\lambda_3 = 0$. This implies $\lambda_4\, d\psi_{4x_2}/dt = 0$ for all t. Since $d\psi_{4x_2}/dt = 1$ at t_1, as the second equation of (10.52) shows, we have $\lambda_4 = 0$, which is a contradiction. Hence, $\lambda_4 = 0$, which implies $\lambda_3\, d\psi_{3x_2}/dt = 0$. Since $d\psi_{3x_1}/dt = 1$ at t_1, we must also have $\lambda_3 = 0$, establishing lincar independence.

From the lincar independence of the ∇g_j it follows that $l_0 = 1$ in (10.24) of the multiplier rule. Thus, $\boldsymbol{l}_x = -\mathbf{J}_x - \sum_1^4 \lambda_j \boldsymbol{\psi}_{jx}$, where not all λ_j are zero. Since $\mathbf{J}_x = (0, 0, 0, 0, 1)$ for all t, we have as the transversality condition (10.26) in this case $\boldsymbol{l}_x(t_1) = (-\lambda_1, -\lambda_2, -\lambda_3, \lambda_4, 1)$. From the necessary conditions (10.27) and (10.47) we find that $2u_1 = \sum_1^4 \lambda_j \psi_{jx_1}$ and $2u_2 = \sum_1^4 \lambda_j \psi_{jx_2}$. Thus, u_1 and u_2 are components of a solution of the adjoint equations, and consequently they must be differentiable functions.

Similar considerations for the escape problem show that $\boldsymbol{l}_x{}^T = -\mathbf{J}_x{}^T - \lambda \boldsymbol{\psi}_x{}^T = (-\lambda\psi_{x1}, -\lambda\psi_{x2}, -\lambda\psi_{x3}, -1)$. Also,

$$\boldsymbol{l}_x{}^T (\partial f/\partial u) = (-\lambda\psi_{x1} - 2u_1, -\lambda\psi_{x2} - 2u_2) = 0 \tag{10.55}$$

Since $\psi_{x1}(t_1) = u(t_1)$ and $\psi_{x2}(t_1) = v(t_1)$, we arrive at the following necessary condition for an optimal solution:

$$a_r(t_1) = (-\lambda/2)\, u(t_1) \qquad \text{and} \qquad a_\theta(t_1) = (-\lambda/2)\, v(t_1) \tag{10.56}$$

i.e., the final thrust vector must be along the final velocity vector, a result obtained by somewhat different techniques in Blum and Irving.[30] For some time it was conjectured that a tangential thrust program was the optimal solution of the escape problem. However, numerical computations have shown this conjecture to be false. Of course, a demonstration by numerical calculation cannot be accepted as a mathematical proof in general, however convincing the data may be. Furthermore, in this type of computation, exact estimates of the error arising from various approximation procedures (e.g., numerical integration) are not available. Perhaps more important, in this particular example, is the fact that all the numerical solutions involve some sort of iteration procedure. Even when the iteration procedure is known to converge (and not all procedures in current use possess this property), in this particular example the neighborhood of convergence is quite large, that is, thrust programs which are quite far from optimum produce escape trajectories having almost the same fuel consumption as the optimum. Therefore, it is difficult to conclude with absolute certainty from an approximate numerical solution that the optimal solution does or does not have certain qualitative properties. The same is true of approximations obtained by various analytic techniques such as linearization and perturbation methods. Therefore, it is of some interest to establish qualitative properties by rigorous mathematical proof whereever possible. Using the results developed here, we can now prove rigorously that the optimal thrust program for the escape problem is not tangential, is not circumferential and is not of constant magnitude, although there are programs of each of these three types which produce escape trajectories having fuel consumptions close to the minimum. We prove these results in the following three theorems.

Theorem 3. *The optimal thrust program for the escape problem is not tangential at all points of the trajectory.*

PROOF. Assume that the optimal thrust program is tangential for all t, that is, suppose that

$$a_r(t) = z(t)u(t), \qquad a_\theta(t) = z(t)\,v(t), \qquad 0 \leqq t \leqq t_1 \tag{10.57}$$

We shall prove that this assumption implies a zero thrust program which, of course, cannot produce escape.

From (10.55) and (10.57) it follows immediately that $z(t)v(t) = (-\lambda/2)\psi_{x2}(t)$. Since ψ_{x2} is the second component of a solution of (10.47), we obtain

$$\frac{d}{dt}(zv) = -\frac{\lambda}{2}\frac{d\psi_{x2}}{dt} = -\frac{\lambda}{2}\left(\frac{u}{r}\psi_{x2} - \frac{2v}{r}\psi_{x1}\right) \tag{10.58}$$

Again, from (10.55) and (10.57), we have $\psi_{x1}(t) = (-2/\lambda)z(t)u(t)$. (We may assume $\lambda \neq 0$, since otherwise $a_r(t) = a_\theta(t) = 0$ by (10.55) and the proof is complete.) Applying this to (10.58), we find

$$\frac{d}{dt}(zv) = \frac{u}{r}\,zv - \frac{2v}{r}\,zu = -\frac{zuv}{r} \tag{10.59}$$

Using the second equation of (10.43), we get

$$\frac{d}{dt}(zv) = v\frac{dz}{dt} + z\left(a_\theta - \frac{uv}{r}\right) \tag{10.60}$$

Equating these two expressions for $d(zv)/dt$, we obtain, provided that $v \neq 0$,

$$\frac{dz}{dt} = -\frac{za_\theta}{v} = \frac{-z}{v}(zv) = -z^2 \tag{10.61}$$

Proceeding similarly with the first adjoint equation in (10.47), we obtain

$$\frac{d}{dt}(zu) = \frac{v}{r}(zv) + \frac{\lambda}{2}\psi_{x3} \tag{10.62}$$

Using the first equation in (10.43), we get

$$\frac{d}{dt}(zu) = u\frac{dz}{dt} + z\left(\frac{v^2}{r} - \frac{1}{r^2} + zu\right) \tag{10.63}$$

Combining (10.62) and (10.63), we have

$$u\frac{dz}{dt} = \frac{\lambda}{2}\psi_{x3} + \frac{z}{r^2} - z^2 u \tag{10.64}$$

It follows from (10.61) and (10.64) that

$$\Psi_{x3} = -2z/\lambda r^2 \tag{10.65}$$

Finally, the third equation in (10.47) yields

$$\frac{d\psi_{x3}}{dt} = \left(\frac{v^2}{r^2} - \frac{2}{r^3}\right)\left(-\frac{2zu}{\lambda}\right) - \frac{uv}{r^2}\left(-\frac{2zv}{\lambda}\right) - \frac{4zu}{r^3 u} \tag{10.66}$$

But (10.65) implies that

$$\frac{d\psi_{x3}}{dt} = \frac{4zu}{\lambda r^3} - \frac{2}{\lambda r^2}\frac{dz}{dt} = \frac{4zu}{\lambda r^3} + \frac{2z^2}{\lambda r^2} \tag{10.67}$$

Equations (10.66) and (10.67) imply that $2z^2/\lambda r^2 = 0$, which implies that $z(t) = 0$ whenever $v(t) \neq 0$. However, $v(t)$ is a continuous function of t and $v(0) = 1$. Therefore, $v(t) \neq 0$ for $0 \leq t \leq \varepsilon$, where ε is some positive number. Hence, $z(t) = 0$ for $0 \leq t \leq \varepsilon$, so that the orbit remains circular in this time interval. Thus, $v(\varepsilon) = 1$. The same argument can be applied at $t = \varepsilon$ to obtain $v(t) = 1$ for $t > \varepsilon$. In fact, for any interval, $0 \leq t \leq t'$, in which $v(t) = 1$, this argument proves that $v(t) \neq 0$ for t in a small interval beyond $t = t'$. Hence, $z(t) = 0$ and $v(t) = 1$ in this small interval. It follows that $v(t) = 1$ and $z(t) = 0$

for $0 \le t \le t_1$. Thus, the orbit is the initial circle, which is the optimal orbit corresponding to the case $E_1 = -1/2$ in the last equation of (10.44). This proves that the only optimal solution which satisfies (10.57) (i.e., tangential thrust) is the zero thrust program.

Before proving the next theorem, let us consider the Hamiltonian function defined at the end of Sec. 10.5. Since $\mathscr{H} = \boldsymbol{l}_x{}^T\mathbf{f}$, we have, using (10.43), and the expression for $\boldsymbol{l}_x$ given prior to (10.55),

$$\mathscr{H} = -\lambda\psi_{x1}(x_2{}^2/x_3 - 1/x_3{}^2 + u_1) - \lambda\psi_{x2}(u_2 - x_1x_2/x_3) \\ - \lambda\psi_{x3}x_1 - u_1{}^2 - u_2{}^2$$

Rewriting this in terms of the variables of the escape problem and letting $a^2 = a_r{}^2 + a_\theta{}^2$, we have by (10.55),

$$\mathscr{H} = 2a_r\left(\frac{v^2}{r} - \frac{1}{r^2}\right) - 2a_\theta\frac{uv}{r} - \lambda\psi_{x3}u + a^2 \tag{10.68}$$

At time $t = 0$, using the initial conditions (10.41) with $u(0) = 0$ and $v(0) = 1/\sqrt{r(0)}$ for a circular orbit, we find that $\mathscr{H}(0) = a^2(0)$. At time $t = t_1$, by virtue of the end conditions

$$\psi_{x1}(t_1) = u_1, \qquad \psi_{x2}(t_1) = v_1, \qquad \psi_{x3}(t_1) = 1/r_1{}^2 \tag{10.69}$$

previously derived from (10.44) (see above), we have

$$\mathscr{H}(t_1) = -\lambda u_1\left(\frac{v_1{}^2}{r_1} - \frac{1}{r_1{}^2}\right) + \lambda\frac{u_1v_1{}^2}{r_1} - \frac{\lambda u_1}{r_1{}^2} + a_1{}^2 = a_1{}^2$$

Since $\mathscr{H}(t_1) = \mathscr{H}(0)$ on the optimal solution, we obtain

$$a^2(t_1) = a^2(0) \tag{10.70}$$

that is, the initial and final thrust magnitudes must be equal, a result given also in Blum and Irving.[30] It is this result which first led to the conjecture that the optimal thrust program is of constant magnitude at all points of the trajectory. In Theorem 4, we prove that this conjecture is false.

Theorem 4. *The optimal thrust program for the escape problem is not of constant magnitude at all points of the trajectory.*

Proof. We observe that if $u(t) = 0$ for $0 \le t \le t_1$, then the orbit is simply the initial circle and therefore is not an escape trajectory. Hence, we may suppose $u(t) \ne 0$ for some t. Let us set

$$\Delta a^2 = a^2(t) - a^2(0)$$

Since $\mathscr{H}(t) = \mathscr{H}(0) = a^2(0)$ for all t, we may use (10.68) to solve for $\lambda\psi_{x3}/2$. For $u \neq 0$, this yields

$$\frac{\lambda\psi_{x3}}{2} = \frac{a_r}{u}\left(\frac{v^2}{r} - \frac{1}{r^2}\right) - \frac{a_\theta v}{r} + \frac{\Delta a^2}{2u} \tag{10.71}$$

From (10.55) and the first adjoint equation in (10.47), we get

$$\frac{d}{dt}\,a_r = \frac{v}{r}\,a_\theta + \frac{\lambda}{2}\psi_{x3} \tag{10.72}$$

Combining (10.71) and (10.72), we have

$$\frac{d}{dt}\,a_r = \frac{a_r}{u}\left(\frac{v^2}{r} - \frac{1}{r^2}\right) + \frac{\Delta a^2}{2u} \tag{10.73}$$

Similarly, from (10.55) and the second equation of (10.47), we get

$$\frac{d}{dt}\,a_\theta = (ua_\theta - 2va_r)/r \tag{10.74}$$

Differentiation of a^2 and substitution of formulas (10.73) and (10.74) for the derivatives yields

$$\begin{aligned}\frac{d}{dt}\,a^2 &= 2a_r\frac{d}{dt}\,a_r + 2a_\theta\frac{d}{dt}\,a_\theta \\ &= \frac{2{a_r}^2}{u}\left(\frac{v^2}{r} - \frac{1}{r^2}\right) + \frac{\Delta a^2}{u}\,a_r + \frac{2u}{r}\,{a_\theta}^2 - \frac{4v}{r}\,a_r a_\theta\end{aligned}$$

Thus,

$$\frac{d}{dt}\,a^2 = \frac{2}{ru}\,((ua_\theta - va_r)^2 - {a_r}^2/r) + a_r\,\Delta a^2/u \tag{10.75}$$

Now, suppose $\Delta a^2(t) = 0$ for all t, i.e., suppose $a^2(t) = A^2$, where A is a constant. Then $da^2/dt = 0$, and it follows from (10.75) that

$$(ua_\theta - va_r)^2 - {a_r}^2/r = 0$$

Hence,

$$a_\theta = \frac{a_r}{u}\left(v \pm \frac{1}{\sqrt{r}}\right)$$

Together with ${a_r}^2 + {a_\theta}^2 = A^2$, this implies $a_r = Au/w$ and $a_\theta = A(v \pm 1/\sqrt{r})/w$, where $w^2 = u^2 + (v \pm 1/\sqrt{r})^2$. To determine the sign, we recall that $u(0) = 0$ and $v(0) = 1/\sqrt{r(0)}$ in the initial circular orbit. If the minus sign is chosen, then $a_r(0) = a_\theta(0) = 0$, which means that $A = 0$ and the orbit remains circular. Hence, we choose the plus sign, thereby obtaining

$$a_r = \frac{Au}{(u^2 + (v + 1/\sqrt{r})^2)^{1/2}}, \qquad a_\theta = \frac{A(v + 1/\sqrt{r})}{(u^2 + (v + 1/\sqrt{r})^2)^{1/2}} \tag{10.76}$$

From (10.73), with $\Delta a^2 = 0$, we have

$$u \frac{d}{dt} a_r = a_r\left(\frac{v^2}{r} - \frac{1}{r^2}\right) = a_r \left(\frac{du}{dt} - a_r\right)$$

Hence, for $a_r \neq 0$, we have

$$\frac{d}{dt}\left(\frac{u}{a_r}\right) = 1$$

whence,

$$a_r = u/(t + c), \qquad a_\theta = (v + 1/\sqrt{r})/(t + c) \tag{10.77}$$

where c is a constant. Differentiating (10.77) and using the second equation in (10.41), we obtain after some simplification

$$\frac{d}{dt} a_\theta = \frac{-u}{r(t + c)} \left(v + \frac{1}{2\sqrt{r}}\right)$$

Another expression for da_θ/dt is obtained by substituting the expressions for a_r and a_θ given by (10.77) into formula (10.74). This yields

$$\frac{d}{dt} a_\theta = \frac{-u}{r(t + c)} \left(v - \frac{1}{\sqrt{r}}\right)$$

Comparing the two preceding formulas for da_θ/dt, we conclude that

$$\frac{3u}{2r^{3/2}(t + c)} = 0$$

This implies that $u(t) = 0$, which contradicts the assumption that $u(t) \neq 0$ and $a^2(t) = A^2$. Hence, either $a^2(t)$ is not constant or $u(t) = 0$ for all t. In the latter case, the thrust magnitude must be zero and cannot produce escape.

Theorem 5. *The optimal thrust program for the escape problem is not circumferential at all points of the trajectory.*

PROOF. Suppose $a_r(t) = 0$ for $0 \leq t \leq t_1$. Together with (10.55) this implies that $\psi_{x1}(t) = 0$ for $0 \leq t \leq t_1$. The Hamiltonian in (10.68) now becomes

$$\mathscr{H} = -2a_\theta uv/r - \lambda\psi_{x3}u + a_\theta^2 \tag{10.78}$$

Since $\mathscr{H}$ is constant along an optimal solution and $\mathscr{H}(0) = a_\theta^2(0)$, we may set the right side of (10.78) equal to $a_\theta^2(0)$ and solve for $\lambda\psi_{x3}u$. This yields

$$\lambda\psi_{x3}u = a_\theta^2(t) - a_\theta^2(0) - 2a_\theta uv/r \tag{10.79}$$

Since $\psi_{x1}(t) = 0$ for all t, the derivative of ψ_{x1} is also zero. Hence, the first adjoint equation in (10.47) becomes $0 = (v/r)\psi_{x2} - \psi_{x3}$. This yields, using (10.55),

$$\lambda\psi_{x3}u = -2a_\theta uv/r \tag{10.80}$$

Combining (10.79) and (10.80), we conclude that $a_\theta^2(t) = a_\theta^2(0)$ for all t, that is, a_θ is constant. By (10.55), this implies that ψ_{x2} is also constant and therefore $d\psi_{x2}/dt = 0$ for all t. By the second adjoint equation in (10.47), this implies further that $u\psi_{x2}/r = 0$ for all t. If $u(t') \neq 0$ for some t' in the interval $[0, t_1]$, then $\psi_{x2}(t') = 0$. Since ψ_{x2} is constant, it follows that $\psi_{x2} = 0$ for all t. This implies $a_\theta = 0$ for all t and the orbit remains the original circle. On the other hand, if $u = 0$ for all t, then again we have the case of zero thrust. Therefore, the only optimal circumferential program is the zero thrust program.

Remark. Although the constant magnitude thrust program given in (10.76) is not optimal unless $A = 0$, it nevertheless has interesting properties which suggest that it may be a first approximation to the optimal solution. In fact, numerical computations show that (10.76) produces escape trajectories having a value of $J(t_1)$, which is approximately six percent larger than the optimum value of $J(t_1)$. It seems possible to investigate this further analytically. However, we shall not pursue this line here, but rather we turn our attention to the numerical computation of the optimal solution. In the next section we shall describe a rather general procedure for numerical solution which has proven to be suitable for modern digital computers.

10.8 A Convergent Gradient Procedure

The examples discussed in the previous section illustrate the difficulties in obtaining analytic solutions—or even analytic approximations to solutions—of optimal control problems. In all but the simplest problems, to obtain good approximations to a solution one must have recourse to numerical methods. In this section we shall present one such method based on gradients. Gradient-type approximation procedures are not new, but they have received considerable attention recently in a variety of contexts, as in Balakrishnan,[15] Goldstein,[16] Hart and Motzkin,[31] and Kelley,[32] to mention a few recent works. These procedures generate a sequence of approximations to the solution of a minimization problem by using gradients in various ways, but usually involving the direction of steepest descent. The method to be described now is not of the steepest descent type. Furthermore, we shall prescribe sufficient conditions to ensure convergence of the approximating sequence. A convergence proof was first given in Blum.[33] The treatment given here is a slight modification of that work.

We refer to Sec. 10.3 for the basic concepts and definitions to be employed in the abstract formulation of our gradient procedure. Our procedure is based on the multiplier rule as given in the corollary to Theorem 2 and as summarized by Eq. (10.13). It is convenient to restate (10.13) in a somewhat different form. As before, let $J, g_1, \ldots, g_p$ be real functionals on a pre-Hilbert space H. Suppose that the weak gradients $\nabla J(\mathbf{u})$, $\nabla g_i(\mathbf{u})$, $1 \leq i \leq p$ exist at $\mathbf{u} \in H$. Suppose further that the $p \times p$ Gram matrix

$$D(\mathbf{u}) = (\langle \nabla g_i(\mathbf{u}), \nabla g_j(\mathbf{u}) \rangle)$$

is nonsingular. Let $\boldsymbol{\mu}$ be the p-dimensional row vector

$$(\langle \nabla J(\mathbf{u}), \nabla g_1(\mathbf{u}) \rangle, \ldots, \langle \nabla J(\mathbf{u}), \nabla g_p(\mathbf{u}) \rangle)$$

and define $\lambda = (\lambda_1, \ldots, \lambda_p)$ as the vector $\lambda = \boldsymbol{\mu} D^{-1}$. As is well known, the "projection," ∇J_G, of ∇J on the subspace $G \subset H$ spanned by $\{\nabla g_1(\mathbf{u}), \ldots, \nabla g_p(\mathbf{u})\}$ is given by

$$\nabla J_G(\mathbf{u}) = \sum_1^p \lambda_j \nabla g_j(\mathbf{u})$$

The component of ∇J orthogonal to G is $\nabla J_T(\mathbf{u}) = \nabla J(\mathbf{u}) - \nabla J_G(\mathbf{u})$. The multiplier rule states that if $\mathbf{u}^*$ is a relative minimum of J on the constraint $C = \bigcap_1^p C(g_i)$ (and the conditions of the corollary are satisfied), then

$$\nabla J_T(\mathbf{u}^*) = 0 \tag{10.81}$$

Definition 8. Let $J, g_1, \ldots, g_p$ be real functionals on H with weak gradients defined at $\mathbf{u}$ and the Gram matrix $D(\mathbf{u})$ nonsingular. If $\nabla J_T(\mathbf{u}) = 0$ and $g_i(\mathbf{u}) = 0$, $1 \leq i \leq p$, then $\mathbf{u}$ is a *stationary point* of J on the constraint $\bigcap_1^p C(g_i)$.

Remark on Notation. In what follows, for any $\mathbf{u} \in H$, we shall write $\bar{\mathbf{u}}$ to denote the unit vector $(1/\|\mathbf{u}\|)\mathbf{u}$. For any real functional, f, we shall write $f(\mathbf{x}) \gg 0$ to indicate that $f(\mathbf{x}) > a^2 > 0$ for some positive constant a.

Our gradient procedure generates a sequence $\{\mathbf{u}_n\}$ which converges to a stationary point $\mathbf{u}^*$ provided that certain "regularity" conditions are satisfied in a neighborhood of $\mathbf{u}^*$. These conditions are given in the next definition.

Definition 9. Let $\mathbf{u}^*$ be a stationary point of J on the constraint $\bigcap_1^p C(g_i)$. $\mathbf{u}^*$ is a *regular stationary point* if there exists a neighborhood, $N = N(\mathbf{u}^*)$, of $\mathbf{u}^*$ such that the following conditions are satisfied for $\mathbf{u} \in N$:

(1) The strong gradient $\nabla_s J(\mathbf{u})$ exists as a continuous function of $\mathbf{u}$ and $\nabla J_G(\mathbf{u}) \neq 0$;
(2) The strong gradients $\nabla_s g_i(\mathbf{u})$, $1 \leq i \leq p$, exist as continuous functions of $\mathbf{u}$ and $\nabla g_i(\mathbf{u}) \neq 0$;
(3) $D(\mathbf{u})$ is nonsingular;
(4) Let $\theta(\mathbf{u}) = \arcsin\,(\|\nabla J_T(\mathbf{u})\|/\|\nabla J(\mathbf{u})\|)$.
For those $\mathbf{u}$ in N such that $\nabla J_T(\mathbf{u}) \neq 0$ the strong gradient $\nabla_s \theta(\mathbf{u})$ exists and $\|\nabla\theta(\mathbf{u})\| \gg 0$. At $\mathbf{u}^*$, the weak differential $\delta\theta(\mathbf{u}^*; \mathbf{h})$ exists and for $\mathbf{u} = \mathbf{u}^* + \Delta\mathbf{u}$, $\Delta\mathbf{u} \neq 0$, $\langle \nabla\theta(\mathbf{u}), \overline{\Delta\mathbf{u}}\rangle \to \delta\theta(\mathbf{u}^*, \overline{\Delta\mathbf{u}})$ as $\Delta\mathbf{u} \to 0$;
(5) For $\mathbf{u} = \mathbf{u}^* + \Delta\mathbf{u}$, $\Delta\mathbf{u} \neq 0$, let

$$\alpha_i = \alpha_i(\mathbf{u}) = \arccos\langle \overline{\nabla\psi_i(\mathbf{u})}, \overline{\Delta\mathbf{u}}\rangle \qquad 1 \leq i \leq p,$$
$$\alpha_0 = \alpha_0(\mathbf{u}) = \arccos\langle \overline{\nabla J_T(\mathbf{u})}, \overline{\Delta\mathbf{u}}\rangle,$$
$$\beta = \beta(\mathbf{u}) = \arccos\langle \overline{\nabla\theta(\mathbf{u})}, \overline{\Delta\mathbf{u}}\rangle,$$
$$\gamma = \gamma(u) = \arccos\langle \overline{\nabla\theta(\mathbf{u})}, \overline{\nabla J_T(\mathbf{u})}\rangle.$$

There exist positive constants a_1 and a_2, such that
(i) if $\nabla J_T(\mathbf{u}) \neq 0$, then $|\cos\gamma| > a_2$ and $\sum_1^p \cos^2\alpha_i + \cos\alpha_0 \cos\beta/\cos\gamma > a_1$;
(ii) if $\nabla J_T(\mathbf{u}) = 0$, then $\sum_1^p \cos^2\alpha_i > a_1$.

A neighborhood such as N is called a regular neighborhood of $\mathbf{u}^*$.

Remark. In view of our earlier discussion in Sec. 10.3 (see Definition 5 and what follows), we may write ∇J instead of $\nabla_s J$, since the existence of the strong gradient implies the existence of the weak gradient, and the two are equal. Hence, having made it clear that we require the strong gradient, it is simpler to omit the subscripts.

Theorem 6. *Let* $\mathbf{u}^*$ *be a regular stationary point of J on the constraint* $\bigcap_1^p C(g_i)$ *and let N be a regular neighborhood of* $\mathbf{u}^*$ *which contains no other stationary point. For* $\mathbf{u} = \mathbf{u}^* + \Delta\mathbf{u} \in N$, $\Delta\mathbf{u} \neq 0$, *let*

$$\mathbf{h}_G = \mathbf{h}_G(\mathbf{u}) = -\sum_1^p (g_i(\mathbf{u})/\|\nabla g_i(\mathbf{u})\|)\, \overline{\nabla g_i(\mathbf{u})} \tag{10.82}$$

$$\mathbf{h}_T = \mathbf{h}_T(\mathbf{u}) = -(1/\|\nabla J_G(\mathbf{u})\| \cdot \langle \nabla\theta(\mathbf{u}), \overline{\nabla J_T(\mathbf{u})}\rangle)\, \nabla J_T(\mathbf{u}), \qquad \text{if} \quad \nabla J_T(\mathbf{u}) \neq 0,$$
$$= 0, \qquad \text{if} \quad \nabla J_T(u) = 0 \tag{10.83}$$

$$\mathbf{h} = \mathbf{h}(\mathbf{u}) = \mathbf{h}_G + \mathbf{h}_T \tag{10.84}$$

Let $d = 2a_1a_2^2/(a_2^2p^2 + 2p + 3)$, *where* a_1 *and* a_2 *are the constants given in Definition 9 (condition (5)). Let* $\{s_n\}$ *be a sequence of real numbers with*

$d/2 < s_n < d$, $n = 0, 1, 2, \ldots$. There exist positive constants, r and k, with $k < 1$, such that if $\|\mathbf{u}_0 - \mathbf{u}^*\| < r$, then the sequence $\{\mathbf{u}_n\}$ defined by

$$\mathbf{u}_{n+1} = \mathbf{u}_n + s_n \mathbf{h}(\mathbf{u}_n), \qquad n = 0, 1, 2, \ldots \tag{10.85}$$

converges to $\mathbf{u}^*$ and $\|\mathbf{u}_n - \mathbf{u}^*\| < k^n \|\mathbf{u}_0 - \mathbf{u}^*\|$.

PROOF. First we shall prove that there exist r and k, with $k < 1$, such that if $\mathbf{u} = \mathbf{u}^* + \Delta\mathbf{u} \in N$ and $0 < \|\Delta\mathbf{u}\| < r$, then $\|\mathbf{u} + s\mathbf{h} - \mathbf{u}^*\| < k\|\Delta\mathbf{u}\|$ whenever $d/2 < s < d$.

For convenience we shall adopt the notational convention that throughout the proof any quantity designated by ε with appropriate subscripts or superscripts is such that $\varepsilon/\|\Delta\mathbf{u}\| \to 0$ as $\Delta\mathbf{u} \to 0$. We shall make no further mention of this property.

By the definition of strong gradient (see the remark following Definition 5 of Sec. 10.3), we have for $1 \le i \le p$,

$$g_i(\mathbf{u}) = g_i(\mathbf{u}) - g_i(\mathbf{u}^*) = \langle \nabla g_i(\mathbf{u}^*), \Delta\mathbf{u} \rangle + \varepsilon_i$$

By the continuity of ∇g_i at $\mathbf{u}^*$ (condition (2) of Definition 9), $g_i(\mathbf{u}) = \langle \nabla g_i(\mathbf{u}), \Delta\mathbf{u} \rangle + \tilde{\varepsilon}_i$. Using these relations in (10.82), we obtain

$$\mathbf{h}_G = -\sum_1^p \langle \overline{\nabla g_i(\mathbf{u})}, \Delta\mathbf{u} \rangle\, \overline{\nabla g_i(\mathbf{u})} + \varepsilon_G \tag{10.86}$$

Since $\mathbf{u} + s\mathbf{h} - \mathbf{u}^* = \Delta\mathbf{u} + s\mathbf{h}_G + s\mathbf{h}_T$, we have

$$\|\mathbf{u} + s\mathbf{h} - \mathbf{u}^*\|^2 = \|\Delta\mathbf{u}\|^2 + 2s\langle \Delta\mathbf{u}, \mathbf{h}_G \rangle + 2s\langle \Delta\mathbf{u}, \mathbf{h}_T \rangle + s^2(\|\mathbf{h}_G\|^2 + \|\mathbf{h}_T\|^2) \tag{10.87}$$

From (10.86) it follows that

$$\langle \mathbf{h}_G, \Delta\mathbf{u} \rangle = -\|\Delta\mathbf{u}\|^2 \sum_1^p \cos^2 \alpha_i + \langle \varepsilon_G, \Delta\mathbf{u} \rangle \tag{10.88}$$

where the α_i are defined in condition (5) of Definition 9. Applying the Schwarz inequality to (10.86) yields

$$\|\mathbf{h}_G\|^2 \le \|\Delta\mathbf{u}\|^2 \left(p \sum_1^p \cos^2 \alpha_i + w_G(\Delta\mathbf{u}) \right) \tag{10.89}$$

where $w_G(\Delta\mathbf{u}) \to 0$ as $\Delta\mathbf{u} \to 0$. Using (10.83), we find that if $\mathbf{h}_T \ne 0$,

$$\langle \mathbf{h}_T, \Delta\mathbf{u} \rangle = -\frac{\|\nabla J_T(\mathbf{u})\|}{\|\nabla J_G(\mathbf{u})\|} \frac{\|\Delta\mathbf{u}\| \cos \alpha_0}{\|\nabla\theta(\mathbf{u})\| \cos \gamma} = -\frac{\tan \theta(\mathbf{u}) \|\Delta\mathbf{u}\| \cos \alpha_0}{\|\nabla\theta(\mathbf{u})\| \cos \gamma}$$

where α_0 and γ are given in condition (5) of Definition 9. By condition (4) of Definition 9, using the mean-value theorem, $\tan\,\theta(\mathbf{u}) = \tan\,\theta(\mathbf{u}^*) + \sec^2 \theta(\mathbf{u}')\langle \nabla\theta(\mathbf{u}'), \Delta\mathbf{u} \rangle$, where $\mathbf{u}' = \mathbf{u}^* + s\,\Delta\mathbf{u}$, $0 < s < 1$. Again, by condition 4,

$\langle \nabla\theta(\mathbf{u}'), \overline{\Delta\mathbf{u}}\rangle = \langle \nabla\theta(\mathbf{u}), \overline{\Delta\mathbf{u}}\rangle + w'$, where $w' \to 0$ as $\Delta\mathbf{u} \to 0$. Since $\theta(\mathbf{u})$ is continuous at $\mathbf{u}^*$ and $\theta(\mathbf{u})^* = 0$, it follows that $\tan\,\theta(\mathbf{u}) = \langle \nabla\theta(\mathbf{u}), \Delta\mathbf{u}\rangle + \hat{\varepsilon}$. Since $\langle \nabla\theta(\mathbf{u}), \Delta\mathbf{u}\rangle = \|\nabla\theta(\mathbf{u})\|\;\|\Delta\mathbf{u}\| \cos\beta$ we obtain

$$\langle \mathbf{h}_T, \Delta\mathbf{u}\rangle = -\;\|\Delta\mathbf{u}\|^2(\cos\alpha_0 \cos\beta/\cos\gamma + w\,(\Delta\mathbf{u})) \tag{10.90}$$

where $w\,(\Delta\mathbf{u}) \to 0$ as $\Delta\mathbf{u} \to 0$. Similarly, from (10.83) it follows that

$$\|\mathbf{h}_T\| = \frac{\|\nabla J_T(\mathbf{u})\|}{\|\nabla J_G(\mathbf{u})\|\;\|\nabla\theta(\mathbf{u})\| \cos\gamma} = \|\Delta\mathbf{u}\| \left(\frac{\cos\beta}{\cos\gamma} + w_T\right) \tag{10.91}$$

where $w_T \to 0$ as $\Delta\mathbf{u} \to 0$. Combining (10.87)–(10.91), we see that

$$\|\mathbf{u} + s\mathbf{h} - \mathbf{u}^*\|^2 \le \|\Delta\mathbf{u}\|^2(\Phi_1(s) + 2sw_1\,(\Delta\mathbf{u}) + s^2 w_2\,(\Delta\mathbf{u})) \tag{10.92}$$

where $w_1 \to 0$ and $w_2 \to 0$ as $\Delta\mathbf{u} \to 0$ and

$$\begin{aligned}
\Phi_1(s) &= 1 - 2bs + c_1 s^2 \\
b &= \sum_1^p \cos^2\alpha_i + \cos\alpha_0 \cos\beta/\cos\gamma \qquad \text{if} \quad \nabla J_T(\mathbf{u}) \neq 0 \\
&= \sum_1^p \cos^2\alpha_i \qquad \text{if} \quad \nabla J_T(\mathbf{u}) = 0 \\
c_1 &= p\sum_1^p \cos^2\alpha_i + \cos^2\beta/\cos^2\gamma \qquad \text{if} \quad \nabla J_T(\mathbf{u}) \neq 0 \\
&= p\sum_1^p \cos^2\alpha_i \qquad \text{if} \quad \nabla J_T(\mathbf{u}) = 0
\end{aligned}$$

If we replace $\Phi_1(s)$ by $\Phi(s) = 1 - 2bs + cs^2$, where

$$c = c_1 + \left(2\sum_1^p \cos^2\alpha_i + 1 + 1/|\cos\gamma|\right)/|\cos\gamma|$$

the inequality in (10.92) remains valid. Now, $0 < \Phi(s) < 1$ for $0 < s < d$, where $d = 2a_1 a_2^2/(a_0^2 p^2 + 2p + 3)$. For $d/2 < s < d$ and $0 < \|\Delta\mathbf{u}\| < r$ with r sufficiently small, there exists a constant $k^2 < 1$ such that

$$0 < \Phi(s) + 2sw_1(\Delta\mathbf{u}) + s^2 w_2(\Delta\mathbf{u}) < k^2 < 1$$

Hence, $\|\mathbf{u} + s\mathbf{h} - u^*\| < k\|\Delta\mathbf{u}\|$ whenever $d/2 < s < d$, as we wished to prove. The remainder of the theorem now follows directly, for if $\|\mathbf{u}_0 - \mathbf{u}^*\| < r$, then $\|\mathbf{u}_1 - \mathbf{u}^*\| < k\|\mathbf{u}_0 - \mathbf{u}^*\|$ and, by induction, $\|u_n - \mathbf{u}^*\| < k^n\|\mathbf{u}_0 - \mathbf{u}^*\|$. This, of course, implies $\mathbf{u}_n \to \mathbf{u}^*$.

10.9 Computations Using the Convergent Gradient Procedure

We shall illustrate the use of the convergent gradient procedure by applying it to the brachistochrone problem discussed in Sec. 10.2. The equations which define this problem are (10.6′), (10.7′), and (10.8′). In order to apply our gradient procedure, we must calculate gradients according to formulas (10.19) and (10.20). Thus, we must derive the adjoint equations of (10.6′) and the matrix $(\partial f/\partial u)$. According to (10.16), the adjoint equations in the brachistochrone problem are the following:

$$\frac{dy_1}{dt} = \frac{(1+u^2)^{1/2}}{2(2g)^{1/2}x_1^{3/2}}\,y_2, \qquad \frac{dy_2}{dt} = 0 \tag{10.93}$$

The matrix $(\partial f/\partial u)$ is the 2×1 matrix

$$\begin{pmatrix} 1 \\ \\ \dfrac{u}{(2gx_1(1+u^2))^{1/2}} \end{pmatrix}$$

(Here we have written $u = u_1$, since the control function is one-dimensional.) To obtain the function $\mathbf{J}_x(t) = (J_{x_1}(t), J_{x_2}(t))$ we must solve (10.93) with the final values $\mathbf{J}_x(t_1) = (\partial J/\partial x_1(t_1), \partial J/\partial x_2(t_1))$. Hence, from (10.8′) we see that $\mathbf{J}_x(t_1) = (0, 1)$ and the required solution is given by

$$J_{x_1}(t) = -\tfrac{1}{2}\int_t^{t_1} \frac{(1+u^2)^{1/2}}{2(2g)^{1/2}x_1^{3/2}}\,dt, \qquad J_{x_2}(t) = 1 \tag{10.94}$$

With regard to the constraints in (10.7′), we may simplify the problem by considering the initial values as being held fixed. Thus, $x_1(t_0) = 1$ and $x_2(t_0) = 0$ are taken as fixed initial conditions for the solution of Eq. (10.6′). Thus, the "control space" in this problem is the space of functions $u_1(t)$. We must choose $u_1(t)$ to obtain a solution of (10.6′) having the prescribed initial values (1, 0) and satisfying the single constraint

$$\psi = \psi_3 = x_1(t_1) - 2 = 0 \tag{10.95}$$

According to the theory of Sec. 10.5, we must determine a function, $\boldsymbol{\psi}_x(t) = (\psi_{x_1}(t), \psi_{x_2}(t))$, which is a solution of (10.93) and which has final values $\boldsymbol{\psi}_x(t_1) = (\partial\psi/\partial x_1(t_1), \partial\psi/\partial x_2(t_1))$. From (10.95) we have $\boldsymbol{\psi}_x(t_1) = (1, 0)$. The solution of (10.93) having these final values can be by inspection seen to be $\psi_{x_1}(t) = 1, \psi_{x_2}(t) = 0$. Hence, the gradient $\nabla\psi = \boldsymbol{\psi}_x{}^T(\partial f/\partial u)$, as given by (10.20), becomes in this case simply

$$\nabla\psi = 1 \tag{10.96}$$

The gradient $\nabla J = \mathbf{J}_x{}^T(\partial f/\partial u)$ is given by

$$\nabla J = J_{x_1}(t) + \left(\frac{u}{(2gx_1(1+u^2))^{1/2}}\right) \tag{10.97}$$

In order to obtain $\nabla J(t)$, we choose a control function $u = u(t)$ and integrate the control Eqs. (10.6′) with the initial values (1, 0). The solution $x_1 = x_1(t)$ is then used together with u in (10.93) to determine the coefficients. Equation (10.93) is solved for $\mathbf{J}_x(t)$ using the final values (0, 1), as explained previously. Finally, (10.97) yields ∇J as a function of t obtained from u, x_1 and J_{x_1}.

To apply the convergent gradient procedure, we must calculate ∇J_G and ∇J_T. Since there is only one constraint in this example, it is readily seen that $\nabla J_G = \langle \nabla J, \overline{\nabla\psi} \rangle \, \overline{\nabla\psi}$. (As before, the bar denotes the unit vector.) By the definition of the inner product given in Sec. 10.5, we have from (10.96) and (10.97)

$$\langle \nabla J, \nabla\psi \rangle = \int_0^{t_1} \left(J_{x_1}(t) + \frac{u}{(2gx_1(1+u^2))^{1/2}} \right) dt$$

$$\|\nabla\psi\|^2 = \langle \nabla\psi, \nabla\psi \rangle = \int_0^{t_1} 1 \, dt = t_1$$

Applying formula (10.82) with $p = 1$ and $g_1 = \psi$, we have

$$h_G = -(x_1(t_1) - 2)/t_1$$

To compute h_T from (10.83), we require ∇J_T and $\langle \nabla\theta, \overline{\nabla J_T} \rangle$. We have immediately that $\nabla J_T = \nabla J - \nabla J_G$. However, to obtain $\langle \nabla\theta, \overline{\nabla J_T} \rangle$ we use a numerical approximation, therein making use of the fact that $\langle \theta, \overline{\nabla J_T} \rangle = d\theta(u; \overline{\nabla J_T}) = d\theta/ds|_{s=0}$ in the direction $\overline{\nabla J_T}$. Thus we compute $\theta = \arcsin \|\nabla J_T\|/\|\nabla J\|$ for u and again for $u + \Delta s\, \overline{\nabla J_T}$, choosing the value of the scalar Δs to be "sufficiently small." We then approximate $d\theta/ds$ by $\Delta\theta/\Delta s$ and use this in (10.83) to obtain h_T and then obtain h from (10.84).

The iteration procedure defined by (10.85) is carried out by choosing some initial guess $u_0 = u_0(t)$ for the control function and computing all the above quantities for this u_0. To compute the next approximation, u_1, from (10.85) requires an estimate of s_0. In the absence of information about the constant d of Theorem 6, we are forced to guess s_0 by trial and error and then improve the guess by various computational techniques of doubling and halving. These techniques have proved effective in solving the brachistochrone problem and the escape and rendezvous problems.

REFERENCES

1. Galileo, "Dialog über die beiden hauptsächlichsten Weltsysteme," pp. 471–472 (Transl.: Strauss), 1630.
2. Galileo, "Dialogues concerning two new sciences," p. 239 (Transl.: Crew and De Salvio), 1638.
3. G. A. Bliss, "Lectures on the Calculus of Variations." Univ. of Chicago Press, Chicago, Illinois, 1946.
4. J. Bernoulli, "Acta Eruditorium," p. 269. Leipzig, 1696.

5. L. S. Pontryagin, V. G. Boltyanskii, R. V. Gamkrelidze, and E. F. Mischehenko, "The Mathematical Theory of Optimal Processes," (K. N. Trirogoff, transl.; L. W. Neustadt, ed.). Wiley (Interscience), New York, 1962.
6. F. A. Valentine, "The Problem of Lagrange with Differential Inequalities as Added Side Conditions, Contributions to the Calculus of Variations 1933–1937." Univ. of Chicago Press, Chicago, Illinois, 1937.
7. L. Berkovitz, Variational Methods of Control and Programming, *J. Math. Anal. Appl.* **3**, 145–169 (1961).
8. O. Bolza, An Application of the Notions of "General Analysis" to a Problem of the Calculus of Variations, *Bull. Am. Math. Soc.* **16**, 402–407 (1910).
9. M. Fréchet, La notion de différentielle dans l'analyse générale, *Ann. Sci. École Norm. Sup.* **42**, 293–323 (1925).
10. R. Gáteaux, Sur les fonctionelles continues et les fonctionelles analytiques, *Bull. Soc. Math. France* **50**, 1–21 (1922).
11. H. H. Goldstine, A Multiplier Rule in Abstract Spaces, *Bull. Am. Math. Soc.*, (1938).
12. H. H. Goldstine, The Calculus of Variations in Abstract Spaces, *Duke Math. J.* (1942).
13. L. A. Liusternik, On Relative Extrema of Functionals (in Russian), *Mat. Sbornik* **41**, 390–401 (1934).
14. M. R. Hestenes, Hilbert Space Methods in Variational Theory and Numerical Analysis, *Proc. Congr. Math. Amsterdam* **3**, 229–236 (1954).
15. A. V. Balakrishnan, An Operator-Theoric Formulation of a class of Control Problems and a Steepest Descent Method of Solution, *J. SIAM Control Ser. A*, **1**, No. 2 (1963).
16. A. A. Goldstein, Minimizing Functionals on Hilbert Space, *Proc. Symp. Computing Methods in Optimization Probl, UCLA*. Academic Press, New York, 1964.
17. E. K. Blum, Minimization of Functionals with Equality Constraints, *J. SIAM Control Ser. A*, **3**, No. 2, 299–316 (1965). (See also United Aircraft Res. Rept. C-11005-814, 1964).
18. E. Hille, "Functional Analysis and Semi-Groups" (AMS Colloq. Publ. Vol. 31). Am. Math. Soc., Providence, Rhode Island, 1948.
19. L. Liusternik and V. Sobolev, "Elements of Functional Analysis." Ungar, New York, 1961.
20. N. I. Akhiezer, "The Calculus of Variations." Ginn (Blaisdell), Boston, 1962.
21. J. Dieudonné, "Foundations of Modern Analysis." Academic Press, New York, 1960.
22. H. A. Antosiewicz and W. Rheinboldt, Numerical Analysis and Functional Analysis, *in* "Survey of Numerical Analysis" (J. Todd, ed.). McGraw-Hill, New York, 1962.
23. E. A. Coddington and N. Levinson, "Theory of Ordinary Differential Equations." McGraw-Hill, New York, 1955.
24. R. A. Struble, "Nonlinear Differential Equations." McGraw-Hill, New York, 1962.
25. P. C. Rosenbloom, The Method of Steepest Descent, *AMS Proc. Symp. Appl. Math.*, **6**. McGraw-Hill, New York, 1956.
26. L. M. Graves, A Transformation of the Problem of Lagrange in the Calculus of Variations, *Trans. Am. Math. Soc.* **35**, 675–682 (1933).
27. T. H. Hildebrandt and L. M. Graves, Implicit Functions and Their Differentials in General Analysis, *Trans. Am. Math. Soc.* **29**, 127–153 (1927).
28. F. E. Browder, Variational Methods for Nonlinear Elliptic Eigenvalue Problems, *Bull. Am. Math. Soc.* **71**, No. 1, 176–183 (1965).
29. L. W. Neustadt, Optimal Control Problems as Extremal Problems in a Banach Space, USCEE Rept. 133, (1965).
30. E. K. Blum and J. Irving, Comparative Performance of Low-Thrust and Ballistic Rocket Vehicles for Flight to Mars, *in* "Vistas in Astronautics," Vol. II. Pergamon Press, Oxford, 1956.

31. W. Hart and T. S. Motzkin, A Composite Newton-Raphson Gradient Method for the Solution of Systems of Equations, *Pacific J. Math.* **6**, 691–707 (1956).
32. H. J. Kelley, Method of Gradients, *in* "Optimization Techniques" (G. Leitmann, ed.), pp. 205–252. Academic Press, New York, 1962.
33. E. K. Blum, A Convergent Gradient Procedure in Pre-Hilbert Spaces, *Pacific J. Math.* **17**, No. 1 (1966). (See also United Aircraft Rept. D-110058-18 (1965).)

Author Index

Numbers in parentheses are reference numbers and indicate that an author's work is referred to although his name is not cited in the text. Numbers in italics show the page on which the complete reference is listed.

Subject Index